CONCORDIA UNIVERSITY

HA33 .G71952
STATISTICAL QUALITY CONTROL 2D ED.

W9-DEE-183

3 4211 000037297

McGRAW-HILL INDUSTRIAL ORGANIZATION
AND MANAGEMENT SERIES

L. C. Morrow, *Consulting Editor*

★ ★ ★

STATISTICAL QUALITY CONTROL

McGRAW-HILL
INDUSTRIAL ORGANIZATION AND MANAGEMENT SERIES

L. C. MORROW, *Consulting Editor*
Consulting Editor, Factory Management and Maintenance
Assisted by a Board of Industrial and Educational Advisers

BETHEL, ATWATER, SMITH, and STACKMAN—*Industrial Organization and Management*
BIKLEN and BRETH—*The Successful Employee Publication*
BRIDGES—*Job Placement of the Physically Handicapped*
CANTOR—*Employee Counseling*
CARROLL—*How to Chart Timestudy Data*
DRAKE and DRAKE—*A Human Relations Casebook for Executives and Supervisors*
EVANS—*A Program for Personnel Administration*
FEIGENBAUM—*Quality Control: Principles, Practices, and Administration*
GARDINER—*When Foreman and Steward Bargain*
GARDINER and GARDINER—*Vitalizing the Foremen's Role in Management*
GILBRETH and COOK—*The Foreman in Manpower Management*
GRANT—*Statistical Quality Control*
HANNAFORD—*Conference Leadership in Business and Industry*
HEIDE—*Industrial Process Control by Statistical Methods*
HILL—*Pattern for Good Labor Relations*
HILL and HOOK—*Management at the Bargaining Table*
HYDE—*Fundamentals of Successful Manufacturing*
IMMER—*Layout Planning Techniques*
JURAN—*Quality-control Handbook*
KALSEM—*Practical Supervision*
KIMBALL and KIMBALL—*Principles of Industrial Organization*
LANDY—*Production Planning and Control*
LAWSHE—*Principles of Personnel Testing*
LIPPERT—*Accident Prevention Administration*
MAYNARD, STEGEMERTEN, and SCHWAB—*Methods-Time Measurement*
MICHAEL—*Wage and Salary Fundamentals and Procedures*
MORGAN—*Industrial Training and Testing*
NEUSCHEL—*Streamlining Business Procedures*
NEUSCHEL and JOHNSON—*How to Take Physical Inventory*
PRESGRAVE—*The Dynamics of Time Study*
SMITH—*Control Charts*
SMYTH and MURPHY—*Job Evaluation and Employee Rating*
STANIAR—*Plant Engineering Handbook*
STIGERS—*Making Conference Programs Work*
STOWERS—*Management Can Be Human*
THOMPSON—*Engineering Organization and Methods*
THOMPSON—*Inspection Organization and Methods*
TOOTLE—*Employees Are People*
WIREN and HEYEL—*Practical Management Research*
YOUNG—*Personnel Manual for Executives*

STATISTICAL
QUALITY CONTROL

EUGENE L. GRANT

PROFESSOR OF ECONOMICS OF ENGINEERING
STANFORD UNIVERSITY

SECOND EDITION

KLINCK MEMORIAL LIBRARY
Concordia College
River Forest, IL 60305

New York   Toronto   London
McGRAW-HILL BOOK COMPANY, Inc.
1952

STATISTICAL QUALITY CONTROL

Copyright, 1946, 1952, by the McGraw-Hill Book Company, Inc. Printed in the United States of America. All rights reserved. This book, or parts thereof, may not be reproduced in any form without permission of the publishers.

Library of Congress Catalog Card Number: 52-5332

III

THE MAPLE PRESS COMPANY, YORK, PA.

69454
G

To
JOHN CHARLES LOUNSBURY FISH

PREFACE TO THE SECOND EDITION

The most important changes from the first edition of this book are as follows:

1. The chapters dealing with acceptance sampling by attributes have been considerably expanded and largely rewritten. In part, this rewriting has been aimed at including developments in this field since the writing of the first edition, particularly those in multiple and sequential sampling. In part, the rewriting has been aimed at up-to-date coverage of the attributes sampling procedures used by the military services. In part, also, the objective has been to improve the presentation of fundamental principles.

2. The chapter dealing with acceptance sampling by variables has been entirely rewritten. Many recent developments in this field are described, including the Shainin Lot Plot and the variables tables and procedures developed by the Applied Mathematics and Statistics Laboratory of Stanford University under the direction of Dr. A. H. Bowker.

3. The treatment of the cost aspects of quality decisions has been considerably expanded.

4. Less extensive changes have been made in the remainder of the book, chiefly to introduce new material.

5. The number of problems has been more than doubled. Answers are now given to about 30% of the problems with the thought that this may be helpful to those persons who use the book for home study.

6. The master tables from "Military Standard 105A—Sampling Procedures and Tables for Inspection by Attributes" have been included in an appendix. Two tables for use in variables sampling have also been included. One gives representative factors from the Bowker-Goode volume "Sampling Inspection by Variables." The other gives factors recently developed under Dr. Bowker's direction that make it possible to determine the approximate operating characteristics of a wide range of unknown-sigma plans for one-sided specifications.

Much expansion of the use of the techniques of statistical quality control has occurred since the first edition of this book was published in 1946. In hundreds of industrial companies that had made little or no use of these techniques, their use is now accepted as a routine and commonplace cost-saving matter. In procurement by all of the armed services of the United States, the use of statistical sampling tables is standard. It has become evident that many of these statistical techniques originally developed for use in manufacturing can be applied successfully to clerical work and other nonmanufacturing activities.   From small beginnings in 1946, the American Society for Quality Control has grown rapidly to become an active and important organization with an excellent technical journal. The literature of statistical quality control has expanded rapidly.

Nevertheless, from the viewpoint of the over-all contribution of these techniques to industry, persons most competent to judge seem to agree that the surface has only been scratched.   Not only do these techniques appear to be destined for a permanent spot in industry; it is evident that throughout the years they can be expected to make an increasing contribution to the industrial objective of better quality at lower cost.

The thanks of the author are due to a number of users of the first edition who have pointed out errors and made suggestions for improvement. His thanks are also due to his Stanford University colleagues, L. F. Bell, A. H. Bowker, H. P. Goode, C. D. Henderson, and W. G. Ireson, who have made suggestions regarding the manuscript of this second edition. Special acknowledgment and thanks are due to Harold F. Dodge of Bell Telephone Laboratories for many helpful comments and suggestions. However, as in all technical books, the final responsibility for the selection and treatment of material must fall on the shoulders of the author, and he should receive the blame for any deficiencies.

EUGENE L. GRANT

STANFORD, CALIF.
April, 1952

PREFACE TO THE FIRST EDITION

This is a working manual. Its object is to explain simple but powerful statistical techniques that can be widely used in industry to reduce costs and improve product quality. The most effective use of these techniques depends upon their being understood by production and inspection supervisors, by engineers, and by management.

The object has been to write a book that might be immediately useful to all of these groups. No attempt has been made to write for the professional statistician or the mathematician. The aim has been to give just enough theory to supply practical working rules that will enable one to recognize the limitations of the methods as well as their many uses.

The spectacular savings in man power and materials that resulted from certain wartime applications of statistical quality control have often generated much enthusiasm. Nevertheless, the remark of one enthusiast that statistical quality control is the most important event in manufacturing since the development of interchangeable manufacture is undoubtedly an exaggeration. Statistical quality control should be viewed as a useful tool for the solution of many manufacturing problems that cannot be solved so well by any other known method. The many applications developed in war industry have demonstrated its possibilities in a great diversity of situations. However, like any other tool, its limitations should be recognized.

It seems inevitable that at some future date the techniques of statistical quality control will become well-known basic tools for use in nearly all types of manufacturing. It also seems inevitable that there will be many headaches incident to the transition to this future situation from the present condition of full application in a few manufacturing plants, limited experimental application in many others, and no application at all in the great majority. This book has been written with the hope that it may help to ease some of these headaches and possibly prevent others.

From the viewpoint of the best possible service of these techniques to industry, it is important that their possible misuse should not retard the expansion of their application. Sometimes the sponsors of new methods do not realize the length of time required to work out effective applications. Moreover, some people undoubtedly will use the publicity given to successful applications of statistical quality control as a means of promoting as statistical quality control ideas that are really quite different. Because such hazards could conceivably result in temporarily discrediting

ix

these methods in some organizations, this book emphasizes the limitations as well as the uses of statistical quality control.

In part this book has developed from a course in engineering applications of statistical methods that the author has given at Stanford University during the past 17 years. More particularly, it developed from short full-time courses given for key personnel of West Coast war industries in the summer of 1942 and thereafter. These courses were given by Stanford University as part of the Engineering, Science, and Management War Training program sponsored by the U. S. Office of Education. Practically all the West Coast developments in statistical quality control have been made by persons who were first introduced to these techniques in the Stanford courses or by others who were subsequently trained by these persons. The Stanford full-time courses with their subsequent follow-up seminars later became the pattern for a nationwide program of similar courses sponsored by the Office of Production Research and Development of the War Production Board in cooperation with ESMWT.

Before 1942, most statistical quality control applications were made in certain plants in the electrical manufacturing industry, in the textile industry, and in the production of munitions in certain government arsenals. When in 1942 and thereafter the suggestion was made that the methods be applied in other industries, the first reaction of inspection, production, engineering, and management personnel nearly always was, "But our business is different!" This was the reaction in the aircraft industry, in the chemical industry, in the milling industry, in the food canning and preserving industry, and in the container industry, in plants where many successful applications later were made. In fact, it was a common reaction in plants in those very industries where successful applications had already been made elsewhere. Sometimes even successful applications in adjoining departments of a plant did not prevent department heads from raising this objection.

Observation of the introduction of these methods in a great diversity of manufacturing plants convinces the author that no manufacturing business is really so different as to be unable to make some effective use of these techniques. Variation in product quality is inevitable; wherever variation exists, statistical quality control may be expected to be helpful. However, imagination and ingenuity as well as a knowledge of the basic principles of statistical quality control are likely to be required for each successful application.

In the preparation of this book, the author has been primarily influenced by the pioneers in the field of statistical quality control—both by their writings and by personal conversations relative to the general philosophy of the subject and to the treatment of specific problems. In this connection, special acknowledgment is due to A. G. Ashcroft, W. E.

Deming, H. F. Dodge, G. D. Edwards, G. R. Gause, W. A. Shewhart, L. E. Simon, and R. E. Wareham. The book has been particularly influenced by the general point of view of Dr. Deming.

Much help on specific problems has come from friends on the Pacific Coast, in many of whose plants the author has had opportunity to see the evolution of applications of statistical quality control from the first tentative beginnings to routine use of the techniques as a standard tool. Special mention should be made of the help received from E. E. Bates, J. R. Crawford, George Dundas, P. C. Hammer, J. M. Howell, George Lebedeff, W. H. Lewis, Frederick MacKenzie, D. D. Pettit, and W. B. Rice. The entire manuscript has been read by Prof. Paul T. Norton, Jr., of Virginia Polytechnic Institute, former Chief of the Industrial Processes Branch of the Office of Production Research and Development, and by Profs. Henry Goode and Clarkson H. Oglesby of Stanford University. All three have made many helpful suggestions. Prof. Holbrook Working of Stanford University, former Chief of the O.P.R.D. quality control program, has also supplied helpful ideas regarding parts of the manuscript.

Specific acknowledgments of quotations and of some of the examples have been made at the appropriate places in the text. Data for many of the problems and examples have come from sources that may not be disclosed. In such cases the data have sometimes been so altered as to make sure that no confidential information has been given; such alterations have not changed the statistical aspects of the illustrations.

Eugene L. Grant

Gallatin Gateway, Mont.
August, 1946

CONTENTS

LIST OF EXAMPLES

Part One

WHAT WILL STATISTICAL QUALITY CONTROL DO?

CHAPTER I

OBJECTIVES OF STATISTICAL
QUALITY CONTROL

The long-range contribution of statistics depends not so much upon getting a lot of highly trained statisticians into industry as it does in creating a statistically minded generation of physicists, chemists, engineers, and others who will in any way have a hand in developing and directing the production processes of tomorrow.—W. A. SHEWHART and W. E. DEMING[1]

1. The Control-chart Viewpoint. The essential tool in statistical quality control is the Shewhart control chart. In spite of the apparent simplicity of the control chart, most engineers, production men, and inspectors find that its use calls for an entirely new point of view. One purpose of this book is to explain this point of view in some detail. Briefly stated, it is this: *Measured quality of manufactured product is always subject to a certain amount of variation as a result of chance. Some stable "system of chance causes" is inherent in any particular scheme of production and inspection. Variation within this stable pattern is inevitable. The reasons for variation outside this stable pattern may be discovered and corrected.*

The power of the Shewhart technique lies in its ability to separate out these assignable causes of quality variation. This makes possible the diagnosis and correction of many production troubles and often brings substantial improvements in product quality and reduction of spoilage and rework. Moreover, by identifying certain of the quality variations as inevitable chance variations, the control chart tells when to leave a process alone and thus prevents unnecessarily frequent adjustments that tend to increase the variability of the process rather than to decrease it.

Through its disclosure of the natural tolerances of a production process, the control-chart technique permits better decisions on engineering tolerances and better comparisons between alternative designs and between alternative production methods. Through improvement of conventional acceptance procedures, it often provides better quality assurance at lower inspection cost.

2. Specification, Production, and Inspection. Before production starts, a decision is necessary as to what is to be made. Next comes

[1] SHEWHART, W. A. (edited by W. E. Deming), "Statistical Method from the Viewpoint of Quality Control," p. 49, The Graduate School, Department of Agriculture, Washington, D.C., 1939.

the actual manufacturing of the product.   Finally it must be determined whether the product manufactured is what was intended.   It is convenient to think of all matters related to quality of manufactured product in terms of these three functions of specification, production, and inspection.

Much of the publicity regarding statistical quality control has dealt with cost savings made in the inspection function.   This emphasis gives a somewhat distorted picture.   Although under certain favorable conditions inspection savings are spectacular, in other circumstances they may be impossible.

Statistical quality control should be viewed as a tool which may influence decisions related to the functions of specification, production, or inspection.   Its most effective use generally requires cooperation among those responsible for these three different functions or decisions at a higher level than any one of them.   For this reason, the techniques should be understood at a management level that encompasses all three functions.

3. An Aid to Cooperation.   A common complaint among production personnel is that engineers responsible for specifications do not understand production problems.   Inspection personnel often complain not only about the poor quality of manufactured product but also about the unreasonableness of specified tolerances.   In fact, very frequently inspection practices develop that substitute the inspector's views regarding proper tolerances for those actually specified by the engineers.   In many organizations, there is evident need for a basis on which designers, production personnel, and inspectors can understand each other's problems.

In the past many arguments between these three groups have been carried on with more heat than light because of the absence of facts in a form which would provide a basis for agreement.   In many cases these facts can be provided by the use of statistical quality control techniques.   In fact, statistical quality control provides a common language that may be used by all three groups in arriving at a rational solution of mutual problems.

4. Four Tools.   Many of the techniques developed by mathematical statisticians for the analysis of data may be used in the control of product quality.   The expression *statistical quality control* might conceivably cover all uses of statistical techniques for this purpose.   However, it ordinarily refers to the use of four separate but related techniques that constitute the most common working statistical tools in quality control. These tools are

1. The Shewhart control charts for measurable quality characteristics. In the technical language of the subject, these are described as charts for

variables, or as charts for $\bar{X}$* and R (average and range) and charts for $\bar{X}$ and σ† (average and standard deviation). They are the subject matter of Part Two of this book.

2. The Shewhart control chart for fraction defective. In the technical language of the subject, this is described as the p chart. It is explained in Part Three of this book.

3. The Shewhart control chart for number of defects per unit. In the technical language of the subject, this is described as the c chart. It also is explained in Part Three of this book.

4. That portion of sampling theory which deals with the quality protection given by any specified sampling acceptance procedure. This is the subject matter of Part Four of this book.

This book is primarily an exposition of these four simple techniques. In the use of statistical methods to control product quality, these are the tools for cost reduction and quality improvement that are most widely applied. This is particularly true in the first stages of the use of statistical methods; as people dealing with quality matters acquire statistical sophistication, more advanced statistical methods are also used to good advantage. Reference to more advanced methods is made in Chap. XVIII.

5. Variables and Attributes. An important distinction in the technical language of statistics is that between *variables* and *attributes*. When a record is made of an actual measured quality characteristic, such as a dimension expressed in thousandths of an inch, the quality is said to be expressed by variables. When a record shows only the number of articles conforming and the number of articles failing to conform to any specified requirements, it is said to be a record by attributes.

All manufactured products must meet certain quality specifications, express or implied. Many of these specifications may be stated as variables. Examples are dimensions, hardness in Rockwell units, operating temperatures in degrees Fahrenheit, tensile strength in pounds per square inch, per cent of a particular impurity in a chemical compound, weight in pounds of the contents of any container, time in seconds of the blow of a fuse, life in hours of an incandescent lamp. Most specifications of variables give both upper and lower limits for the measured value. Some, such as the per cent of a particular impurity in a chemical compound,

---

* The symbol $\bar{X}$ is read as "X bar" or as "bar X." The bar over any symbol always indicates an average. Thus $\bar{X}$ means an average of the X's.

† σ is the lower-case form of the Greek letter *sigma*. It is universally used by statisticians to represent *standard deviation*. It is always read as "sigma." It should not be confused with the Greek capital letter sigma Σ, which mathematicians use to represent summation. The meaning of standard deviation is explained in Chap. III.

may have an upper limit only, whereas others, such as strength, may have a lower limit only. Variables are dealt with in the Shewhart control charts for $\bar{X}$ and R, and for $\bar{X}$ and σ.

Many specifications are necessarily written in terms of attributes rather than variables. This applies, for example, to many things that may be judged only by visual examination. The glass cover on a pressure gage either is not cracked or it is. A lithographed label either has a certain desired color or it has not. The surface finish of a piece of furniture either presents a satisfactory appearance or it does not. A spot weld in sheet metal either has not caused cracked edges of the sheets or it has. In general, the thing examined either conforms or does not conform to the specifications.

In addition to numerous quality characteristics that are specified without reference to measurement of any quantity, many characteristics that are specified as measurable variables are inspected merely as conforming or nonconforming to specifications. This applies, for example, to gaging of dimensions of machine parts by go and not-go gages. Attributes are dealt with in the Shewhart control chart for fraction defective p.

6. Some Benefits to Be Expected from Use of the Shewhart Control Chart for Variables. Trouble is a common state of affairs in manufacturing. Whenever the trouble consists of difficulty in meeting quality specifications that are expressed in terms of variables, the Shewhart control charts for $\bar{X}$ and R are indispensable tools in the hands of the trouble shooter. They provide information on three matters, all of which need to be known as a basis for action. These are

1. Basic variability of the quality characteristic
2. Consistency of performance
3. Average level of the quality characteristic

No production process is good enough to produce all items of product exactly alike. Some variability is unavoidable; the amount of this basic variability will depend on various characteristics of the production process, such as the machines, the materials, the operators. Where both upper and lower values are specified for a quality characteristic, as in the case of dimensional tolerances, one important question is whether the basic variability of the process is so great that it is impossible to make all the product within the specification limits. When the control chart shows that this is true and when the specifications cannot be changed, the alternatives are either to make a fundamental change in the production process that will reduce its basic variability or to face the fact that it will always be necessary to sort the good product from the bad. Sometimes, however, when the control chart shows so much basic variability that some product is sure to be made outside the tolerances, a review of the situation will show that the tolerances are tighter than necessary for the functioning of the product. Here the appropriate action is to change the specifications to widen the tolerances.

Variability of the quality characteristic may follow a chance pattern, or it may behave erratically because of the occasional presence of assignable causes that can be discovered and eliminated. The control limits on the chart are so placed as to disclose the presence or absence of these assignable causes. Although their actual elimination is usually an engineering job, the control chart tells when, and in some instances suggests where, to look. As previously mentioned, the action of operators in trying to *correct* a process may actually be an assignable cause of quality variation. A merit of the control chart is that it tells when to leave a process alone as well as when to take action to correct trouble. The elimination of assignable causes of erratic fluctuation is described as bringing a process *under control* and is responsible for many of the cost savings resulting from statistical quality control.

Even though the basic variability of a process is such that the *natural tolerance range* is narrower than the specified tolerance range, and even though the process is under control, showing a consistent pattern of variability, the product may be unsatisfactory because the average level of the quality characteristic is too low or too high. This also will be disclosed by the control chart. In some cases the correction of the average level may be a simple matter, such as changing a machine setting; in other situations, such as increasing an average level of strength, it may call for a program of research and development work.

Once the control chart shows that a process is brought under control at a satisfactory level and with satisfactory limits of variability, one may feel confident that the product meets specifications. This suggests the possibility of basing acceptance procedures on the control chart, using it to determine whether this happy state of affairs is continuing. Under these favorable circumstances substantial savings are often possible in costs related to inspection. Where inspection consists of destructive tests, it may be possible to reduce the number of items tested, thus saving both in testing cost and in the cost of the product destroyed. In nondestructive testing, savings may sometimes be made through substitution of sampling inspection by variables (such as measuring actual values of a dimension with a micrometer or dial gage) for 100% inspection by attributes (such as inspection of a dimension with a go and not-go gage).

7. Some Benefits to Be Expected from the Use of the Shewhart Control Chart for Fraction Defective. Most routine inspection of manufactured product is inspection by attributes, classifying each item inspected as either Accepted or Rejected (with possibly a further division of rejects into Spoilage and Rework). This statement applies both to 100% inspection and sampling inspection.   In such inspection it is a common practice to make a record of the number of items rejected.

The practice of recording at the same time the number of items inspected is not so universal.   However, if quality performance at one time is to be compared with that at another time, the record of total number inspected is just as necessary as the record of number rejected. The ratio of the items rejected to items inspected is the *fraction defective*.[1]

Thus the Shewhart control chart for fraction defective generally makes use of data that either are already available for other purposes or that can readily be made available.   Simple statistical calculations provide control limits that tell whether assignable causes of variation appear to be present or whether the variations from day to day (or lot to lot, vendor to vendor, or whatever the classification basis may be) are explainable on chance grounds.

It will be shown in later chapters that this control chart for attributes (the p chart) is somewhat less sensitive than the charts for variables ($\overline{X}$ and R charts) and does not have as great diagnostic value.   Nevertheless, it is an extremely useful aid to production supervision in giving information as to when and where to exert pressure for quality improvement.   It is a common experience for the introduction of a p chart to be responsible for substantial reductions in the average fraction defective. In some instances the p chart will disclose erratic fluctuations in the quality of inspection, and its use may result in improvement in inspection practices and inspection standards.   Moreover, the p chart often serves to point out those situations needing diagnosis of trouble by the control chart for variables.

In addition to its use in process control, the p chart may be of great value in dealing with outside vendors.   Vendors may differ both in the quality level submitted and in the variability of that quality level.   It is particularly desirable to know whether the quality of product submitted by a vendor today is a reliable indication of what he may be expected to submit next month.   The p chart gives useful guidance on this point.

8. Some Benefits to Be Expected from the Use of the Shewhart Control Chart for Defects per Unit.   This type of control chart applies to two rather specialized situations.   One is the case where a count is made of the number of defects of such type as blemishes in a painted or plated surface of a given area, weak spots in the insulation of rubber-covered wire of a given length, or imperfections in a bolt of cloth.   The other is the case of inspection of fairly complex assembled units, such as radio sets, aircraft engines, or machine guns, in which there are a great many opportunities for occurrences of defects of various types, and the total

---

[1] It is commonly expressed as a decimal fraction such as 0.023.   The decimal fraction is often multiplied by 100 to convert it into per cent defective, such as 2.3%.

number of defects of all types found by the inspectors is recorded for each unit.

As in other types of control charts, the control limits are set in a way to detect the presence or absence of assignable causes of variation, and they therefore tell when to take action on the process and when not to do so. Experience indicates that erratic variation in inspection standards and inspection practices seems particularly likely to exist in this type of inspection and that the control chart for defects per unit generally proves helpful in standardizing inspection methods.

Although this type of control chart applies only to a limited number of manufacturing situations involving quality, it has broad application to many other types of situations commonly met in everyday life. Two examples are accident rates and epidemic rates.

9. Acceptance Sampling. Acceptance inspection is a necessary part of manufacturing and may be applied to incoming materials, to partially finished product at various intermediate stages of the manufacturing process, and to final product. Acceptance inspection may also be carried out by the purchaser of manufactured product.

Much of this acceptance inspection is by sampling. Often 100% inspection turns out to be impracticable or clearly uneconomical. Moreover, the quality of the product accepted may actually be better with modern statistical acceptance sampling procedures than would be the case if the same product were subjected to 100% inspection. Sampling inspection has a number of psychological advantages over 100% inspection. Inspectors' fatigue on repetitive operations may be a serious obstacle to good 100% inspection.

It is common knowledge that on many types of inspection, even several 100% inspections will not eliminate all of the defective product from a stream of product a portion of which is defective. The best protection against the acceptance of defective product is, of course, having the product made right in the first place. Good sampling acceptance procedures may often contribute to this objective through more effective pressure for quality improvement than can be exerted with 100% inspection. Some sampling schemes also provide a better basis for diagnosis of quality troubles than is common with 100% inspection.

Despite the merits of good sampling acceptance procedures, poor sampling procedures are in common use in industry. Sampling procedures established without recognition of the laws of probability usually give an unsatisfactory degree of protection against the acceptance of defective product and may have other deficiencies as compared with modern statistical sampling procedures. In spite of their deficiencies, the traditional poor sampling procedures often involve greater inspection costs than would exist if sampling procedures were improved.

It should be recognized that although modern sampling acceptance procedures are generally superior to the traditional sampling methods, anyone who uses acceptance sampling must face the fact that whenever a portion of the stream of product submitted for acceptance is defective, some defective items are likely to be passed by any sampling acceptance scheme. The statistical approach to acceptance sampling frankly faces this fact. It attempts to evaluate the risk assumed with alternative sampling procedures and to make a decision as to the degree of protection needed in any instance. It is then possible to choose a sampling acceptance scheme that gives a desired degree of protection with due consideration for the various costs involved.

Part Four of this book deals with acceptance sampling. The application of the mathematics of probability to acceptance sampling is explained. Several different types of widely used statistical acceptance procedures are described. Reference is made to the published volumes of sampling tables including the Dodge-Romig tables of the Bell Telephone Laboratories and the tables developed during World War II by the Statistical Research Group, Columbia University. Among other matters, Chap. XV discusses attributes acceptance procedures used in the procurement of military supplies by the armed forces of the United States; the master tables from Military Standard 105A are reproduced in Appendix III. Chapter XVI discusses many different types of acceptance sampling by variables.

10. Many Economy Studies Call for the Viewpoint of Statistical Quality Control. Many decisions on matters related to quality are called for in manufacturing. In making such decisions it is desirable to examine the relative economy of the alternatives under consideration. The techniques of statistical quality control may make a useful contribution to such economy studies.

Consider, for example, the question of the filling of containers—a problem for the food industries and all other industries that package their products. Suppose that government regulations require that all or some specified large percentage of the packages contain at least a certain stipulated weight.[1] Where a conscientious attempt is made to meet such a specification, it is usually done by overfilling enough to be on the safe side.

But the question always remains, "How much overfill is necessary?" This question is often answered on a practical basis of, "Make it enough so that we avoid trouble with the government inspectors." If these inspectors really do a critical job, the resulting average overfill is likely to be too much for maximum economy.

---

[1] In the sense used in statistical quality control, a quality of a manufactured product may be any characteristic of that product. Thus the *quantity* of material in a container is a *quality* of the filled container.

This is not to say that the economic answer is to be gained by increasing the amount of trouble with the inspectors. It is rather a matter of finding the facts about the variability of weights and analyzing these facts. This can be done by the Shewhart control chart for variables better than by any other known technique.

Can the variability of the process be reduced without any change in the physical methods being used to fill the containers? In other words, does the process show lack of control (with the word *control* used in its statistical sense)? If so, what are the reasons for the out-of-control points? Perhaps they may be corrected in such a way that they will be unlikely to recur. Or possibly their correction may call for the maintenance of a control chart continuously (rather than briefly as an information-getting and trouble-shooting device) with some attendant cost for measurement, clerical labor, and supervision. It may even be necessary to maintain several such charts (for instance, on weights of filled containers, weights of empty containers, density of filling substance).

If out-of-control points can be eliminated, it is obviously possible to work closer to the minimum specification limit and thus reduce the cost of the overfill. This is a matter of balancing the cost of maintaining control against the cost of the extra overfill. The control-chart data giving the basic variability of the process will provide the information for decision as to the average level to be aimed at in order to meet specifications and will thus provide an estimate of the money saving possible from better control.

If different methods of filling containers are proposed, (for example, automatic vs. hand filling, or improved automatic controls vs. controls that are only partially automatic) one element in the cost comparison is the possible difference in the cost of overfill with each method. This requires the use of the Shewhart control chart to estimate the basic variability of each method.

If the specification of minimum filling weights has not been made either by government regulation or by a customer contracting for the product but must be made by the producer, the economic decision becomes even more complicated. Here the question may be the effect on consumer acceptance in a competitive market of occasional shortages below the amount stated on a package. Although it may be difficult or impossible to place a definite money value on this effect, it is extremely helpful to have an idea of the costs associated with various degrees of consumer protection. This information is provided by the control-chart technique.

Example 33, Chap. XVII, illustrates the use of statistical quality control in a problem dealing with the control of product weight. This brief introduction to the problem is primarily intended to suggest how statistical quality control may often contribute to a clear statement of the cost differences between manufacturing alternatives and thus provide a basis for decisions aimed at maximum economy. This point is discussed at greater length in Chap. XVII.

11. Statistical Quality Control May Have Useful By-products. The techniques of statistical quality control bring certain desirable results that cannot be achieved as well in any other way. These might be described as the direct benefits of statistical quality control. In addition, the introduction of these techniques into any plant often causes certain desirable changes that might be described as *by-products*. These by-products might have been obtained as well without any use of statistical quality control. Nevertheless, statistical quality control does tend to bring them about.

One such by-product may be the establishment or improvement of inspection standards, with the preparation of definite instructions for each inspection procedure. Another may be the periodic evaluation of departmental performance in quality terms.

Still another may be the evaluation of different vendors' quality performance in terms of average fraction defective, with choice of future vendors based on these findings. For instance, the Niagara Frontier Division of Bell Aircraft Corporation analyzed acceptance and rejection records covering nearly 35 million parts purchased from 458 companies.[1] Only 1.95% of these were found defective and rejected. But it was found that

277 companies supplied parts 0 to 1.99% defective
39 companies supplied parts 2 to 4.99% defective
31 companies supplied parts 5 to 9.99% defective
44 companies supplied parts 10 to 19.99% defective
36 companies supplied parts 20 to 49.99% defective
31 companies supplied parts 50 to 100% defective

Still another by-product of statistical quality control may be the establishment of effective process inspection where none has previously existed. In some manufacturing concerns there is little or no process inspection; inspection takes place some days—or even weeks or months— after production with no chance to associate any defective product with possible causes in the production departments. Statistical quality control, with its emphasis (explained in later chapters) on keeping track of the order of production, tends to call for inspection close to the point of production.

Although the introduction of process inspection is sometimes a by-product, it should be noted that a direct object of statistical quality control is

[1] CHASE, HERBERT, Bell Puts Teeth into Quality Control, *Wings*, vol. 3, pp. 1181–1185, September, 1944.

to provide a new tool that makes process inspection more effective. The information obtained by process inspection—either conducted by roving inspectors or by machine operators themselves—is often misused to make too-frequent machine adjustments. As already pointed out under the discussion of the Shewhart control chart for variables, these too-frequent adjustments have the opposite effect from that intended: they increase rather than decrease the variability of the process. In the introduction of statistical quality control, reports such as these are common: "After a week of the control chart we accomplished substantial improvement in product quality by persuading the operator to let the machine run itself rather than changing the settings whenever a critical dimension gets close to the specification limit." "We found the roving inspector was shutting down the machine for resetting three times as often as necessary."

12. Reasons for Use of the Adjective *Statistical*. In the rapid development of statistical quality control since 1942, this technique has acquired some shorter names. A common practice has been to abbreviate *statistical quality control* by calling it simply *quality control*. The British have gone one step further and describe it as *Q.C.*

One reason for the use of *quality control* in the sense of *statistical quality control* has been the desire to shorten the expression by the saving of one word—a word, incidentally, which many people find hard to pronounce. However a stronger reason seems to have been a desire to avoid a popular prejudice against statistics, statisticians, and the word *statistical*.

Statistics is a word with two quite different meanings. In one sense, it refers to any facts stated in terms of numbers; in this sense it is a plural noun. Thus one may say "Statistics *are* kept in the sales department regarding all branch-office sales." In the other sense, it refers to a body of methods by which useful conclusions can be drawn from numerical data. In this sense it is a singular noun. Thus one may say "Statistics *is* based in large part on the law of large numbers and the mathematical theory of probability." It is in this second sense that the adjective *statistical* is accurately used in the expression *statistical quality control*.

The control of quality of manufactured product is a function that existed long before statistical methods were applied to the analysis of quality data and that exists today whether or not statistical techniques are used. Properly used, the expression *quality control* applies to a function much broader than does the expression *statistical quality control*. The use of *quality control* or *Q.C.* in the sense of *statistical quality control* inevitably leads to confusion as to the meaning of the expression.

In the long run this confusion is likely to be more serious than any troubles introduced by the use of an extra word or by prejudices against the word *statistical*. For this reason, throughout this book the expression *quality control* is always used in the broader sense of the control of quality of product by whatever methods may be used, and the adjective *statistical* is always employed where the control of product quality by statistical methods is referred to.

If prejudices[1] against the word *statistical* seem to be a serious obstacle to that cooperation necessary for the most effective use of the techniques presented in this book, it is always possible to avoid the prejudices in another way, *i.e.*, by calling each statistical tool by its own name, such as *control chart, standard sampling table*, etc.

13. The Mathematics Used in Most Applications of Statistical Quality Control Is Only Simple Arithmetic. Although the techniques explained in this book are all based on the work of mathematical statisticians, some of which involves very advanced mathematics, actual applications generally call for nothing more complicated than addition, subtraction, multiplication, and division. Experience shows that the techniques are effectively used by any persons who are able to do these simple arithmetical operations.

The control chart for variables, as originally developed by Shewhart in 1924, called for frequent calculation of squares and square roots in order to obtain standard deviations. This proved to be a definite obstacle to the introduction of the techniques in many places. Subsequent developments by mathematical statisticians made possible the use of the range rather than the standard deviation and substituted a single subtraction for the calculation of the square root of the sum of squares. This made possible shop cooperation in the use of the control chart in many situations where it had previously seemed to be out of the question.

14. Four Different Levels of Understanding Statistical Quality Control. In any manufacturing company, government procurement agency, or other organization in which substantial statistical quality control applications are to be made, experience indicates that there appropriately may be four levels of understanding of the subject.

One is the level of understanding the mathematics on which the control charts and sampling tables are based and their relationship to the many other tools for the analysis of data that have been developed by mathematical statisticians. A person on this level should be able to read the literature of mathematical statistics without great difficulty and should have reasonable familiarity with this literature. One or more persons on this level should be available, at least in an advisory capacity, in any comprehensive statistical quality control program.

The second level is that of general understanding of the principles underlying the various types of control charts and sampling tables. It calls for understanding why these methods work, how to interpret their

---

[1] In one industry the low pay scale associated with the occupational title *statistical clerk* made everyone engaged in the statistical quality control program unwilling to have the adjective *statistical* used as part of his title.

results, and how to decide which method to use in any particular case.

A third level is that of a broad understanding of the objectives and possible uses of statistical quality control, even though this understanding is not sufficiently detailed and precise to permit close supervision of statistical quality control work. This type of understanding is particularly helpful at higher management levels.

The fourth level calls merely for use of one or more of the techniques on a rule-of-thumb basis. In any plant in which many applications are made, there will doubtless be a number of inspectors, some machine operators, and possibly one or more clerks on this level.

This book is aimed at the second level. The success of any statistical quality control program is likely to depend on the number of people in an organization who are competent on this level and on the distribution of these people among various departments. The cooperation among departments necessary for the fullest benefits from statistical quality control has been mentioned and is emphasized throughout succeeding chapters. The more persons in inspection supervision, production supervision, methods engineering, tool engineering, engineering design, and top management who understand the basic principles of statistical quality control, the better the opportunity for effective use of these techniques.

The first two chapters of this book, although intended primarily as an introduction for people interested in the second level, are also intended to be helpful to those who are interested only in the third level. Chapter XVIII is also suggested as reading for individuals primarily interested in the third level.

15. Is Quantity Production Necessary for Effective Use of Statistical Quality Control? Manufacturing executives, confronted by the suggestion that statistical quality control techniques may be helpful in solving some of their problems, often respond somewhat as follows: "I can see how statistical methods may be used effectively in the production of ammunition or telephones where hundreds of thousands of items are to be produced just alike. But in my business the quantities produced of any particular design of part or product are much smaller."

This objection cannot be answered by specifying a definite minimum production below which statistical quality control methods should not be applied and above which they may be used economically. Not only does the answer differ for different statistical techniques, but it also depends on the various costs involved in any particular situation. Nevertheless, some guidance may be given on this matter.

For instance, the Shewhart control chart for variables often may be used to advantage with very few measurements. Under certain favorable conditions, this technique might be used to reduce cost or improve quality where total production of a part or product was as low as 50, or sometimes even lower. This total production might conceivably be spread over several years; it is the total amount to be produced rather than the rate of production that is most significant. Actually, most applications involve production at least in the thousands. The decision involves balancing the costs of statistical quality control against the prospective benefits. This question is discussed at greater length in Chap. XVII.

On the other hand, the control chart for attributes (fraction defective) cannot be used advantageously with so few observations. Possibly 1,000 is the minimum total production for which this technique should be considered for process control; generally its use is limited to situations with total production at least in the tens of thousands.

Control charts based on total defects or defects per unit, and sampling acceptance tables on the same basis, might be used with total production of 100 or more.

Although statistical types of acceptance procedures may be applied to a single lot of product, these procedures should be interpreted as aiming at some stated quality protection in the long run. This point should be kept in mind in the use of such acceptance procedures even though it is not possible to state any minimum value of total production to which they are applicable.

Intermittent production of a part or product is no obstacle to statistical quality control. In fact, many of the most effective uses of the techniques have been made on this type of production.

It is worth pointing out that in the case of assembled products built up from parts, a single product may contain many identical parts. Thus these techniques may often be applied advantageously to the parts even though the production of the final assembled product is not sufficient to justify their application to the product itself.

The preceding statements about quantities are intended only as rough guides. The basis for judgment as to when to apply statistical quality control techniques and when not to apply them is developed as the techniques are explained in later chapters.

15a. Nonmanufacturing Applications of Statistical Quality Control Techniques. Although control charts and statistical types of acceptance sampling procedures were originally developed for use in mass production manufacturing, these techniques are applicable to many other types of activities in business and government. For instance, certain statistical types of acceptance sampling schemes are well adapted to the problem of checking errors in clerical work. Control charts may be applied to many business variables to discover their average values, their range of variation that can be expected as a matter of chance, and the presence or absence of assignable causes of variation. Example 25, Chap. XIV, illustrates a nonmanufacturing application of statistical quality control techniques.

CHAPTER II

SOME REPRESENTATIVE APPLICATIONS

The manufacturer's inspection of his own product serves two purposes: *Purpose A.* To provide a basis for action with regard to the product already at hand; as for instance, to decide whether the particular article or lot of product at hand should be allowed to go out, or some alternative disposition made (inspected further, sorted, repaired, reworked, scrapped, etc.).

Purpose B. To provide a basis for action with regard to the production process, with a view to future product; as for instance, to decide whether the process should be left alone, or action taken to find and eliminate disturbing causes.—AMERICAN WAR STANDARD Z1.3–1942[1]

16. Use of Examples. Throughout this book there are many descriptions of cases involving use of statistical quality control methods. For convenience in reference, these are numbered consecutively, Example 1, Example 2, etc.

Before proceeding in Parts Two, Three, and Four with a detailed description of the four tools of statistical quality control explained in this book, it seems advisable to give a general perspective on the subject by illustrating the use of each tool. Examples 1 and 2 in this chapter illustrate the control chart for variables; Example 3 illustrates the control chart for fraction defective; Example 4 illustrates the control chart for defects per unit; Example 5 illustrates the use of elementary probability theory to evaluate the quality protection given by a common sampling plan.

EXAMPLE 1. $\bar{X}$ AND R CHARTS

Experimental Control Charts for Process Control

17. Facts of the Case. In the kit of tools provided by statistical quality control, the most potent tool for the diagnosis of production problems is the Shewhart control chart for variables. A course in Statistical Quality Control often starts with a brief introduction of this control chart. This chart was the topic for discussion in the third 2-hr. lecture in an evening course given in the subject.

One of the members of the class was a production foreman in a small department in a plant which had never before used any statistical quality control methods. After hearing the 2-hr. lecture, this foreman, in order to familiarize himself with the control chart, made an experimental application to one of the operations in his department.

This operation consisted in thread grinding a fitting for an aircraft hydraulic system. The pitch diameter of the threads was specified as 0.4037 ± 0.0013 in. All these

---

[1] "Control Chart Method of Controlling Quality during Production. American War Standard Z1.3–1942," p. 5, American Standards Association, 70 E. 45th St., New York, 1942.

fittings were later subject to inspection of this dimension by go and not-go thread ring gages. This inspection usually took place several days after production. In order to minimize gage wear in this inspection operation, it was the practice of the production department to aim at an average value a little below the nominal dimension of 0.4037 in.

TABLE 1.. MEASUREMENTS OF PITCH DIAMETER OF THREADS ON AIRCRAFT FITTINGS (Values are expressed in units of 0.0001 in. in excess of 0.4000 in. Dimension is specified as 0.4037 ± 0.0013 in.)

Sample number	Measurement on each item of five items per hour					Average $\bar{X}$	Range R
1	36	35	34	33	32	34.0	4
2	31	31	34	32	30	31.6	4
3	30	30	32	30	32	30.8	2
4	32	33	33	32	35	33.0	3
5	32	34	37	37	35	35.0	5
6	32	32	31	33	33	32.2	2
7	33	33	36	32	31	33.0	5
8	23	33	36	35	36	32.6	13
9	43	36	35	24	31	33.8	19
10	36	35	36	41	41	37.8	6
11	34	38	35	34	38	35.8	4
12	36	38	39	39	40	38.4	4
13	36	40	35	26	33	34.0	14
14	36	35	37	34	33	35.0	4
15	30	37	33	34	35	33.8	7
16	28	31	33	33	33	31.6	5
17	33	30	34	33	35	33.0	5
18	27	28	29	27	30	28.2	3
19	35	36	29	27	32	31.8	9
20	33	35	35	39	36	35.6	6
Totals..						671.0	124

To make actual measurements of pitch diameter to the nearest ten-thousandth of an inch, the foreman borrowed a visual comparator that had been used for other purposes. Approximately once every hour he measured the pitch diameter of five fittings that had just been produced. For each sample of five he computed the average and the range (largest value in sample minus smallest value). The figures he obtained are shown in Table 1.

18. Two Charts That Are Not Control Charts. If these measurements had been made without benefit of the foreman's introduction to the control-chart technique, he might well have calculated the averages for each sample but probably would not have calculated the ranges. Figure 1 shows two types of charts that are not control charts but that sometimes are made from information of this type. These charts may be of interest to production supervision, but they do not give the definite basis for action that the control chart supplies.

Figure 1a shows individual measurements plotted for each sample. It also shows the nominal dimension and upper and lower tolerance limits. With the exception of one fitting in sample 8, all the fittings examined met the specified tolerances.

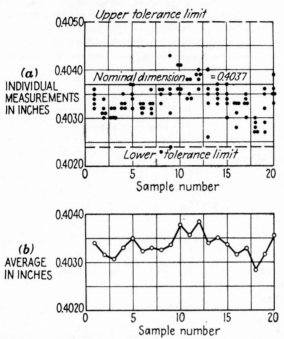

Fig 1. Pitch diameter of threads of fitting for aircraft hydraulic system: (a) individual measurements, (b) averages of samples of five.

Figure 1b shows the averages of these samples. A chart of this type may be useful to show trends more clearly than one of the type of Fig. 1a. However, without the limits provided by the Shewhart technique, it does not indicate whether the process shows lack of control in the statistical sense of the meaning of *control*.[1]

---

[1] The word *control* has a special technical meaning in the language of statistical quality control. A process is described as *in control* when a stable system of chance causes seems to be operating. This meaning is developed more fully in Part Two of this book. However, the word is often misused and misinterpreted, particularly by those who have been briefly exposed to the jargon of statistical quality control without having had a chance to learn its principles.

For example, a government inspection officer in a certain war plant was shown a chart that gave average values of an important quality characteristic of successive lots of a certain munitions item manufactured in this plant. This chart, prepared by one of his inspectors, was similar to Fig. 1b in showing averages but no control limits. "Any fool could see this process is in control," the officer exclaimed. Later one of his assistants calculated control limits and plotted them on the chart, showing many points out of control. A few minutes later the inspection officer was overheard giving

It should be noted that because Fig. 1b shows averages rather than individual values, it would have been misleading to indicate the tolerance limits on this chart. It was the individual article that had to meet the tolerances, not the average of a sample. Averages of samples often fall within tolerance limits even though some of the individual articles in the sample are outside the limits. This was true in sample 8, in which the average was close to the nominal dimension even though one item was below the minimum limit. Therefore, a chart for averages that shows tolerance limits tends to give a false sense of security on the question of whether tolerances have been met. Even though some observers of such a chart appreciate this danger and thus avoid incorrect inferences, experience shows that someone is certain to be misled whenever tolerance limits are shown on a chart for averages.

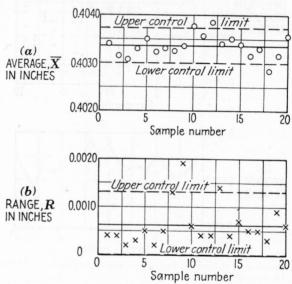

Fig. 2. Pitch diameter of threads of fitting for aircraft hydraulic system: (a) control chart for averages ($\overline{X}$), (b) control chart for ranges (R).

19. Two Control Charts. Figure 2a shows the control chart for averages $\overline{X}$. It will be noted that this is Fig. 1b with the addition of control limits and with the elimination of the irregular line connecting the points. Figure 2b shows the control chart for range R.

Each of these control charts has a solid line to indicate the average value of the statistic that is plotted. The grand average $\overline{\overline{X}}$ (*i.e.*, the average of the averages) is 33.6 (measured—as in Table 1—in units of 0.0001 in. in excess of 0.4000 in.) This is the sum of the averages, 671.0, divided by the number of samples, 20. The average of the ranges is 6.2. This is the sum of the ranges, 124, divided by the number of samples, 20.

Each chart also shows two dotted lines marked *upper control limit* and *lower control*

---

advice to the plant manager. "Any fool can see that this process is out of control," he said.

As a matter of fact no one—fool or otherwise—can tell by inspection of a chart such as Fig. 1b whether or not the process is in statistical control.

limit. The distance of the control limits from the line showing the average value on each chart depends on the average range ($\bar{R} = 6.2$) and makes use of two factors, A_2 and D_4 from Table C, Appendix III. These factors are explained in Chap. IV.

On the $\bar{X}$ chart this distance is $A_2\bar{R} = 0.58(6.2) = 3.6$. Thus the upper control limit is 37.2 (3.6 above the grand average of 33.6) and the lower control limit is 30.0 (3.6 below the grand average of 33.6).

On the R chart the lower control limit for samples of five is always 0. The upper control limit is $D_4\bar{R} = 2.11(6.2) = 13.1$.

These limits thus calculated and shown on Fig. 2 are what are described in Chap. VI as *trial limits*. Before projecting them into the future (*i.e.*, past sample 20) to control future production, they need to be slightly modified by methods that are there explained.

20. The Charts Show Lack of Control. Three points (samples 10, 12, and 18) are outside the control limits on the chart for averages. Two points (samples 9 and 13) are outside the control limits on the chart for ranges. This indicates the presence of assignable causes of variation in the manufacturing process, *i.e.*, factors contributing to the variation in quality which it should be possible to identify and correct. Of course not much could be done about these past assignable causes, as the control limits were not established until the end of the 20-hr. record. The control charts in Fig. 2 merely give evidence that there should be a good opportunity to reduce the variability of the process.

The dividends from the control chart come in the application of the control limits to future production. The prompt hunting for assignable causes as soon as a point goes out of control gives opportunity for their immediate discovery. Action may be taken not only to correct them at once but in many cases to prevent their recurrence.

This lack of control was evident to the production foreman who prepared this chart. A continuation of the chart permitted the identification of the assignable causes of variation in the average—mostly related to machine setting—and the assignable causes of variation in the range—mostly related to carelessness of a particular operator. An effort to prevent their frequent recurrence resulted in a substantial improvement in product uniformity.

21. Other Conclusions from This Control Chart. The simplicity of the control chart is evidenced by the fact that this alert foreman was able to use it to advantage after receiving only 6 hr. instruction in statistical quality control with only two of those hours devoted to construction of the control charts for $\bar{X}$ and R. His successful application was to process control, *i.e.*, to the detection and elimination of assignable causes of quality variation. However, several conclusions that might have been suggested by the control-chart analysis were not evident to him, although they doubtless would have been evident to someone with additional training and experience in this subject. These conclusions, the basis for which will be developed in later chapters, are as follows:

1. If control (in the statistical sense) can be maintained, the natural tolerances of this process appear to be about ± 0.0006 in. Thus, by maintaining statistical control there should be no difficulty in making all the product well within the specified tolerances of ± 0.0013 in.

2. As the practice has been to center the process at a dimension somewhat below the nominal dimension of 0.4037 in. in order to minimize gage wear on 100% inspection with go and not-go thread ring gages, the question arises at what level the process ought to be centered. If statistical control can be maintained, this level must be not less than 0.4030 in. to ensure that practically all product be within the specifications. Actually the level shown by the 20-hr. record was about 0.4034 in. This would be definitely on the safe side if the process could be kept within statistical control. But

with the process out of control, there is always danger of defective product regardless of the level.

3. Whenever natural tolerances are within the specification tolerances, consideration should always be given to the advisability of eliminating 100% inspection and substituting sampling inspection with the use of the control chart. In this case, five measurements of the actual dimension at specified intervals might replace 100% inspection with the go and not-go gages, except where the control chart showed lack of control. Such a change should not be made until the control chart had been maintained on this operation for some time with all points falling inside the control limits. Once this change was made, the motive of reducing wear on the ring gages would be eliminated and the nominal dimension of 0.4037 should be aimed at.

The methods by which one may obtain these conclusions, and similar conclusions of economic importance in other cases, are developed in the following chapters.

22. Some Comments on Example 1. Because management's preconceived ideas on statistical quality control often include a number of misconceptions, it is worth while to make several comments on Example 1 directed at these common misconceptions.

1. One misconception is that because the methods are *statistical* they can only be applied where there is a long period of record. Often this is the basis for the feeling that it is not worth applying them to new operations that are to be continued for only a few months.

It should be noted that the necessary data for a successful application in this case were obtained in 20 hr. As a matter of fact, as past records are seldom in a form for the most effective use of the control chart for variables, it is usually necessary to start securing the required data *after* the decision is made to use this technique. The time needed to get enough information to supply a basis for action depends on how long it will take to manufacture enough units for a suitable chart.

2. Another misconception is that the methods are highly mathematical. This application involved only simple arithmetic.

3. A common misconception is that the methods are so complicated that they cannot be operated by the ordinary production and inspection employees.

As already pointed out, this particular foreman made a useful application after only 2 hr. instruction in the particular technique. This is not to suggest that 2 hr. is sufficient time to devote to explanation of the control chart for variables; it merely is evidence that the essential features of this method can be explained simply in a short time. As also pointed out, this foreman missed some of the possible useful conclusions that might have been drawn from his data. The more persons holding positions of responsibility in an organization who understand statistical quality control and the better they understand it, the better the chance for all the possible cost-saving applications to be made.

4. Another misconception is that the techniques are good to use only when you are conscious that you are in trouble.

It is true that the places where one is conscious of trouble are likely to provide the best opportunities for saving costs. Nevertheless, the techniques often turn up cost-saving opportunities in places where there is no particular awareness of trouble. The possibility in Example 1 of substituting sampling inspection by variables for 100% inspection by attributes is an example. The foreman chose this particular operation somewhat at random in order to provide himself an opportunity to experiment with the techniques.

5. Still another serious misconception is that effective use of the techniques of statistical quality control may be obtained by applying them only in one department.

In Example 1 we have noted that the data secured by the *production* foreman point to a possibility of a saving in *inspection* costs. Budgetary control systems used in industry generally are operated in a way that gives a supervisor credit for a cost saving in his own department but not for cost savings in other departments. In this particular case, if the decision had been made to adopt acceptance sampling by variables at the point of production, with a control chart kept in the production department to be used for process control as well as for acceptance, this decision would have involved the question of whether the measurements were to be made by production or inspection personnel. This question could have been answered only at a management level above both production and inspection. If—as might well have been the case—the decision had been that it was advisable to have the measurements made by production personnel, it would have superficially appeared to *increase* costs in the production department. That is, it would have seemed to increase costs for which the production foreman was held responsible and to decrease costs in a place where—as a matter of budgetary routine—he was given no credit.

Without a full understanding by top management, production supervision, and inspection supervision as to the basis of some of the cost savings that may be effected by statistical quality control, it is evident that the routine operations of a budgetary control system may actually prove an obstacle to securing the savings.

EXAMPLE 2. $\bar{X}$ AND R CHARTS

Revision of Tolerances

23. Facts of the Case. A rheostat knob, produced by plastic molding, contained a metal insert purchased from a vendor. A particular dimension determined the fit of this knob in its assembly. This dimension, which was influenced by the size of the metal insert as well as by the molding operation, was specified by the engineering department as 0.140 ± 0.003 in. Many molded knobs were rejected on 100% inspection with a go and not-go gage for failure to meet the specified tolerances.

A special gage was designed and built to permit quick measurement of the actual value of this dimension.   Five knobs from each hour's production were measured with this gage.   Table 2 shows the measurements obtained on the first 2 days after they were started.

TABLE 2.   MEASUREMENTS OF DISTANCE FROM BACK OF RHEOSTAT KNOB TO FAR SIDE OF PINHOLE

(Values are expressed in units of 0.001 in.   Dimension is specified as 0.140 ± 0.003 in.)

Sample number	Measurement on each item of 5 items per hour					Average $\bar{X}$	Range R
1	140	143	137	134	135	137.8	9
2	138	143	143	145	146	143.0	8
3	139	133	147	148	139	141.2	15
4	143	141	137	138	140	139.8	6
5	142	142	145	135	136	140.0	10
6	136	144	143	136	137	139.2	8
7	142	147	137	142	138	141.2	10
8	143	137	145	137	138	140.0	8
9	141	142	147	140	140	142.0	7
10	142	137	145	140	132	139.2	13
11	137	147	142	137	135	139.6	12
12	137	146	142	142	140	141.4	9
13	142	142	139	141	142	141.2	3
14	137	145	144	137	140	140.6	8
15	144	142	143	135	144	141.6	9
16	140	132	144	145	141	140.4	13
17	137	137	142	143	141	140.0	6
18	137	142	142	145	143	141.8	8
19	142	142	143	140	135	140.4	8
20	136	142	140	139	137	138.8	6
21	142	144	140	138	143	141.4	6
22	139	146	143	140	139	141.4	7
23	140	145	142	139	137	140.6	8
24	134	147	143	141	142	141.4	13
25	138	145	141	137	141	140.4	8
26	140	145	143	144	138	142.0	7
27	145	145	137	138	140	141.0	8
Totals...						3,797.4	233

24. Analysis of the Facts by the Control-chart Technique.   Figures 3b and 3c are control charts for $\bar{X}$ and R, respectively, for the 27 samples taken in these 2 days. Figure 3a is not a control chart, but—like Fig. 1a in Example 1—it shows individual measurements.

If we count all the points outside the tolerance limits that are shown on Fig. 3a, we find that 42 of the 135 knobs measured failed to meet the specifications for this dimension. This is approximately 31 % defective, a very high figure.

At the same time it is evident that all the points on the $\overline{X}$ chart (chart for averages)

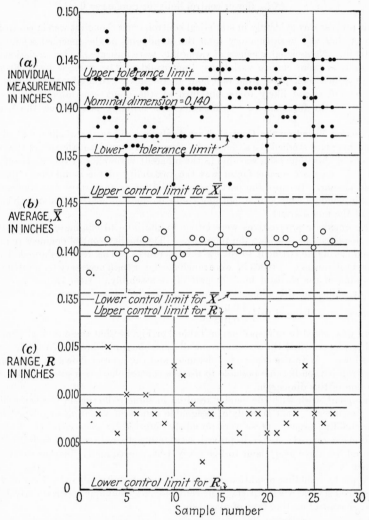

FIG. 3. Measurements of dimension on rheostat knob: (a) individual measurements, (b) control chart for averages ($\overline{X}$), (c) control chart for ranges (R).

and the R chart (chart for ranges) are inside the control limits. As the sample size is five, the same as in Example 1, the calculation of the control limits makes use of the same factors as in that example, as follows:

$$\overline{\overline{X}} \text{ (grand average)} = \frac{3,797.4}{27} = 140.6 \text{ (expressed in units of } 0.001 \text{ in. as in Table 2)}$$

$$\overline{R} \text{ (average range)} = \frac{233}{27} = 8.6$$

$UCL_{\bar{X}}$ (upper control limit for averages) = $\bar{\bar{X}} + A_2\bar{R}$ = 140.6 + 0.58(8.6) = 145.6
$LCL_{\bar{X}}$ (lower control limit for averages) = $\bar{\bar{X}} - A_2\bar{R}$ = 140.6 − 0.58(8.6) = 135.6
$\quad UCL_R$ (upper control limit for ranges) = $D_4\bar{R}$ = 2.11(8.6) = 18.2
$\quad\quad LCL_R$ (lower control limit for ranges) = 0

This process was evidently in statistical control, even though it was in control with a spread that was unsatisfactory from the standpoint of the specified tolerances of ±0.003 in. No assignable causes of variability were indicated. The variations from hour to hour were chance variations; they could not be reduced by hunting for changes which took place from one hour to the next. In a situation of this type, improvement is not likely to be obtained by the plant superintendent's bringing pressure on the foreman, or by the foreman's bringing pressure on the machine operator.

25. Action Based on the Control-chart Analysis. When the quality control engineer in this plant studied the situation, he discovered that although part of the spread in values of this dimension was due to the inherent variability of the plastic molding operation, the most serious factor was the variability of the metal insert from the outside vendor. Because the part was essential for an important war contract and available vendors were scarce, nothing could be done immediately about the variability of the metal insert.

The immediate alternatives were either to continue to eliminate many parts by 100% inspection or to widen the tolerances. The quality control engineer requested the engineering department to review the tolerances. This review showed that the specified tolerances of ±0.003 in. were much narrower than necessary for a satisfactory functioning of the rheostat knob as part of its assembly. After trying knobs with different values of this dimension and judging when the fit was satisfactory, the tolerances were changed to $\begin{cases} +0.010 \\ -0.015 \end{cases}$.

It may be noted from inspection of Table 2 or Fig. 3a that these revised tolerances would have permitted the acceptance of all parts measured in the 27 samples of five there shown. With the change in tolerances and the process shown to be in statistical control, it then became possible to use the control chart as a substitute for 100% inspection of this dimension.

Subsequent work with the vendor resulted in some reduction in the variability of the metal insert. At a later date, assignable causes of variation developed in the plastic molding process; these were promptly detected by the control chart and the conditions corrected. Later it proved satisfactory to reduce the number of parts measured from five every hour to five every 4 hr; subsequently this was cut down to five once in 8 hr.

This plastic molding operation was carried on intermittently with runs of 2 or 3 days spaced several weeks apart. The control-chart technique is particularly helpful in process control on this type of operation.

26. Some Comments on Example 2. This example affords opportunity for some contrasts with the situation described in Example 1 and gives further illustration of some of the uses of the control chart for variables as outlined in Chap. I:

1. In Example 2, the quality control engineer used the control chart as the natural weapon to adopt for the diagnosis of trouble. Without the control chart, and with 31% defectives produced on a critical item, the most common action is for management to "get tough," bringing

pressure on production supervision to do better. The control chart has been described as the substitution of "get smart" for "get tough" in managerial policy in dealing with quality troubles, because it provides supervisors with clues to the causes of correctible day-to-day troubles. In this case, however, the first message of the control chart was to tell management what *not* to do. The chart said, "It's no use to get tough," and it also said, "It's no use to hunt for causes of hour-to-hour or day-to-day variation."

This is the type of situation referred to in the second paragraph of Art. 6 in Chap. I, in which the alternatives presented are (1) to make a fundamental change in the process, (2) to change the specifications, or (3) to resign yourself to the necessity of continuing to try to separate the good product from the bad by 100% inspection. In this case it happened that the specified tolerances had been set arbitrarily without consideration of the particular needs of this assembly; therefore, the appropriate action was to change the specifications.

Some remarks seem appropriate at this point on a matter that will be developed at greater length in later chapters. This is the general relationship between evidence secured from a control chart and a subsequent decision to widen tolerances or otherwise relax specifications.

Any review of tolerances or other specification requirements must look first at the characteristics required in the manufactured part or article. Although presumably this was done when the specifications were written in the first place, designers actually are often too preoccupied with other matters to give much attention to tolerances. Thus it is appropriate to review tolerances whenever they are questioned. Many reviews and relaxations of tolerances do in fact take place without benefit of any control chart.

However, a request for a review of tolerances is on a quite different footing when based on evidence of the control chart that a process is in statistical control than when it is merely based on a statement that a portion of the production has not met the tolerances. In the latter case, there is always the suspicion that the condition may be corrected with no increase in cost if the production department will just make enough effort to do so. In the former case, it is evident that if specifications cannot be changed, either the costs of fundamental changes in the production process (for example, purchasing a new machine, retooling, securing a different material, etc.) must be undertaken, or the costs of making defective product and of doing 100% inspection to try (probably not too successfully) to sort the good product from the bad must be accepted. This whole question is discussed at length in later chapters.

2. In the situation described in Example 2, an active statistical quality control program was in operation. It was in charge of a quality control

engineer who reported directly to the works manager.   Where the information secured from the analysis of control charts points to action by more than one department, such a plan of organization is often advantageous.

3. The contrast between Examples 1 and 2 emphasizes the point that *statistical control* is an expression that describes the pattern of variability of the process rather than the past performance of the process in meeting specifications.   In Example 1, 25% of the samples showed lack of control, whereas only 1% of the product examined failed to meet specifications.   In Example 2, although none of the samples showed lack of control, 31% of the product failed to meet specifications.

4. The point is made in Example 1 (Art. 18) that it is always misleading to show tolerance limits on a chart for averages ($\overline{X}$ chart).   Example 2 emphasizes this point.   Even though many of the individual rheostat knobs measured had dimensions greater than 0.143 or less than 0.137 in., no average of a sample of five was outside these tolerance limits.   Someone who made a comparison between the tolerance limits and the charted values of $\overline{X}$ might well have reached the incorrect conclusion that all the product examined met the specification of 0.140 ± 0.003 in.

EXAMPLE 3.   A CONTROL CHART FOR p THAT RESULTED IN IMPROVEMENT OF PRODUCT QUALITY

27. Description of Situation.   A certain electronic device was subject to 100% final inspection.   In the period immediately preceding the establishment of a control chart for fraction defective, the ratio of rejected devices to total production was 0.315. That is, 31.5% of the product was defective.

Table 3 gives the daily record of the number of devices submitted for final inspection and the number of defective devices found.   This record extends from the start of the maintenance of a control chart on March 6 to the termination of production on July 19 as a result of a change in design.   Final inspection of the device called for the checking of many different qualities.   Although the report form used for final inspection listed some 30 possible causes of rejection, most of the rejections were based on four of these causes.   The daily fractions defective, multiplied by 100 to convert them into per cent defective, are plotted in Fig. 4.

28. The Control Chart for p.   In the technical language of statistical quality control, Fig. 4 is described either as a *control chart for per cent defective* or a *control chart for p*. It is based on *inspection by attributes* in which each item inspected is counted merely as conforming or nonconforming to specifications.   This type of chart may be used to plot the results of sampling inspection with go and not-go gages, or the results of 100% inspection.   Figure 4 applies to 100% inspection of daily output.

Just as in the case of the control charts for $\overline{X}$ and R explained in Examples 1 and 2, the control chart for p has a central line and upper and lower control limits.   From March 6 through April 8, the central line or standard value was set at 31.5% defective, based on the performance just prior to March 6.   Encouraged by the fact that the quality had been at a better level than this during the 3 weeks beginning March 20, the quality control engineer revised the standard value on April 10.

The total number of units inspected from March 20 through April 8 was 3,259.

TABLE 3. RESULTS OF DAILY FINAL INSPECTION OF AN ELECTRONIC DEVICE

Date	Number of units inspected n	Number of units defective np	Fraction defective p	Date	Number of units inspected n	Number of units defective np	Fraction defective p
Mar. 6	198	72	0.364	May 11	162	45	0.278
7	144	53	0.368	12	354	111	0.314
8	342	133	0.389				
9	72	19	0.264	15	36	13	0.361
10	324	136	0.420	16	333	117	0.351
11	198	82	0.414	17	297	91	0.306
				18	190	81	0.426
13	324	132	0.407	19	108	61	0.565
14	165	55	0.333	20	36	14	0.389
15	213	64	0.300				
16	336	129	0.384	23	86	21	0.244
17	252	79	0.313	24	313	101	0.323
18	177	72	0.407	25	126	41	0.325
				26	216	56	0.259
20	162	47	0.290	27	261	75	0.287
21	270	78	0.289				
22	140	38	0.271	29	543	120	0.221
23	158	40	0.253	30	751	152	0.202
24	245	61	0.249	31	213	49	0.230
25	64	16	0.250	June 1	126	24	0.190
				2	141	29	0.206
27	306	92	0.301	3	162	34	0.210
28	108	28	0.259				
29	195	53	0.272	5	177	33	0.186
30	142	34	0.239	6	156	23	0.147
31	126	27	0.214	7	216	28	0.130
Apr. 1	107	36	0.336	8	90	11	0.122
				9	144	17	0.118
3	162	33	0.204	10	249	32	0.129
4	180	27	0.150				
5	321	84	0.262	12	105	11	0.105
6	162	50	0.309	13	126	21	0.167
7	267	80	0.300	14	198	30	0.152
8	144	39	0.271	15	180	27	0.150
				16	180	37	0.206
10	213	81	0.380	17	252	50	0.198
11	144	43	0.299				
12	126	34	0.270	19	270	40	0.148
13	36	11	0.306	20	270	50	0.185
14	270	61	0.226	21	144	24	0.167
15	72	45	0.625	22	141	26	0.184
				23	114	19	0.167
17	108	35	0.324	24	198	27	0.136
18	159	73	0.459				
19	231	103	0.446	26	54	8	0.148
20	105	39	0.371	27	126	27	0.214
21	189	90	0.476	28	159	25	0.151
22	189	53	0.280	29	54	8	0.148
				30	72	14	0.194
24	306	142	0.464	July 1	342	58	0.170
25	198	68	0.343				
26	396	136	0.343	3	255	56	0.220
27	284	85	0.299	4	54	9	0.167
28	199	62	0.312	5	288	56	0.194
29	156	45	0.288	6	155	25	0.161
				7	87	18	0.207
May 1	90	32	0.356	8	225	38	0.169
2	123	77	0.626				
3	267	101	0.378	10	454	90	0.198
4	264	90	0.341	11	159	39	0.245
5	156	53	0.340	12	195	37	0.190
6	132	45	0.341	13	36	6	0.167
8	126	40	0.317	18	69	22	0.319
9	190	70	0.368	19	152	41	0.270
10	261	79	0.303				

(This is the sum of the values of n shown in Table 3 for this period, namely, 162, 270, 140, etc.)   The total number of defective units was 863 (the sum of 47, 78, 38, etc.). For this period of 3 weeks, the average fraction defective p was $863/3,259 = 0.265$. This was adopted by the quality control engineer as the new standard value and was used from April 10 until June 20.   Beginning on June 21, the standard value was again revised, this time to 0.157 based on the record from June 5 to 20 inclusive (410 defectives in 2,613 units).

29. Control Limits.   The control limits on a chart for p provide an answer to the question, "Are the variations in per cent defective from lot to lot (in this case, from day to day) such as might be expected as a matter of chance, if the average quality were maintained at the standard level assumed?"   To answer this question it is necessary to realize that chance fluctuations in per cent defective will be greater with small lots than with large ones.   Hence, if daily production (or other lot size) varies, the position of the control limits must vary.   Figure 4 illustrates the variation of control limits.

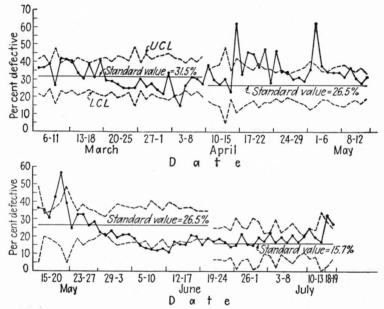

Fig. 4.   Control chart for per cent defective for daily output of an electronic device.

The upper and lower control limits are equally distant from the central line.   Comparison with Table 3 will show that the limits are closest to the central line when the daily production is largest and farthest from the central line when the daily production is smallest.   The methods for calculating limits on a p chart are explained in Chap. X.

30. Reasons for Improvement in Quality.   Analysis of the causes of rejections on March 10, 11, and 13 suggested that these points were out of control because of defects associated with inadequate training of operators on a certain technique.   An intensive program of operator training on this technique was initiated in the following few days.   This training program was responsible for the improvement in the general quality level apparent after March 20.

On April 10, the first day of the new standard value of 26.5%, the day's point was out of control.   On April 15, the defectives skyrocketed to 62.5%.   For the following month, many points were out of control, and the daily per cent defective was continuously higher than the standard of 26.5%.   Nearly all the increase was attributable to a greater number of failures of the device to meet a certain performance test.

Prior to April 10, this test had been responsible for nearly one-third of all rejections. For a period after that date, it caused nearly half the rejections.

This performance test was now set up in a way that permitted the recording of measured values. This made possible the use of control charts for variables, *i.e.*, $\bar{X}$ and R charts. In this case, the diagnostic value of the charts proved to be excellent. As a result of this diagnosis, certain changes were made in production methods that almost completely eliminated failures to pass this performance test. From June 1 until the termination of production on July 20, only two devices out of more than 5,000 produced failed to pass this test. This not only eliminated the erratic points that were out of control because of too many defectives, but also greatly improved the general quality level.

31. Interpretation of Points Out of Control in Direction of Better Quality. Supervisors using control charts for fraction defective sometimes are interested only in out-of-control points on the side of poorer quality. This attitude may result in failure to secure certain useful information that might be obtained from analysis of the "good" out-of-control points.

Occasionally faulty inspection may be the assignable cause producing low values of fraction defective. The quality is not really better; it only appears to be so because the inspectors have not done their work properly. This calls for action by management to correct the situation, just as high out-of-control points call for action to correct faulty production. It should always be kept in mind that the figures analyzed by a Shewhart control chart of any type are figures obtained from an inspection operation. They are influenced by inspection variability as well as by production variability.

If this variability is not the cause of out-of-control points on the good side, they are worth investigating for clues as to how the quality level of the process may permanently be improved. It is worth while to discover the assignable causes of better quality.

However, in Example 3 these points neither indicated inspectors' errors nor gave clues to process improvement. The series of out-of-control points that started on June 6 merely reflected the general improvement in quality level as a result of the elimination of the failures to meet the performance test previously mentioned.

32. Runs or Sequences in Control Charts. Sometimes the chart may suggest the presence of assignable causes of variation, even though no points fall outside the control limits. Statistical techniques, some simple and others complex, have been developed to draw conclusions from data based on the analysis of runs or sequences. One rough but simple rule, which is applicable to the p chart as well as to other control charts, is to view seven or more successive points on the same side of the central line as indicating that the process average has probably changed. In other words, such a sequence is evidence of an assignable cause of variation. On the p chart, such a run of points above or below the standard value suggests a shift in the quality level. (Rules for extreme runs are stated in Art. 88, Chap. V. Their theoretical basis is explained in Art. 179, Chap. IX.)

Figure 4 contains four such runs. One which started March 20 indicated an improvement in the quality level; this resulted from the intensive program of operator training. The evidence given by this run that the process was no longer in control at a standard level of 31.5% defective was confirmed on April 4 by an out-of-control point on the low side. The second run started on April 15 with a high point and contained many such points; it reflected the trouble with the performance tests. The third run began on May 29. Seven successive points below the central line were confirmed by the eighth point (June 6) falling below the control limits. The fourth run extended from June 30 to the completion of production on July 19. It apparently reflected a slight relaxation by production supervisors who knew that the manufacture of this particular model was soon to be terminated.   This run was also confirmed by two high out-of-control points on the final 2 days.

33. Some Comments on Example 3.   This is typical of many industrial uses of the p chart, in that attention to so-called "high spots" (out-of-control points on the high side) resulted in an improvement in the general quality level.   It is also representative of many situations in which the p chart could be started with no change in inspection procedures or in inspection records.

It is noteworthy that this p chart directed attention to an appropriate place for an analysis of one variable by means of an $\bar{X}$ chart and an R chart.   Even though the $\bar{X}$ and R charts are the most useful tools in the statistical quality control kit, it is seldom possible and almost never economical to apply these tools to all variables in the product and in the manufacturing process.   It is sometimes troublesome to decide just where they are likely to be applied most economically.   The p charts frequently suggest the spots for cost-saving applications.

Example 3 describes a situation in which the dollar savings from quality improvement were large.   It is probable that they would not have been made without the stimulus and direction provided by the control chart. It is noteworthy that the benefits of this chart did not terminate with the conclusion of production on July 19; many of the things learned from the studies set in motion by the chart may be expected to be equally useful in the production of a similar product of new design.

This example is not intended to suggest that p charts are applied exclusively to the results of 100% inspection.   They are equally useful with sampling inspection.   Neither is it meant to suggest that p charts always have variable control limits.   As explained in Chap. X, many of them have constant control limits.

EXAMPLE 4.   A CONTROL CHART FOR c ON WELDING OF SEAMS

34. Description of Situation.   In the welding of a certain difficult seam in light metal, practically all seams required some rewelding.   Defects to be corrected included pinholes, cracks, cold laps, excess porosity, etc.   It was decided to make a record of the number of defects found in one seam each hour.   This record was kept for 3 days for each of several welders.   Table 4 gives the results of this inspection of the work of one welder, a man with 2 years experience on similar work.

This is the type of data that may be represented on the control chart for defects per unit, the chart for c.   On this type of chart each unit inspected is represented by one plotted point showing the observed number of defects in that unit.

35. Control Chart for c.   The data of Table 4 are plotted in Fig. 5.   Like the other types of control charts illustrated in Examples 1, 2, and 3, a chart for c has a central line and control limits.   The central line is at the average value of the number of defects per unit.   In this case, 144 defects were observed in 24 units.   The average, designated as $\bar{c}$, is therefore $144/24 = 6$.

On a chart for c, control limits are placed a distance of $3\sqrt{\bar{c}}$ on either side of the average. In this case $3\sqrt{6} = 7.35$.

$$UCL = \bar{c} + 3\sqrt{\bar{c}} = 6 + 7.35 = 13.35$$
$$LCL = \bar{c} - 3\sqrt{\bar{c}} = 6 - 7.35 = -1.35$$

Where a lower control limit is calculated as a negative figure, it is either omitted or indicated on the chart as 0. In Fig. 5 it is omitted.

TABLE 4. NUMBER OF DEFECTS OBSERVED IN WELDED SEAM
(Each count was taken on a single seam. Welder produced 8 seams an hour)

Date	Time of sample	Number of defects c
July 18	8:00 A.M.	2
	9:05 A.M.	4
	10:10 A.M.	7
	11:00 A.M.	3
	12:30 P.M.	1
	1:35 P.M.	4
	2:20 P.M.	8
	3:30 P.M.	9
July 19	8:10 A.M.	5
	9:00 A.M.	3
	10:05 A.M.	7
	11:15 A.M.	11
	12:25 P.M.	6
	1:30 P.M.	4
	2:30 P.M.	9
	3:40 P.M.	9
July 20	8:00 A.M.	6
	8:55 A.M.	4
	10:00 A.M.	3
	11:10 A.M.	9
	12:25 P.M.	7
	1:30 P.M.	4
	2:20 P.M.	7
	3:30 P.M.	12
Total	....	144

36. Conclusions from the Control Chart. This example illustrates a by-product of statistical quality control. Occasionally the act of recording and plotting inspection data will disclose pertinent facts that might have been observed without benefit of any control charts but actually were not known until the control charts were plotted. In Example 4, the attempt to apply statistical quality control disclosed a situation that would have been obvious without control charts if anyone had ever taken the trouble to look into the matter.

All of the points on Fig. 5 fall within control limits. Thus the orthodox use of the control chart did not disclose assignable causes of variation. Nevertheless, a definite pattern of variation suggested the existence of such causes. In Fig. 5 this pattern has been emphasized by connecting the points for each morning and each afternoon and omitting the connections between the end of the morning and the start of the afternoon, and between days.

With the points connected in this way it is evident that the quality tends to deteriorate throughout each 4-hr. period and tends to be worse in the afternoon than in the morning. This same pattern appeared in the *c* charts plotted for other welders. The obvious guess was that fatigue was responsible for the increase in the number of defects throughout each continuous working period. A system of rest periods was inaugurated. This eliminated the fatigue pattern and effected a definite improvement in quality.

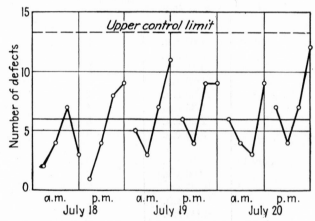

Fig. 5. Control chart for *c*; number of defects in welded seam.

37. Comments on Example 4. Some of the opportunities to reduce costs and improve quality turned up by the first attempts to apply statistical quality control in any manufacturing plant are usually similar to this. Although they might have been disclosed without the use of statistical quality control, no one actually had discovered them. In the early or honeymoon stages of statistical quality control, the persons charged with the responsibility for administering the techniques are likely to receive credit from management for the resulting savings in costs and improvements in quality from these by-product applications, as well as for savings and improvements that are directly dependent on statistical quality control techniques.

Later on, after statistical quality control methods are fully established, the opportunities for apparent by-product cost savings are less frequent. The better the job done by the quality control engineers, the truer will be the preceding statement. An essential point of view in any statistical quality control program is well expressed in the paragraph from the American War Standard pamphlet quoted at the start of this chapter. Inspection must always be viewed as a basis for Purpose *B*, possible action on the production process, as well as for Purpose A, action with regard to the product at hand. This viewpoint tends to secure for the production departments the maximum value from the results of inspection.

One minor comment is suggested by the column in Table 4 that gives the times at which the welded seams were selected for examination. It will be noted that these are not exactly on the hour or half-hour, but that they vary a little one way or the other. The general principle illustrated here is applicable to all process inspection on a sampling basis, and particularly to all sampling for control charts. This principle is that the operator should not be able to be sure in advance just which item is to be selected as the sample for inspection. Hence the need for some irregularity in the times of inspection.

EXAMPLE 5.   WEAKNESS OF A COMMON SAMPLING ACCEPTANCE PROCEDURE

38. Should Sampling Be Used for Acceptance? Two opposite attitudes toward sampling are common in industrial inspection. They are:

1. An uncritical suspicion of all sampling. This is based in part on a belief that a lot may be very different from the sample taken from it.

2. An uncritical acceptance of all sampling. This is based on a belief that a lot will be like the sample taken from it.

The truth is somewhere between these two viewpoints. Samples often give a very inaccurate idea of lot quality. On the other hand, it is possible to devise sampling procedures that do provide a desired quality protection. The basis for distinguishing bad sampling schemes from good ones is developed throughout this entire book. At this point it seems worth while to stimulate curiosity about good sampling schemes by a critical examination of a common sampling acceptance procedure which is bad.

This common procedure calls for inspecting 5 articles from each lot of 50 articles. If every article in this 10% sample conforms to specifications, the lot is accepted. If one or more defective articles are found in the sample of 5, the lot is rejected.

This acceptance procedure gives adequate protection if the articles in a lot are either all good or all bad. (In fact, if lots are either all good or all bad, a sample of one is sufficient.) It gives little protection against product with a moderate percentage of defective articles.

The truth of this latter statement may be demonstrated by assuming that the product submitted for inspection is, on the average, 4% defective; $i.e.$, on the average there will be 2 defective articles in a lot of 50. Some lots will contain more; some less. The expected chance distribution in 1,000 lots submitted would be something like that shown in column B of Table 5. It will be noted that the lots submitted vary from 0% defective to 12% defective, having from 0 to 6 defective articles. In 1,000 lots with 50 articles in each lot, 50,000 articles are submitted for acceptance.

Column D gives for each lot quality the relative frequency of having at least one defective article in a random sample of 5 taken from a lot of 50. The first figure, 0.00, is obvious; there can be no defective in the sample if there is none in the lot. The second figure, 0.10, merely states the reasonable conclusion that if there is only one defective in a lot of 50, that defective will appear in only 10% of the samples of 5 taken from the lot. The source of the remaining figures in column D is not so obvious. They can be calculated by simple probability mathematics as explained in Chap. IX. Or—for those who are skeptical of unfamiliar mathematics—they may be checked approximately by a simple experiment such as dealing 5-card hands from well-shuffled 50-card decks in which certain cards are designated as defective articles, or drawing beads or chips from a bowl of 50 with certain beads or chips marked to indicate defectives.

It is evident that if 10% of the lots are rejected, 90% will be accepted; if 19% are rejected, 81% will be accepted, etc. That is, the sum of the decimals in columns D and E must be 1.00. Columns F, G, H, and I are derived from the preceding columns as indicated in the table.

TABLE 5. RESULTS OF SAMPLING ACCEPTANCE PLAN
(Take sample of 5 from lot of 50. Accept lot if no defectives are found in sample; reject lot if one or more defectives are found in sample. 1,000 lots. Assumed process average 4% defective)

	B	C*	D	E	F	G	H	I
Number of defectives in lot	Number of lots submitted	Number of defectives submitted	Proportion of lots submitted that will be		Number of lots rejected	Number of lots accepted	Number of defectives in rejected lots	Number of defectives in accepted lots
			Rejected	Accepted				
A		$A \times B$			$D \times B$	$E \times B$	$A \times F$	$A \times G$
0	130	0	0.00	1.00	0	130	0	0
1	270	270	0.10	0.90	27	243	27	243
2	275	550	0.19	0.81	52	223	104	446
3	185	555	0.28	0.72	52	133	156	399
4	90	360	0.35	0.65	32	58	128	232
5	35	175	0.42	0.58	15	20	75	100
6	15	90	0.49	0.51	7	8	42	48
Totals	1,000	2,000	....	....	185	815	532	1,468

* Column C gives the total number of defective articles in the lots having each specified number of defectives. The total number of defective articles submitted is 2,000. This is 4% of the 50,000 submitted.

The practical conclusions from the table are obtained from an analysis of the totals of columns F, G, H, and I. Column G tells that 815 of the lots are accepted; this is a total of 40,750 articles. The significant figure desired is the quality of these accepted lots. Column I indicates that they contain 1,468 defective articles. The ratio of 1,468 to 40,750 is 0.036; that is, there are 3.6% defectives in the accepted lots.

It is evident that this acceptance procedure has effected a negligible improvement in quality. The incoming quality submitted was 4% defective, and the outgoing quality after inspection is 3.6% defective. To accomplish this small improvement 18.5% (185 lots out of 1,000) of the submitted product was rejected.

It is also of interest to determine the quality of these rejected lots. These 185 lots contain 532 defectives among 9,250 articles, or 5.75% defective. In them, each sample of 5 contained at least one defective article; calculations based on probability mathematics indicate that 14 of them may be expected to have 2 defectives in the sample of 5. This is a total of 199 defective articles found in the samples. If these

199 defective articles were eliminated from the 185 lots, there would remain 333 defectives among 9,051 articles; this is 3.68% defective. In other words, once the defective articles found in the samples are removed, the quality of the rejected lots is practically as good as that of the accepted lots.

It should be understood that these calculations assume the inspector makes no mistakes, that he does not reject any good articles examined or accept any bad ones. Moreover, they relate to what may be expected on the average in the long run. Although any given set of 1,000 lots submitted will have slightly different results from those shown in the table, they will not differ enough to make any change in the conclusion that this common acceptance plan gives unsatisfactory protection against product that is moderately defective.

39. Some Comments on Example 5. A serious obstacle to sensible and economic acceptance plans is the illusion that perfection (in the sense of 100% conformity to specifications) is possible as the result of *any* inspection plan. This illusion is often cherished both by those who reject all sampling plans in favor of 100% inspection, and by those who adopt sampling plans that accept a lot if a sample is perfect and reject it if the sample contains one or more defectives. Perhaps without being conscious of giving the matter any thought, persons who favor the latter plan would be inclined to have confidence that the 815 accepted lots of Table 5 were perfect or nearly so because the sample was perfect.

In the case of 100% inspection, the belief in perfection through inspection is mistaken for psychological rather than statistical reasons. Where tens of thousands of similar items are to be inspected, even several 100% inspections cannot be expected to weed out every defective. Inspection fatigue on repetitive inspection operations makes even the best inspector fail to catch all the defective articles. For instance, a first screening might eliminate 90% of the defective pieces. On the second 100% inspection, the defectives—being less numerous—would be harder to find, and possibly only 80% of those remaining would be eliminated. For the same reason, a third inspection might catch only 50% of those then remaining. Although the appropriate percentages missed in any given case will depend on the difficulty of the inspection operation and on the skill and diligence of the inspectors,[1] the general principle is sound that if some nonconforming product is submitted for screening inspection, a portion of it will be passed even with several 100% inspections.

If defective product is submitted for lot-by-lot sampling inspection, it is even more certain that there will be some defective product in the accepted lots. This is not primarily for psychological reasons (sampling inspection is likely to be better done than 100% inspection) but for reasons based on the laws of chance. Example 5 is a case in point.

Most sampling plans for lot-by-lot acceptance in small lots that base

---

[1] The best economical check on the efficiency of 100% inspection is a good sampling inspection.

the decision on each small lot on the evidence of a small sample from that lot are likely to have the same defects as the plan examined in Table 5. Under ordinary conditions the product passed by such a scheme will not be substantially better than the product submitted for examination.

Before such acceptance plans, which often delude the user with a promise of perfection they cannot fulfill, can be discarded in favor of better ones, there must be a recognition of the fact that there is a limit to the degree of perfection to be expected. The question of just what this limit is in any case, *i.e.*, just what is an acceptable quality level, is basically a question of economy. Some methods of getting as good an assurance as possible of this acceptable quality level are explained in Part Four. They require as background some understanding of the principles of the Shewhart control chart, which are developed in Parts Two and Three.

Part Two

THE SHEWHART CONTROL
CHART FOR VARIABLES

CHAPTER III

SOME FUNDAMENTAL STATISTICAL CONCEPTS

It seemed to me that there was a defect in the habit of thought of many in the engineering profession, and that some sort of campaign was needed to inculcate in peoples' minds the idea that every number has a fringe, that it is not to be regarded as exact but as so much plus or minus a bit, and that the size of this bit is one of its really important qualities.—C. G. Darwin[1]

40. The Need for Understanding Statistical Principles. This chapter, and the two following, deal with the principles behind the control charts for variables—particularly the charts for $\overline{X}$ and R such as were illustrated in Examples 1 and 2.

At this point, those readers, if any, who think they are not interested in principles but who want descriptions of practical applications, are invited to turn ahead to Chap. VI, which gives concise directions for the $\overline{X}$ and R control charts, and thence to Chap. XIX, in which many varied control-chart applications in different industries are described. Such descriptions may help greatly in suggesting somewhat parallel opportunities in one's own plant—opportunities that might not be evident without this stimulus to the imagination.

Nevertheless, although much good work in statistical quality control has been done by individuals who had only a vague notion of the principles behind the control chart, experience shows that the lack of a clear understanding of these principles may lead to certain costly mistakes that otherwise would be avoided. For this reason the reader who skips ahead will be well advised to return to this chapter and the following ones for an explanation of control-chart principles.

It should be remarked that the theory given in these chapters and elsewhere in this book is not theory at all in the strictly mathematical sense of the word. It is rather what—in the mathematicians' language—is called an *intuitive* explanation of the principles involved.

Few of the many engineers, production men, and inspection supervisors who will make use of statistical quality control techniques in manufacturing will have need to advance the frontiers of theoretical knowledge in this field. For their purpose, it is not necessary that they undertake the study of mathematical statistics. What they do need is a general con-

[1] Darwin, C. G., Statistical Control of Production, *Nature*, vol. 149, pp. 573–575, 1943.

cept of what mathematicians have done and of how it is significant to them. Most of the theory they need can be presented with the use of ordinary arithmetic, with the occasional assistance of algebra on a fairly elementary level. With such a background of theory, they will not only be in a better position to make effective use of statistical quality control techniques, but they will also be better able to recognize those situations in which they may need the advice of a mathematical statistician.

41. Description of Patterns of Variation. Variation seems inevitable in nature. Manufacturing processes are no exception to this. Whether one is attempting to control a dimension of a part which is to go into a precision assembly, the resistance of a relay, the acidity of a solution used for dyeing textiles, the weight of the contents of a container, or any other quality of a manufactured product, it is certain that the quality will vary.

It follows that it is necessary to have some simple methods of describing patterns of variation. Statisticians have developed such methods. One useful method involves a *frequency distribution*. Another involves the determination of an *average* and some measure of the *dispersion* or spread.

This chapter explains and illustrates these methods of describing patterns of variation. It explains that there may be both stable and unstable patterns of variation; it points out that the practical conclusions to be drawn from frequency distributions, averages, and measures of dispersion depend on the stability of the pattern of variation. The control chart, which is a test for this stability, is illustrated. An explanation of why the control chart works and detailed instructions as to its use are deferred till later chapters.

42. Counting the Frequencies of Different Observations. Table 6 gives the results of measurements of drained weights[1] in the canning of tomatoes. Several times during a shift in this particular cannery, a company inspector took from the production line five cans that had been filled and sealed. She opened each can, emptied out and weighed the solid contents, and recorded the results to the nearest half ounce. Table 6 shows such measurements covering 11 days of operation on the day shift, a total of 260 measurements.

One way to organize such figures to show their pattern of variation is to count the number of times each value occurs. This may be done conveniently on a check sheet such as Fig. 6. The results of such a count are called a *frequency distribution*.

---

[1] These are drained weights immediately after filling the cans and before processing them. From a control viewpoint, it is advantageous to determine drained weight at this time in order to provide an immediate basis for action whenever the measurements disclose the existence of trouble. Actual specifications of the U.S. Food and Drug Administration relate to drained weights after processing. A necessary part of the control procedure which is not discussed here is a determination of the relationship between drained weights before and after processing.

TABLE 6. DRAINED WEIGHT AFTER FILLING OF CONTENTS OF SIZE NO. 2½ CANS OF STANDARD GRADE TOMATOES IN PURÉE
(Weight given in ounces)

Sample no.	Date	Hour	Measurement on each can of 5 cans per sample					Average $\overline{X}$	Range R
1	Sept. 21	9:30	22.0	22.5	22.5	24.0	23.5	22.9	2.0
2		10:50	20.5	22.5	22.5	23.0	21.5	22.0	2.5
3		11:45	20.0	20.5	23.0	22.0	21.5	21.4	3.0
4		2:30	21.0	22.0	22.0	23.0	22.0	22.0	2.0
5		5:25	22.5	19.5	22.5	22.0	21.0	21.5	3.0
6	Sept. 22	10:00	23.0	23.5	21.0	22.0	20.0	21.9	3.5
7		1:15	19.0	20.0	22.0	20.5	22.5	20.8	3.5
8		5:00	21.5	20.5	19.0	19.5	19.5	20.0	2.5
9	Sept. 23	9:30	21.0	22.5	20.0	22.0	22.0	21.5	2.5
10		1:15	21.5	23.0	22.0	23.0	18.5	21.6	4.5
11		1:45	20.0	19.5	21.0	20.0	20.5	20.2	1.5
12		3:30	19.0	21.0	21.0	21.0	20.5	20.5	2.0
13	Sept. 25	8:00	19.5	20.5	21.0	20.5	21.0	20.5	1.5
14		10:25	20.0	21.5	24.0	23.0	20.0	21.7	4.0
15		11:30	22.5	19.5	21.0	21.5	21.0	21.1	3.0
16		2:30	21.5	20.5	22.0	21.5	23.5	21.8	3.0
17		3:15	19.0	21.5	23.0	21.0	23.5	21.6	4.5
18		5:30	21.0	20.5	19.5	22.0	21.0	20.8	2.5
19	Sept. 26	2:00	20.0	23.5	24.0	20.5	21.5	21.9	4.0
20		3:00	22.0	20.5	21.0	22.5	20.0	21.2	2.5
21		4:45	19.0	20.5	21.0	20.5	22.5	20.7	3.5
22	Sept. 27	7:30	21.5	25.0	21.0	19.0	21.0	21.5	6.0
23		8:35	22.5	22.0	23.0	22.0	23.5	22.6	1.5
24		10:40	22.5	22.0	22.0	19.5	20.5	21.3	3.0
25		1:45	18.5	22.0	22.5	21.0	21.5	21.1	4.0
26		3:30	21.5	20.5	20.5	16.5	21.5	20.1	5.0
27		4:00	24.0	22.0	17.5	21.0	22.5	21.4	6.5
28		4:40	19.5	22.5	15.5	20.0	22.5	20.0	7.0
29	Sept. 28	7:15	22.0	17.5	21.0	22.0	23.5	21.2	6.0
30		7:45	22.0	20.0	20.5	24.0	21.5	21.6	4.0
31		10:00	22.5	21.0	19.5	21.5	22.5	21.4	3.0
32		1:15	20.0	22.0	20.0	21.5	20.0	20.7	2.0
33		3:30	21.0	19.5	22.0	20.0	20.0	20.5	2.5
34	Sept. 29	9:00	22.5	21.5	21.0	21.5	23.5	22.0	2.5
35		10:50	22.0	21.0	21.0	20.5	21.0	21.1	1.5
36		1:15	25.0	20.0	20.0	20.5	22.5	21.6	5.0
37		2:30	20.5	21.0	21.0	19.0	21.0	20.5	2.0
38		4:10	21.5	22.0	22.0	20.0	21.0	21.3	2.0
39		5:20	21.5	22.0	21.5	20.5	22.5	21.6	2.0
40	Sept. 30	9:30	22.5	24.5	25.5	20.0	21.0	22.7	5.5
41		11:15	21.5	24.0	21.5	21.5	22.5	22.2	2.5
42		2:10	23.0	23.5	21.0	21.5	21.5	22.1	2.5
43		3:30	22.5	19.5	21.5	20.5	20.0	20.8	3.0
44	Oct. 2	8:20	23.5	23.0	24.5	21.5	20.5	22.6	4.0
45		2:30	21.0	21.0	24.5	23.0	22.5	22.4	3.5
46		3:30	24.5	21.5	21.5	22.5	22.5	22.5	3.0
47		5:00	24.0	21.0	24.0	22.0	20.5	22.3	3.5
48	Oct. 3	9:15	23.5	22.5	20.0	20.0	21.0	21.4	3.5
49		10:00	22.0	20.5	21.0	22.5	23.0	21.8	2.5
50		1:00	22.0	23.5	24.0	22.0	22.0	22.7	2.0
51		3:00	23.5	21.0	23.5	21.5	23.0	22.5	2.5
52		4:30	24.5	21.5	21.0	24.5	22.5	22.8	3.5

43. Definitions Relative to Frequency Distributions.[1] A *grouped frequency distribution* of a set of observations is an arrangement which shows the frequency of occurrence of the values of the variable in ordered classes.

The interval, along the scale of measurement, of each ordered class is termed a *cell*.

The *frequency* for any cell is the number of observations in that cell.

The *relative frequency* for any cell is the frequency for that cell divided by the total number of observations.

25.5	I
25.0	II
24.5	‖‖ I
24.0	‖‖ IIII
23.5	‖‖ ‖‖ IIII
23.0	‖‖ ‖‖ IIII
22.5	‖‖ ‖‖ ‖‖ ‖‖ ‖‖ ‖‖ I
22.0	‖‖ ‖‖ ‖‖ ‖‖ ‖‖ ‖‖ IIII
21.5	‖‖ ‖‖ ‖‖ ‖‖ ‖‖ ‖‖ III
21.0	‖‖ ‖‖ ‖‖ ‖‖ ‖‖ ‖‖ ‖‖ ‖‖ I
20.5	‖‖ ‖‖ ‖‖ ‖‖ ‖‖ I
20.0	‖‖ ‖‖ ‖‖ ‖‖ IIII
19.5	‖‖ ‖‖ II
19.0	‖‖ II
18.5	II
18.0	
17.5	II
17.0	
16.5	I
16.0	
15.5	I

FIG. 6. Check sheet to determine frequency distribution from data of Table 6.

44. Cells and Cell Boundaries. In Table 6, each measured weight was recorded to the nearest half ounce, as no greater precision of measurement was required. However, the weight was actually what is called a *continuous variable*. For example, the contents of a given can recorded by this weighing process as weighing 21.0 oz. does not necessarily weigh exactly 21 oz. If more precise methods of measurement were used, it might be found to weigh 20.897 or 21.204 oz. or any other value which is nearer to 21.0 than it is to 20.5 or 21.5. The statement in the frequency distribution that 41 cans had a drained weight of 21.0 oz. really means that the weight in each of the 41 cans was somewhere between 20.75 and

[1] Taken by permission from "Manual on Quality Control of Materials," American Society for Testing Materials, Philadelphia, 1951. This A.S.T.M. manual contains an excellent detailed exposition of matters treated briefly in this chapter.

TABLE 7. EXAMPLES OF GROUPED FREQUENCY DISTRIBUTIONS SHOWING CELL
MID-POINTS AND CELL BOUNDARIES
(Data of Table 6 on drained weights of contents of size No. 2½ cans of tomatoes)

	a. Finer grouping			*b.* Coarser grouping	
Cell mid-points	Cell boundaries	Observed frequency	Cell mid-points	Cell boundaries	Observed frequency
	25.75	—		25.75	—
25.5		1			
	25.25	—	25.25		3
25.0		2			
	24.75	—		24.75	—
24.5		6			
	24.25	—	24.25		15
24.0		9			
	23.75	—		23.75	—
23.5		14			
	23.25	—	23.25		28
23.0		14			
	22.75	—		22.75	—
22.5		31			
	22.25	—	22.25		65
22.0		34			
	21.75	—		21.75	—
21.5		33			
	21.25	—	21.25		74
21.0		41			
	20.75	—		20.75	—
20.5		26			
	20.25	—	20.25		50
20.0		24			
	19.75	—		19.75	—
19.5		12			
	19.25	—	19.25		19
19.0		7			
	18.75	—		18.75	—
18.5		2			
	18.25	—	18.25		2
18.0		0			
	17.75	—		17.75	—
17.5		2			
	17.25	—	17.25		2
17.0		0			
	16.75	—		16.75	—
16.5		1			
	16.25	—	16.25		1
16.0		0			
	15.75	—		15.75	—
15.5		1			
	15.25		15.25		1
				14.75	

Total...................... 260   Total...................... 260

21.25 oz.   The figure of 21.0 oz. is the *mid-point* of a cell the boundaries of which are 20.75 and 21.25.

In grouping data into a frequency distribution, the questions always arise as to how many cells there should be, and where the cell boundaries should be placed.   A rough working rule used by statisticians is to aim to have about 20 cells.   This is often subject to exceptions dictated by other considerations.   The distribution of Fig. 6 has 21 cells.

Cell boundaries should be chosen halfway between two possible observations.   Cell intervals should be equal.   In grouping the data of Table 6, the smallest possible cell size is 0.5 oz., as measurements were not recorded to any smaller unit.   However if measurements had been made to the nearest 0.1 oz., it might still have been advantageous to use a cell size of 0.5 oz.

Table 7 illustrates an appropriate way to present a frequency distribution showing cell mid-points and cell boundaries.   It illustrates also the effect of a coarser grouping, using the cell width as 1.0 oz. instead of 0.5 oz.   With measurements made to the nearest 0.5 oz., no cell size between 0.5 and 1.0 is possible.   Thus these figures must be grouped into either 21 cells or 11 cells.

45. Graphic Representation of a Frequency Distribution.   Three common ways of graphic presentation of frequency distributions are shown in Fig. 7.   Of these, the *frequency histogram* of Fig. 7a is in some respects the best.   In this graph the sides of the columns represent the upper and lower cell boundaries, and their heights (and areas) are proportional to the frequencies within the cells.   Figure 7b, the *frequency bar chart*, uses bars centered on the mid-points of the cells; the heights of the bars are proportional to the frequencies in the respective cells.   Figure 7c, the *frequency polygon*, consists of a series of straight lines joining small circles which are plotted at cell mid-points with a height proportional to cell frequencies.

46. Cumulative Frequency Distributions.   It is sometimes advantageous to tabulate the frequencies of values less than or greater than the respective cell boundaries.   Table 8 illustrates this.   It shows both the number of cans and the percentage of cans having less than a given weight.

Such a *cumulative frequency distribution* may be presented graphically in the manner shown in Fig. 8a.   This type of graph is called an *ogive* because of its similarity to the ogee curve of the architect and the dam designer.

The plotting of relative frequency on a probability scale,[1] as in Fig. 8b,

---

[1] Probability paper is the invention of an engineer, the late Allen Hazen.   It can be purchased from most manufacturers of graph paper.   The probability scale is so designed that the ogive of a normal curve (explained later in this chapter) will plot on it as a straight line.

tends to smooth the ogive to something closer to a straight line.   It also concentrates somewhat more attention on the extreme variations.

47. Frequency Distributions Often Supply a Basis for Action.   A frequency distribution relative to any quality of a manufactured product

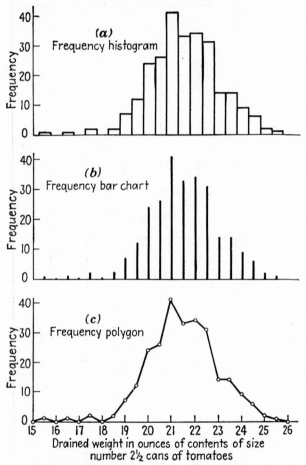

FIG. 7.   Three methods of graphical presentation of a frequency distribution—data of Table 7.

supplies a useful picture of the way in which that quality has varied in the past.   Throughout this book, there are many illustrations of actions that may be taken more intelligently with such a picture than they are likely to be taken without it.   Some of these relate to specification of the quality characteristic and its tolerance limits; others to action on the process; still others to the planning of inspection and acceptance procedures.

A word of caution is required at this point.   Frequency distributions are often used to judge the capability of a manufacturing process. In making such judgments, it is desirable to use the Shewhart control chart to supplement the picture given by the frequency distribution. Otherwise frequency distributions from a process not in statistical control may

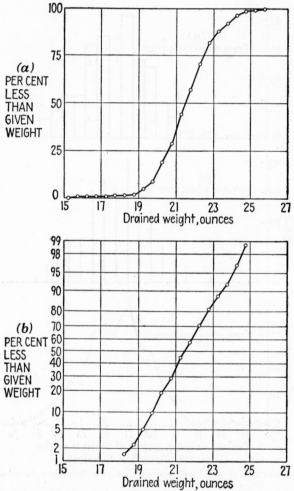

FIG. 8.   Graphical presentation of a cumulative frequency distribution—data of Table 8: (a) rectangular coordinate ruling; (b) probability ruling.

lead to incorrect inferences regarding process capability. The need for the control chart is briefly explained at the end of this chapter and elaborated throughout the remainder of this book.

For most uses in a manufacturing plant, a check sheet such as shown in Fig. 6 gives a graphic picture of a frequency distribution that is good enough for practical purposes. Except for special reports that are to be given wide circulation, the expense of graphic presentations such as those shown in Figs. 7 and 8 is seldom justified.   Example 6 illustrates a practical use of another form of check sheet.

TABLE 8.   EXAMPLES OF CUMULATIVE FREQUENCY DISTRIBUTIONS
(Data of Table 6 on drained weights of contents of size No. 2½ cans of tomatoes)

Weight, oz.	Number of cans having less than given weight	Percentage of cans having less than given weight
25.75	260	100.0
25.25	259	99.6
24.75	257	98.8
24.25	251	96.5
23.75	242	92.3
23.25	228	87.7
22.75	214	82.3
22.25	183	70.4
21.75	149	57.3
21.25	116	44.6
20.75	75	28.8
20.25	49	18.8
19.75	25	9.6
19.25	13	5.0
18.75	6	2.3
18.25	4	1.5
17.75	4	1.5
17.25	2	0.8
16.75	2	0.8
16.25	1	0.4
15.75	1	0.4
15.25	0	0.0

EXAMPLE 6.   A USE OF A FREQUENCY DISTRIBUTION TO ACCOMPLISH A COST SAVING

48. Facts of the Case.   In 100% inspection of completed electron tubes, a certain critical electrical characteristic was measured on a meter.   This meter had a dial gage on which the value of the electrical characteristic was indicated by a pointer. Two fixed red lines were set on the dial, one at the minimum and the other at the maximum specified value.   This permitted the inspector to tell at a glance whether or not each tube met the specifications, so that she could rapidly sort the rejected tubes from the good ones.

Because this characteristic was responsible for a number of rejections and it was desired to study its pattern of variation, the inspector was asked to read the actual value registered on the dial gage for every tube and to make a line on a frequency distribution check sheet indicating this value.   One check sheet was made for each

shift and sent immediately to the quality control engineer of the tube plant.   These
sheets generally looked something like Fig. 9.

One morning the check sheet from the preceding night shift looked like Fig. 10

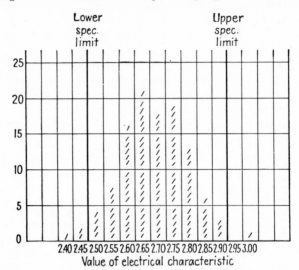

Fig. 9. Typical check sheet showing frequency distribution of electrical characteristic
of vacuum tube.

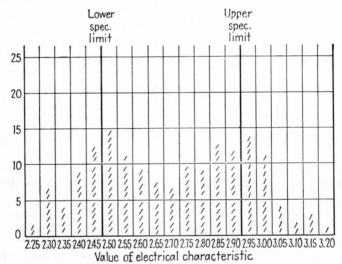

Fig. 10. This check sheet called for investigation of the reasons for the unusual distribution pattern.

This not only indicated a great increase in the proportion of rejected tubes but also
showed an unusual distribution pattern.

49. Analysis and Action.   The quality control engineer suspected that this unusual
distribution pattern might indicate an inspection error.   He went immediately to the

inspection station and rescued from the scrap bin the tubes rejected on the night shift. They were all retested by the day-shift inspector, and nearly all proved to be satisfactory. It developed that there had been a new inspector on the night shift who had not understood how to operate the test equipment. Several hundred dollars worth of good tubes were thus saved from the scrap heap. The new night-shift inspector was instructed in the correct method of testing so that she would not repeat this mistake.

50. Comment on Example 6. Figures 9 and 10 represent a slightly different form of check sheet from that shown in Fig. 6. They are arranged to give a graphic picture of the pattern of variation somewhat like that given by a *frequency histogram* (Fig. 7a).

In this case the inspector made a record of the frequency distribution with a minimum of clerical labor. She did not actually write down any figures for the measured value of the electrical characteristic but merely made a single line in the appropriate cell on the check sheet each time she made a measurement.

It often happens that a person with some understanding of statistics and with a thorough technical knowledge of a process can make a quick and accurate guess at a reason for trouble from looking at the behavior pattern shown on either a frequency distribution or a control chart. The quality control engineer made such a guess in this case. He recognized Fig. 10 as a *bimodal distribution*, that is, one with two cells with high frequencies separated by cells with lower frequencies. This often results from the mixing of two distributions with different modes or averages. From the engineer's technical knowledge of the testing of electron tubes, he recognized how a particular type of inspection error would have this effect. Guesses made in this way are not always correct, but they have a much better chance of being right than hunches unsupported by any statistical evidence.

Frequency distributions of samples may be plotted and examined to guide decisions regarding acceptance of lots of product from which the samples are taken. An informal use of a frequency distribution in this manner is described in Example 27, Chap. XVI. The Shainin Lot Plot method, described in Art. 335, Chap. XVI, provides a formal procedure for acceptance based on analysis of a frequency distribution of a sample of 50 articles.

51. Averages and Measures of Dispersion. In presenting test data, it often happens that showing a series of frequency distributions will require too much space. Some more concise form of presentation must be found. This always requires at least two numbers. One of these is some sort of average or measure of central tendency. The other is some sort of measure of the spread or dispersion of the observations. Many different measures of central tendency and measures of dispersion are used by statisticians. The choice of the measures to be used in any particular case should depend on the probable uses of the statistics. Only those measures of central tendency and dispersion which are important in industrial quality control are explained here.

In the technical language of statistics, the word *average* applies to any measure of central tendency. In popular language, the word *average* applies to that measure of central tendency which in the technical language of statistics is called the *arithmetic mean*.

The arithmetic mean of a set of n observed numbers is the sum of the numbers divided by n. This statement may be expressed in algebraic terms as follows:

$$\overline{X} = \frac{X_1 + X_2 + X_3 + \cdots + X_n}{n} \tag{1}$$

where the symbol $\overline{X}$ represents the arithmetic mean, and X_1, X_2, X_3, etc., represent the specific observed values.

Throughout this book, the word *average* and the symbol $\overline{X}$ (read as "X bar" or "bar X") are used to designate the arithmetic mean.[1]

Other measures of central tendency occasionally referred to in this book are the *median* and the *mode*. The *median* is the magnitude of the middle case, *i.e.*, the value that has half the observations above it and half below it. The *mode* is the value that occurs most frequently; in a frequency histogram or frequency polygon, it is the observed value corresponding to the high point of the graph.

For many statistical purposes the most useful measure of dispersion of a frequency distribution is the *standard deviation*. This is the root-mean-square deviation of the observed numbers from their average. Expressed in algebraic terms, this is

$$\sigma = \sqrt{\frac{(X_1 - \overline{X})^2 + (X_2 - \overline{X})^2 + (X_3 - \overline{X})^2 + \cdots + (X_n - \overline{X})^2}{n}} \tag{2}$$

Throughout this book the symbol σ is used to represent standard deviation. σ is the lower-case form of the Greek letter sigma and is always read simply as "sigma."[2]

Another important measure of dispersion, used particularly in the control chart, is the *range*. This is the difference between the largest observed value and the smallest observed value. Throughout this book, the symbol R is used to represent the range.[3]

---

[1] This use of *average* in its popular sense of arithmetic mean agrees with the usage in the American War Standards on the control-chart method and with the A.S.T.M. "Manual on Quality Control of Materials."

[2] In some of the literature of statistics, the letter s is used for the standard deviation of an observed sample, and the Greek letter σ is reserved for use to represent the standard deviation of a universe from which samples may be drawn.

[3] R is commonly used for this in American practice. An alternative symbol for range is w, used in most British literature on statistical quality control.

52. Calculation of Average and Standard Deviation. Computations for average and standard deviation of a small number of observations may be illustrated with reference to the five weights on the first line of Table 6. The calculation of the average is

$$
\begin{aligned}
X_1 &= 22.0 \\
X_2 &= 22.5 \\
X_3 &= 22.5 \\
X_4 &= 24.0 \\
X_5 &= \underline{23.5} \\
\Sigma X = X_1 + X_2 + X_3 + X_4 + X_5 &= 114.5
\end{aligned}
$$

$$
\overline{X} = \frac{\Sigma X}{n} = \frac{114.5}{5} = 22.9
$$

The calculation of the standard deviation is as follows:

$$
\begin{aligned}
X_1 - \overline{X} &= 22.0 - 22.9 = -0.9; & (X_1 - \overline{X})^2 &= (-0.9)^2 = 0.81 \\
X_2 - \overline{X} &= 22.5 - 22.9 = -0.4; & (X_2 - \overline{X})^2 &= (-0.4)^2 = 0.16 \\
X_3 - \overline{X} &= 22.5 - 22.9 = -0.4; & (X_3 - \overline{X})^2 &= (-0.4)^2 = 0.16 \\
X_4 - \overline{X} &= 24.0 - 22.9 = 1.1; & (X_4 - \overline{X})^2 &= (1.1)^2 = 1.21 \\
X_5 - \overline{X} &= 23.5 - 22.9 = 0.6; & (X_5 - \overline{X})^2 &= (0.6)^2 = \underline{0.36} \\
& & \text{Sum of squares} &= 2.70
\end{aligned}
$$

$$
\sigma = \sqrt{\frac{\Sigma(X - \overline{X})^2}{n}} = \sqrt{\frac{2.70}{5}} = \sqrt{0.54} = 0.73
$$

An alternative form[1] of the expression for standard deviation is

$$
\sigma = \sqrt{\frac{X_1^2 + X_2^2 + X_3^2 + \cdots + X_n^2}{n} - \overline{X}^2} = \sqrt{\frac{\Sigma X^2}{n} - \overline{X}^2} \tag{3}
$$

[1] The identity between the two expressions for σ may be shown algebraically as follows:

$$
\begin{aligned}
(X_1 - \overline{X})^2 &= X_1^2 - 2X_1\overline{X} + \overline{X}^2 \\
(X_2 - \overline{X})^2 &= X_2^2 - 2X_2\overline{X} + \overline{X}^2 \\
(X_3 - \overline{X})^2 &= X_3^2 - 2X_3\overline{X} + \overline{X}^2 \\
&\cdots\cdots\cdots\cdots\cdots\cdots\cdots \\
(X_n - \overline{X})^2 &= X_n^2 - 2X_n\overline{X} + \overline{X}^2 \\
\hline
\Sigma(X - \overline{X})^2 &= \Sigma X^2 - 2\overline{X}\Sigma X + n\overline{X}^2
\end{aligned}
$$

Dividing both sides of the equation by n

$$
\frac{\Sigma(X - \overline{X})^2}{n} = \frac{\Sigma X^2}{n} - 2\overline{X}\,\frac{\Sigma X}{n} + \overline{X}^2
$$

But, as $\dfrac{\Sigma X}{n} = \overline{X}$, this is

$$
\frac{\Sigma(X - \overline{X})^2}{n} = \frac{\Sigma X^2}{n} - 2\overline{X}^2 + \overline{X}^2 = \frac{\Sigma X^2}{n} - \overline{X}^2
$$

Thus

$$
\sqrt{\frac{\Sigma(X - \overline{X})^2}{n}} = \sqrt{\frac{\Sigma X^2}{n} - \overline{X}^2}
$$

The calculation using this alternative expression for σ is as follows:

$$X_1 = 22.0; \qquad X_1^2 = \quad 484.00$$
$$X_2 = 22.5; \qquad X_2^2 = \quad 506.25$$
$$X_3 = 22.5; \qquad X_3^2 = \quad 506.25$$
$$X_4 = 24.0; \qquad X_4^2 = \quad 576.00$$
$$X_5 = 23.5; \qquad X_5^2 = \quad \underline{552.25}$$
$$\Sigma X^2 = 2{,}624.75$$
$$\bar{X} = 22.9; \qquad \bar{X}^2 = \quad 524.41$$

$$\sigma = \sqrt{\frac{\Sigma X^2}{n} - \bar{X}^2} = \sqrt{\frac{2{,}624.75}{5} - 524.41} = \sqrt{524.95 - 524.41}$$
$$= \sqrt{0.54} = 0.73$$

Particularly where a calculating machine and a table of squares are available, this alternative equation (3) will generally prove more convenient. However, in its use one must always carry more significant figures in the squares than are required in the computed standard deviation. For example, in the preceding calculation, the first three significant figures were lost in the subtraction of 524.41 from 524.95. It was necessary to have five significant figures in the squares in order to have two significant figures in the standard deviation.

In the control chart as originally developed by Shewhart in 1924, calculations for σ such as these were necessary for each subgroup. (A subgroup is a small group of measurements, often four or five, usually taken at nearly the same time. The basis for subgrouping is developed throughout Part Two and explained at some length in Chap. VII.) Because the work of mathematical statisticians has made possible the use of the range as a satisfactory measure of dispersion of subgroups, such calculations of standard deviations of subgroups are no longer required.

53. Shifting the Origin to Simplify the Arithmetic. By shifting the zero point of the measuring scale of the variable for purposes of computation, it is often possible to simplify the calculations involved. For example, the variable in the illustration in the preceding article might have been taken as the excess of the weight above 20 oz. The calculation of the average is changed to

$$\bar{X} \text{ (above the origin of 20.0)} = \frac{2.0 + 2.5 + 2.5 + 4.0 + 3.5}{5} = \frac{14.5}{5} = 2.9$$

$\bar{X}$ above the origin 0 is of course $20.0 + 2.9 = 22.9$ oz.

Or, if the origin is assumed at a guessed average of, say, 23.0,

$$\bar{X} \text{ (from the origin 23)} = \frac{-1.0 - 0.5 - 0.5 + 1.0 + 0.5}{5}$$
$$= \frac{-0.5}{5} = -0.1$$

$\bar{X}$ from the origin 0 is $23.0 - 0.1 = 22.9$

By this means, averages such as those of subgroups in the control chart may be calculated rapidly by mental arithmetic.

The addition or subtraction of a constant from all of any set of numbers does not change their standard deviation. For this reason, the same shift of origin can be used to simplify the calculation of σ from equation (3). Assuming an origin at 20.0, $\overline{X}$ measured from this origin $= 2.9$. The calculation of σ becomes

$$\sigma = \sqrt{\frac{2^2 + 2.5^2 + 2.5^2 + 4^2 + 3.5^2}{5} - 2.9^2}$$

$$= \sqrt{\frac{4 + 6.25 + 6.25 + 16 + 12.25}{5} - 8.41} = \sqrt{8.95 - 8.41}$$

$$= \sqrt{0.54} = 0.73$$

Or, assuming the origin at 23.0, $\overline{X} = -0.1$,

$$\sigma = \sqrt{\frac{(-1)^2 + (-0.5)^2 + (-0.5)^2 + 1^2 + 0.5^2}{5} - (-0.1)^2}$$

$$= \sqrt{\frac{1 + 0.25 + 0.25 + 1 + 0.25}{5} - 0.01} = \sqrt{0.55 - 0.01}$$

$$= \sqrt{0.54} = 0.73$$

54. Calculation of Average and Standard Deviation of Grouped Frequency Distributions—Long Method. Although the methods described in Art. 52 might be used for finding the average and standard deviation of the 260 observed weights of Table 6, the computation would be time-consuming, and the chances of an error in calculations would be great. To get the average, one would add the 260 individual values

$$\overline{X} = \frac{\Sigma X}{n} = \frac{5,589.5}{260} = 21.498 \text{ oz.}$$

The first step in calculating the standard deviation would be the squaring of each of the 260 numbers. This long calculation is not illustrated here.

The same results could be obtained with less effort by considering the numbers grouped into a frequency distribution. This is illustrated in Table 9.

The importance of carrying extra significant figures in the calculation of σ by the use of formula (3), pointed out in Art. 52, is again evident here. For any practical conclusions drawn from the average $\overline{X}$, there would be no need to carry it out to three decimal places as 21.498. However, for correct calculation of σ these three decimal places are necessary. If $\overline{X}$ were rounded off to 21.50 for this calculation, the effect would be to make a 2% error in σ, as σ would then appear to be 1.45 instead of the correct figure of 1.48.

An inspection of Table 9 will show that 5,589.5 is necessarily the same sum that would be obtained if the 260 numbers were added one by one, and 120,733.25 is necessarily the same sum that would be obtained if each of the 260 numbers was separately squared and the squares were then added. Consider the numbers in any cell of the frequency distribution. For example, consider the cell corresponding to a weight of 20.0 oz. The 24 observations of 20.0 oz., if added one by one, would contribute $24 \times 20.0 = 480$ to the sum of the numbers. As the square of 20 is 400, these 24 observations would contribute $24 \times 400 = 9,600$ to the sum of the squares.

Although less laborious than calculations from the same data without grouping, calculations of the type of Table 9 are still wasteful of time. Table 9 has been introduced at this point primarily to provide a transition to the common short-cut calculations for frequency distributions from the direct calculations explained in Art. 52 that use the basic formulas defining average and standard deviation. These short-cut calculations are illustrated in Table 10a. If the reader fully understands Table 9, he should have no difficulty in understanding Table 10a.

55. Calculation of Average and Standard Deviation of Grouped Frequency Distributions—Short Method. Just as the shift of origin described in Art. 53 simplifies the arithmetic in the calculation from ungrouped data, so also may a shift of origin greatly simplify calculations of average and standard deviation of frequency distributions. Another change in the direction of simplification is a change of units; one cell is equal to one unit throughout the calculations. At the end of the calculation in cell units from the assumed origin, the results for average and standard deviation are converted into units of the original measurements by multiplying by the value of one cell unit. The average is then converted to its original origin by adding the value of the assumed zero point. This is illustrated in Table 10a.

A further short cut, which may be used when a rapid calculation is more important than accuracy, may be obtained by grouping the frequencies into larger cells. This is illustrated in Table 10b using the grouping of Table 7b which has 1 oz. rather than 0.5 oz. as the cell interval.

In all calculations from grouped data, the assumption is made that the true values of the variable are concentrated at the center of the cell in which they fall.[1] In the coarse grouping of Tables 7b and 10b, this assumption does not agree with the known facts. For example, in the cell with the mid-point 21.25 it is known that there are 41 occurrences in

---

[1] By making certain assumptions about the distribution of cases within cells, mathematicians have developed formulas for corrections to be applied to calculations of σ from grouped data. These corrections, known as *Sheppard's corrections*, are explained in most works on mathematical statistics. However, experience with statistics of qualities of manufactured product indicates difficulty in judging whether

TABLE 9. COMPUTATION OF AVERAGE AND STANDARD DEVIATION OF FREQUENCY DISTRIBUTION—LONG METHOD

(Data of Tables 6 and 7a on drained weights of contents of size No. 2½ cans of tomatoes)

Weight, oz. (mid-point of cell)	Frequency	Total weight	Squared weight	Sum of squares for cell
X	f	fX	X^2	fX^2
25.5	1	25.5	650.25	650.25
25.0	2	50.0	625.00	1,250.00
24.5	6	147.0	600.25	3,601.50
24.0	9	216.0	576.00	5,184.00
23.5	14	329.0	552.25	7,731.50
23.0	14	322.0	529.00	7,406.00
22.5	31	697.5	506.25	15,693.75
22.0	34	748.0	484.00	16,456.00
21.5	33	709.5	462.25	15,254.25
21.0	41	861.0	441.00	18,081.00
20.5	26	533.0	420.25	10,926.50
20.0	24	480.0	400.00	9,600.00
19.5	12	234.0	380.25	4,562.00
19.0	7	133.0	361.00	2,527.00
18.5	2	37.0	342.25	684.50
18.0	0	0.0	324.00	0.00
17.5	2	35.0	306.25	612.50
17.0	0	0.0	289.00	0.00
16.5	1	16.5	272.25	272.25
16.0	0	0.0	256.00	0.00
15.5	1	15.5	240.25	240.25
Totals.....	260	5,589.5	......	120,733.25

$$\bar{X} = \frac{\Sigma fX}{n} = \frac{5,589.5}{260} = 21.498 \text{ oz.}$$

$$\sigma = \sqrt{\frac{\Sigma fX^2}{n} - \bar{X}^2} = \sqrt{\frac{120,733.25}{260} - (21.498)^2}$$
$$= \sqrt{464.36 - 462.16} = \sqrt{2.20} = 1.48 \text{ oz.}$$

the lower half of the cell and only 33 in the upper half. As the values of $\bar{X}$ and σ obtained in Table 10b are practically the same as those obtained in Table 10a, it is evident that in this case no appreciable error resulted from the use of the coarser grouping. In most cases some error will be

---

the assumptions behind these corrections are valid in any particular case; their use sometimes introduces rather than corrects an error. For a pertinent discussion of this point, see W. A. Shewhart, "Economic Control of Quality of Manufactured Product," pp. 78–79, D. Van Nostrand Company, New York, 1931. For reasons pointed out by Shewhart, it seems unnecessary to use Sheppard's corrections in most problems in industrial quality control.

TABLE 10a. COMPUTATION OF AVERAGE AND STANDARD DEVIATION OF FREQUENCY DISTRIBUTION—SHORT METHOD

(Data of Tables 6 and 7a on drained weights of contents of size No. 2½ cans of tomatoes)

Weight, oz., mid-point of cell	Frequency	Deviation in cells from assumed origin		
X	f	d	fd	fd^2
25.5	1	9	9	81
25.0	2	8	16	128
24.5	6	7	42	294
24.0	9	6	54	324
23.5	14	5	70	350
23.0	14	4	56	224
22.5	31	3	93	279
22.0	34	2	68	136
21.5	33	1	33	33
21.0	41	0	0	0
20.5	26	− 1	−26	26
20.0	24	− 2	−48	96
19.5	12	− 3	−36	108
19.0	7	− 4	−28	112
18.5	2	− 5	−10	50
18.0	0	− 6	0	0
17.5	2	− 7	−14	98
17.0	0	− 8	0	0
16.5	1	− 9	− 9	81
16.0	0	−10	0	0
15.5	1	−11	−11	121
Totals.....	260		259	2,541

$$\bar{X} \text{ (in cells from assumed origin of 21.0)} = \frac{\Sigma fd}{n} = \frac{259}{260} = 0.996$$

$$\bar{X} \text{ (in original units from true origin)} = \text{Assumed origin} + \frac{\Sigma fd}{n} \text{ (cell interval)}$$

$$= 21.0 + 0.996(0.5) = 21.498 \text{ oz.}$$

$$\sigma \text{ (in cell unit)} = \sqrt{\frac{\Sigma fd^2}{n} - \left(\frac{\Sigma fd}{n}\right)^2} = \sqrt{\frac{2,541}{260} - (0.996)^2}$$

$$= \sqrt{9.773 - 0.992} = \sqrt{8.781} = 2.96$$

$$\sigma \text{ (in original units)} = (\sigma \text{ in cell units}) \text{ (cell interval)} = 2.96(0.5) = 1.48 \text{ oz.}$$

introduced whenever a coarser grouping is used to shorten computations. In general, it is desirable that the least count of the measuring instrument be such as to permit grouping the data into at least 20 cells.[1]

[1] For a good discussion of this point, see W. E. Deming and R. T. Birge, On the Statistical Theory of Errors, *Reviews of Modern Physics*, vol. 6, p. 124, July, 1934.

56. Inferences about Pattern of Variation to Be Drawn from Average and Standard Deviation. It clearly would be advantageous if substantially all the information contained in a frequency distribution could be packed into two figures, such as a measure of central tendency and a measure of the spread or dispersion. Under favorable circumstances it is

TABLE 10b. COMPUTATION OF AVERAGE AND STANDARD DEVIATION OF FREQUENCY DISTRIBUTION—SHORT METHOD—COARSER GROUPING

(Data of Table 6 and 7a drained weights of contents of size No. 2½ cans of tomatoes)

Weight, oz. (mid-point of cell)	Frequency	Deviation in cells from assumed origin		
X	f	d	fd	fd^2
25.25	3	4	12	48
24.25	15	3	45	135
23.25	28	2	56	112
22.25	65	1	65	65
21.25	74	0	0	0
20.25	50	−1	−50	50
19.25	19	−2	−38	76
18.25	2	−3	− 6	18
17.25	2	−4	− 8	32
16.25	1	−5	− 5	25
15.25	1	−6	− 6	36
Totals.....	260		65	597

$$\bar{X} \text{ (in cells from assumed origin of 21.25)} = \frac{\Sigma fd}{n} = \frac{65}{260} = 0.25$$

$$\bar{X} \text{ (in original units)} = \text{Assumed origin} + \frac{\Sigma fd}{n} \text{ (cell interval)}$$

$$= 21.25 + 0.25(1) = 21.50 \text{ oz.}$$

$$\sigma \text{ (in cell units)} = \sqrt{\frac{\Sigma fd^2}{n} - \left(\frac{\Sigma fd}{n}\right)^2} = \sqrt{\frac{597}{260} - (0.25)^2}$$

$$= \sqrt{2.296 - 0.062} = \sqrt{2.234} = 1.49$$

As the cell unit is 1.0 oz.,

$$\sigma \text{ (in original units)} = 1.49(1.0) = 1.49 \text{ oz.}$$

possible to come close enough to this ideal for many purposes. A practical problem is to judge whether the circumstances are favorable.

Mathematical statisticians have discovered that the best measure of central tendency for this purpose is the *arithmetic mean* (referred to in this book as the *average*). The most common measure of dispersion for this purpose is the *standard deviation*.

The ideal would be to be able to say, given any average and standard deviation, just what proportion of the measurements fell within any specified limits.   For example, if $\overline{X}$ were 0.850 in. for some dimension of a manufactured part and σ were 0.002 in., it would then be possible to tell what proportion of the parts fell between the limits $\overline{X} \pm 2\sigma$, *i.e.*, between 0.846 and 0.854 in.   Or it would be possible to tell the proportion that fell between $\overline{X} - 4\sigma$ and $\overline{X} - 1.5\sigma$, *i.e.*, between 0.842 and 0.847 in., or between any other desired limits.   If this could be done, one could completely reconstruct a frequency distribution provided he knew only two figures, its average and its standard deviation.

For this to be possible, the equation of a frequency curve that described the pattern of variation of the particular quality characteristic would need to be fully defined once the average and standard deviation were known.   These two numbers are, in fact, sufficient to define the so-called *normal curve*.   Many observed frequency distributions of measured qualities of manufactured product, and many other frequency distributions found in nature, do correspond roughly to this normal curve.

57. The Normal Curve.   Figure 7*a* showed a graphical representation of a frequency distribution by means of a frequency histogram.   The area contained in each column of the histogram is proportional to the frequency within its cell.   If there were enough observed numbers in the frequency distribution, the number of cells might be increased more and more and the width of a cell made smaller and smaller.[1]   The series of steps that constitutes the top line of the histogram would then approach a smooth curve.   The height of the curve at any point would be proportional to the frequency at that point, and the area under it between any two limits would be proportional to the frequency of occurrence within those limits.   Such a curve is called a *frequency curve*.

One can imagine frequency curves of many different shapes.   Mathematicians have developed equations that exactly define many common types.   The most useful of these curves is the *normal curve*.   This curve is variously called the normal law, the normal curve of error, the probability curve, the Gaussian curve, the Laplacian curve, and the normal distribution curve.   Its bell-shaped symmetrical form is illustrated in Fig. 11*a*.   Although most of the area under it is included within the limits $\overline{X} \pm 3\sigma$, the curve extends from $-\infty$ (minus infinity) to $+\infty$ (plus infinity).   The curve is fully defined by $\overline{X}$ and σ.

The most commonly quoted limits in connection with the normal curve are as follows:

Limits	Per Cent of Total Area within Specified Limits
$\overline{X} \pm 0.6745\sigma$	50.00
$\overline{X} \pm \sigma$	68.26
$\overline{X} \pm 2\sigma$	95.46
$\overline{X} \pm 3\sigma$	99.73

[1] See Fig. 13 in Chap. IV for an example of a histogram with 61 cells.

This means that in those distributions which roughly approximate the normal curve, about two-thirds of the occurrences fall within one standard deviation on either side of the average, all but about 5 per cent fall within two standard deviations, and practically all fall within three standard deviations.

Table A, Appendix III, gives to four decimal places the proportion of the total area under the normal curve that occurs between $-\infty$ and any chosen point expressed in terms of multiples of σ on either side of $\overline{X}$. It can be used to find the area between any two chosen points. For example, the area between $\overline{X} + 2.00\sigma$ and $\overline{X} - 1.75\sigma$ is found as follows:

$$
\begin{array}{r}
\text{Table } A \text{ reading for } +2.00 = 0.9773 \\
\text{Table } A \text{ reading for } -1.75 = \underline{0.0401} \\
\text{Area enclosed} = 0.9372
\end{array}
$$

Suppose it is desired to check the sum of the frequencies in the cells from 19.5 to 23.0, inclusive, in Table 9 with the frequencies expected for the same region from a normal curve having the same $\overline{X}$ and σ. The upper limit of this group of cells is 23.25 (the upper limit of the cell with the mid-point 23.0) and the lower limit is 19.25. These points must be expressed in terms of multiples of σ from $\overline{X}$.

$$\sigma = 1.48 \text{ oz.}$$

$$\text{Upper limit} = 23.25 - \overline{X} = 23.25 - 21.50 = 1.75 \text{ oz.} = \frac{1.75}{1.48}\sigma = 1.18\sigma$$

$$\text{Lower limit} = 19.25 - \overline{X} = 19.25 - 21.50 = -2.25 \text{ oz.} = \frac{-2.25}{1.48}\sigma$$
$$= -1.52\sigma$$

$$
\begin{array}{r}
\text{Table } A \text{ reading for } +1.18 = 0.8810 \\
\text{Table } A \text{ reading for } -1.52 = \underline{0.0643} \\
\text{Area enclosed} = 0.8167
\end{array}
$$

The total frequency in Table 9 is 260. This multiplied by the figure of 0.8167 above gives a frequency of 212 cases (*i.e.*, occurrences of the variable) to be expected in cells 19.5 to 23.0 if the distribution were normal. This compares with an actual frequency of

$$14 + 31 + 34 + 33 + 41 + 26 + 24 + 12 = 215$$

cases observed in these cells.

58. Other Frequency Curves. The normal curve is useful in many ways in solving practical problems in industry. Some of these ways will be developed in succeeding chapters. Its general pattern, with a concentration of frequencies about a mid-point and with small numbers of occurrences at the extreme values, repeats itself again and again. Nevertheless, the normal curve is frequently misused; it is not safe to assume that unknown distributions are necessarily normal.

There are many other frequency patterns, which are like the normal in that frequencies decrease continuously from the center to the extreme values but—unlike the normal—are not symmetrical. Extreme values occur more frequently in one direction from the center than in the other. Two such distributions are illustrated in Fig. 11b and 11c. In the technical language of statistics, these lopsided frequency curves are known as *skewed* curves. Figure 11b is skewed to the right; *i.e.*, extreme variations occur more frequently above the mode than below it. Figure 11c is

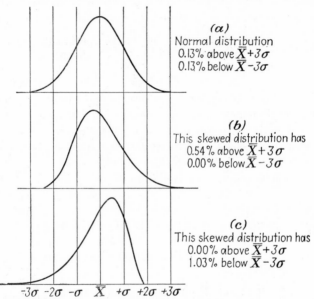

(a)
Normal distribution
0.13% above $\overline{X}+3\sigma$
0.13% below $\overline{X}-3\sigma$

(b)
This skewed distribution has
0.54% above $\overline{X}+3\sigma$
0.00% below $\overline{X}-3\sigma$

(c)
This skewed distribution has
0.00% above $\overline{X}+3\sigma$
1.03% below $\overline{X}-3\sigma$

$-3\sigma \quad -2\sigma \quad -\sigma \quad \overline{X} \quad +\sigma \quad +2\sigma \quad +3\sigma$

Fig. 11. Normal frequency curve (a) and typical skewed frequency curves (b) and (c).

skewed to the left. The distribution of weights shown in the graphs of Fig. 7 also appears to be somewhat skewed to the left.

59. Two Aspects of Practical Uses of Frequency Distributions in Manufacturing. The real purpose of every statistical measurement, tabulation, and analysis in industry should be to find a guide to action. It is worth while to note two different kinds of action that may result from the use of tabulated frequency distributions, as follows:

1. Action which deals only with that product the measurements of which were recorded in the frequency distribution. A good illustration of this was given in Example 6 in which the frequency distribution showed the results of 100% inspection of electron tubes and action was taken calling for reinspection of a group of these tubes.

2. Action relative to product not measured as well as to measured product. This may be action regarding product already produced, as is the case wherever acceptance inspection is based on the evidence of

frequency distributions obtained from samples. Or it may be action relative to product not yet produced; for instance, either continuing a process without change or making some change in it. Or it may be setting or revising tolerance limits to be applied to future production. In all such cases, the product measured is viewed as a sample from a larger total amount, either already produced or to be produced.

There are hundreds of cases where action of this second type is involved for every one where the action is merely on the product measured. Such action calls for knowledge of the probable relationship between the observed quality of the samples and the quality characteristics of the sources from which the samples were taken.

60. The Statistical Concept of a Universe or Parent Distribution. Sometimes the source from which a sample comes is thought of as a finite lot and the only action to be based on the interpretation of the sample is action on the remaining unmeasured portion of the lot. More often, the possible action is not limited in this way. In manufacturing, many of the useful actions relate to future production. The knowledge needed about the quality characteristics of the source of the sample is knowledge of the pattern of variation of the production process from which the sample came. This pattern of variation, if it were known, might be described by a frequency curve that would doubtless smooth out the irregularities inevitable in frequency distributions of moderate size.

It is convenient to have a word or phrase to describe an unknown pattern of variation from which a known sample has been taken. Statisticians use various names for this, calling it the *universe* from which the sample comes, the *parent distribution*, the *population*, or the *bulk*. The word *universe* is used in this connection throughout this book.

In order to be able to draw conclusions about unknown universes by means of samples taken from them, it is helpful to conduct sampling experiments from known universes. A known universe might be represented by a bowl of chips, each chip marked with a number and with the frequencies of the different numbers depending on the assumed pattern of variation. Experiments involving drawing chips from bowls are referred to in Chaps. IV and V.

61. Stable and Unstable Patterns of Variation. At first glance, it might seem that a frequency distribution such as that of the 260 drained weights of contents of cans of tomatoes obtained over the 11-day period would present a satisfactory picture of a pattern of variation that existed throughout that 11 days. Or perhaps some form of smooth frequency curve fitted to these observations by some mathematical process (using $\bar{X}$, σ, and possibly some number to measure the skewness) would give an even better picture of the universe from which the sample of 260 was taken.

Perhaps so, but not necessarily so. The first question to answer here is whether there appears to have been any stable pattern of variation at all. If there is evidence of lack of stability in the variation pattern, it may well be true that there were a number of different universes at different times, and that the frequency distribution of the 260 weights was therefore the result of combining samples from different systems of chance causes. Whenever an unstable pattern of variation exists, the practical

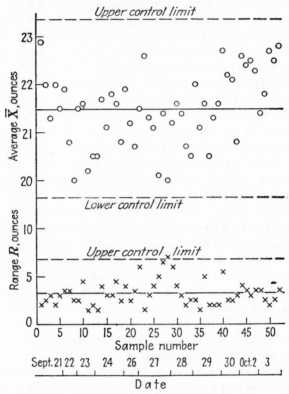

FIG. 12. $\bar{X}$ and R control charts for drained weights of contents of cans of tomatoes—data of Table 6.

basis for the kinds of action previously mentioned (either action for acceptance, or action on the process, or action on the specifications) is quite different from the basis of action in the situation where the variation pattern is stable.

62. Use of the Control Chart in Interpretation of a Frequency Distribution. The best way of judging this stability is by means of the Shewhart control charts for $\bar{X}$ and R. These charts were briefly illustrated in Examples 1 and 2 in Chap. II and are explained in detail in the succeeding chapters.

Figure 12 shows the $\bar{X}$ and R charts for the weight data of Table 6. None of the $\bar{X}$ points is outside the control limits; one of the 52 points for R is outside the limits. In addition to observing whether or not the points fall inside control limits, one may apply so-called "*nonparametric*" tests based on the theory of runs. (These were suggested in the discussion of sequences of seven or more points above or below the central line in the illustration of the p chart in Example 3 of Chap. II. They are explained at greater length in Art. 88, Chap. V, and Art. 179, Chap. IX.) These indicate the possible existence of a slight shift in the pattern of variation during the 11-day period. Beginning with the subgroup at 10:40 A.M. on September 27 (sample 24 on the control chart) 9 out of 10 successive points on the $\overline{X}$ chart fall below the central line. And on the final portion of the record, 12 out of 14 points fall above the central line.

The interpretation of extreme runs as a basis for action is discussed at greater length in Chap. V. An appropriate general comment at this point is that wherever the control chart gives definite evidence of lack of statistical control, any action taken should not be based on the assumption that a single frequency distribution or frequency curve represents the pattern of variation. It may also be stated that even though these figures on drained weights of tomatoes show one point out of 52 out of control plus some evidence of lack of control based on nonparametric tests, it does not necessarily follow that this much departure from a constant pattern of variation is unsatisfactory from a practical standpoint. Many production processes never do as well.

63. Importance of Preserving the Order of Measurement. Whenever a frequency distribution is to be used as a basis for action of the second type mentioned in Art. 59, such as acceptance, changes in process, or review of specifications, a desirable aid in its interpretation is the information given by the control chart. As will be emphasized in later chapters, the control chart without the frequency distribution is often much more useful than the frequency distribution without the control chart.

If the data on drained weights had been presented only as a frequency distribution, such as Table 7, and the record of order of measurement given in Table 6 had been lost, it would not have been possible to have judged whether or not the observations came from controlled conditions. *The order in which the measurements were made should always be preserved in recording data for a frequency distribution.*

64. What the Average and Standard Deviation of a Set of Numbers Really Tell. It has been pointed out that it would be convenient if the combination of average and standard deviation could tell us just what proportion of a set of numbers fell within any specified limits. It has also been pointed out that this combination does supply such information in those cases where it is known that the numbers are distributed according to the normal curve.

What do $\overline{X}$ and σ tell if nothing whatever is known about the pattern of variation? One answer to this question is given by *Tchebycheff's inequality.* This mathematical theorem states that more than $1 - (1/t^2)$ of *any* set of finite numbers must fall within the closed range $\overline{X} \pm t\sigma$ (where t is not less than 1). For example, if $t = 3$, this means that more than $1 - (1/3^2)$ or $\frac{8}{9}$ of any set of numbers must fall within the limits $\overline{X} \pm 3\sigma$, where $\overline{X}$ and σ have been computed from the numbers themselves. In other words, less than $\frac{1}{9}$ of the numbers can fall outside these limits. The actual fraction falling outside of $\overline{X} \pm 3\sigma$ may be much less than $\frac{1}{9}$; the Tchebycheff inequality simply states that it cannot be as much as $\frac{1}{9}$. It should be emphasized that this limit of $\frac{1}{9}$ applies to the *sum* of the fractions above an upper limit of $\overline{X} + 3\sigma$ and below a lower limit of $\overline{X} - 3\sigma$.

Usually it is desired to have $\overline{X}$ and σ tell more about a distribution than can be determined from Tchebycheff's inequality. An adaptation of the inequality by Camp and Meidell states that under certain circumstances more than $1 - (1/2.25t^2)$ of any distribution will fall within the closed range $\overline{X} \pm t\sigma$. These circumstances are that the distribution must have only one mode, that the mode must be the same as the arithmetic mean, and that the frequencies must decline continuously on both sides of the mode. Many distributions that are not normal do actually come close enough to meeting these conditions for the Camp-Meidell inequality to be applied with confidence.

The percentages indicated by the normal curve and by the two inequalities are compared as follows:

Limits	If the distribution is roughly normal, *approximately* the following percentages of cases will be *outside* the limits	If the Camp-Meidell conditions apply, *less than* the following percentages of cases will be *outside* the limits	Under any and all circumstances *less than* the following percentages of cases will be *outside* the limits
$\overline{X} \pm 2\sigma$	4.55	11.1	25.0
$\overline{X} \pm 2.5\sigma$	1.24	7.1	16.0
$\overline{X} \pm 3\sigma$	0.27	4.9	11.1
$\overline{X} \pm 3.5\sigma$	0.05	3.6	8.2
$\overline{X} \pm 4\sigma$	0.006	2.8	6.3
$\overline{X} \pm 4.5\sigma$	0.0007	2.2	4.9
$\overline{X} \pm 5\sigma$	0.00006	1.8	4.0

Problems

1. In the production of an electrical device operated by a thermostatic control, five control switches were tested each hour to determine the "on" temperature at which the thermostat actually operated under a given setting. Results of the test over a 5-day production period were as shown in the table on page 68.

Using a check sheet similar to Fig. 6, make a tally of these 230 measurements to arrange them in a frequency distribution. From this check sheet prepare a table similar to Table 7a showing cell mid-points, cell boundaries, and observed frequencies.

2. Plot the frequency distribution of Problem 1 as (a) a frequency histogram, b) a frequency bar chart, (c) a frequency polygon.

3. (a) Arrange the frequency distribution of Problem 1 into cumulative frequency distributions similar to those in Table 8. Show both "number less than" and "percentage less than" each cell boundary. (b) Plot the ogive on rectangular coordinate paper. (c) Plot the ogive on probability paper.

4. Find the average and standard deviation of subgroup 2 of Problem 1. Compute standard deviation in two ways, using formula (2) for one computation and formula (3) for the other. *Ans.* $\bar{X} = 52.4$; $\sigma = 2.42$

5. (a) Add the 230 numbers listed in the statement of Problem 1. From this sum determine the average "on" temperature. (b) Using the long method illustrated in Table 9, compute the average and standard deviation of the frequency distribution obtained in your solution of Problem 1. (c) Using the short method illustrated in Table 10a, compute the average and standard deviation of this frequency distribution. *Ans.* $\bar{X} = 54.143$; $\sigma = 1.99$

6. A small radio transmitting set is designed so that it may be used to generate a certain automatic signal. The time duration of this signal is one of the specified quality characteristics of the set. At regular intervals, five sets from the production line were tested for this quality characteristic. In the table on page 69, which shows 220 such measurements, the values in each subgroup of five have been arranged in order of magnitude.

Using a check sheet similar to Fig. 6, make a tally of these 220 measurements to arrange them in a frequency distribution. Use cell mid-points of 370, 375, 380, 385, etc. From this check sheet prepare a table similar to Table 7a showing cell mid-points, cell boundaries, and observed frequencies.

7. Plot the frequency distribution of Problem 6 as a (a) frequency histogram, (b) frequency bar chart, (c) frequency polygon.

8. (a) Arrange the frequency distribution of Problem 6 into cumulative frequency distributions similar to those in Table 8. Show both "number less than" and "percentage less than" each cell boundary. (b) Plot the ogive on rectangular coordinate paper. (c) Plot the ogive on probability paper.

9. Find the average and standard deviation of subgroup 1 of Problem 6. Compute standard deviation in two ways, using formula (2) for one computation and formula (3) for the other. *Ans.* $\bar{X} = 400.6$; $\sigma = 10.93$

10. (a) Using the long method illustrated in Table 9, compute the average and standard deviation of the frequency distribution obtained in your solution of Problem 6. (b) Using the short method illustrated in Table 10a, compute the average and standard deviation of this frequency distribution. *Ans.* $\bar{X} = 395.4$; $\sigma = 9.98$

Date	Subgroup number	"On" temperature at which thermostatic switch operates (temperature units not specified)				
		a	b	c	d	e
Apr. 25	1	54	56	56	56	55
	2	51	52	54	56	49
	3	54	52	50	57	55
	4	56	55	56	53	50
	5	53	54	57	56	52
	6	53	47	58	55	54
	7	52	55	54	55	56
	8	56	53	53	54	55
	9	55	52	53	56	55
	10	50	54	53	55	55
Apr. 26	11	57	54	53	52	53
	12	52	52	54	53	55
	13	54	53	55	52	52
	14	54	55	54	53	55
	15	56	53	57	56	54
Apr. 27	16	58	57	56	54	54
	17	55	55	55	56	53
	18	54	57	54	55	54
	19	54	53	56	53	55
	20	53	53	57	54	53
	21	53	55	57	56	55
	22	59	54	53	54	55
	23	54	55	58	55	54
	24	56	53	51	55	59
	25	56	55	55	55	55
Apr. 28	26	54	53	54	55	54
	27	53	52	55	54	53
	28	53	52	53	57	53
	29	53	51	55	50	55
	30	57	54	56	54	55
	31	53	55	52	55	55
	32	56	55	55	53	52
	33	54	50	56	54	56
	34	55	54	53	54	56
	35	54	48	53	55	54
Apr. 29	36	54	53	56	55	55
	37	51	57	55	55	54
	38	57	51	57	55	52
	39	54	55	53	48	49
	40	50	59	58	56	58
	41	55	55	55	54	55
	42	54	55	55	53	55
	43	55	54	54	50	50
	44	51	51	53	52	56
	45	53	56	55	56	55
	46	54	52	55	52	54

Subgroup number	Duration of automatic signal (time units unspecified)				
	a	b	c	d	e
1	390	393	395	405	420
2	376	381	381	383	401
3	380	387	395	397	407
4	377	383	387	390	393
5	393	395	403	405	414
6	376	388	395	397	400
7	387	400	400	403	410
8	391	392	394	397	405
9	390	391	395	401	405
10	379	391	393	394	410
11	390	397	400	406	428
12	380	382	389	391	399
13	375	383	392	395	404
14	387	390	398	400	408
15	390	395	395	397	403
16	382	399	401	406	406
17	390	395	395	400	410
18	381	390	394	397	399
19	387	389	398	401	415
20	372	378	396	400	405
21	387	389	391	391	400
22	376	380	391	406	412
23	395	396	397	400	400
24	392	394	397	399	400
25	385	390	390	392	392
26	388	395	395	400	415
27	385	391	400	407	425
28	379	390	392	411	414
29	390	399	402	406	411
30	392	395	400	400	406
31	386	395	401	401	411
32	372	397	398	400	402
33	388	395	395	401	403
34	382	386	390	395	408
35	380	382	400	406	406
36	385	391	399	406	412
37	370	389	392	401	409
38	377	390	396	400	400
39	390	395	398	399	401
40	382	391	394	399	409
41	386	397	399	402	405
42	377	390	397	399	401
43	386	400	402	407	413
44	386	388	390	399	406

11. The mean value of the modulus of rupture of a large number of test specimens of green Sitka spruce has been found to be 5,600 psi. If the standard deviation is 840 psi and the distribution is approximately normal, the modulus of rupture will fall between 5,000 and 6,200 for what percentage of the specimens? For what percentage will it be above 4,000? Below 3,500?

12. Compute the average and the standard deviation of the following distribution, which shows the result of the measurement of the resistance of 500 units of a certain electrical product:

Resistance, ohms	Frequency
2.7–2.9	2
3.0–3.2	16
3.3–3.5	46
3.6–3.8	88
3.9–4.1	138
4.2–4.4	113
4.5–4.7	71
4.8–5.0	22
5.1–5.3	4

13. A normal curve has an average of 140.6 and a standard deviation of 3.70. What percentage of the area under the curve will fall between limits of 135.5 and 142.5?

14. A normal curve has the same average and standard deviation as those calculated in Problem 5. What percentage of the area under the curve will fall between limits of 51.5 and 57.5? Compare this with the percentage of cases observed between these limits in the frequency distribution of Problem 1.

Ans. Normal, 86.2; Prob. 1, 87.8.

15. A normal curve has the same average and standard deviations as those calculated in Problem 10. What percentage of the area under the curve will fall within limits of 382.5 and 412.5? Compare this with the percentage of cases observed between these limits in the frequency distribution of Problem 6.

16. What can you tell about the percentage of cases outside the limits $\bar{X} \pm 2.7\sigma$ in a frequency distribution (*a*) if it is known that the distribution is approximately normal? (*b*) If it is known that the distribution satisfies the conditions of the Camp-Meidell inequality? (*c*) If nothing at all is known about the form of the distribution?

Ans. (*a*) 0.7%; (*b*) 6.1%; (*c*) 13.7%.

17. Raymond T. Birge made 500 observations of a spectral line. (The resulting frequency distribution is discussed by Birge in *Physical Review*, vol. 40, pp. 17–227, 1932. He has kindly lent the original measurements for reproduction here.) Comparator settings were read to thousandths of a millimeter. Only the last two digits are recorded in the table shown on pages 72–74. Thus the actual first reading is 65.177 mm., of which only 77 is recorded.

Using a check sheet similar to Fig. 6, make a tally of these 500 measurements to arrange them in a frequency distribution.

Using the short method illustrated in Table 10*a*, compute the average and standard deviation of this frequency distribution.

18. What percentage of the observations in Problem 17 fall between the limits $\bar{X} \pm \sigma$? Between $\bar{X} \pm 2\sigma$? Between $\bar{X} \pm 3\sigma$? In answering these questions, assume that the observations are distributed uniformly in each cell of the frequency distribution. For example, if the cell from 83.5 to 84.5 contains 20 observations, 15 would be between 83.5 and 84.25 and 5 between 84.25 and 84.5 Compare the actual percentages between these limits with the percentages to be expected from a normal distribution.

19. The frequencies for the data of Table 2 (page 24) are:

Measure-ment	Fre-quency	Measure-ment	Fre-quency	Measure-ment	Fre-quency	Measure-ment	Fre-quency
148	1	143	14	138	7	135	5
147	5	142	22	138	8	134	2
146	3	141	8	137	19	133	1
145	12	140	15	136	4	132	2
144	7						

Compute $\bar{X}$ and σ for this distribution. What percentage of a normal distribution having this $\bar{X}$ and σ would fall between the specification limits of 136.5 and 143.5? What percentage of the actual distribution falls between these limits?

20. Tests of the stiffness of a number of aluminum-alloy channels gave the following frequency distribution. Stiffness was measured in "effective EI in psi."

Stiffness	Frequency	Stiffness	Frequency	Stiffness	Frequency
2,640	1	2,440	33	2,280	14
2,600	2	2,400	41	2,240	5
2,560	7	2,360	35	2,200	3
2,520	11	2,320	22	2,160	1
2,480	25				

The stated values of stiffness all refer to the mid-points of the respective cells. Compute $\bar{X}$ and σ. If a normal distribution had this $\bar{X}$ and σ, what percentage of the distribution would fall below 2,150?

21. Tests have indicated that the tensile strengths of certain aluminum-alloy castings average 22,300 psi with a standard deviation of 2,700 psi. If the distribution is normal, what percentage of the castings will have tensile strengths less than 17,000 psi?

Reading number	a	b	c	d	e
1–5	77	74	73	84	77
6–10	78	85	80	81	80
11–15	75	69	72	83	79
16–20	75	80	79	74	78
21–25	70	74	83	72	79
26–30	73	81	87	82	79
31–35	78	79	78	74	85
36–40	83	79	83	81	84
41–45	81	88	79	80	78
46–50	77	80	85	80	78
51–55	72	75	73	85	79
56–60	78	82	80	76	76
61–65	79	75	83	81	78
66–70	82	76	78	78	79
71–75	86	79	79	84	74
76–80	76	75	77	82	77
81–85	79	77	72	77	81
86–90	83	75	82	90	77
91–95	80	78	83	81	74
96–100	79	80	79	75	84
101–105	81	74	73	74	86
106–110	77	82	75	74	75
111–115	75	74	83	76	84
116–120	72	84	73	77	77
121–125	76	75	81	79	74
126–130	80	75	81	78	83
131–135	75	89	75	73	81
136–140	76	82	77	81	82
141–145	82	75	81	79	77
146–150	71	74	84	81	81
151–155	80	75	77	83	84
156–160	73	73	77	78	81
161–165	80	74	81	78	77
166–170	80	76	80	77	78
171–175	78	82	84	80	79

Reading number	a	b	c	d	e
176–180	79	77	78	81	83
181–185	83	73	81	74	78
186–190	82	78	82	77	73
191–195	80	85	78	81	84
196–200	78	77	79	72	82
201–205	78	77	79	77	82
206–210	76	77	83	81	79
211–215	82	75	77	74	76
216–220	82	81	72	74	77
221–225	78	79	80	84	80
226–230	77	76	76	79	78
231–235	74	83	80	75	73
236–240	76	80	77	82	73
241–245	82	76	79	78	79
246–250	81	79	75	78	80
251–255	78	82	75	81	85
256–260	82	82	81	73	75
261–265	79	77	78	79	77
266–270	79	77	80	82	73
271–275	70	76	83	76	75
276–280	88	85	77	79	84
281–285	74	78	77	76	79
286–290	77	78	73	75	80
291–295	77	74	78	78	80
296–300	76	82	81	81	81
301–305	82	78	73	83	78
306–310	79	81	76	80	85
311–315	83	81	76	76	79
316–320	81	78	77	79	84
321–325	76	77	72	73	80
326–330	83	74	76	84	78
331–335	78	75	82	80	77
336–340	77	75	82	76	72
341–345	78	79	73	75	80
346–350	82	76	77	84	84

Reading number	a	b	c	d	e
351–355	79	82	78	79	78
356–360	83	83	81	75	80
361–365	80	78	77	77	82
366–370	82	75	80	81	79
371–375	82	85	84	81	81
376–380	82	83	79	81	77
381–385	83	83	75	79	83
386–390	78	83	80	79	83
391–395	81	78	87	82	74
396–400	80	81	79	77	83
401–405	79	75	73	85	85
406–410	77	80	83	79	79
411–415	79	76	80	82	80
416–420	84	85	79	77	81
421–425	73	74	81	79	82
426–430	82	83	81	78	81
431–435	79	84	77	76	78
436–440	77	85	79	77	79
441–445	77	76	77	82	78
446–450	77	86	83	83	82
451–455	79	78	83	82	79
456–460	82	76	78	78	76
461–465	80	79	79	81	85
466–470	81	79	73	79	78
471–475	82	84	79	70	72
476–480	78	79	80	85	85
481–485	80	72	81	70	75
486–490	80	87	82	78	77
491–495	88	79	82	78	80
496–500	83	87	81	82	79

CHAPTER IV

WHY THE CONTROL CHART WORKS.
EXAMPLE OF A PROCESS IN CONTROL

There is no such thing as constancy in real life. There is, however, such a thing as a *constant-cause system*. The results produced by a constant-cause system vary, and in fact may vary over a wide band or a narrow band. They vary, but they exhibit an important feature called *stability*. Why apply the terms *constant* and *stability* to a cause system that produces results that vary? Because the same percentage of these varying results continues to fall between any given pair of limits hour after hour, day after day, so long as the constant-cause system continues to operate. It is the *distribution* of results that is constant or stable. When a manufacturing process behaves like a constant-cause system, producing inspection results that exhibit stability, it is said to be in *statistical control*. The control chart will tell you whether your process is in statistical control.—W. E. DEMING[1]

65. Bowl Drawing to Illustrate a Constant-cause System. One good way to illustrate a constant-cause system is by actual conduct of the chance operation of drawing chips from a bowl. Write a number on each of a group of physically similar poker chips. Put the chips in a bowl, mix them thoroughly, draw one out, and record the number written on the chip. Replace the chip, stir the chips well, draw again, and record. By repeating this process enough times, a series of numbers may be obtained which, if the chips are stirred well enough between each drawing, will have been obtained in a chance or random manner. By examining the behavior of this variable that seems to be influenced only by a constant system of chance causes, it is possible to understand the way in which all constant-cause systems operate.

This type of demonstration is nearly always made in courses in statistical quality control. If the chips are all alike, so that each one has as good a chance as any other to be drawn, it is also possible to illustrate the meaning of many of the formulas used in control-chart work. These formulas, developed by mathematical statisticians, deal with the relationship between a universe and samples taken from it.

It is appropriate that bowl drawings should be part of most explanations of how to use the control chart, as Shewhart used them in the early stages of his work on the applications of statistical methods in manu-

---

[1] DEMING, W. E., Some Principles of the Shewhart Methods of Quality Control, *Mechanical Engineering*, vol. 66, pp. 173–177, March, 1944.

facturing. In his original treatise on the subject, he gives the data from 4,000 drawings of chips from each of three bowls, one containing a norma universe, one a rectangular universe, and one a triangular universe.1 The following discussion makes use of the first 400 drawings from Shew[1]

TABLE 11. MARKING ON CHIPS IN SHEWHART'S NORMAL BOWL

Marking on chip X	Number of chips	Marking on chip X	Number of chips	Marking on chip X	Number of chips
60	1	39	27	19	22
59	1	38	29	18	19
58	1	37	31	17	17
57	1	36	33	16	15
56	1	35	35	15	13
55	2	34	37	14	11
54	2	33	38	13	9
53	3	32	39	12	8
52	4	31	40	11	7
51	4	30	40	10	5
50	5	29	40	9	4
49	7	28	39	8	4
48	8	27	38	7	3
47	9	26	37	6	2
46	11	25	35	5	2
45	13	24	33	4	1
44	15	23	31	3	1
43	17	22	29	2	1
42	19	21	27	1	1
41	22	20	24	0	1
40	24				

hart's normal bowl. (His rectangular and triangular universes are explained and the results of his drawings from them are briefly summarized in Art. 71 and Fig. 15.)

66. Contents of Shewhart's Normal Bowl. Table 11 gives the distribution of the markings on the 998 chips in this bowl. Figure 13a shows

[1] SHEWHART, W. A., "Economic Control of Quality of Manufactured Product," Appendix II, Tables *A*, *B*, and *C*, D. Van Nostrand Company, Inc., New York, 1931. These bowl drawings from Table *A* are used here by permission of the author and publishers. Shewhart's normal bowl contained numbers from −3.0 to +3.0. Numbers from 0 to 60 have been substituted here, to simplify the presentation by elimination of negative numbers and decimals.

the histogram for this frequency distribution.   Figure 13*b* shows a more conventional histogram for the same distribution with a coarse grouping into 13 cells rather than 61; it illustrates the effect of coarse grouping on the histogram of a normal distribution.

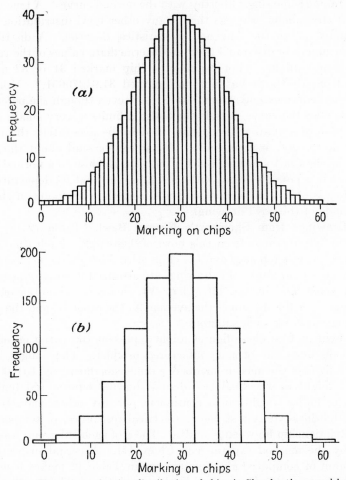

FIG. 13.   Histograms showing distribution of chips in Shewhart's normal bowl.

The average $\bar{X}'$ (read as "X bar prime") of this symmetrical distribution is obviously 30.   The standard deviation σ' (read as "sigma prime") is 9.954, or, in round numbers, 10.   The symbol ' (prime), used with $\bar{X}$ or σ, means that the average or standard deviation referred to is that of the universe.   It may be applied to a known statistic of a universe, as in a bowl-drawing experiment where the distribution in the bowl is known.   Or it may refer to an estimated statistic of an unknown universe. Or, in quality control work it may be an assumed or aimed-at value adopted at any time to serve as a norm for computing limits on a control chart.

In referring to the distribution in this bowl as a normal distribution, we are taking some slight liberties with the normal curve. A true normal curve is continuous, whereas this or any other bowl distribution is discontinuous (or, in the language of statistics, *discrete*). A distribution is discontinuous or discrete if there are intermediate values of the variable which cannot occur. (For example, a chip marked 31 or 32 may be drawn from the bowl but not one marked 31.94279651.) Moreover, the normal curve extends from $-\infty$ to $+\infty$ even though the percentage of area under the curve outside the 3-sigma limits is very small; a bowl would require several million chips to describe accurately the normal curve out to, say, 5-sigma limits. What can be said about the distribution in Shewhart's normal bowl is that it is as close to a normal distribution as it is possible to get with 998 chips, and that its departure from normality is of no practical significance from the standpoint of the uses to be made of the bowl drawings.

67. Drawings from Shewhart's Normal Bowl. Table 12 gives the results of 400 drawings from this bowl of 998 chips. Each time a chip was drawn, it was replaced and the chips stirred before the next drawing. For purposes of analysis, the drawings are arranged in subgroups of four. (As explained later in Art. 110, Chap. VI, this is an advantageous subgroup size.) Table 12 shows the average $\overline{X}$, the range R, and the standard deviation σ, for each subgroup.

It is evident that these figures might represent the variation of some quality characteristic of a manufactured product. They might be the last two digits of the measurements of a dimension measured to 0.0001 in. Or they might be the final two digits, showing ounces and tenths of ounces, of filling weights of a container. Or any other characteristic, such as hardness, tensile strength, electrical resistance, or temperature.

68. Relationship between σ' and $\bar{\sigma}$. The σ of each subgroup was computed by the method explained in Chap. III. A casual inspection of the column of computed σ's of subgroups in Table 12 makes it evident that they are subject to considerable variation. The smallest one observed was 0.5 and the largest was 17.7. Moreover, it is clear that more of them fall below 10, the standard deviation of the distribution in the bowl, than fall above it.

In the long run, the standard deviations of samples of any size from a normal universe will follow a chance pattern which can be predicted by mathematics. Statistical theory also predicts the ratio between $\bar{\sigma}$, the average of the standard deviations of samples of any given size (such as the subgroups of four) and σ', the standard deviation of the universe

TABLE 12. 400 DRAWINGS FROM SHEWHART'S NORMAL BOWL ARRANGED INTO SUBGROUPS OF FOUR

Numbers of drawings	Markings on chips in subgroup				Average $\bar{X}$	Range R	Standard deviation σ
1–4	47	32	44	35	39.50	15	6.2
5–8	33	33	34	34	33.50	1	0.5
9–12	34	34	31	34	33.25	3	1.3
13–16	12	21	24	47	26.00	35	12.9
17–20	35	23	38	40	34.00	17	6.6
21–24	19	37	31	27	28.50	18	6.5
25–28	23	45	26	37	32.75	22	8.8
29–32	33	12	29	43	29.25	31	11.2
33–36	25	22	37	33	29.25	15	6.0
37–40	29	32	30	13	26.00	19	7.6
41–44	40	18	30	11	24.75	29	11.1
45–48	21	18	36	34	27.25	18	7.9
49–52	26	35	31	29	30.25	9	3.3
53–56	52	29	21	18	30.00	34	13.3
57–60	26	20	30	20	24.00	10	4.2
61–64	19	1	30	30	20.00	29	11.9
65–68	28	34	39	17	29.50	22	8.2
69–72	29	25	24	30	27.00	6	2.5
73–76	21	37	32	25	28.75	16	6.2
77–80	24	22	16	35	24.25	19	6.9
81–84	28	39	23	21	27.75	18	7.0
85–88	41	32	46	12	32.75	34	13.0
89–92	14	23	41	42	30.00	28	11.9
93–96	32	28	46	27	33.25	19	7.6
97–100	42	34	22	34	33.00	20	7.1
101–104	20	38	27	32	29.25	18	6.6
105–108	30	14	37	43	31.00	29	10.8
109–112	28	29	32	35	31.00	7	2.7
113–116	35	30	37	26	32.00	11	4.3
117–120	51	13	45	55	41.00	42	16.6
121–124	34	19	11	16	20.00	23	8.6
125–128	32	28	41	40	35.25	13	5.4
129–132	14	31	20	35	25.00	21	8.4
133–136	25	44	29	27	31.25	19	7.5
137–140	18	22	20	33	23.25	15	5.8

TABLE 12. 400 DRAWINGS FROM SHEWHART'S NORMAL BOWL ARRANGED INTO SUBGROUPS OF FOUR.—(*Continued*)

Numbers of drawings	Markings on chips in subgroup				Average $\bar{X}$	Range R	Standard deviation σ
141–144	21	31	39	25	29.00	18	6.8
145–148	17	44	54	13	32.00	41	17.4
149–152	36	48	19	41	36.00	29	10.7
153–156	25	31	38	30	31.00	13	4.6
157–160	35	21	20	34	27.50	15	7.0
161–164	21	22	44	19	26.50	25	10.2
165–168	39	22	24	29	28.50	17	6.6
169–172	40	44	24	18	31.50	26	10.8
173–176	23	25	46	29	30.75	23	9.1
177–180	23	37	44	34	34.50	21	7.6
181–184	36	52	30	28	36.50	24	9.4
185–188	35	23	11	5	18.50	30	11.5
189–192	33	15	40	29	29.25	25	9.1
193–196	18	30	22	25	23.75	12	4.4
197–200	23	30	20	19	23.00	11	4.3
201–204	7	32	36	38	28.25	31	12.5
205–208	29	30	39	31	32.25	10	4.0
209–212	36	12	34	25	26.75	24	9.5
213–216	36	37	39	32	36.00	7	2.5
217–220	38	9	25	39	27.75	30	12.2
221–224	11	44	29	29	28.25	33	11.7
225–228	31	18	31	25	26.25	13	5.4
229–232	22	47	12	27	27.00	35	12.7
233–236	29	24	32	44	32.25	20	7.4
237–240	42	26	32	27	31.75	16	6.3
241–244	29	40	43	29	35.25	14	6.3
245–248	23	22	23	39	26.75	17	7.1
249–252	34	27	52	28	35.25	25	10.0
253–256	27	40	23	24	28.50	17	6.8
257–260	34	38	16	28	29.00	22	8.3
261–264	39	19	39	32	32.25	20	8.2
265–268	42	25	25	42	33.50	17	8.5
269–272	30	25	38	39	33.00	14	5.8
273–276	43	22	10	28	25.75	33	11.9
277–280	17	31	10	16	18.50	21	7.7

TABLE 12. 400 DRAWINGS FROM SHEWHART'S NORMAL BOWL ARRANGED INTO SUBGROUPS OF FOUR.—*(Continued)*

Numbers of drawings	Markings on chips in subgroup				Average $\bar{X}$	Range R	Standard deviation σ
281–284	40	49	38	37	41.00	12	4.7
285–288	22	39	26	18	26.25	21	7.9
289–292	30	36	34	18	29.50	18	7.0
293–296	41	37	27	32	34.25	14	5.3
297–300	5	20	43	26	23.50	38	13.6
301–304	38	26	38	25	31.75	13	6 3
305–308	27	38	40	33	34.50	13	5.0
309–312	20	23	28	35	26.50	15	5.7
313–316	29	29	34	29	30.25	5	2.2
317–320	25	35	37	42	34.75	17	6.2
321–324	42	59	38	28	41.75	31	11.2
325–328	24	32	22	22	25.00	10	4.1
329–332	38	40	31	52	40.25	21	7.6
333–336	22	52	33	27	33.50	30	11.4
337–340	46	32	20	50	37.00	30	11.9
341–344	27	29	24	15	23.75	14	5.4
345–348	31	26	34	35	31.50	9	3.5
349–352	32	46	30	32	35.00	16	6.4
353–356	35	20	34	46	33.75	26	9.2
357–360	55	25	33	54	41.75	30	13.1
361–364	22	46	52	42	40.50	30	11.3
365–368	14	24	2	43	20.75	41	15.0
369–372	36	52	19	50	39.25	33	13.2
373–376	29	21	17	9	19.00	20	7.2
377–380	33	31	32	18	28.50	15	6.1
381–384	52	34	17	5	27.00	47	17.7
385–388	23	41	21	29	28.50	20	7.8
389–392	28	22	45	21	29.00	24	9.6
393–396	32	27	16	30	26.25	16	6.2
397–400	23	23	27	36	27.25	13	5.3
Totals.................................					3,007.50	2076	807.8

from which the samples are taken.   This ratio, represented by the symbol c_2,* is given in Table B of Appendix III.

The value of c_2 for samples of four is 0.7979.   This factor may be used to estimate an unknown universe standard deviation σ' from $\bar{\sigma}$, the average observed standard deviation of any given set of subgroups.   From the 100 subgroups of Table 12, $\bar{\sigma}$ = 807.8/100 = 8.078.   This gives an estimate of σ' as

$$\frac{\bar{\sigma}}{c_2} = \frac{8.078}{0.7979} = 10.12$$

Because, in this case, the frequency distribution in the bowl is known, it is possible to compare this estimated σ' of 10.12 with the known σ' of 9.954.   The error in estimate is a little less than 2%.

It is of interest to observe that, even with the use of this c_2 factor, the σ of an individual small subgroup gives no reliable information about σ'.   For instance, the estimate of σ' from the first subgroup (drawings 1–4) is 6.2/0.7979 = 7.8; from the second subgroup, it is 0.5/0.7979 = 0.6; from the third it is 1.3/0.7979 = 1.6; from the fourth it is 12.9/0.7979 = 16.2; etc.

If the 100 subgroups are divided into 5 sets of 20 subgroups each, the resulting estimates of σ' are as follows:

Set of subgroups	$\bar{\sigma}$	Estimate of σ'
1–20 (drawings 1–80).........	7.155	8.97
21–40 (drawings 81–160)........	8.49	10.64
41–60 (drawings 161–240)........	8.36	10.48
61–80 (drawings 241–320)........	7.225	9.06
81–100 (drawings 321–400)........	9.16	11.48

Whereas some of the estimates from individual subgroups missed the true σ' by as much as 100%, none of the estimates from the sets of 20 subgroups missed it by more than 16%.   The use of all 100 subgroups gave an estimate within 2%.   It seems evident that the larger the number of subgroups included in the calculation of $\bar{\sigma}$, the greater should be

* In so far as possible, the symbols used in this book are those generally used in statistical quality control work in the United States.   Unfortunately, the lower-case form of the letter c is commonly used with three different meanings. c_2 is used for the ratio of $\bar{\sigma}$ to σ'; c is used to represent number of defects in the control chart for defects per unit; c, c_1, and c_2 are used to indicate acceptance numbers in the Dodge-Romig single and double sampling tables described in Chap. XIV.   The first two uses have the authority of the American Standards Association and the American Society for Quality Control; the third is common in the literature and usage of sampling tables. As the possible confusion arising from departure from standard usage seems more serious than the confusion from the use of the same symbol in different ways, c is used in all three senses in this book.   The three uses relate to such different situations that the context should always make clear which meaning of c is intended.

the confidence in the estimate from $\bar{\sigma}$ of the unknown standard deviation of the universe.

69. Relationship between σ' and $\bar{R}$. Given n, the sample or subgroup size, statistical theory gives the expected ratio between $\bar{\sigma}$ and σ' in random sampling from a normal universe. Similarly, it gives the expected ratio between the average range $\bar{R}$ and σ'. This latter ratio, designated as d_2, is also given in Table B, Appendix III.

One practical use of this d_2 factor is to provide an alternative method of estimating an unknown universe standard deviation σ' from a series of samples or subgroups. It is of interest to compare the estimates of σ' obtained from $\bar{R}$ with those obtained from $\bar{\sigma}$ in the bowl drawings of Table 12.

For the 100 subgroups of four, $\bar{R} = 2076/100 = 20.76$. The d_2 factor given for $n = 4$ in Table B is 2.059. Hence the estimate of σ' from $\bar{R}$ is $\bar{R}/d_2 = 20.76/2.059 = 10.08$. If the 100 subgroups are divided into five sets of 20 as was done in the estimates from $\bar{\sigma}$, the estimates of σ' are as follows:

Set of subgroups	$\bar{R}$	Estimate of σ'
1–20 (drawings 1–80)........	18.40	8.94
21–40 (drawings 81–160)........	21.65	10.51
41–60 (drawings 161–240)........	21.65	10.51
61–80 (drawings 241–320)........	18.30	8.89
81–100 (drawings 321–400)........	23.80	11.56

With ranges distributed all the way from 1 to 47, it is evident that estimates of σ' made from a single range could vary all the way from 0.5 to 22.8. The comments made in Art. 68 regarding the unreliability of estimates of σ' from the σ of a single small sample apply with even greater force to estimates of σ' from a single value of R. The range of one small subgroup gives little information about the standard deviation of the universe.

A comparison of the two estimates of σ' from each set of 20 subgroups shows a close agreement between the estimate based on $\bar{\sigma}$ and the one based on $\bar{R}$.

	Estimate of σ' from σ	Estimate of σ' from $\bar{R}$
First set....	8.97	8.94
Second set..	10.64	10.51
Third set...	10.48	10.51
Fourth set..	9.06	8.89
Fifth set....	11.48	11.56

In only one of the five cases is the difference between the two estimates as great as 1% of σ'. In four of the five cases, the estimate of σ' from $\bar{\sigma}$ is a little closer to the true value of σ' (9.954) than is the estimate from $\bar{R}$. On the other hand, the estimate from the $\bar{R}$ of the 100 subgroups, 10.08, happens to be a little closer to the true value than the estimate, 10.12, from the $\bar{\sigma}$ of 100 subgroups. In all cases the differences seem negligible for practical purposes.

A practical point is that it is much easier[1] to compute R for a subgroup by making a single subtraction than it is to compute σ by calculating several squares and a square root. In control-chart work, this ease of calculation of R is usually much more important than any slight theoretical advantage that might come from the use of σ as a measure of dispersion of subgroups. However, in some cases where the measurements themselves are costly (for example, destructive tests of valuable items) and it is necessary that the inferences from a limited number of tests be as reliable as possible, the extra cost of calculating standard deviations of subgroups is justified.

70. Relationship between $\bar{X}'$, σ', and the Values of $\bar{X}$. In statistics, the bar above any symbol means an average. Thus $\bar{X}$ is an average of the values of X. In the control chart for variables, each subgroup has its $\bar{X}$. The symbol $\bar{\bar{X}}$ thus refers to an average of the $\bar{X}$ values, i.e., an average of the averages of values of X.

For the 100 subgroups of Table 12, $\bar{\bar{X}} = 3,007.50/100 = 30.08$. This is very close to 30.00, $\bar{X}'$, the average of the distribution in the bowl. (In fact it is considerably closer to the universe average than would ordinarily be obtained in 400 drawings.) The averages of sets of 80 drawings (20 subgroups of 4) may be shown to vary from 28.89 to 31.46. The averages of subgroups of 4 vary from 18.50 to 41.75, and the individual drawings run from 1 to 59.

The more drawings averaged, the more likely it is that their average will be close to the average in the bowl. Or, stated in more general terms, the larger the sample taken from any universe, the more likely it is that the average of the sample will be close to the average of the universe. This would seem to be an acceptable proposition on common-

---

[1] The statement that it is easier to compute R than σ for a subgroup calls for one reservation. In this statement, "easier" means that the arithmetic is less laborious; hence, less time consuming and less costly. It does not mean that there is any less likelihood of mathematical error in computing R than in computing σ. To compute R, the largest and smallest numbers in a subgroup must first be identified. Whenever an error is made in picking either the largest or the smallest number, the calculated value of R is less than the correct value. Such errors are common in the rapid calculations made for control-chart purposes in industrial plants. As there is no reason for compensating errors making R greater than its true value, computed values of $\bar{R}$ are frequently in error on the low side.

sense grounds even without the support given by statistical theory or by experimental bowl drawings.

Table 13 uses an analysis of the 400 drawings from Shewhart's bowl to show how the spread of the averages depends on sample size. These

TABLE 13. RELATIVE FREQUENCIES OF $\bar{X}$ VALUES IN SAMPLES OF VARIOUS SIZES FROM 400 DRAWINGS FROM SHEWHART'S NORMAL BOWL

(All frequencies expressed as percentages of total)

Cell* boundaries	Distri-bution in bowl	$\bar{X}$ $n = 2$	$\bar{X}$ $n = 4$	$\bar{X}$ $n = 8$	$\bar{X}$ $n = 16$	$\bar{X}$ $n = 40$	$\bar{X}$ $n = 80$	$\bar{X}$ $n = 400$
58.31– 61.31	0.2							
55.31– 58.31	0.3							
52.31– 55.31	0.8							
49.31– 52.31	1.3	1.0						
46.31– 49.31	2.4	0.5						
43.31– 46.31	3.9	2.0						
40.31– 43.31	5.8	3.5	5					
37.31– 40.31	8.0	9.0	3					
34.31– 37.31	9.9	11.5	11	8	4			
31.31– 34.31	11.3	17.0	21	22	32	20	20	
28.31– 31.31	12.0	18.5	23	34	36	60	80	100
25.31– 28.31	11.3	12.0	21	26	28	20		
22.31– 25.31	9.9	11.0	10	4				
19.31– 22.31	8.0	8.5	3	4				
16.31– 19.31	5.8	2.0	3					
13.31– 16.31	3.9	0.5						
10.31– 13.31	2.4	2.0						
7.31– 10.31	1.3	1.0						
4.31– 7.31	0.8							
1.31– 4.31	0.3							
−1.69–+1.31	0.2							

* Following the rule stated in Art. 44 that cell boundaries should always be located half-way between two possible values, the cell boundaries for the distribution in the bowl should properly be 58.5 to 61.5, 55.5 to 58.5, etc., rather than 58.31 to 61.31, etc. However, in making frequency distributions of the averages, it was necessary to choose the cells in such a way that no average fell on a cell boundary. In choosing one set of cell boundaries to apply to all the frequency distributions compared in Table 13, it was necessary to violate the rule stated in Art. 44.

400 drawings were divided into 200 subgroups of 2, the averages calculated for each subgroup, and a frequency distribution made of the averages. The same was done for subgroups of 4, 8, 16, 40, and 80. To permit easy comparisons of these distributions having different total frequencies, Table 13 shows them all expressed in *percentage* of total frequency. Tables 14 and 15 show the individual $\bar{X}$ values for subgroups of 2 and 8 respectively.

Table 13 suggests certain ideas about averages of samples. It is evident that if many random samples of any given size n are taken from a universe, the averages ($\overline{X}$ values) of the samples will themselves form a frequency distribution. This frequency distribution of $\overline{X}$ values is similar to all frequency distributions in having its own central tendency and dispersion or spread, which might be expressed in terms of average and standard deviation. The average $\overline{\overline{X}}$ of such a frequency distribution of $\overline{X}$ values apparently tends to be near $\overline{X}'$, the average of the universe. The spread of this frequency distribution of $\overline{X}$ values seems to depend not only on the spread of the universe but also on the sample size n; the larger the value of n, the less the spread of the $\overline{X}$ values.

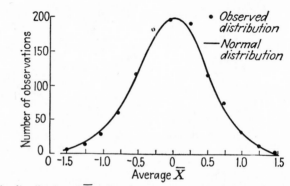

FIG. 14. The distribution of $\overline{X}$ values from 1,000 samples of four from Shewhart's normal bowl was a very close fit to the normal curve. (*Reproduced by permission from "Economic Control of Quality of Manufactured Product" by W. A. Shewhart, published by D. Van Nostrand Company, Inc.*)

Statistical theory gives us some very definite information about these matters. It tells us that in the long run the average of the $\overline{X}$ values will be the same as $\overline{X}'$, the average of the universe. And in the long run, the standard deviation of the frequency distribution of $\overline{X}$ values will be $\sigma'/\sqrt{n}$, *i.e.*, the standard deviation of the universe divided by the square root of the sample size. Thus if $n = 4$, the standard deviation of the frequency distribution of the $\overline{X}$ values will tend to be only half as great as the standard deviation of the universe. If $n = 16$, the spread of the frequency distribution of the $\overline{X}$ values will be one-fourth as great as that of the universe. If $n = 400$, it will be one-twentieth as great. A picture of how this works in a sampling experiment may be obtained by comparing the distributions of $\overline{X}$ values given in Table 13 with the distribution in the bowl.

This standard deviation of the expected frequency distribution of the averages is represented by the symbol $\sigma_{\overline{X}}$. It is referred to in textbooks on statistics as the *standard error of the mean*, or standard error of the average.

Regardless of the form of the universe, whether normal or otherwise, it is true that the expected $\sigma_{\bar{X}} = \sigma'/\sqrt{n}$ and that the expected $\bar{\bar{X}} = \bar{X}'$. If the universe is normal, statistical theory tells us that the expected frequency distribution of the $\bar{X}$ values will also be normal. This is reinforced by experimental evidence from bowl drawings. Figure 14, taken from Shewhart's book,[1] shows the observed frequencies of averages of 1,000 samples of four from his normal bowl and indicates the excellent fit of this distribution to the normal curve.

As pointed out in Art. 57, any distribution is completely specified if it is known to be normal and its average and standard deviation are known. This means that in sampling from a normal distribution that has a known average and standard deviation, statistical theory gives a complete picture of the expected pattern of variation of the averages of samples of any given size.

71. Importance of the Normal Curve in Sampling Theory. Even though the distribution in the universe is not normal, the distribution of the $\bar{X}$ values tends to be close to normal. The larger the sample size and the more nearly normal the universe, the closer will the frequency distribution of averages approach the normal curve.

However, even if n is as small as 4 and the universe is far from normal, the distribution of the averages of samples will be very close to normal. Shewhart illustrates this by showing the distributions of averages of 1,000 samples of four from each of two bowls of chips, one containing a rectangular and the other a triangular distribution. Figure 15, taken from Shewhart,[2] compares these universes, neither of which even faintly resembles the normal curve, with the close fit of the normal curve to the distribution of averages of samples of four.

[1] Reproduced from Shewhart, *op. cit.*, p. 181, by permission of the author and publishers.

[2] Reproduced from Shewhart, *op. cit.*, p. 182, by permission of the author and publishers. The rectangular universe contained 122 chips, with two chips marked −3.0, two marked −2.9, two marked −2.8, and so on to two marked +3.0. The triangular universe contained 820 chips with 40 chips marked −1.3, 39 chips marked −1.2, 38 marked −1.1, and so on to one chip marked +2.6.

The main point to be noted here from Fig. 15 is that even with a great departure from normality in the universe, the distribution of $\bar{X}$ values with $n = 4$ is approximately normal; in sampling from most distributions found in nature and industry, the distribution of $\bar{X}$ values will be even closer to normal. However, it is of interest to observe that distributions similar to the rectangular and triangular distributions sometimes are found in industry. Although they seldom occur as a result of production alone, they may be found as a result of production followed by 100% inspection. For example, if a production operation gives a distribution on a certain dimension which is roughly normal with a standard deviation of 0.0010 in. and the specified

It has already been stated that many observed distributions of industrial characteristics do correspond roughly to the normal curve.   Nevertheless, many others do not.   Serious mistakes are often made when it is assumed that the distribution of an industrial quality characteristic is necessarily normal.

The great practical importance of the normal curve arises even more from its uses in sampling theory than from the fact that some observed

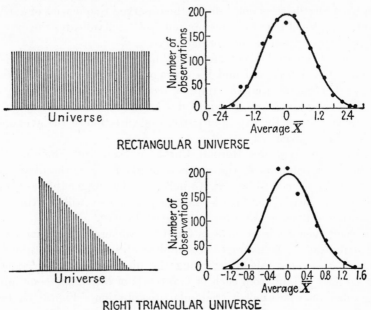

RECTANGULAR UNIVERSE

RIGHT TRIANGULAR UNIVERSE

Fig. 15.   Even from rectangular and triangular universes, the distribution of $\overline{X}$ values from samples of four is approximately normal.   (*Reproduced by permission from "Economic Control of Quality of Manufactured Product" by W. A. Shewhart, published by D. Van Nostrand Company, Inc.*)

distributions are described by it well enough for practical purposes.   One may say with much more confidence that the distribution of averages of samples from an unknown universe will be close to normal than that the universe itself is normal.

72. Is Statistical Distribution Theory of Practical Use?   At this point some critically minded reader might comment somewhat as follows: "What of it?   It may be of academic interest to know that distributions

---

tolerances on the dimension are ± 0.0010 in., it is obvious that only about 68% of the product will meet the specifications.   If the production operation accurately centers the dimension at its specified nominal value, about 16% of the product will be rejected by the go gage and another 16% by the not-go gage.   The distribution of the accepted product will not be far from rectangular.   There will be two distributions something like the triangular, one of the product rejected by the go gage, the other of the product rejected by the not-go gage.

of averages tend to be normal with an average equal to $\bar{X}'$ and a standard deviation equal to $\sigma'/\sqrt{n}$, but what practical good is this information? It is hard to conceive of any situation, outside of bowl sampling experiments, in which $\bar{X}'$ and σ' are actually known. Moreover, if these statistics of the universe were really known, there would be no need to use the evidence of samples to make judgments about the universe, and we would not care about the expected variation among the samples."

True enough; in practice, we always want to make estimates about an unknown universe on the basis of one or more known samples, rather than to estimate from a known universe how samples will be distributed. However, in doing this there are always two pertinent questions that can be better answered with the knowledge given by statistical theory about the distribution of $\bar{X}$ values than they could be answered without it. The first question is, "Do we have a universe at all?" The second question is, "If so, how reliable is our estimate of the average of that universe?" Some ways in which statistical distribution theory helps to answer these two questions are explained in the remainder of this chapter. The first question is answered by means of the control chart; the second by the interpretation of the standard error of estimate of the average.

73. The Appropriateness of 3-sigma Limits for Control Charts for $\bar{X}$. The question to be answered by the control limits on a control chart for $\bar{X}$ might be phrased in a number of different ways, such as, "Were all these samples drawn from the same bowl?" or "Is there one universe from which these samples appear to come?" or "Do these figures indicate a stable pattern of variation?" or "Is this variation the result of a constant-cause system?" or merely "Do these measurements show statistical control?"

Any rule that might be established for providing a definite "Yes" or "No" answer to these questions is bound to give the wrong answer part of the time. The decision where to draw the line between a "Yes" and a "No" answer must be based on the expected action to be taken if each answer is given.

In quality control in manufacturing, the answer, "No, this is not a constant-cause system," leads to a hunt for an assignable cause of variation, and an attempt to remove it, if possible. The answer, "Yes, this is a constant-cause system," leads to leaving the process alone, making no effort to hunt for causes of variation. The rule for establishing the control limits that will determine the "Yes" or "No" answer in any case should strike an economic balance between the costs due to two kinds of errors—the error of hunting for trouble when it is absent (whenever the "No" answer is incorrect) and the error of leaving a process alone because of not hunting for trouble when it really is present (whenever the "Yes" answer is incorrect).

Any rule for establishing control limits for $\bar{X}$ for use in manufacturing should be a practical one based on experience as to this point of economic balance.   In the United States, the control limits on $\bar{X}$ charts are generally placed at $3\sigma_{\bar{X}}$ on either side of the central line.   Experience indicates that in most cases these 3-sigma limits do actually strike a satisfactory economic balance between the two kinds of errors.

It has already been pointed out in this chapter that the distribution of the $\bar{X}$ values of random samples drawn from one universe tends to be normal when the sample size is four or more, even though the universe

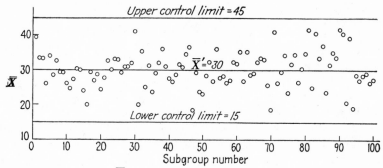

FIG. 16.   Control chart for $\bar{X}$ for 100 subgroups of four drawn from Shewhart's normal bowl.

is not normal.   It has also been pointed out that nearly all the cases (all but 0.27%) in a normal distribution will fall within 3-sigma limits on either side of the average.

It follows that as long as a series of samples (or subgroups) are really random samples from one universe, their averages will nearly always fall within limits $\bar{X}' \pm 3\sigma_{\bar{X}}$.   This is illustrated by Fig. 16 which is a control chart for the averages of 100 samples of 4 from Shewhart's normal bowl, using data of Table 12.   No points fall outside the control limits of 45 and 15.   In Shewhart's 1,000 drawings of samples of four from this bowl, only 2 of the 1,000 points fell outside these control limits.[1]

In Fig. 16, the central line on the chart could be set at 30, *i.e.*, at $\bar{X}'$, the known average of the universe.   The 3-sigma limits could be based

---

[1] It is of interest to examine the distribution of markings on chips as given in Table 11.   These markings extended from 0 to 60, with 60 of the 998 chips below 15 and another 60 above 45.   Obviously in any random series of drawings, occasional subgroups of 4 will contain chips with numbers low enough for the average to be below 15; others will have the average above 45.   The point to be emphasized is that if the chips are drawn in a random manner, the laws of chance operate in a way that these averages below 15 or above 45 will be infrequent.   Whenever one of these infrequent events occurs, the control chart will seem to say, "The universe has changed; look for trouble," when in reality the composition of the universe is unchanged and no trouble can be found.

on a calculation from the known value of σ', the standard deviation in the bowl, which in round numbers was 10. The standard error of the average

$$\sigma_{\overline{X}} = \sigma'/\sqrt{n} = 10/\sqrt{4} = 5$$

The 3-sigma limits were therefore $3\sigma_{\overline{X}} = 3(5) = 15$ on either side of the average of 30. This placed the upper control limit at 45 and the lower control limit at 15.

It is not strictly accurate to say that in the long run 3-sigma limits on an $\overline{X}$ chart will show points out of control only 27 times in 10,000 (*i.e.*, 0.27% of the time) provided the universe is really unchanged. This would be strictly true only if the distribution of the $\overline{X}$ values were exactly normal and the control limits were based on known values of $\overline{X}'$ and σ'. Actually, although the distribution of $\overline{X}$ values is roughly normal, it is not exactly so unless the universe is normal; the 3-sigma limits are necessarily calculated from the observed data rather than from statistics of the universe. Hence 3-sigma limits may give false indications of lack of control somewhat oftener than is indicated by the normal curve.

Nevertheless, such false indications of lack of control will be infrequent. The 3-sigma limits seldom make the error of indicating trouble (*i.e.*, indicating an assignable cause of variation) when there is no trouble to be found. If points on the $\overline{X}$ chart fall outside 3-sigma limits, there is good reason for confidence that they point to some factor contributing to quality variation that can be identified.

74. Calculation of 3-sigma Limits on Control Charts for $\overline{X}$. The use of Tables B, C, and D of Appendix III for the calculation of control limits may be illustrated by using the first 20 subgroups of the bowl drawings of Table 12.

After calculating the averages and ranges of subgroups, the next step in the calculation of limits is to find $\overline{\overline{X}}$ and $\overline{R}$. For the first 20 subgroups, these are

$$\overline{\overline{X}} = \frac{\Sigma \overline{X}}{20} = \frac{577.75}{20} = 28.9$$

$$\overline{R} = \frac{\Sigma R}{20} = \frac{368}{20} = 18.4$$

If Table B is to be used, the next step is to estimate σ'. For this it is necessary to find in Table B the d_2 factor for the subgroup size. In this case $n = 4$, and Table B gives $d_2 = 2.059$.

$$\text{Estimate of } \sigma' = \frac{\overline{R}}{d_2} = \frac{18.4}{2.059} = 8.94$$

Then $3\sigma_{\bar{X}}$ can be calculated from the relationship $\sigma_{\bar{X}} = \sigma'/\sqrt{n}$:

$$3\sigma_{\bar{X}} = \frac{3\sigma'}{\sqrt{n}} = \frac{3(8.94)}{\sqrt{4}} = 13.4$$

Upper Control Limit$_{\bar{X}}$ = $\bar{\bar{X}} + 3\sigma_{\bar{X}}$ = 28.9 + 13.4 = 43.3
Lower Control Limit$_{\bar{X}}$ = $\bar{\bar{X}} - 3\sigma_{\bar{X}}$ = 28.9 - 13.4 = 15.5

The two steps in the calculation of $3\sigma_{\bar{X}}$ might be consolidated as

$$3\sigma_{\bar{X}} = \frac{3\bar{R}}{d_2\sqrt{n}} = \frac{3}{2.059\sqrt{4}}\bar{R} = 0.73\bar{R} = 0.73(18.4) = 13.4$$

To shorten the calculation of control limits from $\bar{R}$, this factor $3/d_2\sqrt{n}$, the multiplier of $\bar{R}$ in the preceding calculation, has been computed for each value of n from 2 to 20 and tabulated in Table C of Appendix III. This factor is designated A_2. The formulas for 3-sigma control limits on charts for $\bar{X}$ then become

$$UCL_{\bar{X}} = \bar{\bar{X}} + A_2\bar{R} \tag{4}$$
$$LCL_{\bar{X}} = \bar{\bar{X}} - A_2\bar{R} \tag{5}$$

If control limits are to be calculated from $\bar{\sigma}$ rather than from $\bar{R}$, the calculations for the first 20 subgroups of Table 12 are as follows:

$$\bar{\bar{X}} = 28.9$$

$$\bar{\sigma} = \frac{\Sigma\sigma}{20} = \frac{143.1}{20} = 7.155$$

Using the c_2 factor from Table B to estimate σ'

$$\text{Estimate of } \sigma' = \frac{\bar{\sigma}}{c_2} = \frac{7.155}{0.7979} = 8.97$$

$$3\sigma_{\bar{X}} = \frac{3\sigma'}{\sqrt{n}} = \frac{3(8.97)}{\sqrt{4}} = 13.5$$

$$UCL_{\bar{X}} = 28.9 + 13.5 = 43.4$$
$$LCL_{\bar{X}} = 28.9 - 13.5 = 15.4$$

As in the calculation from $\bar{R}$, the two steps in the calculation of $3\sigma_{\bar{X}}$ can be consolidated as

$$3\sigma_{\bar{X}} = \frac{3\bar{\sigma}}{c_2\sqrt{n}} = \frac{3}{0.7979(\sqrt{4})}\bar{\sigma} = 1.88(7.155) = 13.5$$

To shorten the calculations for control limits from $\bar{\sigma}$, this factor $3/c_2\sqrt{n}$, the multiplier of $\bar{\sigma}$ in the above calculation, has been computed for each value of n from 2 to 25, thence by 5's to 100, and tabulated in

Table D of Appendix III. This factor is designated A_1. The formulas for 3-sigma control limits using this factor are

$$UCL_{\overline{X}} = \overline{\overline{X}} + A_1\bar{\sigma} \tag{6}$$
$$LCL_{\overline{X}} = \overline{\overline{X}} - A_1\bar{\sigma} \tag{7}$$

For those situations where it is desired to calculate control limits directly from known or standard values of σ' and $\overline{X}'$, the factor $3/\sqrt{n}$ has been computed and tabulated in Table E, Appendix III. This factor is designated as A. The formulas for 3-sigma control limits using this factor are

$$UCL_{\overline{X}} = \overline{X}' + A\sigma' \tag{8}$$
$$LCL_{\overline{X}} = \overline{X}' - A\sigma' \tag{9}$$

As applied to the control chart of Fig. 16, using the known values $\overline{X}' = 30$ and $\sigma' = 10$ and the value $A = 1.50$ given by Table E for a sample size of 4,

$$UCL_{\overline{X}} = 30 + 1.50(10) = 45.0$$
$$LCL_{\overline{X}} = 30 - 1.50(10) = 15.0$$

75. Estimates of σ' from $\bar{R}$ and $\bar{\sigma}$ from Various Subgroup Sizes in a Controlled Process. In industrial use of the control chart for $\overline{X}$, either the factors given in Table C or those given in Table D will be used to determine the position of control limits. The preceding discussion makes it clear that the width of the band between upper and lower control limits depends entirely on the variability within the subgroups, measured either by the average range $\bar{R}$ or the average standard deviation $\bar{\sigma}$. Both $\bar{R}$ and $\bar{\sigma}$ lead to estimates of σ', the standard deviation of the universe. It is of interest to examine data from a controlled process to see whether subgroup size seems to influence these estimates of σ'.

As the chips were drawn one by one from Shewhart's bowl and as each chip drawn was replaced and the chips stirred before the next drawing, there is no natural subgroup size; it is permissible to group the drawings into subgroups of any size. To illustrate the effect of different sizes of subgroups, the 400 drawings have been divided into subgroups of 2 and 8 as well as 4. Table 14 gives the values of average and range for the 200 subgroups of 2. (It is unnecessary to give each standard deviation, as the standard deviation for a subgroup of 2 is always half the range.) Table 15 gives the average, standard deviation, and range for the 50 subgroups of 8.

Consider the first 40 subgroups of Table 14:

$$\Sigma R = 389$$
$$\bar{R} = {}^{389}\!/_{40} = 9.725$$
$$\text{Estimate of } \sigma' \text{ from } \bar{R} = \frac{\bar{R}}{d_2} = \frac{9.725}{1.128} = 8.62$$

TABLE 14. $\bar{X}$ AND R FOR SUBGROUPS OF 2
(Data of Table 12 for 400 drawings from Shewhart's normal bowl)

Numbers of drawing	$\bar{X}$	R	Numbers of drawing	$\bar{X}$	R	Numbers of drawing	$\bar{X}$	R
1–2	39.5	15	71–72	27.0	6	141–142	26.0	10
3–4	39.5	9	73–74	29.0	16	143–144	32.0	14
5–6	33.0	0	75–76	28.5	7	145–146	30.5	27
7–8	34.0	0	77–78	23.0	2	147–148	33.5	41
9–10	34.0	0	79–80	25.5	19	149–150	42.0	12
11–12	32.5	3	81–82	33.5	11	151–152	30.0	22
13–14	16.5	9	83–84	22.0	2	153–154	28.0	6
15–16	35.5	23	85–86	36.5	9	155–156	34.0	8
17–18	29.0	12	87–88	29.0	34	157–158	28.0	14
19–20	39.0	2	89–90	18.5	9	159–160	27.0	14
21–22	28.0	18	91–92	41.5	1	161–162	21.5	1
23–24	29.0	4	93–94	30.0	4	163–164	31.5	25
25–26	34.0	22	95–96	36.5	19	165–166	30.5	17
27–28	31.5	11	97–98	38.0	8	167–168	26.5	5
29–30	32.5	21	99–100	28.0	12	169–170	42.0	4
31–32	36.0	14	101–102	29.0	18	171–172	21.0	6
33–34	23.5	3	103–104	29.5	5	173–174	24.0	2
35–36	35.0	4	105–106	22.0	16	175–176	37.5	17
37–38	30.5	3	107–108	40.0	6	177–178	30.0	14
39–40	21.5	17	109–110	28.5	1	179–180	39.0	10
41–42	29.0	22	111–112	33.5	3	181–182	44.0	16
43–44	20.5	19	113–114	32.5	5	183–184	29.0	2
45–46	19.5	3	115–116	31.5	11	185–186	29.0	12
47–48	35.0	2	117–118	32.0	38	187–188	8.0	6
49–50	30.5	9	119–120	50.0	10	189–190	24.0	18
51–52	30.0	2	121–122	26.5	15	191–192	34.5	11
53–54	40.5	23	123–124	13.5	5	193–194	24.0	12
55–56	19.5	3	125–126	30.0	4	195–196	23.5	3
57–58	23.0	6	127–128	40.5	1	197–198	26.5	7
59–60	25.0	10	129–130	22.5	17	199–200	19.5	1
61–62	10.0	18	131–132	27.5	15	201–202	19.5	25
63–64	30.0	0	133–134	34.5	19	203–204	37.0	2
65–66	31.0	6	135–136	28.0	2	205–206	29.5	1
67–68	28.0	22	137–138	20.0	4	207–208	35.0	8
69–70	27.0	4	139–140	26.5	13	209–210	24.0	24

TABLE 14. $\bar{X}$ AND R FOR SUBGROUPS OF 2.—(*Continued*)

Numbers of drawing	$\bar{X}$	R	Numbers of drawing	$\bar{X}$	R	Numbers of drawing	$\bar{X}$	R
211–212	29.5	9	281–282	44.5	9	351–352	31.0	2
213–214	36.5	1	283–284	37.5	1	353–354	27.5	15
215–216	35.5	7	285–286	30.5	17	355–356	40.0	12
217–218	23.5	29	287–288	22.0	8	357–358	40.0	30
219–220	32.0	14	289–290	33.0	6	359–360	43.5	21
221–222	27.5	33	291–292	26.0	16	361–362	34.0	24
223–224	29.0	0	293–294	39.0	4	363–364	47.0	10
225–226	24.5	13	295–296	29.5	5	365–366	19.0	10
227–228	28.0	6	297–298	12.5	15	367–368	22.5	41
229–230	34.5	25	299–300	34.5	17	369–370	44.0	16
231–232	19.5	15	301–302	32.0	12	371–372	34.5	31
233–234	26.5	5	303–304	31.5	13	373–374	25.0	8
235–236	38.0	12	305–306	32.5	11	375–376	13.0	8
237–238	34.0	16	307–308	36.5	7	377–378	32.0	2
239–240	29.5	5	309–310	21.5	3	379–380	25.0	14
241–242	34.5	11	311–312	31.5	7	381–382	43.0	18
243–244	36.0	14	313–314	29.0	0	383–384	11.0	12
245–246	22.5	1	315–316	31.5	5	385–386	32.0	18
247–248	31.0	16	317–318	30.0	10	387–388	25.0	8
249–250	30.5	7	319–320	39.5	5	389–390	25.0	6
251–252	40.0	24	321–322	50.5	17	391–392	33.0	24
253–254	33.5	13	323–324	33.0	10	393–394	29.5	5
255–256	23.5	1	325–326	28.0	8	395–396	23.0	14
257–258	36.0	4	327–328	22.0	0	397–398	23.0	0
259–260	22.0	12	329–330	39.0	2	399–400	31.5	9
261–262	29.0	20	331–332	41.5	21	Totals.	6,015.0	2,240
263–264	35.5	7	333–334	37.0	30			
265–266	33.5	17	335–336	30.0	6			
267–268	33.5	17	337–338	39.0	14			
269–270	27.5	5	339–340	35.0	30			
271–272	38.5	1	341–342	28.0	2			
273–274	32.5	21	343–344	19.5	9			
275–276	19.0	18	345–346	28.5	5			
277–278	24.0	14	347–348	34.5	1			
279–280	13.0	6	349–350	39.0	14			

TABLE 15. $\bar{X}$, R, AND σ FOR SUBGROUPS OF 8
(Data of Table 12 for 400 drawings from Shewhart's normal bowl)

Numbers of drawings	$\bar{X}$	R	σ	Numbers of drawings	$\bar{X}$	R	σ
1–8	36.500	15	5.3	201–208	30.250	32	9.5
9–16	29.625	35	9.9	209–216	31.375	27	8.3
17–24	31.250	21	7.1	217–224	28.000	35	11.9
25–32	31.000	33	10.2	225–232	26.625	35	9.8
33–40	27.625	24	7.0	233–240	32.000	20	6.9
41–48	26.000	29	9.7	241–248	31.000	21	8.0
49–56	30.125	34	9.7	249–256	31.875	29	9.2
57–64	22.000	29	9.1	257–264	30.625	23	6.9
65–72	28.250	22	6.2	265–272	33.250	17	7.3
73–80	26.500	21	6.9	273–280	22.125	33	10.6
81–88	30.250	34	10.7	281–288	33.625	31	9.8
88–96	31.625	32	10.1	289–296	31.875	23	6.6
97–104	31.125	22	7.1	297–304	27.625	38	11.4
105–112	31.000	29	7.9	305–312	30.500	20	6.5
113–120	36.500	42	12.9	313–320	32.500	17	5.1
121–128	27.625	30	10.5	321–328	33.375	37	11.9
129–136	28.125	30	8.6	329–336	36.875	30	10.2
137–144	26.125	21	6.9	337–344	30.375	35	11.3
145–152	34.000	41	14.6	345–352	33.250	20	5.4
153–160	29.250	18	6.2	353–360	37.750	35	12.0
161–168	27.500	25	8.6	361–368	30.625	50	16.5
169–176	31.125	28	9.6	369–376	29.125	43	14.7
177–184	35.500	29	8.6	377–384	27.750	47	13.3
185–192	23.875	35	11.7	385–392	28.750	24	8.8
193–200	23.375	12	4.4	393–400	26.750	20	5.8
				Totals..	1,503.750	1,433	457.2

As σ for a subgroup size of 2 is always one-half R,

$$\bar{\sigma} = 4.8625$$

$$\text{Estimate of } \sigma' \text{ from } \bar{\sigma} = \frac{\bar{\sigma}}{c_2} = \frac{4.8625}{0.5642} = 8.62$$

(For $n = 2$, c_2 is half of d_2 and $\bar{\sigma}$ is half of $\bar{R}$.   The two estimates of σ' are necessarily the same.)   These estimates from the first 80 drawings arranged in subgroups of 2 may be compared with the estimates of σ' already obtained from the same drawings arranged in subgroups of 4.

In Table 15 these 80 drawings are divided into 10 subgroups of 8.

$$\Sigma R = 263$$
$$\bar{R} = {}^{263}\!/_{10} = 26.3$$
$$\text{Estimate of } \sigma' \text{ from } \bar{R} = \frac{\bar{R}}{d_2} = \frac{2.63}{2.847} = 9.24$$
$$\Sigma \sigma = 81.1$$
$$\bar{\sigma} = \frac{81.1}{10} = 8.11$$
$$\text{Estimate of } \sigma' \text{ from } \bar{\sigma} = \frac{\bar{\sigma}}{c_2} = \frac{8.11}{0.9027} = 8.98$$

Similar calculations have been made for each set of 80 drawings and for the entire set of 400 drawings. The resulting estimates of σ' are compared in Table 16.

The fairly close agreement among the different estimates of σ' from any given set of drawings is striking. The variation in estimates of σ' from one set of 80 drawings to another is evidently much greater than the variation among the different estimates from any set. It would seem that, at least from the standpoint of estimating the dispersion of the universe, many different subgroup sizes are acceptable.

TABLE 16. COMPARISON OF ESTIMATES OF UNIVERSE STANDARD DEVIATION σ',
BASED ON SUBGROUP SIZES OF 2, 4, AND 8
(Data of Tables 12, 14, and 15. Known value of $\sigma' = 9.95$)

Drawings	Estimates of σ' Subgroup size of 2		Estimates of σ' Subgroup size of 4		Estimates of σ' Subgroup size of 8	
	From $\bar{R}$	From $\bar{\sigma}$	From $\bar{R}$	From $\bar{\sigma}$	From $\bar{R}$	From $\bar{\sigma}$
1–80	8.62	8.62	8.94	8.97	9.24	8.98
81–160	10.75	10.75	10.51	10.64	10.50	10.58
161–240	9.73	9.73	10.51	10.48	9.76	9.89
241–320	8.86	8.86	8.89	9.06	8.85	9.02
321–400	11.68	11.68	11.56	11.48	11.98	12.17
1–400	9.93	9.93	10.08	10.12	10.07	10.13

There may, however, be a number of reasons why some one particular subgroup size may be the best to use in any given instance. Some advantages of four, recommended by Shewhart as the ideal subgroup size, are brought out in Chap. V in connection with the discussion of processes out of control. Various practical considerations entering into choice of subgroup size are discussed in Chaps. VI and VII.

76. An Interpretation of the Standard Error of the Average. If the control chart on any measured variable indicates a state of statistical control, it is reasonable to take action as if all the measurements came from one universe. How good are the estimates that can be made about this unknown universe?   We know that the observed average $\bar{X}$ of any set of measured values is the best estimate that these values can give us regarding $\bar{X}'$, the universe average.   Is it possible to find a basis for judgment as to how far $\bar{X}$ departs from $\bar{X}'$?

An answer to these questions is given by the standard error of the average $\sigma_{\bar{X}}$.   The formula for $\sigma_{\bar{X}}$ is always $\sigma'/\sqrt{n}$ with σ' representing the universe standard deviation and n representing the total number of observations that have been averaged.   In industrial quality control work σ' is not known but is usually estimated from $\bar{R}$ or from $\bar{\sigma}$.   In the case of a frequency distribution with no basis for rational subgrouping σ' is usually estimated from the σ of the distribution.

Suppose that for the data of Table 2 it is desired to find the standard error of the average obtained for the particular measured dimension of a rheostat knob.   This average is given in Art. 24 as 140.6 (expressed in thousandths of an inch). $\bar{R}$ is 8.6.

$$\text{Estimate of } \sigma' \text{ from } \bar{R} = \frac{\bar{R}}{d_2} = \frac{8.6}{2.326} = 3.7$$

$$\sigma_{\bar{X}} = \frac{\sigma'}{\sqrt{n}} = \frac{3.7}{\sqrt{135}} = 0.3$$

It should be noted that n is 135, the total number of individual observations that went into the average, and not 27, the number of subgroups.

Statistical theory tells us that as n gets larger, the distribution of averages tends to be closer and closer to normal, even though the universe is not normal.   The standard error may therefore be interpreted using the characteristics of the normal curve.   A precise statement of the interpretation might be made somewhat as follows:

During the period covered by Table 2, there was a constant-cause system—a stable pattern of variation, a universe.   This universe had an unknown average $\bar{X}'$.   If this universe remained unchanged and many random samples of 135 rheostat knobs were measured, their averages would form a frequency distribution the standard deviation of which would be, according to our best estimate, 0.3.   As this frequency distribution of averages would be closely fitted by the normal curve, about two-thirds of the averages would fall within the limits $\bar{X}' \pm 0.3$; about 95% would fall within the limits $\bar{X}' \pm 0.6$; and practically all would fall within the limits $\bar{X}' \pm 0.9$.

A less precise but more common interpretation is to say that it is practically certain the true average is within the limits of 139.7 and 141.5 ($\bar{X} \pm 3\sigma_{\bar{X}}$), that there are 95 chances out of 100 that it is within the limits of 140.0 to 141.2 ($\bar{X} \pm 2\sigma_{\bar{X}}$) and that there are two chances out of three that it is within the limits 140.3 and 140.9 ($\bar{X} \pm \sigma_{\bar{X}}$).   This statement might be useful for the purpose of judging whether the process was closely enough centered on the specified nominal dimension of 140.

A figure related to the standard error is the *probable error*, defined as $0.6745\sigma_{\overline{x}}$. It will be remembered that in the normal curve exactly half the cases were within the limits of $\overline{X} \pm 0.6745\sigma$. Hence the idea of an error that will be exceeded half the time. Experience shows that the adjective *probable* is often misinterpreted to mean maximum probable error. Most modern writers on statistics have discarded the concept of probable error. The phrase is not used elsewhere in this book.

77. Where Not to Use the Standard Error. Although it was appropriate to compute the standard error of the average of the dimensions given in Table 2, it would not have been correct to compute the standard error of $\overline{\overline{X}}$ for Table 1. The measurements in Table 2 showed a state of statistical control; those in Table 1 did not. As there was no constant-cause system in operation throughout the period of measurement in Table 1, it would have been misleading to have considered $\overline{\overline{X}}$ as a measure of the average of *one* universe. Where measurements show lack of statistical control the standard error of estimate of $\overline{X}'$ has no meaning, as there is no one universe that has an average $\overline{X}'$. The statement of a standard error in such a case tends to lead to a false confidence in the reliability of the average.

Nevertheless, in the application of statistics to other fields than industrial quality control, standard errors of averages are often calculated for measurements which, if tested by the Shewhart techniques, would show lack of control. Even writers of textbooks on statistics sometimes make this mistake.[1]

There are obvious limitations to an estimate of the standard error of the $\overline{X}$ of a single subgroup of four or five observations where the only evidence of σ' is the standard deviation (or range) of the subgroup. If the reader examines the variability of the σ's for the subgroups in Table 12, he will see how often it would be possible to get a very misleading estimate of σ' from the σ of one subgroup. By examining Table 16 he will realize how estimates of σ' vary from sets of 80 observations taken

---

[1] There seem to be two reasons why the standard error is so frequently misused in applications outside the field of quality control in manufacturing. One reason is that Shewhart's contributions to statistical theory, originally applied in manufacturing, are not so well known as they ought to be to statisticians in other fields. In fact, many textbooks on statistics are written with no mention of the Shewhart techniques. The other reason is that statisticians in other fields are not subject to the immediate check on the accuracy of their predictions which is so common in manufacturing. In many other fields, if a statistician, by computing a standard error where none is justified, gives a false assurance of the accuracy of a given average, it is likely everyone will have forgotten about it by the time subsequent facts show that he was wrong.

under controlled conditions. The computed figure for standard error can never be better than the estimate of σ'.

78. The Distribution of the Standard Deviation. Gen. Leslie Simon,[1] in his presentation of sampling by variables, introduces his subject with the following quotation from De Morgan's "A Budget of Paradoxes":

> Great fleas have little fleas upon their backs to bite 'em,
> And little fleas have lesser fleas, and so ad infinitum.

Whether or not De Morgan was right about the fleas, a somewhat parallel idea certainly applies to distribution theory in mathematical statistics. Universes seem to give nourishment to many other distributions that have less spread, such as distributions of averages, standard deviations, and ranges. And just as each universe has its average and standard deviation, so also does each distribution of averages, standard deviations, or ranges have its own average and standard deviation.

TABLE 17. DISTRIBUTION OF RELATIVE FREQUENCIES OF STANDARD DEVIATIONS OF SAMPLES OF 2, 4, AND 8 FROM 400 DRAWINGS FROM SHEWHART'S NORMAL BOWL
(All frequencies expressed as percentages of total)

Cell boundaries	Values of σ		
	$n = 2$	$n = 4$	$n = 8$
19.95–21.95	1.0		
17.95–19.95	0.5		
15.95–17.95	1.0	3	2
13.95–15.95	2.5	1	4
11.95–13.95	4.0	9	6
9.95–11.95	5.5	16	22
7.95– 9.95	13.5	13	30
5.95– 7.95	16.0	33	26
3.95– 5.95	15.5	17	10
1.95– 3.95	20.0	6	
0.00– 1.95	20.5		

The reader may get a feeling for what is meant by *the distribution of standard deviations* by examining three such frequency distributions compared in Table 17. This table, based on the 400 bowl drawings and the computed values of σ for the three subgroup sizes, shows how the distribution pattern of σ changed with change in subgroup size. It is evident that for $n = 2$, the distribution of values of σ centers consider-

[1] SIMON, L. E., "An Engineers' Manual of Statistical Methods," p. 41, John Wiley & Sons, Inc., New York, 1941.

ably below the universe standard deviation of 10, and that as n increases this centering approaches closer to the universe standard deviation. The spread of the distribution of σ seems to decrease as n increases. The distribution of σ is evidently not symmetrical (and therefore cannot be normal), particularly for low values of n.

Unfortunately, statistical theory cannot give us such useful generalizations about the distribution of σ as it can about the distribution of $\overline{X}$. In the case of the distribution of $\overline{X}$, theory gave the expected average $(\overline{X}')$ and the expected standard deviation $(\sigma'/\sqrt{n})$, both of which were independent of the form of the universe. Moreover, theory told us that if the universe distribution were normal the distribution of $\overline{X}$ values would be normal regardless of sample size, and that even if the universe distribution were not normal, the distribution of $\overline{X}$ values would approach normality as sample size increased.

However, if the universe is normal, statistical theory can tell us the expected average and the expected standard deviation of the distribution of σ. As has already been pointed out, in samples from a normal universe the expected average $\bar{\sigma}$ is $c_2\sigma'$.* A commonly used approximate estimate of σ_σ, the expected standard deviation of the distribution of σ for samples from a normal universe, is $\sigma'/\sqrt{2n}$. It is also known that as n increases, the distribution of σ becomes closer and closer to a symmetrical distribution.

Theoretical knowledge of the distribution of σ in samples from a normal universe is the basis for 3-sigma limits on the control chart for σ. The central line on the control chart is set at $\bar{\sigma}$. The limits are set at $\bar{\sigma} \pm 3\sigma_\sigma$.

The approximate value of σ_σ for a normal universe is

$$\sigma_\sigma = \sigma'/\sqrt{2n} \tag{10}$$

Modern statistical theory gives the exact value as[1]

$$\sigma_\sigma = [2(n - 1) - 2nc_2^2]^{1/2}\,\frac{\sigma'}{\sqrt{2n}} \tag{11}$$

When n is large, the difference between equations (10) and (11) is negligible. Tables D and E, Appendix III, give factors designated as

*Where
$$c_2 = \sqrt{\frac{2}{n}}\,\frac{\left(\dfrac{n-2}{2}\right)!}{\left(\dfrac{n-3}{2}\right)!}$$

In this formula, the symbol ! means factorial. See Chap. IX for an explanation of factorials.

[1] See "ASTM Manual on Quality Control of Materials," p. 111, American Society for Testing Materials, Philadelphia, Pa., 1951. See also Frederick Mosteller, On Some Useful "Inefficient" Statistics, *The Annals of Mathematical Statistics*, vol. 17, pp. 377–408, December, 1946.

B_1, B_2, B_3, and B_4, to simplify the calculation of 3-sigma control limits on a control chart for standard deviation. Equation (11) is the basis for these factors where n is 25 or less; equation (10) is used where n exceeds 25.

When 3-sigma limits on a σ chart are calculated from an observed $\bar{\sigma}$, they are

$$UCL_\sigma = \bar{\sigma} + 3\sigma_\sigma = B_4\bar{\sigma} \tag{12}$$
$$LCL_\sigma = \bar{\sigma} - 3\sigma_\sigma = B_3\bar{\sigma} \tag{13}$$

When limits are based on a known or assumed value of universe standard deviation σ', they are

$$UCL_\sigma = c_2\sigma' + 3\sigma_\sigma = B_2\sigma' \tag{14}$$
$$LCL_\sigma = c_2\sigma' + 3\sigma_\sigma = B_1\sigma' \tag{15}$$

In computing σ_σ for the B_4 and B_3 factors given in Table D, σ' is assumed to be $\bar{\sigma}/c_2$. The B_2 and B_1 factors are given in Table E.

79. The Distribution of the Range.   Although no simple formula gives either the expected average range $\bar{R}$ or the standard deviation of the range σ_R, statistical theory does give the ratio of these figures to universe standard deviation σ' in sampling from a normal universe. Theory also fully defines the expected distribution of R in sampling from a normal universe.[1]

The ratio $\bar{R}/\sigma'$, designated as d_2, is given in Table B, Appendix III. It has already been used to estimate σ' from $\bar{R}$.

Table C gives two factors, D_3 and D_4, which are used in the calculation of control limits on a control chart for R. The upper control limit is $D_4\bar{R}$ and the lower control limit is $D_3\bar{R}$.

Table E may be used whenever, for some reason, it is desired to calculate control limits on a chart for R directly from known or assumed values of σ'.   Here the upper control limit is $D_2\sigma'$ and the lower control limit is $D_1\sigma'$.

80. Control Charts for Standard Deviation and Range.   Figure 17 shows control charts for σ and R for the 100 subgroups of four given in Table 12.   The similarity between the variation from subgroup to subgroup shown in the σ and R charts is emphasized here by the use of lines[2]

---

[1] See SIMON, *op. cit.*, p. 204, and E. S. Pearson, The Probability Integral of the Range in Samples of n Observations from a Normal Population, *Biometrika*, vol. 32, 1942.

[2] In practical control-chart work in industry, the points on $\bar{X}$ and R charts are sometimes connected and sometimes not.   In this book points on the charts are not connected except in special cases such as Fig. 17.   Generally speaking, experience shows that the connection of points on control charts for variables is likely to lead to their misinterpretation, particularly by many people who are not familiar with the principles behind the control chart.   It is usually advantageous if control charts for $\bar{X}$ and R do not look like ordinary trend charts.

connecting the successive points. It seems clear that these two charts tell practically the same story. Either one may be used in any instance to tell the story; there is no need to use both.

In subsequent illustrations throughout this book, only one measure of subgroup dispersion will be calculated. Usually this will be R, although occasionally it may be σ. The purpose of calculating both R and σ for the subgroups in Tables 12 and 15 was to illustrate that R and σ were alternative measures of the same thing, that they led to similar estimates

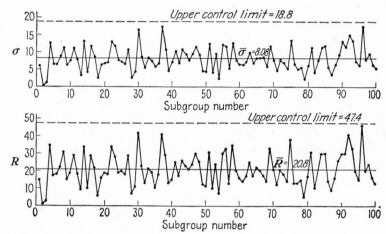

Fig. 17. Control charts for standard deviations and range—drawings from Shewhart's normal bowl.

of σ', similar control limits on $\overline{X}$ charts, and similar control charts showing subgroup dispersion.

In practical control-chart work in industry, R rather than σ should nearly always be used as a measure of subgroup dispersion. As has already been stated, this is partly because R is easier to compute. Equally important is the advantage that R is easier to explain; almost everyone can understand range, whereas many people have difficulty understanding standard deviation.

R as a measure of subgroup dispersion is always necessary to provide a basis for calculating limits on a control chart for $\overline{X}$ and to permit estimates of σ'. However the control chart for R may often be omitted. For many industrial quality characteristics, experience shows that R never goes out of control even though $\overline{X}$ does so frequently. In such cases the keeping of an R chart merely adds to cost without supplying any useful information.

81. Practical Meaning of 3-sigma Limits on Control Charts for Variables. Suppose that, following the 100 subgroups of 4 that are tabulated in Table 12 and charted in Fig. 16, the 101st subgroup drawn had contained chips marked 55, 52, 46, and 47.   The $\overline{X}$ of such a subgroup would be 50.   Would this prove that the universe had changed (possibly by someone substituting different chips in the bowl)?

A study of statistical theory would show us that the correct answer to this kind of question cannot be "Yes" or "No."   An $\overline{X}$ of 50 from Shewhart's normal bowl is not impossible; however, the evidence provided by the 100 subgroups already drawn indicates that it would occur infrequently.   For this reason, the answer given by the statistician must be expressed in terms of probability, *i.e.*, in terms of relative frequency in the long run.   When the statistician is asked, "Does this prove that the universe has changed?" he must answer, "It all depends on what you consider satisfactory proof.   I can tell you that *either* the universe has changed *or* that an unlikely event, one that would not occur as a matter of chance more than once in about 30,000 trials, has occurred."

If the question is asked only to satisfy idle curiosity, as might be the case if it were asked about a bowl drawing (provided no one were gambling on the results of the drawing), there is no need to worry about the practical limitations of this kind of conditional answer.   But if the answer is to provide a basis for action, it often is necessary to have either a "Yes" or a "No" answer, even though it is recognized that each answer will sometimes be wrong.   To get a "Yes" or "No" answer, it is necessary to decide what will be accepted as satisfactory proof.

The question, "Has the universe changed?" asked about a manufacturing process is intended to provide a basis for choice between two possible actions, either looking for trouble (*i.e.*, an assignable cause of variation) if the answer is that the universe has changed, or leaving the process alone if the answer is that the universe has not changed.   As pointed out in Art. 73, the question of what constitutes satisfactory proof of change (in other words, the question of where to establish limits on the control chart) is really the economic one of balancing the costs associated with two kinds of errors.

Trouble, in the sense of the existence of assignable causes of variation in quality, is a common state of affairs in manufacturing.   Under such circumstances, it seldom pays to hunt for trouble without a strong basis for confidence that trouble is really there.   The real basis for the use of 3-sigma limits on control charts for variables in industrial quality control is experience that when closer limits, such as 2-sigma, are used, the control chart often gives indication of assignable causes of variation that simply cannot be found, whereas when 3-sigma limits are used and points fall out of control, a diligent search will usually disclose the assignable causes of variation.

82. Two Points of View on Control Limits for Control Charts for Variables.   Two different points of view have developed among writers on statistical quality control with respect to the real basis for establishing limits on control charts for variables.

One, which might be called *the engineering point of view*, is that the real basis for control-chart limits is experience regarding those limits which strike the economic balance between the two kinds of errors previously mentioned. Such experience has generally led to the use of 3-sigma limits. This point of view holds that the numerical values of probabilities associated with these limits are only of incidental interest. It is not a serious matter if an exact numerical value cannot be placed on these probabilities; it is merely necessary that there be a definite basis for the calculation of the limits.

The other might be called *the statistical point of view*. This holds that the appropriate decision to make in establishing control limits is a numerical value of a probability. This preferably should be the probability (*i.e.*, relative frequency in the long run) that, with no change in the universe, a point will fall outside the control limits. The advocates of this point of view have frequently adopted 0.998 (corresponding to a relative frequency of 99.8%) as the desired probability that a point should fall within the control limits as long as the universe remains unchanged. As 99.8% of the area under the normal curve falls within the limits $\overline{X} \pm 3.09\sigma$, this has been interpreted as setting the limits on $\overline{X}$ charts at $\overline{\overline{X}} \pm 3.09\sigma_{\overline{x}}$ rather than at $\overline{\overline{X}} \pm 3\sigma_{\overline{x}}$.

Because of the assumption that the distribution of $\overline{X}$ is normal, probability limits on $\overline{X}$ charts, like 3σ limits, are at equal distances from the central line. However, even from a normal universe the distributions of σ and R are not symmetrical (see Table 17). This is recognized in the setting of probability limits on control charts for σ and R. These limits are based on the known theoretical distributions of σ and R in sampling from a normal universe. The upper limit is often set at a point where the probability is 0.001 that a point will fall above the upper limit if the universe is unchanged, and the lower limit is set at a point where the probability is 0.001 that a point will fall below the lower limit if the universe is unchanged. Because of the unsymmetrical distributions of σ and R, this gives upper and lower limits that are at unequal distances from the central line on the chart.

The American standards[1] on the control chart use 3-sigma control limits on charts for variables. The standards prepared by the British

---

[1] Two pamphlets have been published by the American Standards Association, 70 East 45th St., New York. The first pamphlet contains American War Standards Z1.1 and Z1.2, 1941, "Guide for Quality Control" and "Control Chart Method of Analyzing Data." The second contains American War Standard Z1.3, 1942, "Control Chart Method of Controlling Quality During Production." These standards were prepared by a committee consisting of H. F. Dodge, Quality Results Engineer, Bell

Standards Institution[1] use probability limits. Nevertheless, the difference in point of view is not primarily an international one. Probability limits as well as 3-sigma limits are used in the United States; 3-sigma limits as well as probability limits are used in Great Britain.

83. Reasons for Using 3-sigma Limits Rather than Probability Limits. An objection that may be made to stating control-chart limits in terms of probabilities is that the probabilities are really not known. The stated probabilities generally used are based on two assumptions. One is that the universe is normal; the other is that the σ' estimated from $\bar{R}$ or from $\bar{\sigma}$ is the true standard deviation of the universe. In industrial quality control, in which sampling is always from an unknown universe, it is impossible to judge just how much error in the stated probabilities is introduced by these assumptions. This error may be substantial— frequently as much as several hundred per cent in a probability stated as 0.001. The description of limits as 3-sigma limits avoids this statement in precise terms of a probability that really is uncertain.[2]

Moreover, it really is not the exact value of a probability that constitutes the basis for action. For instance, it would be practically impossible to have any sense of the difference between the effect of probabilities of 0.0010 and 0.00135 that a point would fall above the upper control limit by chance. The real basis for acceptance of control limits, whether called 3-sigma limits or something else, is experience that the operational procedure involved in their computation gives limits that provide a satisfactory basis for action.

As far as the practical use of the control charts in manufacturing is concerned, it makes very little difference whether limits are at 3-sigma

---

Telephone Laboratories, Chairman; A. G. Ashcroft, Director of Research, Alexander Smith and Sons Carpet Co.; W. Edwards Deming, Mathematical Adviser, Bureau of the Budget; Gen. Leslie E. Simon, Ordnance Department, U.S. Army; Ralph E. Wareham, Consultant on Quality Control, and John Gaillard, Secretary, American Standards Association.

[1] DUDDING, B. P., and W. J. JENNETT, "Quality Control Charts," British Standard 600R: 1942, British Standards Institution, 28 Victoria St., London, 1942 An earlier standard by E. S. Pearson, "The Application of Statistical Methods to Industrial Standardization and Quality Control," British Standard 600: 1935, is out of print, as the plates were destroyed in the bombing of London. The British Standards Institution also reprinted the earlier American standards as B.S. 1008.

[2] A similar objection may be made that so-called "3-sigma limits" are not exactly at the 3-sigma points. Their calculation involves the use of c_2 and d_2 factors based on a normal universe; they are based on an estimate of σ' from $\bar{R}$ or $\bar{\sigma}$; in the case of charts for R or σ they use the standard deviation of the distribution of R and σ from a normal universe. However, it seems less misleading to describe as a 3-sigma limit one that may really be at a slightly different multiple of sigma, than to describe as an 0.001 probability limit one that may really be at several times that stated probability.

or at 3.09-sigma, and it makes even less difference whether they are called 3-sigma limits or probability limits. Both types of limits are used in the same manner and give very nearly the same results. This book, following the American standards on the subject, uses 3-sigma limits for all control charts for variables. The only exceptions to this usage are a few examples using probability limits that have been taken from British literature, and a brief explanation of the calculation of probability limits given in Art. 158, Chap. VIII.

Problems

22. Control charts for $\bar{X}$ and R are maintained on the tensile strength in pounds of a certain yarn. The subgroup size is 5. The values of $\bar{X}$ and R are computed for each subgroup. After 25 subgroups, $\Sigma\bar{X} = 514.8$, and $\Sigma R = 120.0$. Compute the values of 3-sigma limits for the $\bar{X}$ and R charts. *Ans.* 23.4, 17.8; 10.1, 0.

23. All of the points on the control charts of Problem 22 fell within the control limits. From $\bar{R}$, estimate the value of σ'. From this σ' compute the standard error of the average of the 125 measurements of tensile strength. *Ans.* 2.06; 0.18.

24. Control charts for $\bar{X}$ and σ are maintained on the weight in ounces of the contents of a certain container. The subgroup size is 10. The values of $\bar{X}$ and σ are computed for each subgroup. After 18 subgroups, $\Sigma\bar{X} = 595.8$, and $\Sigma\sigma = 8.24$. Compute the values of the 3-sigma limits for the $\bar{X}$ and σ charts. *Ans.* 33.57, 32.63; 0.79, 0.12.

25. All of the points on the control charts of Problem 24 fell within the control limits. From $\bar{\sigma}$, estimate the value of σ'. From this σ' compute the standard error of the average of the 180 measurements. *Ans.* 0.496; 0.037.

26. Control charts for $\bar{X}$, R, and σ are to be maintained on drawings from a bowl of chips the distribution of which is approximately normal. The subgroup size is 5. $\bar{X}'$ is 60, and σ' is 8. Assume that 3-sigma control limits are to be based on $\bar{X}'$ and σ'. Compute the value of the upper control limit, the central line, and the lower control limit for the $\bar{X}$, R, and σ charts, respectively. *Ans.* 70.7, 60.0, 49.3; 39.4, 18.6, 0; 14.3, 6.7, 0.

27. Control charts for $\bar{X}$ and R are maintained on a certain dimension of a manufactured part, measured in inches. The subgroup size is 4. The values of $\bar{X}$ and R are computed for each subgroup. After 20 subgroups, $\Sigma\bar{X} = 41.283$, and $\Sigma R = 0.339$. Compute the values of the 3-sigma limits for the $\bar{X}$ and R charts, and estimate the value of σ' on the assumption that the process is in statistical control.

28. Control charts for $\bar{X}$ and R are maintained on the shear strength in pounds of test spot welds. The subgroup size is 3. The values of $\bar{X}$ and R are computed for each subgroup. After 30 subgroups, $\Sigma\bar{X} = 12,870$, and $\Sigma R = 1,350$. Compute the values of the 3-sigma limits for the $\bar{X}$ and R charts, and estimate the value of σ' on the assumption that the process is in statistical control.

29. Control charts for $\bar{X}$ and σ are maintained on the breaking strength in pounds in a certain destructive test of a particular type of ceramic insulator used in vacuum tubes. The subgroup size is 15. The values of $\bar{X}$ and σ are computed for each subgroup. After 12 subgroups, $\Sigma\bar{X} = 1,307$, and $\Sigma\sigma = 191.5$. Compute the values of the 3-sigma limits for the $\bar{X}$ and σ charts, and estimate the value of σ' on the assumption that the process is in statistical control.

30. Control charts for $\bar{X}$ and σ are maintained on the resistance in ohms of certain electrical parts. The subgroup size is 25. The values of $\bar{X}$ and σ are computed for each subgroup. After 20 subgroups, $\Sigma\bar{X} = 1,612.9$, and $\Sigma\sigma = 61.4$. Compute the values of the 3-sigma limits for the $\bar{X}$ and σ charts, and estimate the value of σ' on the assumption that the process is in statistical control.

31. Control charts for $\bar{X}$, R, and σ are to be maintained on drawings from a bowl of chips the distribution of which is approximately normal.   The subgroup size is 4. $\bar{X}'$ is 40, and σ' is 5.   Assume that 3-sigma control limits are to be based on $\bar{X}'$ and σ'. Compute the value of the upper control limit, the central line, and the lower control limit for the $\bar{X}$, R, and σ charts, respectively.

32. After the bowl drawing referred to in Problem 31 has continued for some time, a frequency distribution is made of the $\bar{X}$ values.   Estimate the average and standard deviation of this distribution.   A frequency distribution is also made of the σ values. Estimate the average and standard deviation of this distribution.

33. The statement is made on page 93 that the standard deviation of a subgroup of 2 is always half the range.   Explain why this is true.

34. On a single sheet of graph paper plot control charts for σ and R for the 50 subgroups of 8 given in Table 15 (page 96).   Connect the points as in Fig. 17, (page 103) to make possible a quick visual comparison of the similarity of the two charts.   Use $\bar{\sigma}$ and $\bar{R}$ to compute the respective control limits.

35. Plot a control chart for $\bar{X}$ for the 50 subgroups of 8 given in Table 15.   Base the control limits on the observed values of $\bar{\bar{X}}$ and $\bar{R}$.

36. Make frequency distributions of the ranges given in Tables 12, 14, and 15, respectively.   Use cells 0 to 4, 5 to 9, 10 to 14, etc.   Compare these three frequency distributions by a tabulation of relative frequencies similar to Table 17.

37. Plot control charts for $\bar{X}$ and R for the first 20 subgroups of Problem 1 (pages 67 and 68).

38. Plot control charts for $\bar{X}$ and R for the first 20 subgroups of Problem 6 (pages 67 and 69).

39. Compute R for each of the 100 subgroups of Problem 17 (pages 70 to 74). Compute $\bar{R}$, and estimate σ' from this.   How does this estimate of σ' compare with the σ of the distribution of the 500 measurements as found in your solution of Problem 17?

40. Compute $\bar{R}$ for each set of 20 subgroups in your solution of Problem 39.   Make estimates of σ' from each $\bar{R}$.   Compare these with the estimate from the entire 100 subgroups made in Problem 39.

CHAPTER V

WHY THE CONTROL CHART WORKS.
EXAMPLES OF PROCESSES OUT
OF CONTROL

Statistical methods serve as landmarks which point to further improvement beyond that deemed obtainable by experienced manufacturing men. Hence, after all obvious correctives have been exhausted and all normal logic indicates no further gain is to be made, statistical methods still point toward a reasonable chance for yet further gains; thereby giving the man who is doing trouble shooting sufficient courage of his convictions to cause him to continue to the ultimate gain, in spite of expressed opinion on all sides that no such gain exists.—G. J. MEYERS, JR.[1]

84. Contribution of the Control Chart to Elimination of Causes of Trouble. As pointed out in Chap. I and briefly illustrated in Chap. II, actions based on the control chart for variables are of many kinds. Some of these actions, particularly those related to specifications and tolerances and to acceptance procedures, need to start from evidence that a process is in control. For such actions, it is satisfactory to understand the behavior of constant-cause systems, such as were discussed in Chap. IV, which dealt with processes under control.

Other useful actions start from evidence of the control chart that a process is out of control. Trouble shooting in manufacturing is a particularly important example of this. In this type of control-chart application, the control chart sometimes says, "Leave this process alone," and at other times it says, "Hunt for trouble and try to correct it."

A major virtue of the control chart is that it tells—within reasonably satisfactory limits—*when* to hunt for the cause of variation. It is always helpful to know *when;* sometimes this may be sufficient to indicate *where* to look. Nevertheless, there is often a fair amount of hard work between the decision to hunt for trouble and the actual discovery and correction of the cause of the trouble. This fact is responsible for H. F. Dodge's frequently quoted statement that "Statistical quality control is 90% engineering and only 10% statistics."[2]

---

[1] MEYERS, G. J., JR., Discussion of E. G. Olds, On Some of the Essentials of the Control Chart Analysis, *Transactions, American Society of Mechanical Engineers*, vol. 64, pp. 521–527, July, 1942.

[2] This statement has occasionally been misinterpreted to belittle the practical con-

The control chart unaided cannot put its finger on exactly *where* the cause of trouble can be found. Nevertheless, users of the control-chart technique sometimes develop an ability to diagnose causes of production troubles with surprising accuracy. This ability usually depends on a combination of an understanding of the principles of the control chart with an intimate knowledge of the particular manufacturing processes to which the control chart is applied.

No general book on statistical quality control can supply the necessary knowledge of various manufacturing processes. However, some guidance may be given on the statistical aspects of interpretation of the control chart for purposes of trouble shooting. It is the purpose of this chapter to provide this guidance by examining several general ways in which lack of control may occur and noting the effect of each on the appearance of control charts for $\bar{X}$ and R.

85. Lack of Statistical Control Implies a Shift in the Universe. Drawing chips from a bowl is a helpful analogy in clarifying what really happens when a manufacturing process shows lack of control. The system of chance causes in operation at any particular moment corresponds to the universe, that is, to the distribution of chips in the bowl. The items actually manufactured at that moment correspond to a sample drawn from that bowl or universe. When points fall outside the limits on the control charts, this is evidence that the universe has changed; it is as if samples were being drawn from a different bowl.

Usually the items *produced* in any period constitute a much larger sample from the universe than do the items actually *measured* for control-chart purposes during the same period. Thus the control chart gives evidence not only regarding the universe (that is, the chance cause system operating) but also regarding the items produced which were not measured.

86. A Classification of Ways in Which Lack of Control May Occur. Because lack of control corresponds to the substitution of a new bowl, a classification of different types of lack of control may be thought of as

---

tributions of statistics in statistical quality control.

When statistics—by means of the control chart—points to the need to hunt for trouble, it often is true that 90% of the hard work remains to be done; the tough engineering job of hunting for causes and eliminating them is still ahead. In cases where this trouble shooting has led to spectacular reductions in scrap and rework, these cost reductions would not have been made without the hard engineering work. It is sometimes forgotten that neither would they have been made without the statistics.

A fair analogy is to think of the use of the control chart in trouble shooting as a chain with ten links. One of them is the statistical link; the other nine are engineering links. From the standpoint of the strength of the chain, weakness in the statistical link is just as serious as weakness in one of the engineering links.

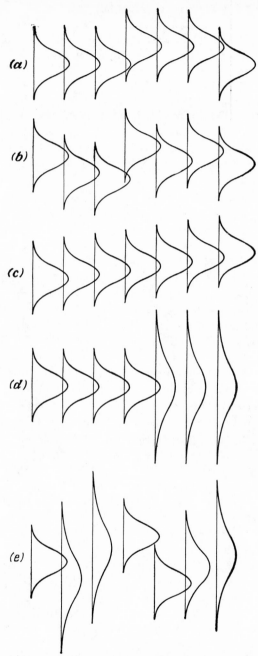

FIG. 18. Chance cause systems (represented here by frequency curves) may change in different ways: (a) sustained shift in universe average with constant spread; (b) irregular shifts in universe average with constant spread; (c) steady trend in universe average with constant spread; (d) change in universe spread with no change in average; (e) irregular changes in both average and spread.

111

a classification of ways in which two bowls may differ in their distribution of chips.   It is helpful to give separate consideration to three ways in which universes may differ, as follows:

1. They may differ in average only.
2. They may differ in dispersion only.
3. They may differ in both average and dispersion.

Shifts in universe average influence the control charts for $\bar{X}$ and R in one way; shifts in universe dispersion influence them in another way.

Shifts in the universe may be sustained shifts over a period of time, as if many subgroups were drawn from one bowl and then many more drawn from another bowl.   Or shifts may be frequent and irregular, as if there were a great many bowls with the drawings from each bowl continued for periods of different lengths.   Or shifts may be gradual and systematic.

In Fig. 18, the frequency curves are intended to represent the universe or bowl, *i.e.*, the chance cause system in operation at any moment.   Figure 18*a* shows a situation in which the universe continued for a while at one average, then shifted for a while to a higher average, and finally was brought back to the original average.   Figure 18*b* shows a situation in which the universe average varies erratically and universe dispersion remains constant.   Figure 18*c* shows the universe average gradually increasing.   Figure 18*d* shows a situation in which, although the universe average remained unchanged, the universe dispersion doubled.   Figure 18*e* shows universe average and dispersion both varying erratically.

87. Changes in Universe Average.   A common type of lack of control observed in manufacturing is a shift in universe average with little or no change in universe dispersion.   In such cases, the control chart is often of great value to the machine setter, helping him to center the machine setting in order to produce at a desired process average.   This type of lack of control is shown on the $\bar{X}$ chart; unless the changes in universe average take place within a subgroup, the R chart will show control.   Where lack of control is practically never shown on the R chart, the R chart is often omitted.

In those cases where the main reason for keeping a control chart is to detect changes in the universe average, the appropriate scheme of selection of subgroups differs from those cases in which the control chart has several purposes, including acceptance inspection.   Various possible schemes of subgrouping and the basis of their selection are discussed in Chap. VII.

Because, as explained in Chap. IV, control limits are set far enough from the central line on the chart for there to be very few points outside the limits without a real change in the universe, small shifts in universe average will not cause many points to fall out of control.   For this reason, it is often useful to supplement the evidence given by the position of the points relative to the control limits by evidence given by tests based on the statistical theory of runs or sequences.

88. Tests for Lack of Control Based on Runs of Points above or below the Central Line on the Control Chart. Examples 3 and 4 in Chap. II pointed out the importance of looking for sequences in control-chart data even though all points fall within the control limits. Some of these sequences permit the use of simple definite rules as a basis for action; others, as in Example 4, call for a common-sense analysis in light of possible causes of the observed order.

Considerable work has been done by mathematicians on the development of various types of statistical tests based on the theory of runs.[1] Many of these tests involve a complete tabulation of all of the runs, long and short alike, in any definite sequence of observations. Such tests provide useful tools for the study of research data.

In order to detect shifts in a process average in manufacturing, the most practical plan is to use a few simple rules that depend only on the extreme runs. The following are suggested:

Consider that grounds exist for suspicion that the process average has shifted

Whenever in 7 successive points on the control chart, all are on the same side of the central line.

Whenever in 11 successive points on the control chart, at least 10 are on the same side of the central line.

Whenever in 14 successive points on the control chart, at least 12 are on the same side of the central line.

Whenever in 17 successive points on the control chart, at least 14 are on the same side of the central line.

Whenever in 20 successive points on the control chart, at least 16 are on the same side of the central line.

The theoretical basis for these rules is discussed in Art. 179, Chap. IX.

The sequences mentioned in these rules will occur as a matter of chance with no change in the universe more frequently than will a point outside of 3-sigma control limits. (In fact, such sequences did occur in the 400 drawings from Shewhart's normal bowl.) For this reason they provide a less reliable basis for hunting for trouble than does the occurrence of a point outside of control limits. Their use as a basis for action on the process should perhaps be limited to those instances where because the

---

[1] An informative discussion of this subject with an excellent bibliography is given in J. Wolfowitz, On the Theory of Runs with Some Applications to Quality Control, *Annals of Mathematical Statistics*, vol. 14, pp. 280–288, 1943. For a good example of an application of theory of runs to a research problem, see W. E. Campbell, Use of Statistical Control in Corrosion and Contact Resistance Studies, *Bell Telephone System Technical Publications*, Monograph B-1350, 1942.

specification tolerances are tight compared to the natural tolerances of the process, it is of great importance that there be no fluctuations in the process average.

However, even though such sequences of points on one side of the central line are not always used as a basis for hunting for assignable causes of variation and taking action on the process, they should always lead to consideration of possible action on the control chart. That is, they call for a review of the position of the central line to determine whether or not its position should be changed.

89. Sustained Shift in Universe Average. In the control chart for $\overline{X}$ given in Fig. 19, the universe varied in the manner indicated in Fig. 18a. The universe average for the first 40 subgroups was 30; for the

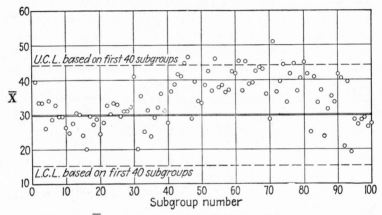

FIG. 19. $\overline{X}$ chart showing sustained shift in universe average.

next 40 subgroups it was 40; for the final 20 subgroups it went back to 30. The universe standard deviation was 10 throughout the entire period.

Figure 19 was made by adding 10 to each drawing from the 161st to the 320th in Table 12. This has the same effect as if subgroups 41 to 80 were drawn from a bowl in which each chip was marked with a number 10 higher than a corresponding chip in the distribution described in Table 11. Of course subgroups 1 to 40 and 81 to 100 were drawn from the bowl described in Table 11. Figure 19 is similar to Fig. 16 except that points 41 to 80 have been raised 10 units. However, the control limits are drawn on Fig. 19 as if they were established by the $\overline{X}$ and R of the first 40 subgroups.

During the period in which the universe average has changed, namely, subgroups 41 to 80, occasional points are above the upper control limit. Tests based on the theory of runs also give clear evidence that the universe average has shifted.

This shift in average was equal to one standard deviation of the universe. It is obvious that the greater this shift in the average, the stronger will be the evidence of lack of control, and the sooner the shift is likely to be detected by the control chart.

When sustained shifts of process average occur *after* the control limits have been established, they result in all the out-of-control points falling outside *one* control limit, and all suspicious runs occurring on the *same* side of the central line. However, if the shift occurs *during* the period from which the control limits were established, the evidences of lack of control shift from one side to the other at the time of shift in process average.

No R chart has been given to accompany the $\overline{X}$ chart of Fig. 19. With this type of shift in process average, the R chart gives no indication of lack of control. It is evident that without a change of universe dispersion, the dispersion within the subgroups will not be affected.

Examples 7, 8, and 9 illustrate situations involving shifts in process average.

EXAMPLE 7. SHIFT IN PROCESS AVERAGE OF ACIDITY OF DYE LIQUOR

90. Facts of the Case. In the dyeing of woolen yarns, it is desirable to control the acidity of the dye liquor. Unless the dye liquor is sufficiently acid, the penetration

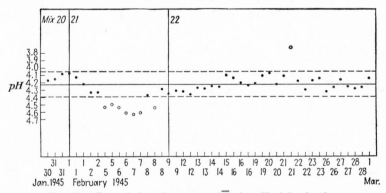

FIG. 20. Control chart for average ($\overline{X}$) for pH of dye kettles.

of color is unsatisfactory; on the other hand, a too-acid liquor affects the durability of the products made from the yarn. Acidity is conveniently measured as pH (hydrogen ion concentration). A low pH corresponds to high acidity, and vice versa. In any dyeing operation there is a band of pH values within which the best results as to both color penetration and durability are obtained. A control chart for pH is helpful in maintaining acidity within the desired band.

Such a control chart is shown in Fig. 20. On this chart are plotted the average $\overline{X}$ values of pH of dye liquor from five Hussong kettles used for the dyeing of blanket wool. Table 18 gives the actual $\overline{X}$ and R values for the period of approximately 5 weeks covered by this chart. Generally, two determinations of pH were made from each kettle every day, although a few days show one or three determinations.

The central line on the chart at $\bar{X}' = 4.22$ and the control limits of 4.05 and 4.39 were established by previous data. This process average and dispersion had proved to be satisfactory from the standpoint of the desired characteristics of the dye liquor. The chart is plotted with high acidity (*i.e.*, low pH) at the top of the graph.

TABLE 18. pH OF DYE LIQUOR USED FOR DYEING OF BLANKET WOOLS
(Averages and ranges of subgroups composed of samples from five Hussong kettles)

Date	$\bar{X}$	R	Date	$\bar{X}$	R
Jan. 30	4.17	0.14	Feb. 14a	4.25	0.11
31a	4.15	0.30	14b	4.26	0.26
31b	4.08	0.20	15a	4.10	0.18
Feb. 1a	4.07	0.09	15b	4.14	0.23
1b	4.13	0.10	16a	4.20	0.52
1c	4.22	0.24	16b	4.24	0.17
2a	4.33	0.65	19a	4.21	0.46
2b	4.33	0.17	19b	4.11	0.20
5a	4.54	0.58	20a	4.07	0.40
5b	4.50	0.22	20b	4.22	0.12
6a	4.54	0.22	21a	4.11	1.34
6b	4.61	0.18	21b	3.72	0.96
7a	4.63	0.44	22a	4.18	0.35
7b	4.61	0.20	22b	4.29	0.31
8a	4.37	0.23	23a	4.17	0.20
8b	4.54	0.23	23b	4.14	0.13
8c	4.29	0.32	26a	4.32	0.26
9a	4.35	0.62	26b	4.26	0.08
9b	4.31	0.28	27a	4.16	0.51
12a	4.32	0.20	27b	4.25	0.25
12b	4.36	0.40	28a	4.28	0.09
13a	4.27	0.40	28b	4.26	0.15
13b	4.28	0.38	Mar. 1	4.14	0.11

91. Analysis and Action. The acidity of the dyeing solution depends not only on the constituents put into the dye liquor but also on the characteristics of the wool being dyed. From time to time it is necessary to use wools from sources that have different characteristics. Although blends of wools from various sources are made, successive blends will differ somewhat from one another.

On February 1 a new blend of entirely different wools was introduced. Immediately the acidity dropped. On February 5, after the old surplus stock had been used up, acidity fell below the control limit and continued out of control thereafter until corrective measures were taken on February 8. At this time the amount of acid introduced into the dye liquor was changed. Although after this all points fell within the control limits, the run of points below the central line indicated that the previous average was not restored until February 15.

Thereafter, with the exception of a brief departure from control on February 21, the pH values continued in satisfactory control. The temporary difficulty on February 21 was traced to two batches of improperly neutralized carbonized (baked with concentrated sulphuric acid) stock. Such stock is acid in relation to stock normally used.

EXAMPLE 8. SHIFT IN QUALITY LEVEL OF STEEL CASTINGS

92. Facts of the Case. Certain specially treated steel castings were required to meet rigid requirements as to strength and ductility. As part of the acceptance procedure for these castings, the purchaser required that two tensile specimens from each heat be tested to destruction in the testing laboratory. Specifications regarding the results of these tests covered tensile strength, yield point, per cent elongation, and reduction in area. $\bar{X}$ and R charts were maintained on yield point and per cent elongation. Whenever these charts showed control for a sufficient number of heats and the tests were otherwise satisfactory, the amount of required testing was reduced to two specimens from every fourth heat.

The tests did in fact show control at a satisfactory level for a number of months. Suddenly points on both $\bar{X}$ charts went out of control.

93. Analysis and Action. The responsible supervisors in the production department were sure no changes had been made in production methods. Nevertheless, all the following heats continued out of control on the $\bar{X}$ charts. An attempt was made to throw the blame on the testing laboratory; however, tests made by other personnel on other machines showed the points continuing to fall out of control. This condition continued for some time despite pressure brought by supervisors on operating personnel. Finally someone remarked that a change in the source of quench water for heat treatment had been made just before the time when the first points fell out of control. Although no one believed that this could be the source of the trouble, as a last resort the original source of quench water was restored. Immediately the results of tensile tests of specimens from subsequent heats gave points that fell within the original control limits. From this time on, the process continued in control at the original satisfactory level.

EXAMPLE 9. SHIFT IN QUALITY LEVEL OF TENSILE STRENGTH OF YARN

94. Facts of the Case. A small manufacturer producing a certain type of yarn supplied this yarn to a large textile mill. This relationship between vendor and purchaser had continued for many years without the purchase contract including any formal specifications for physical tests. However, as a matter of precaution, the purchaser occasionally made physical tests of yarns purchased from various sources. In the case of regular vendors, control charts were maintained for each vendor.

The control chart for tensile strength of the yarn purchased from this vendor had shown continuous control for several years, with an average and dispersion that the purchaser considered satisfactory. Suddenly on one lot the average tensile strength fell substantially below the lower control limit. The lots that followed gave similar results, with tensile strength continuing at this unsatisfactory level.

95. Analysis and Action. The product engineer for the purchaser informed the vendor's sales manager of this change in quality of the yarn. After discussing the matter with his production department, the sales manager reported that production operations were carried on in exactly the same way as they had been for many years. He suggested that there must be some mistake about the tests. The product engineer insisted that further investigation be made, but without constructive results; the yarn continued to show low tensile strength.   Finally the vendor was informed that unless quality was improved, future purchases would be from another source.

This brought an invitation to the product engineer to attend a meeting of the top executives of the vendor's plant to discuss the matter.   At the meeting each executive made the same point in different words, namely, that as there had been no change in the plant's raw material or production methods, there could have been no change in the quality of its product.   Finally the foreman of the spinning room was brought into the meeting to reinforce this testimony.

The product engineer mentioned the date on which his control chart had first indicated lack of control.   "Can't you recall anything which may have happened just before that date?" he asked.   "Well," said the foreman, "I remember now that we *did* make a machine adjustment that slightly changed the twist given the yarn."

This turned out to be the clue to the trouble.   The machine was readjusted to give the yarn its original twist.   After this the tensile strength of the yarn produced fell within the original control-chart limits.

96. Comment on Examples 7, 8, and 9.   These examples all describe cases in which the average values of the measured quality definitely moved outside control-chart limits.   Even though in such cases the actual trouble shooting may encounter many difficulties, from a statistical viewpoint these are the simplest type of examples.   In fact, when such cases are described in presenting the advantages of control-chart techniques, the question is likely to be asked, "Would not the need for action have been just as clear from the tests as a matter of common sense even if there has been no control chart?   Just how did the control chart itself really help?"

This question implies that the tests would have been carried out and that their results would have been conveniently available for analysis, regardless of whether or not a control chart was used.   This assumption is often contrary to the facts.   Experience shows that the use of the control chart sometimes leads to a more systematic program of testing and measurement; it nearly always leads to a tabulation of test results in a way that makes them more readily available as a basis for action.

But the control chart's contribution to effective action in cases like Examples 7, 8, and 9 does not depend on any stimulus that it may have given to more systematic procedures in making and recording measurements of quality.   The control chart provides a graphic presentation of quality history that gives a clearer picture than could be obtained from any tabulation of test data.   Of course the primary contribution of the control chart to such trouble shooting lies in the information given by the control limits.   These provide rules for action that are much more definite and much more reliable than any so-called "common-sense" judgments.   When the control chart shows a long period of control followed by several points out of control, the evidence is conclusive that there is a discoverable cause of variation.   Such evidence may be followed with confidence in the face of assertions, such as those in Examples 8 and 9, that no change has really taken place. Moreover, the limits provide a definite basis for judgment as to whether or not the cause of trouble has been corrected.

It will be noted that in both Examples 8 and 9 the production men first insisted there was no trouble; in each case the cause of trouble was found only because some individual whose job was entirely outside production insisted that the hunt be continued. These two examples are not intended to suggest that an outsider using the control chart can succeed where men intimately connected with production will fail. What the outsiders provided here was *insistence* that the source of trouble could be found; in both cases the actual identification of the source was made by individuals connected with production.

Experience shows that those closest to production sometimes have blind spots with respect to certain sources of trouble. A quality control engineer with wide experience states that in production conferences regarding processes which the control chart shows have gone out of control, it is common for someone close to the production operation to state "It may be cause A or cause B or cause C. One thing I am sure of is that it isn't cause D." In such instances, about half the time the source of trouble turns out to be cause D.

Examples 7, 8, and 9 are alike in that it was the evidence of the control chart as to *when* the process went out of control that was the basis of discovering *why* it went out control.

Examples 8 and 9 illustrate cases in which a purchaser's control chart gave guidance to a vendor. This is a common occurrence and often leads to the use of the control-chart technique by the vendor himself. Examples 40 and 41 in Chap. XIX illustrate this.

Example 7 represents a common situation characteristic of the food industry, the chemical industry, and the ceramic industry as well as the textile industry. This is the situation in which some variation in raw material quality is inevitable. In spite of this variation (such as that of wool from different sources) it is desired to maintain a certain quality level (as of pH of dye liquor) at some stage of the manufacturing operations. This quality level may in itself not be a quality of the finished product, but, as in the case of the dye liquor, may influence various desired qualities of the product.

In the case of Example 7, control limits on the $\bar{X}$ chart were set on the basis of a previous $\bar{R}$ of 0.30. No R chart was kept, as previous experience had indicated that troubles were always with process average and not with process dispersion. However if an R chart is plotted for the data of Table 18, it will show lack of control on February 2 and 21. Both cases coincide with times when $\bar{X}$ went out of control and result from an unequal influence on different members of the subgroup by a

change in the process average.   To use the analogy of drawing from a
bowl, it is as if while switching from one bowl to another, a few subgroups
were drawn with some chips from the old bowl and the remaining chips
from the new bowl.

**97. Frequent Irregular Changes in Universe Average with Constant
Universe Standard Deviation.**   Figure 21 is derived from the data of

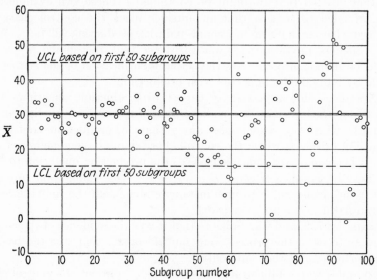

FIG. 21. $\overline{X}$ chart showing the effect of frequent irregular changes in universe average.

Table 12 in a way intended to produce an illustration of the effect of
numerous changes in the universe average.   Table 12 gave drawings
from a bowl with a constant average of 30 and standard deviation of 10.
Figure 21 uses these drawings for the first 50 subgroups.   The remaining
50 subgroups show irregular variation in universe average, with the
amount and duration of each shift having been determined from a table
of random numbers.   The universe standard deviation continues at 10
throughout all 100 subgroups.   The averages used were as follows:

Subgroups	Universe Average
1–50	30
51–57	20
58–61	10
62	45
63–69	25
70–72	5
73–81	35
82–85	15
86–93	40
94–96	10
97–100	30

This type of situation is often a result of carelessness in machine setting. As indicated in Fig. 21, it results in points falling outside *both* control limits on the $\overline{X}$ chart. If the shifts in universe average occur between subgroups and never happen to fall within a subgroup, the R chart will continue to show control regardless of the variations shown on the $\overline{X}$ chart.

At first glance it might seem that a situation such as that pictured in the control chart of Fig. 21 should always be a cause for action on the manufacturing process. However, this is not necessarily true. It all depends on the relationship between the specified tolerances, on the one hand, and the constant universe dispersion and the fluctuations of the universe average on the other.

Assume, for example, that the data of Table 12 referred to the final two digits of a dimension measured to ten-thousandths of an inch; let us say a figure of 27 in Table 12 would correspond to a dimension of 2.1527 in. If the engineering specification were 2.153 ± 0.003, it would be evident that the tolerances were so tight that careful attention would always have to be paid to machine setting; any points falling out of control limits on the $\overline{X}$ chart would indicate that some product was being made outside tolerance limits. On the other hand, if the engineering specification were 2.153 ± 0.010, the situation shown in Fig. 21 would not have caused any rejected product; in this case there would be quite a range of possible carelessness in machine setting without causing any product to fall outside the tolerances.

In control of dimensions in manufacturing, the great usefulness of the control charts for $\overline{X}$ and R is in those situations where the specification tolerances are tight compared to the inherent variability of the manufacturing process. Fortunately, in most manufacturing operations this is true of only a small proportion of specified dimensions.

98. Steady Trend in Universe Average with Constant Universe Standard Deviation. In some machining operations tool wear occurs at a uniform rate over the period of use of a tool. This tool wear may be one of the factors influencing the average value of some dimension of the product manufactured and may be responsible for a trend in this average. Where subgroups are selected in a way that spaces them uniformly with respect to this wear, control charts for $\overline{X}$ often look something like Fig. 22. This corresponds to the pattern of universe variation shown in Fig. 18c.

Figure 22 has been made by adapting the data of Table 12 to an assumed steady increase in universe average. For subgroup 1, this average was assumed as 30.5, for subgroup 2 as 31.0, and so on, increasing by 0.5 each subgroup until the average of 50.0 was reached for subgroup 40. Subgroup 41 started at 30.5 again and the cycle repeated. It is as if there were a row of 40 bowls of chips, each having the same universe standard deviation of 10 but differing in universe average from the adjacent bowls by 0.5.   Drawings are made in succession from one bowl after another.

For such a chart the central line and control limits should be sloping rather than horizontal.   In Fig. 22 these have been determined from

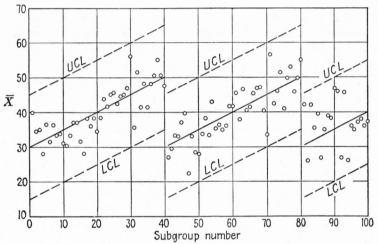

FIG. 22. $\overline{X}$ chart showing the effect of a trend in universe average.

the known characteristics of the universe.   The sloping central line is at the known universe average; the limits are at 15 units

$$\left[3\sigma_{\overline{x}} = 3\left(\frac{\sigma'}{\sqrt{n}}\right) = 3\left(\frac{10}{\sqrt{4}}\right) = 15\right]$$

on either side of the central line.   In practice the position of the universe is never known and the position of the central line and the limits must be determined from the measurements themselves.   The methods of making this calculation are illustrated in Example 46, Chap. XIX.

Once the slope of the central line has been determined and the σ' has been estimated from $\overline{R}$, it becomes possible to determine an initial setting and length of run that together will give the maximum period between tool settings consistent with making all product within specified tolerances.   The initial setting and length of run in Fig. 22 correspond to a lower tolerance limit of 0 and an upper tolerance limit of 80, as (assuming a normal distribution) nearly all individual values may be expected to vary from $3\sigma'$ below the initial average to $3\sigma'$ above the final average.

Although the most common application of this type of chart is in connection with tool wear, other situations occur in which uniform wear creates a trend in measurable quality characteristics.   An example is the influence of wear of a gun tube on the muzzle velocity of the projectile. In this case, one value of the control chart lies in its indication of the appropriate time of replacement of the gun tube.

99. Shift in Universe Dispersion with No Change in Universe Average. The inherent variability of a process may change from time to time even though there is no change in the process average. On any process where

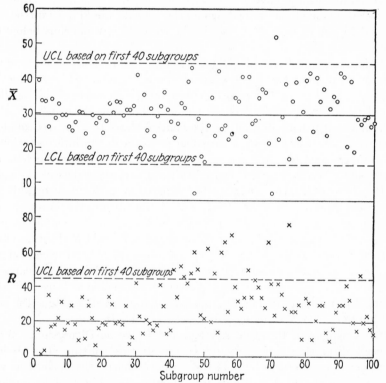

FIG. 23. Control charts for $\overline{X}$ and R showing the effect of a sustained shift in universe dispersion.

the skill and care of the operator is an important factor, a common cause of increase in variability is a change from one operator to another who is less skillful or less careful. In fact, an operator's skill and care may sometimes vary from day to day or from hour to hour.

This type of shift in universe is illustrated in Fig. 23, which has been adapted from the data of Table 12. For the first 40 subgroups, universe standard deviation is 10; for subgroups 41 to 80, universe standard deviation is 20; for the final 20 subgroups it is 10 again. The universe average has been held constant at 30 throughout. Figure 23 gives both $\overline{X}$ and R charts. Both charts show lack of control, with more points outside control limits on the R chart than on the $\bar{X}$ chart. Extreme runs above the central line on the R chart also give strong evidence of lack of control.

The central lines and control limits on Fig. 23 have been set using the data from the first 40 subgroups. If they had been set using the data from the first 80 subgroups, $\bar{R}$ would have been larger and the limits on both the $\bar{X}$ and R charts would have been wider. With these limits fewer points would have fallen outside the control limits. However, the higher value of the central line on the R chart would have introduced other evidence of lack of control in the form of extreme runs below the central line.

On hand-operated machines, it is a common experience that the influence of a control chart on the operator results in a gradual reduction in the variability of the quality characteristic charted. This is illustrated in Example 11 in Chap. VI and in Example 44 in Chap. XIX. This is a useful contribution by the control chart to improved quality. However, such cases create a practical problem in the interpretation of the control chart for R. As long as the subgroup size is six or less, the lower control limit on the R chart is always zero regardless of the value of $\bar{R}$. Thus, with the usual size of subgroups, a decrease in universe dispersion cannot be reflected in points falling below the lower control limit on the R chart. Here reliance must be placed on regular reviews of the value of $\bar{R}$ used to set limits on both the $\bar{X}$ and R charts. Often the need to review $\bar{R}$ is suggested by extreme runs below the central line on the R chart. It should be remembered that whenever, because of evidence of a decrease in universe dispersion, the value of $\bar{R}$ used in computing control limits is recalculated and reduced, this tightens the control limits on the $\bar{X}$ chart as well as on the R chart.

100. Changes in Universe Average and Universe Dispersion. When universe dispersion as well as universe average is shifting, it is obvious that lack of control will be indicated in both charts, the R chart as well as the $\bar{X}$ chart. Such a situation is illustrated in Fig. 2 of Example 1. Such examples are common in the first stages of the use of the control chart for variables for analysis of many manufacturing operations.

Where several assignable causes of variation exist, the elimination of some of the causes will decrease the number of out-of-control points but will not eliminate all of them. In such circumstances, the continuance of some points out of control may be discouraging to anyone anxious for quick results. Rather than be discouraged, it is better to view the control chart as an indication that further improvement is possible and as an incentive to keep hunting for more sources of trouble.

101. Assignable Causes of Variation May Be Due to Errors of Measurement. In Examples 8 and 9, the production departments first tried to lay the blame on faulty inspection as the source of the indication of lack of control. In both cases, this common production alibi proved to be wrong. Nevertheless, there is always the possibility that it may be right.

It should be emphasized that the control-chart analysis, like any other statistical test, is applied to a set of numbers. Anything that affects these numbers affects the control chart. The numbers are influenced by variations in the measurements, just as they are influenced by variations in the quality being measured. The universe from which samples are being drawn is the result of a cause system that includes measurement causes as well as production causes.

Therefore, an error in measurement may be an assignable cause of variation in the figures resulting from the measurements. In describing the various types of lack of control, reference was made to production situations that might give rise to each type. Similarly, each might have been associated with some sort of inspection error. An error in setting a measuring device may make a sudden shift in universe average. Frequent errors in setting may make irregular shifts in the average. Some types of wear of measuring devices may increase universe dispersion. Other types of wear may give rise to trends in averages.

102. Use of the Control Chart as a Basis for Sorting Sub-lots into Homogeneous Grand Lots. If some quality of a manufactured product shows unsatisfactory variability and if the control chart shows that lack of control is responsible for this variability, the natural action seems to be to make a strong effort to bring about a state of control. However, it may turn out that for some reason it is impracticable to achieve control. Sometimes a satisfactory alternative may exist in the sorting of sub-lots of product into grand lots that seem to be statistically homogeneous. The variability from one grand lot to another may then become the basis for different correction factors somehow applied in the use of each grand lot. Conceivably, even though control could actually be obtained at a cost, it might be more economical to carry out this sorting.

This sorting is a logical procedure, for example, in the case of artillery ammunition. Experience shows that the variation in ballistic properties from one lot to another is greater than the variation within any lot. (In other words, the averages show lack of statistical control.) Successive lots, the samples from which under ballistic tests all fall within control-chart limits, may be treated as sub-lots of one grand lot. Different corrections in the powder charge, or in the firing tables used by the artilleryman, could then be made for each grand lot.

In the case of chemical or bacteriological tests that different laboratories make of the same product, experience shows it is often impracticable to get control. The variation from one laboratory to another will be greater than the variation in successive tests made by any one laboratory.   Here also, correction factors might be applied to the results given by any laboratory that did not seem to be part of the grand lot.[1]

Although the control chart provides the best way to sort sub-lots into homogeneous grand lots, it sometimes happens that people who do not fully understand the principles behind the control chart use it for sorting in ways that are incorrect.   This point is illustrated in Example 10.

EXAMPLE 10.   AN UNSOUND PROPOSAL FOR SORTING PRODUCT INTO CLASSES

103. Facts of the Case.   This example is adapted from an actual case with slight modifications intended to disguise the source and to simplify the situation in a way that will concentrate attention on the important principle involved.

A certain munitions product, which for purposes of this story will be called the XYZ-77, was subject to destructive testing in order to determine a particular quality characteristic.   Four of these XYZ-77's from each lot of 500 were tested to establish a basis for acceptance.   Control charts were plotted using each set of four tests as a subgroup.   These exhibited good control with only an infrequent point falling outside control limits.

The specifications stated that the average value of this quality characteristic should be 540.   Tolerances were ±20.   It proved possible to hold the average (*i.e.*, $\overline{X}$ on the control chart) at 540.   The upper control limit on the $\overline{X}$ chart was 549; the lower control limit was 531.   This indicated that 3σ limits on individual values were 558 and 522.   From this it seemed reasonable to believe that, if the distribution were normal or nearly so, as long as control was maintained practically all the product would fall within the specification limits of 560 and 520.   As the process showed good control, this was a very satisfactory state of affairs.

Suddenly there was a demand for some XYZ-77's that would hold the much closer tolerances of 540 ± 6.   Not all the product was required to meet these specifications, but it was desired that a substantial portion of it do so.

One of the men who had been working with the control chart had a suggestion that he thought would solve the problem.   His suggestion called for no change in production methods, and for a continuance of destructive testing of four out of each lot of 500 with the control chart carried on as before.   However, he proposed adding two new inner limits to the control chart.   These were to be set at a distance from $\overline{X}$ equal to the tolerance limits divided by $\sqrt{n}$.   This meant inner limits at $540 \pm 6/\sqrt{4}$, *i.e.*, at 543 and 537.

He proposed that whenever the average of a sample plotted within these inner limits, the lot was to be classified as meeting the new specifications of 540 ± 6.   Whenever the average of the sample plotted within control limits but above 543 or below 537, the lot was to be classified as meeting the original specifications of 540 ± 20.

104. Comment on Error in Reasoning Involved in Example 10.   This suggestion could not have been made except by someone who had completely misunderstood the correct interpretation of the control chart.

When $\overline{X}$ and R charts for some quality characteristic of a manufactured product exhibit control over a long period, this means that the successive subgroups behave like random samples drawn from a single bowl.   The

[1] See Example 13, Chap. VII, for an ingenious application of this correction factor technique to a manufacturing problem.

existence of control indicates that for all practical purposes the bowl was unchanged throughout the period. If, as in Example 10, each subgroup is a small sample from a large lot, the evidence is that the large lots are practically alike. The variation from one subgroup to another is simply a chance variation to be expected in random sampling.

With all points on the control chart for $\bar{X}$ falling between control limits of 549 and 531, the fact that the sample from one lot has an $\bar{X}$ of 545 and the sample from the next lot has an $\bar{X}$ of 540 is an indication that the lots are *alike*, not that they are different. It is only in the case of lack of control that the control chart can be used to sort lots into grand lots having different dispersions or different averages.

In Example 10, the control chart gave conclusive evidence that the manufacturing process, as it was then carried on, could not meet the proposed new tolerances of ± 6. If 100% inspection were possible, the product meeting these close tolerances (about two-thirds of the total product if the distribution were approximately normal) could be sorted from the product not meeting the tolerances. As the test was destructive, this was not possible. It was necessary, therefore, either to make some fundamental change in the manufacturing process that would reduce the variability of the product, or to devise some nondestructive test that gave substantially the same information as the destructive test and would thus permit 100% inspection.

105. Basis of Selection of Subgroups. The discussion throughout this chapter has implied *time* of production as the basis for selection of rational subgroups. This is a natural and logical basis, but, for reasons explained in Chap. VII, it is not always a sufficient one. As pointed out there, the conclusions to be drawn from any control chart depend on the basis of selection of subgroups; a process may appear to show control with one plan of subgrouping and not show control with some other plan.

Moreover, there are many situations in which the order of production is no longer known but where it is still possible to use the control chart to advantage. Some comments on this are made in Art. 151, Chap. VII.

Problems

41. Calculate the position of the central lines and control limits for $\bar{X}$ and R charts for the data of Table 18, assuming that no information prior to January 30 was available. Plot both $\bar{X}$ and R charts with these limits.

42. Compute control limits for $\bar{X}$ for Fig. 19, basing the limits on the first 80 subgroups rather than on the first 40. For these 80 subgroups $\bar{\bar{X}} = 34.7$ and $\bar{R} = 20.0$. What change does this make in the points falling outside the control limits?

43. The next to the last paragraph of Art. 97 states that a specification of 2.153 $\pm$ 0.003 calls for close attention to machine setting whereas a specification of 2.153 $\pm$

0.010 permits a considerable range of carelessness in machine setting. Explain why an analysis of Table 12 and Fig. 21 makes this evident.

44. The next to the last paragraph in Art. 98 states that the initial setting and length of run in Fig. 22 corresponds to a lower tolerance limit of 0 and an upper tolerance limit of 80. Explain the basis of this statement. With tool wear at the rate indicated in Fig. 22, what should be the initial setting and length of run if the lower tolerance limit was 5 and the upper tolerance limit 95?

45. Compute control limits for $\bar{X}$ and R for Fig. 23, basing the limits on the first 80 subgroups rather than the first 40. For these 80 subgroups $\bar{\bar{X}} = 29.5$ and $\bar{R} = 30.0$. What points fall outside the control limits? Are there any significant extreme runs above or below the central line?

46. Why is it that an increase in universe dispersion with no change in universe average throws the $\bar{X}$ chart out of control as well as the R chart?

47. Mark 500 chips as follows:

Marking	Frequency	Marking	Frequency	Marking	Frequency
28	1	22	58	16	22
27	2	21	73	15	11
26	5	20	78	14	5
25	11	19	73	13	2
24	22	18	58	12	1
23	39	17	39		

Place the chips in a bowl and stir thoroughly. Draw five chips and record the readings. Replace the chips, stir thoroughly, and draw five more. Repeat this until you have a record of 50 subgroups of 5 each. Compute $\bar{X}$ and R for each subgroup as you go along, and plot a control chart. After the first 20 subgroups, compute control limits and put them on the chart. After the 50 subgroups have been drawn, compute $\bar{R}$ for the entire set of 50. From this estimate σ'. Compute the true σ' from the distribution in the bowl and compare with the σ' estimated from the drawings. (This is suggested as a class exercise.)

48. Mark 500 chips as follows:

Marking	Frequency	Marking	Frequency	Marking	Frequency
32	1	26	58	20	22
31	2	25	73	19	11
30	5	24	78	18	5
29	11	23	73	17	2
28	22	22	58	16	1
27	39	21	39		

Continue the control charts for $\bar{X}$ and R that were started in Problem 47 by drawing 25 subgroups of 5 chips each from this new bowl. Replace the chips after each drawing. Continue to use the control limits established in Problem 47. How many points fall out of control on each chart? Do you get any extreme runs on either side of the central line? What has happened to universe average and universe dispersion? (This is suggested as a class exercise.)

49. Mark 500 chips as follows:

Marking	Frequency	Marking	Frequency	Marking	Frequency
36	1	25	24	14	19
35	1	24	29	13	15
34	1	23	33	12	11
33	1	22	36	11	8
32	2	21	39	10	6
31	4	20	40	9	4
30	6	19	39	8	2
29	8	18	36	7	1
28	11	17	33	6	1
27	15	16	29	5	1
26	19	15	24	4	1

Continue the control charts for $\bar{X}$ and R that were started in Problem 47 by drawing 25 subgroups of 5 chips each from this new bowl. Replace the chips after each drawing. Continue to use the control limits established in Problem 47. (For purposes of this problem neglect your drawings in Problem 48.) How many points fall out of control on each chart? Do you get any extreme runs on either side of the central line? What has happened to universe average and universe dispersion? (This is suggested as a class exercise.)

50. The $\bar{X}$ and R charts of Fig. 2, Example 1 (page 20) show lack of control. Of the various types of shifts in the universe illustrated in Fig. 18 (page 111), which ones might be expected to result in control charts such as these. Explain.

CHAPTER VI

DIRECTIONS FOR SIMPLE $\overline{X}$ AND R CHARTS

Scientific data are not taken for museum purposes; they are taken as a basis for doing something. If nothing is to be done with the data, then there is no use collecting any. The ultimate purpose of taking data is to provide a basis for action or a recommendation for action. The step intermediate between the collection of data and the action is prediction.—W. E. DEMING[1]

106. Outline of Necessary Steps in Connection with Using the Control Charts for $\overline{X}$ and R for Any Quality Characteristic of Manufactured Product. It is helpful to visualize the decisions and calculations that must be made and the actions that must be taken, as occurring in a sequence somewhat as follows. (The numbers of the articles in which each step is discussed are given in parentheses.)

I. Decisions preparatory to the control charts
    A. Some possible objectives of the charts (107)
    B. Choice of the variable (108)
    C. Decision on the basis of subgrouping (109)
    D. Decision on the size and frequency of subgroups (110)
    E. Setting up the forms for recording the data (111)
    F. Determining the method of measurement (112)
II. Starting the control charts
    A. Making the measurements (113)
    B. Recording the measurements and other relevant data (113)
    C. Calculation of average $\overline{X}$ for each subgroup (114)
    D. Calculation of range R for each subgroup (115)
    E. Plotting the $\overline{X}$ chart (116)
    F. Plotting the R chart (116)
III. Determining the trial control limits
    A. Decision on required number of subgroups before control limits are calculated (117)
    B. Calculation of $\overline{R}$, the average of the ranges (118)
    C. Calculation of upper and lower control limits for R (118)
    D. Calculation of $\overline{\overline{X}}$, the average of the $\overline{X}$ values (118)
    E. Calculation of upper and lower control limits for $\overline{X}$ (118)
    F. Plotting the central lines and limits on the charts (119)
IV. Drawing preliminary conclusions from the charts
    A. Indication of control or lack of control (120)

[1] DEMING, W. E., On a Classification of the Problems of Statistical Inference, *Journal of the American Statistical Association*, vol. 37, pp. 173–185, June, 1942.

I. DECISIONS PREPARATORY TO THE CONTROL CHARTS

107. Some Possible Objectives of the Charts. In general, where control charts for variables, either $\bar{X}$ and R or $\bar{X}$ and σ, are undertaken, some or all of the following purposes are present:

1. To analyze a process with a view to one or more of the following objectives:

a. To secure information to be used in establishing or changing specifications or in determining whether a given process can meet specifications. This was illustrated in Example 2.

b. To secure information to be used in establishing or changing production procedures. Such changes may be either elimination of assignable causes of variation or fundamental changes in production methods that may be called for whenever the control chart makes it clear that specifications cannot be met with present methods. Production changes of one or the other of these types are referred to in Examples 1, 7, 8, 9, 10, and 11.

c. To secure information to be used in establishing or changing inspection procedures or acceptance procedures, or both. This objective is referred to in Examples 1, 2, 8, 10, and 11.

2. To provide a basis for current decisions during production as to when to hunt for causes of variation and take action intended to correct them, and when to leave a process alone. This is nearly always one of the purposes of any control chart for variables. It is illustrated in Examples 1, 2, 7, 8, 9, and 11.

3. To provide a basis for current decisions on acceptance or rejection of manufactured or purchased product. This is illustrated in Examples 8 and 9 and discussed further in Chap. XVI. Sometimes, as in Example 8, the control chart is undertaken primarily for this purpose. Often when it is undertaken for other purposes, there is a hope that, as time goes on and the other purposes are accomplished, it will ultimately be possible to reduce inspection costs by using the control chart for variables for acceptance. This was actually accomplished in Example 2. It was suggested as a possibility in the comments on Example 1.

4. To familiarize personnel with the use of the control charts. Al-

though this would seem to be a legitimate purpose only in the early stages of the use of statistical quality control techniques in any organization, control charts undertaken for this purpose often disclose opportunities for cost savings.

108. Choice of the Variable. The variable chosen for control charts for $\bar{X}$ and R must be something that can be measured and expressed in numbers, such as a dimension, hardness number, tensile strength, weight, etc. The real basis of choice is always the prospect of reducing or preventing costs. From the standpoint of the possibility of reducing *production* costs, a candidate for a control chart is any quality characteristic that is causing rejections or rework involving substantial costs. From the *inspection and acceptance* standpoints, destructive testing always suggests an opportunity to use the control chart to reduce costs. Expensive analytical procedures also suggest the possibility of reducing inspection costs with the control charts.

In general, if acceptance is on a sampling basis and the quality tested can be expressed as a measured variable, it is likely to be worth while to examine inspection costs to form a basis for judgment as to the possibilities of reducing these costs by basing acceptance on the control chart for variables. Where 100% inspection takes place on an attributes basis, as with go and not-go gages, the chances for savings in costs depend on considerations outlined in Chap. XVII.

Frequently the best chances to save costs are in places that would not be suggested either by an examination of costs of spoilage and rework or of inspection costs. These depend on the use of the control chart to analyze a process (purpose 1 of Art. 107). The discussion in Art. 10 of the problem of filling containers illustrates this type of opportunity. Concealed costs often exist that are not apparent in any cost statement.

In the introduction of the control-chart technique in any organization, the choice of the right variables is often troublesome (see Example 38, Chap. XVIII). Occasionally the large number of possible variables is a source of confusion. One large manufacturing plant counted several hundred thousand specified dimensions on the many parts going into its products. Obviously only a very small fraction of these were legitimate candidates for control charts for $\bar{X}$ and R. In selecting variables for initial application of the control-chart technique, it may be important not only to choose those with opportunities for cost savings but to select carefully a type of saving that everyone in a supervisory or managerial capacity will readily accept as being a real saving. This usually—although not always—suggests starting where the spoilage and rework costs are high.

109. Decision on the Basis of Subgrouping. The key idea in the Shewhart method is the division of observations into what Shewhart called *rational subgroups.* The success of the Shewhart technique depends in large measure on the discrimination used in the selection of these subgroups. The principles of subgroup selection are discussed at length in Chap. VII.

Generally speaking, subgroups should be selected in a way that makes each subgroup as homogeneous as possible and that gives the maximum opportunity for variation from one subgroup to another. As applied to control charts on production, this means that it is of vital importance not to lose track of the order of production. Particularly if the primary purpose of keeping the charts is to detect shifts in the process average, one subgroup should consist of items produced as nearly as possible at one time; the next subgroup should consist of items all produced at a single later time; and so forth.

This basis of subgrouping was illustrated in Examples 1 and 2 in which five items constituting one subgroup were produced in succession at about 8 o'clock; five items constituting the next subgroup were produced in succession at about 9 o'clock; none of the items produced between the 8 and 9 o'clock subgroups were measured for purposes of the control charts. (As pointed out in Art. 37, some irregularity is desirable in the exact time of taking such samples.) This type of subgrouping is sometimes modified by the practical difficulties in taking such samples and by consideration of the various purposes to be served by the control chart.

For instance, if one of these purposes is to provide a basis for acceptance, it may be desirable to have each subgroup as nearly representative as possible of the production over a given period of time. For this purpose it would be better to inspect five items selected at random from the production in some given period of time than to inspect five items produced in succession at the beginning or end of the period. Or, if each item takes a considerable period of time to produce, it may be more convenient for the items inspected for each subgroup to be spaced approximately uniformly over the production of a given period. This is illustrated in Example 11.

110. Decision on the Size and Frequency of Subgroups. Shewhart suggested four as the ideal subgroup size. In the industrial use of the control chart, five seems to be the most common size. Because the essential idea of the control chart is to select subgroups in a way that gives minimum opportunity for variation *within* a subgroup, it is desirable that subgroups be as small as possible. On the other hand, a size of four is better than three or two on statistical grounds; the distribution of $\bar{X}$ is nearly normal for subgroups of four or more even though the samples are taken from a nonnormal universe; this fact is helpful in the interpretation of control-chart limits. A reason sometimes advanced for the use of five is ease of computation of the average, which can be obtained by multiplying the sum by two and moving the decimal point one place to the left.

Subgroups of two or three may often be used to good advantage, particularly where the cost of measurements is so high as to veto the use of larger subgroups.

Larger subgroups such as 10 or 20 are sometimes advantageous where it is desired to make the control chart sensitive to small variations in the process average. The larger the subgroup size, the narrower the control limits on charts for $\overline{X}$ and the easier it is to detect small variations; this is true only if subgroups are selected in a way that these variations in process average occur between and not within subgroups. Generally speaking, the larger the subgroup size, the more desirable it is to use standard deviation rather than range as a measure of subgroup dispersion. A practical working rule is to use $\overline{X}$ and σ charts rather than $\overline{X}$ and R charts whenever the subgroup size is greater than 15.

In the introduction of the control-chart technique in any organization, charts for variables are often applied to data already collected for some other purpose. Often it is wise to start the control charts with no change in the method of collecting data, putting off any changes that might improve the control charts until such time as the charts have proved their usefulness to management. In such cases the subgroup size is likely to be determined by the way in which the data are collected. Sometimes this involves variable subgroup sizes; methods of determining limits and plotting charts for these are explained in Art. 153, Chap. VIII.

Where the control-chart analysis is applied to past data already tabulated, this may necessitate much larger subgroups than would ordinarily be selected. This is illustrated in Art. 156, Chap. VIII.

No general rules may be laid down for frequency of subgroup. Each case must be decided on its own merits, considering both the cost of taking and analyzing measurements and the benefits to be derived from action based on the control charts. In the initial use of a control chart for analyzing a process, it may be desirable to arrive at conclusions quickly by taking frequent samples. Later on, after the troubles have been diagnosed and corrected and the function of the control chart has become the maintenance of process control on current production, it may be advisable to reduce the frequency of sampling. This was illustrated in Example 2, in which the frequency of sampling was ultimately reduced from one sample every hour to one sample every 8 hr.

The frequency of taking a subgroup may be expressed either in terms of time, such as once an hour (as in Examples 1 and 2), or as a proportion of the items produced, such as 5 out of each 100 (as in Example 11).

111. Setting up the Forms for Recording the Data. Although the exact details of forms used will vary from one organization to another, two general types of forms are in common use. Both types are shown in Example 11 at the end of this chapter. The type shown in Fig. 30, in which the successive measurements in each subgroup are recorded one below the other, avoids the necessity of mental arithmetic (or calculations on scratch paper) in figuring averages.

Figure 31 shows the other common type of form, in which each line contains all the measurements in one subgroup. This type avoids the necessity of copying the $\bar{X}$ and R values to compute the grand averages and generally allows room for more subgroups on a page. Where only the final two digits of the measurement are subject to variation, the mental arithmetic involved in obtaining averages is not complicated.

All forms need spaces for indicating the item measured, the unit of measurement, and other relevant information. It is particularly important to provide opportunity for remarks regarding any production changes (for example, changed machine setting, changed operator, tool sharpened, etc.), inspection changes, or other matters observed by the quality control inspector that might give clues to the causes of any out-of-control points.

112. Determining the Method of Measurement. Decision must be made as to the measuring instruments to be used and the way in which the measurements are to be made. Usually it is desirable to prepare definite written instructions on this point.

II. STARTING THE CONTROL CHARTS

113. Making and Recording the Measurements and Recording Other Relevant Data. The actual work of the control chart starts with the first measurements. As emphasized in the preceding chapter, it should always be remembered that the information given by the control chart is influenced by variations in measurement as well as by variations in the quality being measured. Any method of measurement will have its own inherent variability; it is important that this not be increased by mistakes in reading measuring instruments or errors in recording data. As suggested in Art. 111, it is also important that notes be made about any occurrences which, if the control chart later shows lack of control, might provide help on the investigation of assignable causes of variation.

114. Calculation of Average $\bar{X}$ for Each Subgroup. As already explained, the measurements in each subgroup are added together and the sum is divided by the number of items in the subgroup.

$$\bar{X} = \frac{X_1 + X_2 + X_3 + \cdots + X_n}{n}$$

115. Calculation of the Range R for Each Subgroup. The highest and lowest numbers in the subgroup must first be identified. With large subgroups it is helpful to mark the highest value with the letter H and the lowest with the letter L. The range is computed by subtracting the lowest value from the highest.

116. Plotting the $\bar{X}$ and R Charts. Many $\bar{X}$ and R charts have already been illustrated in the preceding chapters and many others are given throughout this book. Such charts are often plotted on rectangular cross-section paper having 8 or 10 rulings to the inch. Profile paper may also be used. Some special forms developed for this purpose have used rulings similar to profile paper, with vertical lines spaced $\frac{1}{6}$ in. apart and horizontal lines spaced $\frac{1}{20}$ in. apart.

The vertical scale at the left is used for the statistical measures $\bar{X}$ and R. The horizontal scale is used for subgroup numbers. Dates, hours, or lot numbers may also be indicated on the horizontal scale. Each point may be indicated on the chart by a dot, circle, or cross. In this book the general practice is to use a circle for points on $\bar{X}$ charts and a cross for points on R charts; there are some exceptions, however. There is no standard practice in industry in this regard. Points on control charts may or may not be connected. In this book they are not connected except where the connecting line serves some definite purpose or where published charts having connecting lines are being reproduced.

Points on both $\bar{X}$ and R charts should be kept plotted up to date. This is particularly important where the charts are posted in the shop and are used by machine operators, setters, and foremen.

As explained in Chap. V, the objectives of the control chart can sometimes be fully served by the $\bar{X}$ chart alone. In such cases the R chart may be omitted.

III. DETERMINING THE TRIAL CONTROL LIMITS

117. Decision on Required Number of Subgroups before Control Limits Are Calculated. The determination of the minimum number of subgroups required before control limits are calculated is a compromise between a desire to obtain the guidance given by averages and control limits as soon as possible after the start of collecting data, and a desire that the guidance be as reliable as possible. The fewer the subgroups used, the sooner the information thus obtained will provide a basis for action but the less the assurance that this basis for action is sound.

On statistical grounds it is desirable that control limits be based on at least 25 subgroups. Moreover, experience indicates that the first few subgroups obtained when a control chart is initiated may not be representative of what is measured later; the mere act of taking and recording measurements is sometimes responsible for a change in the pattern of variation.

For these reasons, if 25 subgroups can be obtained in a short time, it is desirable to wait for 25 or more subgroups; this would be true, for example, where a new subgroup was measured every hour.

However, where subgroups are obtained slowly there is a natural desire on the part of those who initiated the control charts to draw some conclusions from them within a reasonable time. This impatience for an answer frequently leads to the policy of making preliminary calculations of control limits from the first 8 or 10 subgroups, with subsequent modification of limits as more subgroups are obtained.

118. Calculation of Trial Limits. First it is necessary to compute the average range $\bar{R}$. This is the sum of the ranges of the subgroups divided by the number of subgroups. The D_3 and D_4 factors from Table C, Appendix III, should then be used to calculate control limits for R

$$UCL_R = D_4\bar{R}$$
$$LCL_R = D_3\bar{R}$$

Then $\bar{X}$, the average of the $\bar{X}$ values, should be computed. This is the sum of the $\bar{X}$ values divided by the number of subgroups. The A_2 factor from Table C, Appendix III, should be used to calculate control limits for $\bar{X}$

$$UCL_{\bar{X}} = \bar{\bar{X}} + A_2\bar{R}$$
$$LCL_{\bar{X}} = \bar{\bar{X}} - A_2\bar{R}$$

The trial limits thus obtained are appropriate for analyzing the past data which were used in their calculation. They may require modification before extending them to apply to future production.

The preceding formulas for limits for $\bar{X}$ and R assume a constant subgroup size. Chapter VIII explains the necessary calculations where the subgroup size is variable.

119. Plotting the Central Lines and Limits on the Charts. The central line on the R chart should be drawn as a solid horizontal line at $\bar{R}$. The upper control limit should be drawn as a dotted horizontal line at the computed value of UCL_R. If the subgroup size is seven or more, the lower control limit should be drawn as a dotted horizontal line at LCL_R. If the subgroup size is six or less, the lower control limit for R is zero.

The central line on the $\bar{X}$ chart should be drawn as a solid horizontal line at $\bar{\bar{X}}$. The upper and lower control limits for $\bar{X}$ should be drawn as dotted horizontal lines at the computed values.

IV. DRAWING PRELIMINARY CONCLUSIONS FROM THE CHARTS

120. Indication of Control or Lack of Control. Lack of control is indicated by points falling outside the control limits on either the $\bar{X}$ or R charts. Some users of the control charts identify such out-of-control points by a special symbol. For instance, if each point is represented by a circle, a cross is made in the circles designating out-of-control points; if each point is represented by a dot, a circle may be drawn around the dot for out-of-control points.

When, because points fall outside the control limits, we say a process is "out of control," this is equivalent to saying, "Assignable causes of variation are present; this is not a constant-cause system." As explained in Chap. IV, with 3-sigma limits we can make this statement with considerable confidence that it is correct; a constant-cause system will seldom be responsible for points falling outside control limits.

In contrast to this, when all points fall inside the control limits we cannot say with the same assurance, "*No* assignable causes of variation are present; this *is* a constant-cause system." No statistical test can give us this positive assurance. When we say, "This process is in control," the statement really means, "For practical purposes, it pays to act as if no assignable causes of variation were present."

Moreover, even in the best manufacturing processes, occasional errors occur that constitute assignable causes of variation but that may not constitute a basis for action. This fact may lead to various practical working rules on the relationship between satisfactory control and the number of points falling outside limits. One such rule is to consider 0 out of 25 points, not more than 1 out of 35, or 2 out of 100 points outside control limits as evidence of excellent control.

Even though all points fall within control limits, lack of control may be indicated by runs of seven or more points in succession on the same side of the central line, or by the presence of other extreme runs such as were listed in Art. 88.

The actions suggested by the evidence of the control chart depend on the relationship between what the process is doing and what it is supposed to do. That is, the apparent pattern of variation as shown by the control chart needs to be compared with the specifications. This comparison is simplest if the process appears to be in control.

121. Interpretation of Processes in Control. With evidence from the control chart that a process is in control, we are in a position to judge what is necessary to permit the manufacture of product that meets the specifications for the quality characteristic charted. The control chart data give us estimates of

1. The centering of the process ($\bar{X}'$ may be estimated from $\bar{\bar{X}}$).
2. The dispersion of the process (σ' may be estimated as $\bar{R}/d_2$).

The discussion in Chap. IV made it clear that estimates of $\bar{X}'$ and σ' are subject to sampling errors. For this reason, any conclusions obtained from a short period (such as 25 points on the control chart) must be regarded as tentative, subject to confirmation or change as the control chart is continued and as more evidence becomes available. However, the reasonable thing to do at any stage in the proceedings is to make the best interpretation possible of the data already available. Once it is evident what actions are suggested by this interpretation, decision can be made whether action should be taken at once or whether it should await more data. In applying the following analysis of processes in control, the limitations of the current estimates of $\bar{X}'$ and σ' should always be kept in mind.

In Chap. IV it was pointed out that practically all (all but 0.27%) of a normal distribution falls within limits of $\bar{X}' \pm 3\sigma'$; *i.e.*, for practical purposes the spread of the distribution may be thought of as approximately $6\sigma'$. In the preliminary analysis of control-chart data, there is hardly enough evidence to permit judgment whether or not the distribution is approximately normal. Certainly the evidence is seldom sufficient to tell whether 0.27% or 0.6% or 1.1% or some other small percentage of the distribution will fall outside $\bar{X}' \pm 3\sigma'$. Evidence of the exact form of the frequency distribution and the percentage of the distribution outside these limits may be obtained only after a long accumulation of data under control. In the meantime a satisfactory rough guide to judgment is provided by the assumption that $6\sigma'$ is a measure of the spread of the process.

Actions based on the relationship between the specifications and the centering and dispersion of a controlled process depend somewhat on whether there are two specification limits, X_{max} and X_{min}, as is always true of dimensions, or only one specification limit, either X_{max} or X_{min}, as might be true of a specified minimum tensile strength, or minimum weight of the contents of a container, or maximum per cent of a particular chemical impurity. Some of the various possible situations that may exist with two limits are shown in Figs. 24, 25, and 26. Some situations that may exist with a single limit are shown in Figs. 27, 28, and 29.

122. Possible Relationships of a Process in Control to Upper and Lower Specification Limits. When a controlled process must meet two specification limits on individual values, X_{max} and X_{min}, all possible situations may be grouped into three general classes, as follows:

1. The spread of the process ($6\sigma'$) is appreciably less than the difference between the specification limits ($X_{max} - X_{min}$).

2. The spread of the process ($6\sigma'$) is approximately equal to the difference between the specification limits ($X_{max} - X_{min}$).

3. The spread of the process ($6\sigma'$) is appreciably greater than the difference between the specification limits ($X_{max} - X_{min}$).

The first situation is illustrated in Fig. 24, in which the specification limits are shown by the upper and lower horizontal lines. Frequency curves A, B, C, D, and E indicate various positions in which the process might be centered. With any of the positions A, B, or C, practically all the product manufactured will meet specifications as long as the process stays in control.

In general the conditions represented in Figs. 24A, B, and C represent the ideal manufacturing situation. When the control chart shows that one of these conditions exists, many different possible actions may be considered; the choice among the various actions is a matter of relative economy.

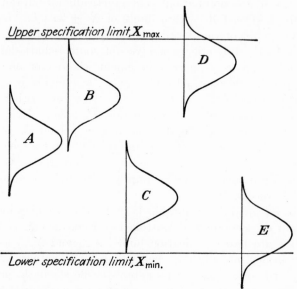

FIG. 24. Some cases where the spread of a process is less than the difference between specification limits.

For example, it may be considered economically advisable to permit $\overline{X}$ to go out of control if it does not go too far; that is, the distribution may be allowed to move between positions B and C. This may avoid the cost of frequent machine setups and of delays due to hunting for assignable causes of variation that will not be responsible for unsatisfactory product. In Art. 163, Chap. VIII, the use of so-called "modified control limits" for this purpose is explained.

Or, where acceptance has been based on 100% inspection, it may be economical to substitute acceptance based on the control chart for $\overline{X}$ and R.

Or, if there is an economic advantage to be gained by tightening the specification limits, such action may be considered.

If none of these things is to be done, it may be economical to discontinue the use of the control chart, or at least to increase the time interval between control-chart inspections. The larger the ratio of $(X_{max} - X_{min})$

to the process spread ($6\sigma'$), the more favorable is the situation to getting good product without assistance from any control chart.

With the process in position D of Fig. 24, some product will fall above the upper specification limit; in position E some product will fall below the lower specification limit. In either case the obvious action is to try to change the centering of the process, bringing it closer to position A. Once this has been done, consideration may be given to the various actions just enumerated.

The second type of situation is illustrated in Fig. 25. Only if the process is exactly centered between the specification limits, as in position

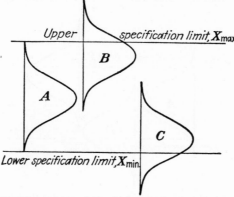

FIG. 25. Some cases where the spread of a process is approximately equal to the difference between specification limits.

A, will all the product be good. If the distribution shifts away from this exact centering, as in B or C, some of the product will fall outside the specifications.

Here the obvious action is to take all steps possible to maintain the centering of the process. This usually calls for continuous use of the control charts for $\bar{X}$ and R with subgroups at frequent intervals and immediate attention to points out of control. If fundamental changes can be made that reduce process dispersion, they will ease the pressure. Consideration should also be given to the question of whether the tolerances are tighter than is really necessary.

The third type of situation is illustrated in Fig. 26. Here the specification limits are so tight that even with the process in control and perfectly centered as in position A, some nonconforming product will be made. This calls for a review of tolerances, as was illustrated in Example 2. It also calls for efforts to make fundamental changes that will reduce process dispersion. It is still important to maintain the centering of the process; the curves in positions B and C show how a shift in process average will increase the per cent defective.

If 100% inspection is possible, the nonconforming product may be sorted out and eliminated. (This is subject to the limitations of the human error involved in any 100% inspection.) But if such 100% sorting is impossible because acceptance is based on destructive tests, there is no chance to obtain product all of which conforms to specifications. The alternatives are to make fundamental changes in the process in order to reduce the process dispersion or to widen the specification limits to fit the process.

However, in some cases (for example, certain dimensions of mating parts, certain electrical characteristics of electrical components) a twilight zone exists just beyond the specification limits within which a

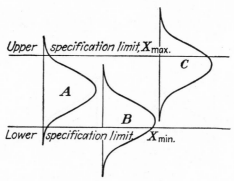

Fig. 26.   Some cases where the spread of a process is greater than the difference between specification limits.

moderate percentage of out-of-tolerance articles may be used without causing trouble; this situation usually calls for continued action to maintain the centering of the process.

123. Possible Relationships of a Process in Control to a Single Specification Limit.   The key to the most useful classification of the situations involving two specification limits was the process dispersion.   A similar key to the classification of situations involving a minimum limit is the position of $\overline{X}' - 3\sigma'$ with respect to $X_{\min}$.   Again three situations may be considered:

1. The low value of the process distribution $(\overline{X}' - 3\sigma')$ is appreciably above the specification minimum $(X_{\min})$.   This is illustrated in Fig. 27.

2. The low value of the process distribution $(\overline{X}' - 3\sigma')$ is approximately at the specification minimum $(X_{\min})$.   This is illustrated in Fig. 28.

3. The low value of the process distribution $(\overline{X}' - 3\sigma')$ is appreciably below the specification minimum $(X_{\min})$.   This is illustrated in Fig. 29.

The first situation is one in which there is a margin of safety, the second is one in which the specification is just barely met as long as the

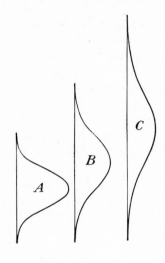

Specification limit, $X_{min.}$

FIG. 27.   Some cases where the low value of the process distribution is above the specification minimum.

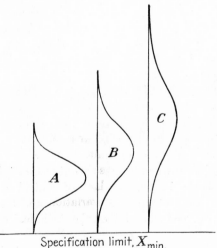

Specification limit, $X_{min.}$

FIG. 28.   Some cases where the low value of the process distribution is approximately at the specification minimum.

process stays in control, and the third is one in which some nonconforming product is inevitable unless a fundamental change is made in the process. The fundamental change may be either a decrease in process dispersion or an increase in the process average.

Three curves, A, B, and C, with different dispersions have been shown in Figs. 27, 28, and 29 to emphasize the interrelationship of process average, process dispersion, and specification minimum.   All three distributions, A, B, and C have the same low value.   However, distribution B with a greater dispersion must have a greater process average than A for the low points to be at the same level; similarly C must have a greater process average than B.   It is evident that the greater the dispersion, the higher must be the average for the entire distribution to fall above the specification minimum.   This relationship between average and dispersion is an important matter related to costs in many instances; for example, in the filling of containers a reduction in dispersion may reduce cost by reducing the average overfill.

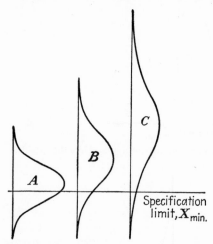

On the other hand, the less the dispersion the more important it is that the process average not go out of control.   This is illustrated by comparing distributions A and C in Figs. 28 and 29.   In Fig. 29 both process averages have shifted an equal amount below their position in Fig. 28.   However, the proportion of bad product, as indicated by the area of the distribution below the specification limit, is much greater in A than in C.

Fig. 29.   Some cases where the low value of the process distribution is below the specification minimum.

The preceding discussion has related to a single lower specification limit X_{min}, with no upper limit.   Similar reasoning would apply if there were an upper limit with no lower limit.

124. Relationships between Processes out of Control and Specification Limits.   If the control chart shows lack of control one obvious step is to hunt for the assignable causes of variation and try to correct them. Some guidance was given in Chap. V on the statistical aspects of detection of assignable causes.

It is also pertinent to enquire into the process centering and dispersion that may be expected if control is obtained.   If the out-of-control points on the R chart are eliminated, what evidence does the control chart give about process dispersion?   In view of this process dispersion and of the specification limits, where ought the process average to be?   The same type of analysis of the relationship between process average, process dispersion, and specification limits that was discussed for controlled processes is appropriate for processes not yet brought under control.   The practical differences are that it may not be certain whether control can actually be attained and that there is less confidence in the estimates of $\bar{X}'$ and σ' at which it might be attained.

125. Some Specific Suggestions about Preliminary Conclusions and Actions Based on the Control Charts. If the charts show control, estimate σ' as $\bar{R}/d_2$. If there are minimum and maximum specification limits, compare $6\sigma'$ with $(X_{max} - X_{min})$. Compare $(\bar{\bar{X}} + 3\sigma')$ with X_{max}, and compare $(\bar{\bar{X}} - 3\sigma')$ with X_{min}. Determine from these comparisons which class of situation described in Arts. 122 and 123 is applicable. Consider the possible actions suggested.

If the charts show lack of control, try to judge from the charts and all other pertinent information what may be the assignable causes and whether or not it is likely they can be eliminated. After removing the subgroups that showed lack of control on the R chart, calculate a revised $\bar{R}$ and new control limits for R. If these limits show additional subgroups out of control, remove those subgroups and repeat the calculation. Estimate σ' as $\bar{R}/d_2$, using the final revised $\bar{R}$ after all out-of-control values of R have been eliminated. Consider this as a value of σ' that might be obtained if the process were brought into control.

Consider whether or not the process average can readily be set at any desired level. (In some cases, as in dimensions resulting from machining operations, this may be merely a matter of machine setting; in other cases, as in tensile strengths or percentages of chemical impurities, this may be a difficult matter involving costly changes in the process.) If so, decide on the desired value of $\bar{X}'$ at which to aim, assuming that control could be attained with σ' as estimated. If not, in the light of the known value of $\bar{\bar{X}}$, decide on an attainable $\bar{X}'$. Use the values of $\bar{X}'$ and σ' thus obtained as a basis for an analysis of the relationship of the specification limits to the process average and dispersion.

Decisions as to whether to take action now on the basis of the control-chart data already at hand, or to defer action until more data are obtained, should give weight to the uncertainties in the estimates of $\bar{X}'$ and σ' and to the costs and possible consequences of the proposed action.

V. CONTINUING TO USE THE CHARTS

126. Revision of Central Lines and Control Limits. The trial control limits served the purpose of determining whether past operations were in control. The continuing use of the control chart, with each out-of-control point used as a possible basis for hunting for an assignable cause of variation and taking action to eliminate that cause, may require revised limits.

If the process has been in control with both average and dispersion satisfactory from the standpoint of the specification limits, the trial control limits should be extended to apply to future production. As more data accumulate, the limits may be reviewed from time to time and revised whenever necessary. It is desirable to establish regular periods for this review, such as once every week, once every month, once every 25, 50, or 100 subgroups.

If the dispersion has been in control, as evidenced by the R chart, but the average $\bar{X}$ has been out of control, the trial central line and trial limits on the R chart should continue to be used, and control limits on the $\bar{X}$ chart should continue to be a distance of $A_2\bar{R}$ on either side of the central line. The location of the revised central line on the $\bar{X}$ chart calls for a decision whether this should be at an aimed-at level (sometimes called a standard level), designated as $\bar{X}'$, or whether it should be based on the past data, a revision of $\bar{\bar{X}}$. When making this choice it should be recognized that wherever the central line (*i.e.*, the assumed process average for purposes of the control chart) is placed, a point outside control limits is interpreted as meaning, "This variation is more than would be expected as a matter of chance if the assumed process average is maintained."

If the process average may be changed by a fairly simple adjustment of the manufacturing process, such as a machine adjustment influencing a dimension, it is nearly always desirable to decide on a standard or aimed-at value $\bar{X}'$. This aimed-at process average should be determined by consideration of the relationship between process average, process dispersion, and specification limits, along the lines discussed in Arts. 122 and 123. Where there are upper and lower specification limits and product falling outside one limit may be reworked whereas product falling outside the other limit must be scrapped, the aimed-at average should be chosen with due consideration for the difference between costs of spoilage and rework.

Unless the process average can be changed by a definite simple adjustment, $\bar{\bar{X}}$ is likely to be the result of a complex set of factors, with the influence of each factor not clearly known. In such instances, a control chart based on an aimed-at value of $\bar{X}'$ which was different from the past $\bar{\bar{X}}$ might show many points out of control; these out-of-control points would simply indicate that the aim had been poor without giving much help in correcting the aim. For this reason it is more sensible in such cases to use the past $\bar{\bar{X}}$ as the new central line, or possibly a revised $\bar{\bar{X}}$ corrected by the elimination of the past out-of-control points. Then if different changes in the process are undertaken one after another with the purpose of finding a way to bring the process average to a new desired level, the control chart based on the past process average will give evidence whether each change constitutes an assignable cause of variation from past performance. If these assignable causes move the process average closer to the desired average, they should be continued rather than eliminated. Each change that is continued may call for a new central line on the $\bar{X}$ chart based on the changed performance. This is illustrated in Example 33, Chap. XVII.

Where the R chart shows that the process dispersion is out of control, it is desirable to estimate the value of $\bar{R}$ and σ' that might be attained if the dispersion were brought into control. This estimate is necessary even though it cannot be made with great assurance that it is correct. A method that is usually satisfactory is to eliminate the values of R outside the control limits and make a new calculation of $\bar{R}$. If new limits calculated from this $\bar{R}$ throw more points outside the control limits, the calculation of revised $\bar{R}$'s may be repeated as many times as necessary until all remaining points fall inside the limits. This is illustrated in Example 11.

This revised $\bar{R}$ may be used as the new central line on the R chart, as the basis for calculating the new limits on the R chart and as the basis for calculating $A_2\bar{R}$ to get the distance of the control limits from the central line on the $\bar{X}$ chart. This has the effect of tightening the limits on both the R and $\bar{X}$ charts, making them consistent with a σ' that may be estimated from the revised $\bar{R}$ as $\bar{R}/d_2$. This σ' may also serve as a basis for analyzing the relationship between process average, process dispersion, and specification limits, as outlined in Arts. 122, 123, and 124.

Where both R and $\bar{X}$ are out of control and new limits on the $\bar{X}$ chart are to be based on an aimed-at $\bar{X}'$, the calculation of the revised $\bar{R}$ should be made before making a decision regarding the value of $\bar{X}'$ to be used. This is illustrated in Example 11.

Revised limits should be reviewed from time to time as additional data are accumulated.

127. Use of the Control Charts for Action on the Process. In continuing the use of the control charts, there may be three different kinds of action on the process, as follows:

1. Action to remove assignable causes of variation that are brought to attention by out-of-control points.

2. Action to establish the process average.

3. Action to establish the process dispersion.

Once a process is brought into control with a satisfactory average and dispersion, an important purpose of the control chart is to help continue this happy state of affairs. The most common routine use of the control chart for variables is for this purpose. This involves simply leaving a process alone as long as it stays in control, and hunting for and removing assignable causes of variation whenever the control charts show lack of control. Uses of the control chart for this purpose were illustrated in Examples 7, 8, and 9.

Actions to establish a process average at some desired level follow the lines suggested in Art. 126. It should be emphasized that whenever an aimed-at value $\bar{X}'$ is used for the central line on the control chart, there should be an actual effort made to aim at that value in the manufacturing process itself. It does no good to put such a line on the control chart unless this forms a basis for action by those who carry out the manufacturing operations.

Actions to reduce process dispersion often call for fundamental changes in machines or methods. Action may also be undertaken to match various process dispersions with different jobs to be undertaken. The information given by control charts about the natural tolerances that will be held by various machines or various production methods may make it possible to fit the process dispersion to the job in hand. Operations calling for close tolerances may be assigned to the machines that will hold the close tolerances, and operations on which wide tolerances are satisfactory may be assigned to those machines that will hold only wide tolerances. This use of the control chart in production planning may be its chief contribution in some jobbing shops.

128. Use of the Control Chart for Variables as a Basis for Acceptance. Obviously variables charts may be used as a basis for acceptance only for those quality characteristics subject to actual measurement. For such quality characteristics, two very different types of situation exist.

In one type, inspection by attributes is available at relatively low cost with gages or other measuring devices that use the go and not-go principle. This is true of nearly all dimensions and of many other quality characteristics. For sampling inspection based on the control chart for variables to be a satisfactory basis for acceptance in this situation, the relationship of the process to the specification limits must be a favorable one, such as that shown in Fig. 24A or Fig. 27. Even in cases where sampling inspection using the control chart for variables will do a satisfactory job, it may not do the most economical one. Here relative costs and performances should be compared to decide among many different possible acceptance plans, such as 100% inspection by attributes, various schemes involving acceptance by sampling inspection by attributes, and the various possible schemes for acceptance sampling by variables.

In the other type of situation, acceptance tests are destructive or so costly that they may be applied only to a small percentage of the product. Here the information given by the control chart for variables should always be used as a part of the acceptance procedure.

This entire subject is discussed at length in Part Four of this book and illustrated further in Part Five.

129. Use of the Charts for Action on the Specifications. The control charts for variables may influence specifications in two ways.

They may be used to determine the capabilities of a manufacturing process before the specification limits are set. This is often a sensible procedure. This is discussed in Arts. 233 to 236, Chap. XII.

They may also be used to give evidence that, because of the inability of a manufacturing process to meet existing specification limits even when it is in control, a review of specification limits is called for.

A general principle applicable here is that the basis of all specification limits should be the prospective use of the part or product for which the limits are specified. Ideally, all specification limits should be exactly right from the standpoint of what is really needed. Actually, as illustrated in Example 2, many specification limits are made tighter than really necessary, often because no time or effort has been given to finding out what is necessary. Moreover, in most cases there is no one right value of specification limits which can be settled independently of cost factors involved; these cost factors cannot be properly judged without information regarding the capabilities of the manufacturing process such as is given by the control chart. For these reasons, many cases exist in which the appropriate conclusion from the control chart is to change the specifications.

EXAMPLE 11. MILLING A SLOT IN AN AIRCRAFT TERMINAL BLOCK

An Example to Illustrate the Steps in the Use of $\bar{X}$ and R Charts on a Manufacturing Operation

130. Decisions Preparatory to the Control Chart. High percentages of rejections for many of the parts made in the machine shop of an aircraft company indicated the need for examination of the reasons for trouble. As most of the rejections were for failure to meet dimensional tolerances, it was decided to try to find the causes of trouble by the use of $\bar{X}$ and R charts.

These charts, which of course required actual measurement of dimensions, were to be used only for those dimensions which were causing numerous rejections. Among many such dimensions, the ones selected for control charts were those having high costs of spoilage and rework, and those on which rejections were responsible for delays in assembly operations. Although the initial purpose of all the $\bar{X}$ and R charts was to diagnose causes of trouble, it was anticipated that some of the charts would be continued for routine process control and possibly for acceptance inspection.

This example deals with one of these dimensions, the width of a slot on a duralumin forging used as a terminal block at the end of an airplane wing spar. The final machining of this slot width was a milling operation. The width of the slot was specified as $0.8750 \begin{cases} +0.0050 \\ -0.0000 \end{cases}$ in. The designing engineers had specified this dimension with a unilateral tolerance because of the fit requirements of the terminal block; it was essential that the slot width be at least 0.8750 in. and desirable that it be as close to 0.8750 as possible.

Most of the aircraft parts produced in this machine shop were large parts fabricated in lots the size of which varied from a few hundred to several thousand. It was felt that practical considerations called for a single decision as to the method of subgrouping and the size and frequency of sample to apply to all the $\bar{X}$ and R charts to be used.

One limiting factor was the small number of available personnel for the control-chart inspection in relation to the number of control charts it was desired to keep. On this basis it was decided that for each chart the sample inspected would be approximately 5% of the total production of the part in question. Because of the many general

<table>
<tr><td colspan="10" align="center">$\bar{X}$ AND R CONTROL CHART DATA SHEET</td></tr>
<tr><td colspan="10">Product _Terminal block_   Dept No. _78_   Order No. _54321_
Characteristic _Width of slot_   Specified limits { _0.8800 in_ Max.
Unit of measurement _0.0001in. over 0.8000_   { _0.8750 in._ :Min.</td></tr>
</table>

Subgroup No.	1	2	3	4	5	6	7		$\bar{X}$	R
a	772	756	756	744	802	783	747	1	770	85
b	804	787	773	780	726	807	766	2	750	54
c	779	733	722	754	748	791	753	3	751	51
d	719	742	760	774	758	762	758	4	765	36
e	777	734	745	774	744	757	767	5	756	76
Total	3851	3752	3756	3826	3778	3900	3791	6	780	50
Average, $\bar{X}$	770	750	751	765	756	780	758	7	758	20
Range, R	85	54	51	36	76	50	20	8	771	38
								9	748	16
Date or time	3/7	3/7	3/7	3/8	3/8	3/8	3/9	10	717	25
Subgroup No.	8	9	10	11	12	13	14	11	737	36
								12	740	36
a	788	757	713	716	746	749	771	13	769	38
b	750	747	730	730	727	762	767	14	772	20
c	784	741	710	752	763	778	785	15	768	13
d	769	746	705	735	734	787	772	16	777	27
e	762	747	727	751	730	771	765			
Total	3853	3738	3585	3684	3700	3847	3860			
Average, $\bar{X}$	771	748	717	737	740	769	772			
Range, R	38	16	25	36	36	38	20		12,129	621
Date or time	3/9	3/9	3/10	3/10	3/10	4/2	4/2		Calculation of limits	
Subgroup No.	15	16							$\bar{\bar{X}} = 12,129 \div 16 = 758$	
a	771	767							$\bar{R} = 621 \div 16 = 39$	
b	758	769							$A_2\bar{R} = .58(39) = 23$	
c	769	770							$UCL_{\bar{X}} = \bar{\bar{X}} + A_2\bar{R}$	
d	770	794							$= 758 + 23 = 781$	
e	771	786							$LCL_{\bar{X}} = \bar{\bar{X}} - A_2\bar{R}$	
Total	3839	3886							$= 758 - 23 = 735$	
Average, $\bar{X}$	768	777							$UCL_R = D_4\bar{R}$	
Range, R	13	27							$= 2.11(39) = 82$	
Date or time	4/3	4/3							$LCL_R = D_3R = 0$	

FIG. 30. $\bar{X}$ and R data sheet for Example 11.

considerations favoring five as the subgroup size, this size was adopted. It was considered essential that, wherever possible, all measurements be made at the point of production. As lots of five of these large parts did not accumulate at the machine, it was decided that one part would be measured out of approximately every 20 produced, and that a subgroup would consist of five such measurements.

The type of form used for recording the data is illustrated in Fig. 30. It was chosen as a result of the decision to measure many of the dimensions to the nearest ten-thousandth of an inch; it was believed that with so many significant figures, delays and errors would be introduced by any type of form calling for much mental arithmetic. If measurements had been made only to thousandths of an inch, the other type of form would have been appropriate. This is illustrated in Fig. 31, in which

RECORD SHEET FOR $\overline{X}$ & R CHART

Material or part name __Terminal block_____ Part No. _1-2345___
Characteristic measured __Width of slot_____ *_____ Plant _6____ Dept. _78___
Unit of measurement __0.001 in. over 0.800_____ Recorded by _J. S.____

Series No.	Date pro- duced	Measurements on each of five items in series					$\overline{X}$ Av. of items	R Range of items	Record of inspection
		A	B	C	D	E			
1	3/7	77	80	78	72	78	77.0	8	
2		76	79	73	74	73	75.0	6	
3		76	77	72	76	74	75.0	5	
4	3/8	74	78	75	77	77	76.2	4	
5		80	73	75	76	74	75.6	7	
6		78	81	79	76	76	78.0	5	
7	3/9	75	77	75	76	77	76.0	2	
8		79	75	78	77	76	77.0	4	
9		76	75	74	75	75	75.0	2	
10	3/10	71	73	71	70	73	71.6	3	
11		72	73	75	74	75	73.8	3	
12		75	73	76	73	73	74.0	3	
13	4/2	75	76	78	79	77	77.0	4	Operator's check measure-
14		77	77	78	77	76	77.0	2	ments have been made
15	4/3	77	76	77	77	77	76.8	1	on hot part.
16		77	77	77	79	79	77.8	2	Instructed to wait until part
17									has cooled before making
18									check measurement, and to
19									center process at 0.8775 inches
20									
	Totals						1212.8	61	

$\overline{\overline{X}} = \dfrac{1212.8}{16} = 75.8$

$\overline{R} = \dfrac{61}{16} = 3.8$

$A_2\overline{R} = 0.58(3.8) = 2.2$

$D_4\overline{R} = 2.11(3.8) = 8.0$

$\begin{cases} UCL_{\overline{X}} = 75.8 + 2.2 = 78.0 \\ LCL_{\overline{X}} = 75.8 - 2.2 = 73.6 \end{cases}$

$\begin{cases} UCL_R = 8.0 \\ LCL_R = 0 \end{cases}$

Fig. 31. An alternate form of $\overline{X}$ and R data sheet.

the same measurements as in Fig. 30 have been recorded to the nearest thousandth of an inch.

The method of inspection to secure data for each $\overline{X}$ and R chart was stated in written instructions. In the case of the slot width of the terminal block, this was to measure the width with a micrometer at two specified positions in the slot. The recorded slot width was the average of these two measurements.

131. Starting the Control Charts. The actual measurements for the first 16 subgroups are shown in Fig. 30. This number of subgroups corresponds to a production order for 1,600 of these terminal blocks.   Averages and ranges were calculated as shown in Fig. 30 and were plotted as shown in Fig. 32.

At the time of the twelfth subgroup, before the completion of this production order and before the calculation of central line or control limits, the quality control inspector noticed that the machine operator was occasionally checking his performance by a micrometer measurement on width of slot on a terminal block which had just come off the machine.   As the block was still hot from the milling operation, this dimension as measured by the operator was too high because of the expansion of the metal

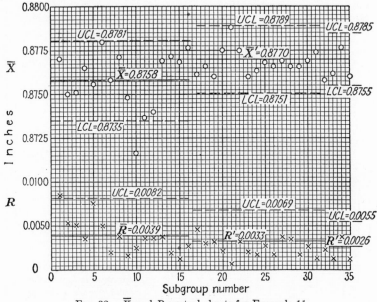

FIG. 32. $\overline{X}$ and R control charts for Example 11.

due to temperature.   Moreover, the operator was influenced by the unilateral tolerance to aim at a dimension at or very slightly above the nominal dimension of 0.8750 in.

Even without a central line or control limits, it was evident from the chart and the data sheet that this was producing many slots that were too narrow.   After the twelfth subgroup the operator was instructed to make his check measurements on parts that had cooled to room temperature and to aim at a dimension of 0.8775, halfway between the upper and lower tolerance limits.   This was reflected in the results in subgroups 13 to 16.

132. Determining the Trial Control Limits.   Calculation of trial control limits was made after the first 16 subgroups which completed the production order.   As shown in Fig. 30, this was done using the A_2 and D_4 factors and formulas from Table C, Appendix III.   These trial control limits are shown for the first 16 subgroups in the control charts in Fig. 32.

133. Drawing Preliminary Conclusions from the Charts.   Subgroup 1 is above the upper control limit on the R chart.   Subgroup 10 is below the lower control limit on the $\overline{X}$ chart.   Moreover, the last 10 of the 16 points on the R chart all fall below the central line.   It is evident that the measurements obtained are not the result of a constant system of chance causes.

If subgroup 1 is eliminated from consideration, $\bar{R}$ for the remaining 15 subgroups is $536/15 = 36$. This gives as the revised upper control limit $D_4\bar{R} = 2.11(36) = 76$. Subgroup 5 falls exactly on the control limit.

A common experience on hand-operated machines, where the dispersion of a controlled process is dependent in part on the care taken by the operator, is that the introduction of the control chart increases the care taken by the operator and thus reduces process dispersion. For this reason the ranges of the first few subgroups may not be representative of what may be expected as time goes on. The general appearance of this R chart with its run of the last 10 points below $\bar{R}$ suggests this as probably true of the slot width. Hence a second revision of $\bar{R}$, with subgroup 5 eliminated, seems reasonable. This gives $\bar{R} = 460/14 = 33$; *i.e.*, $\bar{R} = 0.0033$ in.

From this second revision of $\bar{R}$ an estimate may be made of σ', the process standard deviation that might be anticipated if the process were controlled in the future. This estimate of $\sigma' = \bar{R}/d_2 = 0.0033/2.326 = 0.0014$ in. If this should be the value of σ', the natural tolerance or spread of the controlled process, $6\sigma'$, will be

$$6(0.0014) = 0.0084$$

This spread may be compared with the tolerance spread:

$$X_{max} - X_{min} = 0.8800 - 0.8750 = 0.0050$$

It is evident that the natural tolerance of this process is considerably greater than the specified tolerance. Unless the process dispersion can be reduced, it is evident that even though the process can be brought into control a high percentage of nonconforming product will be produced.

It is evident that this situation is like the one shown in curve B of Fig. 26, namely, the dispersion is too wide and the process average ($\bar{\bar{X}} = 0.8758$) is too low. It is also evident that the process average is capable of adjustment; the instructions given to the operator after subgroup 12 seemed definitely to raise the average. At first glance, it would seem that the most desirable thing to do is to aim at minimum rejections by trying to hold the process in control at an average midway between the upper and lower specification limits, namely, at 0.8775.

However, this conclusion fails to give weight to the fact that a slot that is too narrow can be widened but a slot that is too wide cannot be narrowed. In other words, rework is less costly than spoilage. It is therefore desirable to center the process at a level that results in few slots over the upper specification limit of 0.8800 in., even though a number may be under the lower specification limit of 0.8750 in. The upper 3-sigma limit on individual values might be placed at 0.8800 to make a trial calculation of the aimed-at $\bar{X}'$. If this is done

$$\bar{X}' + 3\sigma' = 0.8800$$
$$\bar{X}' + 3(0.0014) = 0.8800$$
$$\bar{X}' = 0.8758$$

By chance, this is exactly the $\bar{X}$ of the first 16 subgroups. It is evident that such a centering will continue to result in considerable rework.

Experience on similar jobs indicates that it is reasonable to expect that process dispersion may be further reduced. Hence it seems wise to center the process somewhat above 0.8758. Just how much above depends on how much improvement is expected and on the relative costs of spoilage and rework. A figure of 0.8770 was selected.

134. Continuing to Use the Charts. For the continuation of the control chart for the next production order, which started several weeks later, the central line was set as $\bar{X}' = 0.8770$. The 3-sigma control limits were based on assuming $\sigma' = 0.0014$. Using Table E of Appendix III,

$$UCL_{\bar{X}} = \bar{X}' + A\sigma' = 0.8770 + 1.34(0.0014) = 0.8789$$
$$LCL_{\bar{X}} = \bar{X}' - A\sigma' = 0.8770 - 1.34(0.0014) = 0.8751$$
$$UCL_R = D_2\sigma' = 4.92(0.0014) = 0.0069$$
$$\text{Central Line}_R = d_2\sigma' = 2.326(0.0014) = 0.0033$$
$$LCL_R = D_1\sigma' = 0$$

(As σ' was estimated from an $\bar{R}$ of 0.0033, the same limits would have been obtained using the factors and formulas from Table C of Appendix III, with an $\bar{R}$ of 0.0033.)

These limits are shown for subgroups 17 to 32 on the control charts of Fig. 32. The averages and ranges of these subgroups were as follows: (As in the data sheet shown in Fig. 30, $\bar{X}$ is in units of 0.0001 in. above 0.8000 and R is in units if 0.0001 in.)

Subgroup number	$\bar{X}$	R
17	761	47
18	766	31
19	760	32
20	775	22
21	788	7
22	775	32
23	760	21
24	763	18
25	768	27
26	766	17
27	769	38
28	766	35
29	766	17
30	769	26
31	774	14
32	758	24
Totals.....	12,284	408

None of the pieces inspected for control-chart inspection in subgroups 17 to 32 fell outside the specification limits.   The average values for these 16 subgroups are

$$\bar{\bar{X}} = \frac{12,284}{16} = 768 \ (i.e., \ 0.8768 \ \text{in.})$$
$$\bar{R} = {}^{408}\!/_{16} = 26 \ (i.e., \ 0.0026 \ \text{in.})$$

It is evident that there has been a further narrowing of the process dispersion. This should be recognized by a revision of control limits starting with subgroup 33. As there seems to be no reason for a change in the aimed-at average, these revised control limits should be computed from an $\bar{X}'$ of 0.8770 and an $\bar{R}$ of 0.0026, using the factors from Table C of Appendix III.

$$UCL_{\bar{X}} = \bar{X}' + A_2\bar{R} = 0.8770 + 0.58(0.0026) = 0.8785$$
$$LCL_{\bar{X}} = \bar{X}' - A_2\bar{R} = 0.8770 - 0.58(0.0026) = 0.8755$$
$$UCL_R = D_4\bar{R} = 2.11(0.0026) = 0.0055$$
$$LCL_R = D_3\bar{R} = 0$$

These limits are shown on the control chart of Fig. 32 as applying to sub-groups 33, 34, and 35. With $\bar{R}$ reduced to 0.0026, the estimate of σ' is now

$$\frac{0.0026}{2.326} = 0.0011 \text{ in.}$$

If control can be maintained at this level, $\bar{X}' + 3\sigma' = 0.8803$ and $\bar{X} - 3\sigma' = 0.8737$. This indicates that a small amount of spoilage and a moderate amount of rework will still be produced; however, the situation is greatly improved as compared to that which existed before the start of the control chart. As time went on it proved possible to maintain control and to decrease $\bar{R}$ (and σ') further to the point where nearly all the product fell within specification limits.

In situations where the specification limits are as tight as this in relation to the process dispersion, it is not appropriate to use the control chart for acceptance as a substitute for 100% inspection. Neither was this a situation in which the tolerance limits could be widened; the required fit of the part properly controlled the specifications despite the fact that the natural tolerance of the process seemed to be wider than the specified tolerance.

135. Comment on Example 11. The reader should be warned against the inference that a reduction in universe dispersion can always be readily attained, even though it was actually attained in this case. Although such reduction in σ' is possible in certain machine-shop operations in which the skill and care of the operator are controlling factors, it is not possible in many operations on automatic machines where the process dispersion is almost entirely a matter of what the machine will do and of the variability of the materials being machined. Neither is it possible in operations on many quality characteristics other than dimensions.

Example 11 has been explained at some length. The purpose of this full explanation has been not only to show forms and computations involved in the simple control charts for $\bar{X}$ and R, but also to show the way in which judgment enters into interpretation of these charts and into the action based on this interpretation.

A point to be emphasized is that no fixed rules may be laid down regarding the appropriate action based on interpretation of a control chart. The person who makes decisions about action, whether he be quality control engineer, foreman, methods engineer, or machine operator, must understand both the process being analyzed and the general principles underlying the control-chart analysis. Even though all situations may be grouped into a few simple classes from the statistical viewpoint, each actual case is somewhat different from all others; decisions regarding action are economic decisions that should be based on all the facts of each particular case.

It is recommended that all users of $\bar{X}$ and R charts examine the American Standards Association pamphlets on control charts referred to on page 105. The presentation of the subject in this and the three preceding chapters has been greatly influenced by these standards.

Problems

51. The process for the manufacture of a certain yarn referred to in Problems 22 and 23, (page 107) appears to be in control with respect to the quality characteristic tensile strength. There is .a single specification limit, $X_{min} = 15$ lb. Make the necessary calculation, based on the control-chart data given in Problem 22, to determine whether or not you would expect this product to meet its specification. If not, approximately what percentage would you expect to find below the specification limit? Assume the normal distribution is applicable. *Ans.* About 0.3%.

52. In the statistically controlled container-filling process referred to in Problems 24 and 25 (page 107), $X_{min} = 32$ oz. It is desired to hold the overfill to as low a value as possible consistent with meeting this specification. What was the average overfill during the period covered by the control chart? Make the necessary calculation, based on the control-chart data given in Problem 24, to determine what percentage of the containers you would expect to contain less than 32 oz. Assume the normal distribution is applicable. If it were permissible for 4% to be below 32 oz., how much could the average overfill be reduced below its present value?
Ans. 1.1 oz.; about 1.5%; 0.23 oz.

53. The dimension referred to in Problem 27 (page 107) is specified as 2.050 ± 0.030. If the dimension falls above X_{max}, rework is required; if below X_{min}, the part must be scrapped. If the process is in control and normally distributed, what can you conclude regarding its ability to meet specifications? Can you make any suggestions for improvement?

54. In Problem 28 (page 107) the specified minimum strength for a weld is 350 lb. If the process is in statistical control and normally distributed, what can you conclude regarding its ability to meet this specification?

55. In Problem 29 (page 107) $X_{min} = 90$ lb. If the process is in statistical control and normally distributed, what can you conclude regarding its ability to meet this specification?

56. The resistance referred to in Problem 30 (page 107) is specified as 80 ± 5 ohms. If the process is in statistical control and normally distributed with average and standard deviation as indicated by the control-chart data, what percentage would you expect to find above X_{max}? Below X_{min}? What improvement in the total percentage outside of specifications would be made if the process average could be held at 80 ohms rather than at the $\bar{\bar{X}}$ of the control-chart data?

57. Problem 37 (page 108) involved the plotting of $\bar{X}$ and R charts for the first 20 subgroups of Problem 1 (pages 67 and 68). All points on the $\bar{X}$ chart fell within the control limits; one point on the R chart fell outside of the limits. Compute a revised $\bar{R}$, eliminating this out-of-control value of R. From this revised $\bar{R}$, estimate the value of σ' that might be expected if the process dispersion could be held under statistical control.

The specification for the "on" temperature of this thermostatically controlled switch is 54 ± 4. If the process could be centered at 54 with the σ' you have just estimated, and if statistical control could be maintained, what percentage of switches would you expect to fall outside of these specification limits? Assume the normal distribution is applicable.

58. Continue the control charts of Problem 37, plotting subgroups 21 to 46. Base the new control limits on an aimed-at average of 54 and on the revised $\bar{R}$ computed in Problem 57. Are there further evidences of lack of statistical control with respect to these limits? What is the actual percentage of product outside of the specification limits in the entire 46 subgroups? Why is it reasonable to expect this to be somewhat higher than the percentage computed in Problem 57?

59. Problem 38 (page 108) involved the plotting of $\bar{X}$ and R charts for the first 20 subgroups of Problem 6 (pages 67 and 69). All points fell within control limits. The specification for the duration of this time signal is 400 ± 30. All of the 100 observed values in these 20 subgroups fell within specification limits. What general conclusion can you draw from your analysis of the control-chart data regarding the ability of this process to meet its specifications? Which of the distributions in Figs. 24, 25, and 26 (pages 140 to 142) is most closely representative of this process? In continuing these $\bar{X}$ and R charts to apply to future subgroups, what control limits would you recommend?

60. Continue the control charts of Problems 38 and 59 for the final 24 subgroups given on page 69. Use the control limits recommended in your solution to Problem 59. What conclusions can you now draw regarding the presence or absence of statistical control?

61. In Problem 39 (page 108), the values of R were computed for the 100 subgroups of Problem 17 (pages 72 to 74). The 500 measurements in these subgroups were all measurements of the same length. The variation from one measurement to another was presumably due to the inherent variability of the particular measuring process. Prepare $\bar{X}$ and R charts to provide a basis for judgment on the question of whether or not a constant system of chance causes was operating throughout this entire series of 500 measurements.

62. Subgroups of five items each are taken from a manufacturing process at regular intervals. A certain quality characteristic is measured, and $\bar{X}$ and R values are calculated for each subgroup. After 25 subgroups, $\Sigma\bar{X} = 357.50$, and $\Sigma R = 9.90$. Compute the control-chart limits. All points on both charts fall within these limits. What are the apparent 3-sigma "natural tolerance" limits of the process? If the specification limits are 14.40 ± 0.45, what conclusions can you draw regarding the ability of the process to produce items within these specifications? Suggest possible ways in which the situation could be improved.

63. What were the apparent 3-sigma "natural tolerance" limits of the controlled process described in Example 2 (pages 23 to 26)? The revised tolerances stated near the middle of page 26 represented what multiple of σ'?

64. Article 21 (page 21) states three conclusions from the data of Example 1 but does not explain the analysis on which these conclusions are based. Explain the calculations that may be made to provide the basis for these three conclusions.

65. (a) If in Example 1 it were decided to work as close as possible to the lower specification limit in order to minimize gage wear on 100% inspection, what would you recommend for central lines and control limits on $\bar{X}$ and R charts for future production?

(b) If in Example 1 it were decided to eliminate 100% inspection and substitute sampling inspection with acceptance based on the control charts for $\bar{X}$ and R, how would you use the $\bar{X}$ and R charts for this purpose? In this case what would you recommend for central lines and control limits for $\bar{X}$ and R charts for future production?

66. In Example 11, if the slot width were below the lower specification limit of 0.8750, the part could be reworked to bring it within specifications. However, if above 0.8800, it would have to be scrapped. After the first 16 subgroups, an estimate was made that the standard deviation σ' of a controlled process would be 0.0014. This called for an $\bar{X}'$ of 0.8758 if the process average were to be $3\sigma'$ below the upper specification limit.   However, the decision was made to aim at 0.8770 as the process average.

(a) If the distribution of slot width were normal with σ' of 0.0014, approximately what percentage of rework could be expected if $\bar{X}'$ were 0.8758?

(b) With $\bar{X}'$ at 0.8770, what percentage of spoilage would be expected?   What percentage of rework?

(c) In what way do the answers in (a) and (b) suggest an economic basis for establishing the process average in cases of this type?

(d) How would your decision as to process average to be aimed at in Example 11 be influenced if you knew that terminal blocks with slot widths up to 0.8830 had been accepted by the plant salvage committee for use in the airplane and had been used satisfactorily?

CHAPTER VII

THE SELECTION OF RATIONAL SUBGROUPS

. . . The ultimate object is not only to detect trouble but also to find it, and such discovery naturally involves classification. The engineer who is successful in dividing his data initially into *rational* subgroups based upon rational hypotheses is therefore inherently better off in the long run than the one who is not thus successful.—W. A. Shewhart[1]

136. The Information Given by the Control Chart Depends on the Basis Used for Selection of Subgroups. A control chart may be thought of as a statistical test to determine whether the variation from subgroup to subgroup is consistent with the variation within the subgroups. If it is desired to determine whether or not a group of measurements is statistically homogeneous (*i.e.*, whether they appear to come from a constant system of chance causes), subgroups should be chosen in a way that appears likely to give the maximum chance for the measurements in each subgroup to be alike and the maximum chance for the subgroups to differ one from the other.

This may be demonstrated in a striking way. Take a set of measurements which have been subgrouped according to order of production and which show definite lack of control as based on the evidence of $\bar{X}$ and R charts. Write each measurement on a chip, put the chips in a bowl, mix them thoroughly, and draw the chips out one by one without replacement. Record the values written on the chips in the order drawn. Plot $\bar{X}$ and R charts from these recorded values. If you have done a good job of mixing the chips, these new charts will show control. By this mixing you have substituted chance causes for the original assignable causes as a basis for the differences between subgroups.

The basis of subgrouping calls for careful study, with a view to obtaining the maximum amount of useful information from any control chart. As already pointed out, the most obvious rational basis for subgrouping is the order of production.

137. Two Schemes Involving Order of Production as a Basis for Subgrouping. As explained in Art. 109, where order of production is used as a basis for subgrouping, two fundamentally different approaches are possible:

1. The first subgroup consists of product all produced as nearly as

---

[1] Shewhart, W. A., "Economic Control of Quality of Manufactured Product," p. 299, D. Van Nostrand Company, Inc., New York, 1931.

possible at one time; the next subgroup consists of product all produced as nearly as possible at a later time; and so forth.   For example, if the quality control inspector makes his measurements at hourly intervals and the subgroup size is five, he may measure the last five items that were produced just before each hourly visit to the machine.   This is possible on machine parts, for example, if the parts are placed in trays in the order of production.   Otherwise the same result may be obtained by the inspector waiting for five items to come off the machine and measuring them as they come.

2. One subgroup consists of product intended to be representative of all the production over a given period of time; the next subgroup consists of product intended to be representative of all the production of approximately the same quantity of product in a later period; and so forth.   Where product accumulates at the point of production, the inspector may choose a random sample from all the product made since his last visit.   If this is not practicable, he may make five visits (if $n = 5$) approximately equally spaced over a given production quantity or time, with one measurement made at each visit; these five measurements constitute one subgroup.

The first method follows the rule for selection of rational subgroups of permitting a minimum chance for variation within a subgroup and a maximum chance for variation from subgroup to subgroup.   It can be expected to give the best estimate of a value of σ' that represents the ideal capabilities of a process obtainable if assignable causes of variation from one subgroup to another can be eliminated.   Moreover, it provides a more sensitive measure of shifts in the process average; it makes the control chart a better guide to machine setting or to other actions intended to maintain a given process average.   Thus the first method is more ideally suited to analysis of a process and to process control.

However, if subgrouping is by the first method and a change in process average takes place after one subgroup is taken and is corrected before the next subgroup, the change will not be reflected in the control chart. For this reason, the second method is sometimes preferred where acceptance is to be based on the control chart.   For acceptance purposes, the question to be asked before choosing between the two schemes is whether or not two compensating shifts in process average are really likely to occur between subgroups.   If so, and if there is no other way to detect bad product that might be produced between subgroups (for instance, failure of a part to fit into an assembly), the second method of subgrouping is desirable in spite of the other advantages of the first method.   In machining operations, such compensating shifts between subgroups are more likely to occur on hand-operated machines than on automatic machines.

Where the second method of subgrouping is used, the interpretation of points out of control on the R chart is somewhat different from that in the first method. With the second method a shift in the process average during the period covered by a subgroup may cause out-of-control points on the R chart even though there has been no real change in the process dispersion.

In many cases where the first method of subgrouping is really better, it may be necessary to use the second method because of practical reasons associated with the taking of the measurements. This was illustrated in Example 11.

138. Order of Production Is Not Always a Sufficient Basis for Sub-grouping. The reason why order in time is a good basis of subgrouping is that its use tends to disclose assignable causes of variation that come and go. However, there may be other assignable causes of variation that are not disclosed merely by taking subgroups in the order of production.

Two or more apparently identical machines may have different process averages, different process dispersions, or other differences in their patterns of variation. If these machines contribute to a stream of product in a way that subgroups taken from that stream contain approximately constant numbers from each machine, the differences among the machines will not be disclosed by the control charts. The principle here is that assignable causes, if they are to be indicated by the charts, must influence some but not all of the subgroups.

For this reason, consideration often needs to be given to the question of different subgroups for different machines each doing the same operation, or for different spindles on the same machine, or for different cavities in a mold, or for different operators or different inspectors or different shifts. In some cases separate control charts may be needed rather than merely separate subgroups.

The extent to which it pays to make this type of breakdown is a matter for judgment in each individual case. The decision depends on whether it is normally difficult or easy to meet specified tolerances, on the costs of keeping and analyzing the control charts, on whether it is practicable or economical to correct certain known assignable causes of variation, and on other matters that vary from case to case. Two cases in which it did pay to make this breakdown are described in Examples 12 and 13.

EXAMPLE 12. ECCENTRICITY OF PUNCHED HOLES

An Example Illustrating the Use of Separate Control Charts for Each of Several Similar Machines

139. Facts of the Case. This example is a quotation from an article[1] by the Supervisor of Quality Control and Inspection, SKF Industries, Inc.

[1] GOTWALS, C. S., Control Charts, *Metal Progress*, vol. 45, pp. 290–292, February, 1944.

"In the grinding of rollers for spherical bearings it is necessary to have a center hole in one end of the roller. This is done on a Bliss vertical punch press before the roller is hardened. This hole has a tolerance of 0.0025 in. off center, or 0.005 in. eccentric with O.D. (indicator reading). The other end of the roller is not centered. In the grinding operation the roller is supported by a dead center in the countersunk hole on one end, and a cup arrangement as a live center on the other end; thus excessive eccentricity of the center hole or countersunk hole will cause the greater portion of stock to be removed from one side of the roller and leave the machined surface (called "black") not 'cleaned up' on the other side. This roller is then scrap, or must be re-operated to a smaller diameter, which is not desirable.

"Examination of the daily and weekly scrap and re-operation records, together with the control reports, indicated a gradual upward trend in scrap rollers. The rollers were checked to determine if the correct amount of stock was being allowed in machining, and this was found to be within tolerance. The end grinding operations were checked to determine if an out-of-square condition was present. This did not seem to be the cause. Thus by simple elimination of possible assignable causes, we had left only the eccentricity of the center to investigate.

"Small distributional measurements were made in the machining division of lots of rollers. The mean eccentricity of the center hole proved to be about 0.004 in., the extremes of the pattern extending to about 0.007 in. This extreme variability was not present in all lots, and observations seemed to indicate that only one machine was producing to this pattern.

"Control charts were placed on each of the three machines producing this work, as this appeared to be the quickest and easiest way to find out where the trouble was occurring. Control chart procedure is as follows:

"Averages of five pieces were plotted on an 'average and range' chart every 15 minutes on the three presses. Control limits were established after about six hours study, which gave us about 25 readings, and experience has shown that 25 subgroups of five pieces each is enough evidence to establish our limit lines."

140. Analysis and Action. "The analysis of our three charts showed us that we did have trouble. Two machines did not have any points outside of control limits, indicating that they were operating to a controlled pattern and within limits. The third chart clearly showed points outside of the control limits and therefore no reliable prediction could be made of this machine; in other words, it might suddenly get a number of bad pieces and just as suddenly produce good parts. The floor inspector or even the operator may not notice or catch the deviation.

"The action taken in this instance was to study the machine. It was found that the indexing plate on the press was loose and the centering bell slightly ridged. These were quickly corrected."

EXAMPLE 13.   SETTING OF THERMOSTATIC CONTROLS

Compensation for the Differences between Operators

141. Facts of the Case. Thermostatic controls for an electrical device were all adjusted on two banks of units which soak the thermostats at a given heat level. After soaking for a few minutes, each thermostat was adjusted by an operator until a light flashed in the adjusting unit; a lock nut was subsequently put on the control to hold this adjustment. Each bank of units required its own operator. These controls were produced on two shifts. Thus four operators used two banks of units.

The specifications stated the temperatures at which the thermostatically controlled switches should turn the electrical device on and off and gave tolerances for these temperatures.   Each finished device was checked by a testing set operating on the go and not-go principle to determine whether these tolerances were met.   Whenever an out-of-tolerance thermostat was found on this final inspection, it had to be removed from the completed device, reset, and reassembled into the device.

Several weeks might elapse between the original adjustment of a thermostatic control and its final assembly into a completed device.   Hence it was not economical to depend only on the 100% inspection at final assembly as a check on the thermostat setting; any continued systematic error in setting could be responsible for many defective thermostats before it was detected at final assembly and hence could cause much costly rework.

For this reason, samples of the thermostatic controls were taken immediately after setting and checked on a test panel that permitted the measurement of actual on and off temperatures.   Control charts for $\bar{X}$ and R were plotted.   At first the scheme of subgrouping was to take five thermostats that had just been set; a subgroup would generally contain some thermostats adjusted by each of the two operators on the current shift.

This proved successful in detecting trouble from time to time and in obtaining prompt correction of the trouble.   Usually the assignable causes were of a type that could be corrected by maintenance work on one of the adjusting banks.

142. Analysis and Action.   However, even when the process stayed in control, some of the thermostats were outside specified tolerances.   With σ' estimated from the $\bar{R}$ of the control charts, the tolerance spread $X_{max} - X_{min}$ appeared to be about $5\sigma'$.

It was decided to use a plan of subgrouping by operators and by adjusting banks; all the thermostats in any subgroup came from one operator and one bank.   This disclosed the fact that on each shift the thermostats from one operator showed a consistently higher average on and off temperature than those from the other operator.   By shifting operators from one bank to the other it was determined that this was a personal difference between operators and not a difference between banks.   It was evidently a difference in reaction time to the flashing of the light in the adjusting unit.

The heat levels in the adjusting banks were then established in a way that allowed the difference in heat level to compensate for the difference between the "hot" and "cold" operators.   The scheme of subgrouping by operators reduced $\bar{R}$ and σ'. The change in heat level of the banks to compensate for differences between operators tended to keep the same process average for all operators and thus kept the process in control with the narrower control limits.   As the new σ' was about $\frac{5}{6}$ of the previous σ', the tolerance spread $X_{max} - X_{min}$ was now six times the new σ'.   With careful attention to routine use of the control charts to prevent shifts in the process average, it was now possible to make all the thermostats within tolerances and to avoid rework costs at final assembly.

143. Comment on Examples 12 and 13.   In both examples, order in time was a necessary but not a sufficient basis for subgrouping.   In Example 12, subgroups by machines involved separate control charts for each machine.   In Example 13, after it proved possible to compensate for differences in operators, a single chart was maintained with each subgroup representing a single bank and one operator.

If in Example 13 the tolerances had not been so tight compared to the dispersion of the process, it would not have been necessary to go to the extra trouble of keeping subgroups by operators.

It is noteworthy that in Example 12 the trouble shooting by the $\overline{X}$ and R charts was completed in 6 hr. by taking subgroups every 15 min.

144. Need for Discrimination in the Selection of Subgroups. Where there is trouble in meeting tolerances and control is shown by a control chart based merely on the order of production, it may still be possible to diagnose and correct trouble by changing the basis of subgrouping or by keeping separate charts for different sources of measurements, such as different machines, different spindles on the same machine, or different operators. But because such breakdowns usually increase the costs of taking and analyzing data, it may pay to avoid them in cases where tolerances are easily held most of the time.

Moreover, there is no point in continuing to take subgroups in a way that has the effect of disclosing assignable causes of variation that it is impracticable or uneconomical to remove. The need for discrimination in selection of subgroups is illustrated in Examples 14 and 15.

EXAMPLE 14. WEIGHT OF PRIMER PELLETS

An Example of the Need for Separate Control Charts

145. Facts of the Case. The following quotation is from an article[1] describing applications of statistical quality control in the manufacture of small-arms ammunition in ordnance plants managed by the United States Rubber Co.:

FIG. 33.

"In the manufacture of small-arms primers, it is customary to charge each primer by forming pellets of the explosive mixture in a pill plate. The equipment used in this operation is shown in Fig. 33. The pill plate is seen at the right. The primer composition is spread over the plate and worked into the holes by hand, using tools shown at the extreme right. The primer cups are positioned open end up in a plate

[1] SMALLWOOD, H. M., Quality Control in Manufacture of Small-arms Ammunition, *Mechanical Engineering*, vol. 66, pp. 179–182, March, 1944.

to the left of the pill plate. After excess primer composition has been wiped from the pill plate, the entire plate, containing a pellet of explosive in each hole, is swung over the plate of cups by means of a hinged joint on the left-hand side of the pellet plate. At the extreme left of Fig. 33 may be seen knock-out pins, mounted in a plate which is carried on hinges. When this plate is swung down, the pellets are knocked from the pill plate into the primer cups.

"The most important variable in this operation is the pellet weight. Primer sensitivity varies with pellet weight to such an extent that it is necessary to maintain this quantity within fairly narrow limits. Apart from the dimensions of the holes in the

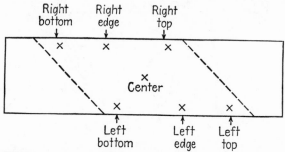

FIG. 34. Locations from which primer pellets are sampled.

pill plate, the pellet weight is determined by physical properties of the primer composition, and by rather minute details of working the composition into the holes of the pill plate.

"Customary inspection schedules call for weighing pellets from the edges and center of the pill plate. The approximate locations used for this inspection are shown in Fig. 34.

"An unusual feature of this operation is that small but consistent differences are usually noticed between the various positions in the plate. These may depend upon the individual characteristics of the operators carrying out the charging operation."

Because of these consistent differences, seven separate control charts were maintained, one for each of the seven sampling locations indicated in Fig. 34. The separate charts supplied evidence of any tendency to charge heavily in one portion of the plate and lightly in another portion.

EXAMPLE 15. THICKNESS OF PADS ON HALF-RING ENGINE MOUNT

An Example in Which Subgroups Were Taken in a Way That Made Evidence of Lack of Control Have No Practical Value

146. Facts of the Case. Figure 35 shows a rough sketch of a half-ring that is part of an assembly used in connection with the mounting of an airplane engine. This half-ring contained four contact pads. It was desired to control the thickness of these pads. All four pads were machined at the same time and were supposed to have the same thickness.

The thickness of each pad was measured with a micrometer to the nearest ten-thousandth of an inch. The four pads on one half-ring were considered to be one subgroup. The measurements for 36 half-rings are shown in Table 19. The $\bar{X}$ and R charts plotted from these measurements are shown in Fig. 36.

These charts appeared to show the process badly out of control.   However, a more critical consideration of the matter showed that it was practically certain this type of subgrouping would show lack of control, and that this showing of lack of control did not provide a useful guide to action.

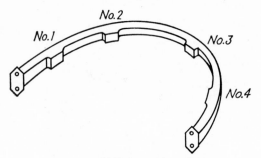

FIG. 35.   Half-ring engine mount.

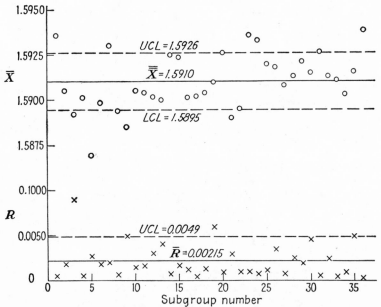

FIG. 36. $\overline{X}$ and R charts for thickness of pads on half-ring engine mount—data of Table 19.

Control charts answer the question, "Is the variation among the sub-groups consistent with the variation within the subgroups?"   With sub-groups taken as they were, this question might have been phrased, "Is the variation among the half-rings consistent with the variation from pad to pad within each half-ring?"   The answer, "No," given by the control chart might have been guessed without help from any control charts.   That is, it was to be expected from the fact that the four pads on any half-ring were machined together; it was reasonable to expect more variation among the half-rings than among the pads.   Moreover, it was no help to know that this was true, as nothing could be done about it by attention to out-of-control points.

TABLE 19. THICKNESS OF EACH OF FOUR PADS ON HALF-RING ENGINE MOUNT
(Measurements in units of 0.0001 in. above 1.5000 in.)

Half-ring number	Pad 1	Pad 2	Pad 3	Pad 4	$\bar{X}$	R
1	933	937	938	935	936	5
2	897	898	915	913	905	18
3	840	900	900	930	892	90
4	900	905	902	900	901	5
5	879	852	873	871	869	27
6	903	890	892	908	898	18
7	930	940	930	920	930	20
8	890	895	897	895	894	7
9	890	900	850	900	885	50
10	900	915	900	905	905	15
11	901	916	901	900	904	16
12	920	890	905	895	902	30
13	920	890	910	880	900	40
14	929	921	924	928	925	8
15	927	914	925	931	924	17
16	907	896	895	908	901	13
17	902	900	903	905	902	5
18	903	900	914	900	904	14
19	870	930	920	920	910	60
20	925	930	920	930	926	10
21	880	895	910	885	890	30
22	890	900	895	895	895	10
23	940	935	930	940	936	10
24	930	935	938	930	933	8
25	915	921	918	927	920	12
26	895	930	925	925	918	35
27	910	907	905	913	908	8
28	905	916	902	928	913	26
29	925	930	910	925	922	20
30	924	928	882	927	915	46
31	925	931	924	930	927	7
32	900	905	925	925	913	25
33	910	910	915	910	911	5
34	900	905	900	910	903	10
35	900	950	920	900	916	5ᶜ
36	940	938	940	938	939	2
Totals...................................					32,772	774

147. Comment on Examples 14 and 15. In both cases what might have appeared at first glance to be a natural plan of subgrouping was, in fact, an unsatisfactory plan. In Example 14 it might have seemed that each set of seven primer pellets from one charge should be a subgroup. In Example 15 the subgroup was actually taken as four pads on one half-ring. In Example 14, seven separate control charts, one for each sampling location, were properly used. Similarly in Example 15, four control charts, one for each pad, might well have been used.

A particular difficulty, which was not present in Example 15, entered into the situation in Example 14. This was the observed consistent difference in weights of pellets from the seven locations; this apparently could not be eliminated. This was somewhat similar to the case of the "hot" and "cold" operators in Example 13.

Many situations exist like Examples 14 and 15. In such situations the decision regarding the number of control charts to be used cannot be made without studying the behavior of the variables and having a clear idea of the objectives of the charts. For example, if the pellet weights at the seven sampling locations had tended to vary in unison, with an increase or decrease in weight at the center location accompanied by equal increases or decreases at the top and bottom locations, a single chart for the center location would have served to control the general level of weight of pellets. If the variations from one location to another had been completely unrelated, it is clear that one chart could not have done the job. Actual situations are nearly always somewhere between these two extremes. Whether one chart or several are required depends on the degree of relationship (in statistical language, the correlation) between the fluctuations at the several points and on the tightness of the tolerances.

In the situation described in Example 15, a slight change in tooling resulted in a reduction in the variation of pad thickness from pad to pad within a half-ring. It then proved satisfactory to use a single control chart on which the variable was thickness of pad 2, and a subgroup consisted of the measured thickness of this pad from four successive half-rings.

It may be remarked that it is always an advantage if one control chart can be made to do the work of four. Not only is there a saving in the cost of clerical labor in computing and charting; the practical difficulties in having charts analyzed and in securing action based on that analysis are also reduced. It is easier to get people to study one chart and take action on it than it is to get them to study four related charts and take action on them.

Sometimes in this type of situation a practical answer may be to take enough data to permit the several control charts to be made, but actually to keep only one chart as a routine matter. Then if at any time the situation calls for critical study, the data will be available for the construction of the other charts for purposes of analysis.

148. Identification on a Control Chart of Different Sources of Subgroups. In Example 13, subgrouping was finally by operators and by banks of adjusting units. Four sources of subgroups were possible, namely, operator A and bank 1, operator B and bank 2, operator C and bank 1, and operator D and bank 2. However, subgroups for all four combinations were plotted on the same control chart. It is common for different subgroups to come from different shifts and is not unusual for them to come from different machines or different operators.

In all such cases it is desirable to differentiate the various subgroup sources on the control charts, so that any consistent differences may be readily observed by someone looking at the charts. This may be done by the use of different types of symbols (such as circles, dots, and crosses) or different colors to represent each source of subgroups.

149. Group Control Charts. The British have developed an ingenious method for combining a number of subgroups from different sources in a single simplified chart.[1] Although developed by the British for control of dimensions on multiple-spindle automatics where each spindle is performing the same operation as all the other spindles, the technique used is broadly applicable.

Figure 37 shows $\bar{X}$ and R group control charts based on the data of Table 19. The method of calculation is illustrated in Table 20, which shows the detailed calculations for the first two and the last two subgroups.

A subgroup size of 2 is used in this illustration. The calculations are made for averages and ranges as if four control charts were to be plotted, one for each pad thickness. For example, the thickness of pad 1 on the first half-ring was 933, and on the second was 897. These two constitute a subgroup with average of 915 and range of 36. For half-rings 1 and 2, there are three other subgroups, one for each of the other pads. Each subgroup has its own average and range.

The special idea of the group chart is to plot only the highest and lowest of the averages and ranges, all on one chart, rather than to plot four separate charts that would show all the averages and ranges. Thus for the four subgroups 1 (half-rings 1 and 2) the highest average is 926, corresponding to pad 3, and the lowest average is 915, corresponding to pad 1. Only these two values are plotted on the $\bar{X}$ chart, each identi-

---

[1] SEALY, E. H., "A First Guide to Quality Control for Engineers," pp. 24–28, Ministry of Supply Advisory Service on Quality Control, Berkeley Court, Glentworth Street, London, N.W.1.

See also an article, Group Control Charts, *Production and Engineering Bulletin*, vol. 3, pp. 49–54, February, 1944.

fied with the number of its respective pad. Similarly, the highest and
lowest ranges are plotted on the R chart. One line connects the high
values of $\overline{X}$; another line connects the low values. Similar high and
low lines are drawn on the R chart.

The central lines and limits are obtained by combining the subgroups
from all the pads. The totals shown in Table 20 include the averages

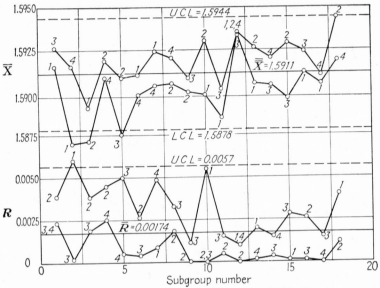

Fig. 37. Group control charts for data of Table 19.

and ranges for subgroups 3 to 16, which were omitted from the table.
The averages are calculated from these totals as follows:

$$\overline{\overline{X}} = \frac{65,579}{72} = 911$$

$$\bar{R} = \frac{1,256}{72} = 17.4$$

It should be noted that in the above fractions, the denominator, 72,
is the total number of subgroups, including 18 subgroups from each of
four pads. Calculation of control limits uses the formulas and factors
from Table C, Appendix III.

$$UCL_{\overline{X}} = 911 + A_2\bar{R} = 944$$
$$LCL_{\overline{X}} = 911 - A_2\bar{R} = 878$$
$$UCL_R = D_4\bar{R} = 57$$
$$LCL_R = D_3\bar{R} = 0$$

The $\bar{X}$ limits, like the figures in Tables 19 and 20, are expressed in units of 0.0001 in. above 1.5000 in. Expressed in inches, these limits are 1.5944 and 1.5878.

TABLE 20. ILLUSTRATION OF CALCULATIONS FOR GROUP CONTROL CHARTS USING DATA FROM TABLE 19

Subgroup number	Half-ring numbers	Pad number	Pad thickness		Average $\bar{X}$	Range R
			a	*b*		
1	1–2	1	933	897	915*L*	36
1	1–2	2	937	898	918	39*H*
1	1–2	3	938	915	926*H*	23
1	1–2	4	935	913	924	22*L*
2	3–4	1	840	900	870*L*	60*H*
2	3–4	2	900	905	902	5
2	3–4	3	900	902	901	2*L*
2	3–4	4	930	900	915*H*	30
..	.....	..	...	...	....	....
17	33–34	1	910	900	905*L*	10
17	33–34	2	910	905	908	5
17	33–34	3	915	900	908	15*H*
17	33–34	4	910	910	910*H*	0*L*
18	35–36	1	900	940	920	40*H*
18	35–36	2	950	938	944*H*	12*L*
18	35–36	3	920	940	930	20
18	35–36	4	900	938	919*L*	38
Totals..					65,579	1,256

150. Applicability of Group Control Charts. Three necessary conditions for the advantageous use of group control charts are as follows:

1. There must be several subgroup sources that contribute approximately equal numbers of subgroups at approximately the same rate. These sources may be, as in the British development of the technique, different spindles on one automatic machine. Or they may be several identical machines or several operators each doing the same operation. Or they may be several different operations done on the same machine. One example of this latter classification is Fig. 37 in which the subgroup sources were the thicknesses of the four different pads on the half-ring. Another such example might be the pellet weights of Example 14.

Generally speaking, the more parallel subgroups, the greater the advantage of the group charts.

2. All these subgroup sources must be aiming at the same value of the measured quality characteristic. Otherwise, there would be no

point in comparing them and no justification for combining the sub-groups to get one set of limits to apply to all.

3. There should be no differences among the averages or dispersions of the various subgroup sources that cannot be corrected. For instance, if there were five machines operating in parallel and two of these were able to hold much closer tolerances than the other three, the group chart would not be appropriate. Or if, in Example 14, nothing could be done about the consistent differences among the pellet weights from the various sampling locations, the group control charts should not be used even though they would otherwise seem to be well adapted to this situation. If the universes corresponding to the various subgroup sources have such differences, it is not desirable to combine them for the calculation of central lines and limits. Moreover, there is no use in having a chart continue to point out differences that do not constitute a practical basis for action.

Where they are applicable, the group charts would seem to have three advantages over presenting the same information with one set of charts for each subgroup source.

1. They involve less work in plotting the charts.

2. The more compact presentation of all the information in a single chart makes the charts somewhat easier to interpret, once the basis of the group charts is understood.

3. It is easier to judge whether certain subgroup sources are running consistently high or low, either on average or range. This may be judged by inspecting the high and low lines on each chart to observe the numbers written adjacent to each point. If there is no real difference among the subgroup sources, the numbers corresponding to the various subgroup sources should occur in any one of these lines approximately an equal number of times. In Fig. 37 there seems to be no indication that any subgroup source runs consistently high or low in either average or range.

The British use of the charts involves taking two successive components from each spindle on an automatic machine; therefore the subgroup size is two. The example given here in Table 20 and Fig. 37 also uses a subgroup size of two. However, there is nothing in the principle of the group control chart that requires two as the subgroup size. Any other subgroup size may be used as well.

151. The Control Chart as a General Test for Homogeneity. It is impossible to give too much emphasis to the importance of keeping track of the order of production whenever measurements are made of any quality of manufactured product. Ideally, measurements should be planned with this in view. Practically this may not be possible. This is particularly true when a purchaser wishes to apply the control-chart analysis to an incoming shipment of product regarding which there is no knowledge of the order of production.

Suppose, for instance, that an aircraft manufacturer receives a shipment of 100,000 bolts packed in 50 boxes each containing 2,000 bolts. He wishes to test 200 of these for some quality, such as Rockwell hardness number or tensile strength. He will naturally pick four bolts from each of the 50 boxes.

Suppose the results of his tests are plotted on $\bar{X}$ and R charts, with the four bolts from each box constituting a subgroup, and these control charts show a state of control. The interpretation of this showing of control is not the same as if the basis of subgrouping had been the order of production. Here the control charts are simply a test for homogeneity. This homogeneity may have been obtained by a constant-cause system during production with the bolts packed in boxes in order of production, or it may have been obtained by a thorough mixing of the bolts before they were packed even though they came from several different cause systems.

The control-chart analysis may also be applied to data already at hand that were taken with no thought of the control chart, provided there is some rational basis for subgrouping. Here also the control charts are a general test for homogeneity. For example, they have been applied by Shewhart to published data regarding the determination of fundamental physical constants such as the velocity of light.[1] This type of application in a manufacturing setting is illustrated in Art. 156, Chap. VIII, in an example dealing with the shear strength of spot welds.

Problems

67. In Example 13, why should $\bar{R}$ have been decreased by the change in the method of subgrouping? With the subgrouping by operators but with no change in the heat levels of the adjusting banks to compensate for the differences among operators, what would have been the appearance of the $\bar{X}$ and R charts? With the original plan of subgrouping, how was it that the differences between operators did not cause points to go out of control on the $\bar{X}$ chart?

68. In Example 15 someone made the suggestion that the variable (X) used for the control charts should be the average of the four pad thicknesses on a half-ring, and that a subgroup should consist of four such averages. What objection can you see to this suggestion?

69. Prepare $\bar{X}$ and R control charts for the thickness of pad 2 in Table 19, Example 15. Use a subgroup size of two. This will give you 18 subgroups. How are these control charts related to the ones in Fig. 37?

70. Make the remaining calculations necessary for the group control charts of Fig. 37, filling in the subgroups corresponding to half-rings 5 to 32 that were omitted in Table 20.

[1] SHEWHART, W. A., edited by W. E. Deming, "Statistical Method from the Viewpoint of Quality Control," p. 68, The Graduate School, Department of Agriculture, Washington, 1939.

71. Plot a group control chart for the following record of measurements of the diameters of a part produced on each of the six spindles of an automatic screw machine. The figures given are dimensions in units of 0.0001 in. in excess of 0.4900 in.

Sub-group number	Spindle number	Diameter		Sub-group number	Spindle number	Diameter	
		Part *a*	Part *b*			Part *a*	Part *b*
1	1	55	67	4	1	50	61
1	2	44	59	4	2	57	50
1	3	57	43	4	3	48	47
1	4	48	40	4	4	45	36
1	5	57	45	4	5	55	44
1	6	37	51	4	6	48	65
2	1	55	56	5	1	45	60
2	2	59	59	5	2	46	35
2	3	52	58	5	3	57	52
2	4	46	45	5	4	69	42
2	5	48	62	5	5	72	64
2	6	64	52	5	6	48	69
3	1	52	61	6	1	52	45
3	2	63	55	6	2	59	47
3	3	50	53	6	3	39	65
3	4	54	53	6	4	65	60
3	5	51	53	6	5	50	54
3	6	56	60	6	6	60	51

CHAPTER VIII

DIFFERENT ADAPTATIONS OF THE CONTROL CHART FOR VARIABLES

You need not be a mathematical statistician to do good statistical work, but you will need the guidance of a first class mathematical statistician. A good engineer, or a good economist, or a good chemist, already has a good start, because the statistical method is only good science brought up to date by the recognition that all laws are subject to the variations which occur in nature. Your study of statistical methods will not displace any other knowledge that you have; rather, it will extend your knowledge of engineering, chemistry, or economics, and make it more useful.—W. E. Deming[1]

152. Some Miscellaneous Topics. This chapter deals with a number of more or less unrelated topics that should be covered in any presentation of the control chart for variables. Some of these are forms of the control chart that vary slightly from the simple $\overline{X}$ and R charts described in the preceding chapters. Other topics deal with schemes for plotting and analysis which, although they make use of some of the features of the Shewhart control charts, are not, strictly speaking, control charts at all.

153. Control Charts with Variable Subgroup Size. Wherever possible it is desirable to have a constant subgroup size. If this cannot be done, the limits on both $\overline{X}$ and R charts (or $\overline{X}$ and σ charts) should be variable limits. Such variable limits are illustrated in the $\overline{X}$ chart of Fig. 38,* which shows limits corresponding to subgroup sizes of 10, 15, and 20 for ultimate strength of suspension insulators.

Once σ' has been estimated, these limits for various sample sizes may be obtained by using the factors and formulas of Table E, Appendix III. Where the data used to estimate σ' include subgroups of various sizes, a satisfactory working rule (although not precisely correct as a matter of statistical theory) is to calculate R/d_2 for each subgroup, using the appropriate d_2 factor from Table B, Appendix III, for the size of the subgroup in question. The estimate of σ' is the average of these values of R/d_2. If standard deviation, rather than range, is the measure used

---

[1] Deming, W. E., Some Principles of the Shewhart Methods of Quality Control, *Mechanical Engineering*, vol. 66, pp. 173–177, March, 1944.

* Reproduced from J. J Taylor, Statistical Methods Applied to Insulator Development and Manufacture, *Transactions American Institute of Electrical Engineers*, vol. 64, pp. 495–499, July, 1945.

for subgroup dispersion, σ/c_2 may be computed for each subgroup; the estimate of σ' is the average value of σ/c_2.

154. R Charts or σ Charts Where $\overline{X}$ Charts Are Not Appropriate. In some cases subgroups may be comparable in their dispersion even though not comparable in their averages. This is true, for example, of many standard chemical analyses that are made in duplicate, triplicate, or quadruplicate. Each two, three, or four analyses of a given sample may be thought of as a subgroup. If samples having somewhat different chemical content are analyzed, the averages of the subgroups are not

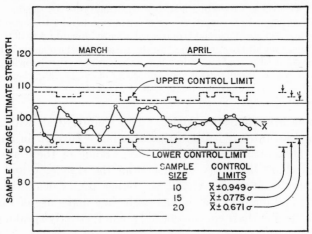

FIG. 38. $\overline{X}$ chart illustrating variation of control limits with sample size. The variable X is the ultimate strength of suspension insulators.

comparable. The dispersion of the subgroups, however, reflects the ability of an analyst and an analytical procedure to reproduce results by several similar determinations. The control chart for R or σ provides a basis for judging whether this dispersion seems to be influenced by a constant-cause system. Calculations for the central lines and control limits for R or σ are no different from such calculations for any other control charts.

155. General Comments on the Use of σ as a Measure of Subgroup Dispersion. Table 16, Chap. IV, showed the close agreement between two estimates of σ', one obtained from $\bar{\sigma}$, the average of the standard deviations of a set of subgroups, and the other obtained from $\bar{R}$, the averages of the ranges of the same set of subgroups. An illustration was given in Fig. 17 of the similarity of the control charts for R and σ for the same set of data. It was explained that as the charts for R and σ were substitutes for one another, there was no need to use both in any particular case. In Art. 80 it was recommended that for ordinary use of the control charts in manufacturing, range rather than standard deviation be used as a measure of subgroup dispersion. Subgroup range had the practical advantages of being easier to understand and to calculate, which more than offset the fact that subgroup standard deviation is slightly more desirable as a matter of statistical theory.

From the statistical theory viewpoint, however, the advantage of using subgroup standard deviation increases as the subgroup size increases. This fact was reflected in the recommendation in Art. 110 that $\bar{X}$ and σ charts, rather than $\bar{X}$ and R charts, be used wherever subgroup size was over 15.

As explained in Chap. IV, estimates of σ' from $\bar{\sigma}$ may be obtained by the use of the c_2 factor of Table B, Appendix III. Limits for control charts for $\bar{X}$ and σ may be obtained by the use of the factors and formulas of Table D, Appendix III. In cases where these limits are to be based on an assumed value of universe standard deviation σ', rather than on average subgroup standard deviation $\bar{\sigma}$, the factors and formulas of Table E must be used.

The specific directions in Chap. VI for simple control charts for $\bar{X}$ and R may be readily adapted to $\bar{X}$ and σ charts by the use of the appropriate factors and formulas from Tables B, D, and E.

156. $\bar{X}$ and σ Charts with Large Subgroups. It sometimes happens that data are at hand on averages and standard deviations of some measured variable from a number of different sources. It may be desired to apply a test for homogeneity to these figures to see if there is clear evidence that the different sources seem to represent different cause systems. The control charts for $\bar{X}$ and σ constitute a simple test for this purpose.

For example, in a certain manufacturing plant it was desired to compare the strength and uniformity of spot welds made on nine apparently identical machines. A number of specimen welds of sheet aluminum alloy of a certain gage were made on each machine. The ultimate strength of each weld was determined by testing to destruction in a shear testing machine. The averages and standard deviations of the welds from each machine were tabulated in a report summarizing this investigation. They are shown in Table 21. Because the investigator was not acquainted with the Shewhart techniques, no record was preserved of the order of production of welds or of order of measurement.

The shear strengths from each machine constitute one rational subgroup. The subgroups are large, ranging from 111 to 128. With such large subgroups, the c_2 factor (see Table B) is practically unity, and the best estimate of σ' (*i.e.*, $\bar{\sigma}/c_2$) becomes $\bar{\sigma}$. A_1 therefore becomes $3/\sqrt{n}$, B_4 becomes $1 + (3/\sqrt{2n})$, and B_3 becomes $1 - (3/\sqrt{2n})$. These expressions, stated in Table D, are evident from the explanation of the A_1, B_4, and B_3 factors as given in Chap. IV.

TABLE 21.   SHEAR STRENGTHS OF SPOT WELDS MADE BY NINE DIFFERENT MACHINES

Machine	Number of tests n	Average shear strength, lb. $\bar{X}$	Standard deviation σ
A	128	743	63
B	127	695	47
C	126	711	67
D	114	668	51
E	126	736	80
F	126	791	58
G	126	686	50
H	111	801	92
J	119	604	64
Totals.........	1,103	6,435	572

Where the subgroup sizes are different, it may be advisable to use weighted averages for the calculation of $\bar{X}$ and $\bar{\sigma}$. The formulas for these are as follows:

$$\bar{\bar{X}} = \frac{n_1\bar{X}_1 + n_2\bar{X}_2 + n_3\bar{X}_3 + \cdots + n_m\bar{X}_m}{n_1 + n_2 + n_3 + \cdots + n_m}$$

$$\bar{\sigma} = \sqrt{\frac{n_1\sigma_1^2 + n_2\sigma_2^2 + n_3\sigma_3^2 + \cdots + n_m\sigma_m^2}{n_1 + n_2 + n_3 + \cdots + n_m}}$$

However, unless the differences in subgroup size are large, the calculations are simpler and the results are nearly the same if $\bar{X}$ is estimated as the simple unweighted average of the $\bar{X}$ values and $\bar{\sigma}$ is estimated as the simple unweighted average of the σ values.   No absolute rule may be given as to when this simplification is satisfactory; a rough rule is to figure unweighted averages unless the largest subgroup is at least twice the smallest.   It is clearly satisfactory to compute unweighted averages for the data of Table 21.   Thus

$$\bar{\bar{X}} = \frac{\bar{X}_1 + \bar{X}_2 + \bar{X}_3 \cdots + \bar{X}_m}{m} = \frac{6,435}{9} = 715$$

$$\bar{\sigma} = \frac{\sigma_1 + \sigma_2 + \sigma_3 \cdots + \sigma_m}{m} = 57\frac{2}{9} = 64$$

The question now arises whether, because of the different subgroup sizes, different limits should be computed for each subgroup.   Again the computations are much simpler if one set of limits is computed based on average subgroup size.   This simplification is usually satisfactory for a start; separate limits for individual subgroups may be calculated later for any doubtful cases. The average subgroup size $\bar{n}$ must be computed

$$\bar{n} = \frac{1,103}{9} = 123$$

The factors A_1, B_4, and B_3 may now be computed

$$A_1 = \frac{3}{\sqrt{n}} = \frac{3}{\sqrt{123}} = 0.27$$

$$B_4 = 1 + \frac{3}{\sqrt{2n}} = 1 + \frac{3}{\sqrt{246}} = 1.19$$

$$B_3 = 1 - \frac{3}{\sqrt{2n}} = 1 - \frac{3}{\sqrt{246}} = 0.81$$

From these factors, the control limits may be computed

$$UCL_{\bar{X}} = \bar{\bar{X}} + A_1\bar{\sigma} = 715 + 0.27(64) = 732$$
$$LCL_{\bar{X}} = \bar{\bar{X}} - A_1\bar{\sigma} = 715 - 0.27(64) = 698$$
$$UCL_{\sigma} = B_4\bar{\sigma} = 1.19(64) = 76$$
$$LCL_{\sigma} = B_3\bar{\sigma} = 0.81(64) = 52$$

These limits are plotted on the control charts of Fig. 39. Both charts definitely show lack of control; in fact, only one point falls within the control limits on the $\bar{X}$ chart. It is quite evident that even though these spot-welding machines are identical in their design, they perform differently both with regard to average strength and uniformity of strength of welds.

It should be remarked in passing that a tabulation of averages and standard deviations of large numbers of measurements such as that in Table 21 is of little value for prediction without the knowledge that each source of measurements is itself in control. For example, without any evidence of control on machine A, it is not safe to assume that the strength of future spot welds on machine A will fall within limits suggested by the average of 743 lb. and the standard deviation of 63 lb. It would have been much better if the order of production had not been lost and the results on each machine had been subjected to the control-chart analysis.

157. The Use of Control Limits for Moving Averages. In manufacturing plants many schemes other than the Shewhart control chart have been used for plotting data on quality characteristics. For example, a chemical plant may maintain charts on which are plotted the results of daily analyses made to determine the percentages of certain chemical constituents in its incoming materials, product in process, and finished product. A common variation of this is to plot moving averages rather than daily values. The moving average is particularly appropriate in

continuous process chemical manufacture when applied to quality characteristics of raw materials and product in process. The smoothing
effect of the moving average often has an effect on the figures similar to
the effect on the product of the blending and mixing that take place in
the remainder of the production process.

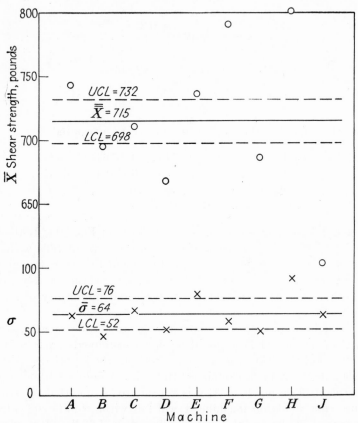

FIG. 39. $\overline{X}$ and σ control charts for shear strength of spot welds—data of Table 21.

In the introduction of Shewhart techniques into chemical plants, it
may be desirable not to disturb the custom of plotting moving averages.
However it is appropriate to apply control limits to such moving average charts and to add charts for moving ranges. The calculations for
these limits and the interpretation of these charts are similar to the conventional $\overline{X}$ and R charts but differ in certain respects.

Table 22 illustrates the calculation of moving averages and moving
ranges. The figures given are the daily analyses of percentages of
unreacted lime (CaO) at an intermediate stage in a continuous manu-

facturing process. The average given for September 3 is the average of the percentages on the first, second, and third; the average for the fourth is the average of the values on the second, third, and fourth; and so forth. (From a technical statistical viewpoint, the average should

TABLE 22. CALCULATION OF MOVING AVERAGE AND MOVING RANGE
(Data on per cent of unreacted CaO at an intermediate stage in a chemical manufacturing process)

Date		Daily value	3-day moving total	3-day moving average	3-day moving range	Combination (for conventional control charts)
Sept.	1	0.24				
	2	0.13				
	3	0.11	0.48	0.160	0.13	*A*
	4	0.19	0.43	0.143	0.08	*B*
	5	0.16	0.46	0.153	0.08	*C*
	6	0.17	0.52	0.173	0.03	*A*
	7	0.13	0.46	0.153	0.04	*B*
	8	0.17	0.47	0.157	0.04	*C*
	9	0.10	0.40	0.133	0.07	*A*
	10	0.14	0.41	0.137	0.07	*B*
	11	0.16	0.40	0.133	0.06	*C*
	12	0.14	0.44	0.147	0.02	*A*
	13	0.17	0.47	0.157	0.03	*B*
	14	0.15	0.46	0.153	0.03	*C*
	15	0.20	0.52	0.173	0.05	*A*
	16	0.26	0.61	0.203	0.11	*B*
	17	0.16	0.62	0.207	0.10	*C*
	18	0.00	0.42	0.140	0.26	*A*
	19	0.18	0.34	0.113	0.18	*B*
	20	0.18	0.36	0.120	0.18	*C*
	21	0.20	0.56	0.187	0.02	*A*
	22	0.11	0.49	0.163	0.09	*B*
	23	0.30	0.61	0.203	0.19	*C*
	24	0.21	0.62	0.207	0.19	*A*
	25	0.11	0.62	0.207	0.19	*B*
	26	0.17	0.49	0.163	0.10	*C*
	27	0.18	0.46	0.153	0.07	*A*
	28	0.13	0.48	0.160	0.05	*B*
	29	0.28	0.59	0.197	0.15	*C*
	30	0.16	0.57	0.190	0.15	*A*
Oct.	1	0.14	0.58	0.193	0.14	*B*
	2	0.16	0.46	0.153	0.02	*C*
	3	0.14	0.44	0.147	0.02	*A*
	4	0.10	0.40	0.133	0.06	*B*
	5	0.13	0.37	0.123	0.04	*C*
	6	0.20	0.43	0.143	0.10	*A*
	7	0.14	0.47	0.157	0.06	*B*
	8	0.10	0.44	0.147	0.10	*C*
	9	0.18	0.42	0.140	0.08	*A*
	10	0.11	0.39	0.130	0.08	*A*
	11	0.08	0.37	0.123	0.10	*C*
	12	0.12	0.31	0.103	0.04	*A*
	13	0.13	0.33	0.110	0.05	*B*
	14	0.12	0.37	0.123	0.01	*C*
	15	0.17	0.42	0.140	0.05	*A*
	16	0.10	0.39	0.130	0.07	*B*
	17	0.09	0.36	0.120	0.08	*C*

always be plotted at the *mid-point* of the period; for instance, the average of the first, second, and third should be assigned to the second, not to the third. In this case, however, practical psychology takes precedence over statistical correctness. The reason for the common practice in manufacturing of assigning the moving average to the final date rather than the middle date is to have the average always seem up to date rather than behind time.) The calculation of a 3-day moving average is sim-

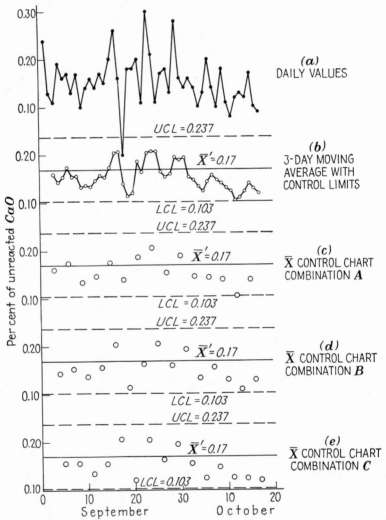

FIG. 40. Per cent of unreacted CaO. Comparison of (a) daily values, (b) graph of 3-day moving average, and (c), (d), and (e) the three $\overline{X}$ control charts combined in the moving average graph (b).

plified by carrying a moving total to which is added each day the algebraic difference between the value today and the value 3 days ago.

The daily values are plotted in Fig. 40a; the moving averages in Fig. 40b. A comparison of these two graphs shows the effect of the moving average in smoothing the curve. The more successive points averaged, the greater this smoothing effect and the more the curve emphasizes trends rather than point-to-point fluctuations. The moving range for the same data is plotted in Fig. 41a.

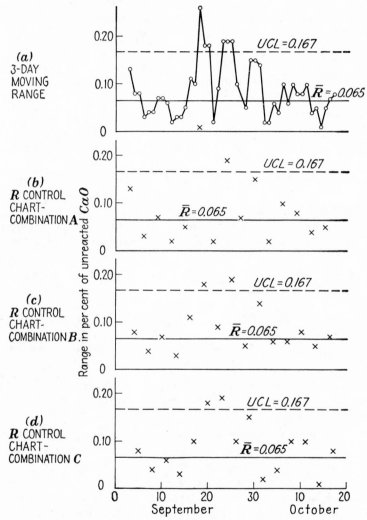

Fɪɢ. 41. Comparison of graph for 3-day moving range with the three *R* control charts combined in the moving-range graph-data from Table 22.

The control limits in Figs. 40 and 41 are computed from an $\bar{X}'$ of 0.17 and an $\bar{R}$ of 0.065. These figures were established on the basis of the record of the two preceding months. The calculation of limits uses the factors and formulas of Table *C*, Appendix III.

If the same data had been subgrouped for conventional $\overline{X}$ and R charts with a subgroup size of three, the decision as to the date of starting the subgroups would have been entirely arbitrary. The first subgroup might have been September 1, 2, and 3; the next the fourth, fifth, and sixth; and so forth; this is identified in Table 22 as combination A. Or September 2, 3, and 4 might have been combined; this is combination B. Or September 3, 4, and 5; this is combination C.

A moving average chart with $n = 3$ is as if the points from three conventional $\overline{X}$ charts were superimposed. That is, Fig. 40b combines the points of Figs. 40c, 40d, and 40e. Similarly, the moving range chart Fig. 41a combines the points in the three conventional R charts, Figs. 41b, 41c, and 41d.

It follows that the interpretation of a point outside control limits on moving average and moving range charts is the same as a point outside control limits on conventional $\overline{X}$ and R charts. However, because successive points on moving average and moving range charts are not independent of one another, the interpretation of several points in a row outside control limits is obviously not the same. For example, three points in a row outside control limits in Fig. 41a correspond roughly to one point outside limits on each of the conventional R charts, Figs. 41b, 41c, and 41d. Similarly, runs above or below the central line do not have the same significance on moving average and moving range charts as on conventional $\overline{X}$ and R charts.

As pointed out in previous chapters, whenever a shift in universe average occurs *within* a subgroup rather than *between* subgroups, the R chart tends to show lack of control. Changes of short duration that do not persist through one entire subgroup may be shown only on the R chart and not on the $\overline{X}$ chart. This was evidently the case in Figs. 40 and 41, as both indications of lack of control are on the R chart.

158. Computing Probability Limits on Control Charts for $\overline{X}$, R, and σ. It was pointed out in Chap. IV that one school of thought in the field of statistical quality control advocates the use of so-called "probability limits," rather than 3-sigma limits, on control charts for variables. Reasons were given for preferring the use of 3-sigma limits.

However, if probability limits are desired on $\overline{X}$ charts, the A_2, A_1, and A factors of Tables C, D, and E, respectively, may be changed by the use of a suitable multiplier. The appropriate multiplier to fit any desired probability may be computed by the use of Table A, Appendix III.

For instance, if it is desired that the probability be 0.001 that without a change in the universe a point will fall above the upper control limit, look in Table A for the multiplier of σ corresponding to 0.001. This is 3.09. As the factors A_2, A_1, and A are based on 3-sigma limits, it is merely necessary to multiply them by $3.09/3 = 1.03$ to obtain corresponding factors based on 0.001 probability limits. It should be remembered that to the probability of 0.001 that a point will fall above the upper limit must be added the equal probability of 0.001 that a point will fall below the lower limit. This means a probability of 0.002 of a point outside limits, or 0.998 within limits. The British particularly have used limits based on 3.09σ.

Or if it is desired that the probability be 0.025 that a point fall above the upper limit (corresponding to 0.05 that it fall outside limits), Table A gives 1.96 as the appropriate multiple of σ. The multiplier to be applied to the A_2, A_1, and A factors is then $1.96/3 = 0.653$. Factors based on 1.96σ have been used by the British as inner control limits or warning limits.

As pointed out in Chap. IV, the distribution of averages from a normal universe is normal and therefore symmetrical. Hence, like 3-sigma limits, probability limits for $\bar{X}$ are symmetrical. But because the distributions of R and σ are not symmetrical, it is necessary to have separate factors for the upper and lower control limits if the probabilities of extreme variations are to be made equal. Table 23 gives such factors for probability limits for σ charts; Table 24 gives them for R charts. Three sets of symmetrical probabilities (giving unsymmetrical limits) are 0.001 and 0.999, corresponding to a 0.002 probability that with no change in the universe a point will fall outside of the limits; 0.005 and 0.995, corresponding to a 0.01 probability of a point falling outside; and 0.025 and 0.975, corresponding to an 0.05 probability of a point falling outside.

Table 23 gives multipliers for the assumed or estimated value of σ' to obtain limits on a chart for σ. σ' may be estimated as $\bar{\sigma}/c_2$.

TABLE 23. FACTORS FOR PROBABILITY LIMITS TO BE USED IN CONTROL CHARTS FOR STANDARD DEVIATION

(To obtain limits, multiply the estimated value of σ' by the B factor with subscript corresponding to the desired probability)

Size of subgroup n	Lower limits			Upper limits		
	$B_{.001}$	$B_{.005}$	$B_{.025}$	$B_{.975}$	$B_{.995}$	$B_{.999}$
2	0.00	0.00	0.02	1.59	1.99	2.33
3	0.03	0.06	0.13	1.57	1.88	2.15
4	0.08	0.13	0.23	1.53	1.79	2.02
5	0.13	0.20	0.31	1.49	1.72	1.92
6	0.19	0.26	0.37	1.46	1.67	1.85
7	0.23	0.31	0.42	1.44	1.63	1.79
8	0.27	0.35	0.46	1.42	1.59	1.74
9	0.31	0.39	0.49	1.40	1.56	1.70
10	0.34	0.42	0.52	1.38	1.54	1.67

TABLE 24. FACTORS FOR PROBABILITY LIMITS TO BE USED IN CONTROL CHARTS FOR
RANGE

(To obtain limits, multiply $\bar{R}$ by the D factor with subscript corresponding to the desired probability)

Size of subgroup n	Lower limits			Upper limits		
	$D_{.001}$	$D_{.005}$	$D_{.025}$	$D_{.975}$	$D_{.995}$	$D_{.999}$
2	0.00	0.01	0.04	2.81	3.52	4.12
3	0.04	0.10	0.18	2.17	2.58	2.98
4	0.10	0.18	0.29	1.93	2.26	2.57
5	0.16	0.25	0.37	1.81	2.08	2.34
6	0.21	0.31	0.42	1.72	1.97	2.21
7	0.26	0.35	0.46	1.66	1.90	2.11
8	0.29	0.39	0.50	1.62	1.84	2.04
9	0.32	0.41	0.52	1.58	1.79	1.99
10	0.35	0.44	0.54	1.56	1.76	1.93

Table 24 gives multipliers for a computed or assumed value of $\bar{R}$ to obtain limits on a chart for R. If the R chart is to be based on an assumed universe standard deviation σ', $\bar{R}$ may be estimated as $d_2\sigma'$.

It should be emphasized that the probabilities given for these limits are strictly accurate only when sampling from a normal universe. They are also based on the assumption that a σ' estimated from the data is the true universe standard deviation. For practical control-chart work in industry, where the exact form of the universe is hardly ever known and control limits are often based on the evidence of short series of observations, it must be recognized that these probabilities are approximate rather than exact and may often be substantially in error.

159. Warning Limits on Control Charts. Some writers on statistical quality control have advocated the use of two sets of limits on $\bar{X}$ charts. The outer limits, sometimes called *action limits*, are the conventional limits, usually at 3-sigma, or—if 0.002 probability limits are used—at 3.09 sigma. The inner limits are recommended as warning limits and are usually at 2-sigma, or—if 0.05 probability limits are used—at 1.96 sigma.

On the conventional $\bar{X}$ chart with only one set of limits, the chart seems to give only two kinds of advice. It either says, "Look for trouble," or it says, "Leave the process alone." This has the virtue of definiteness. However, as pointed out in Chap. IV any such definite advice is sure to be wrong part of the time. Limits placed at 3-sigma or 3.09-sigma are seldom wrong when they say, "Look for trouble," but are much oftener wrong when they say, "Leave the process alone."

The inner limits or warning limits seem to add a third kind of advice. This might be phrased, "Start being suspicious that trouble is brewing."

At first thought, the idea of having warning limits on $\bar{X}$ charts may seem attractive. Nevertheless, there is a sound reason for the common practice of having only one set of limits and having these limits at or near 3-sigma. This reason is the greater definiteness of a single set of limits. Two sets of limits tend to be confusing with regard to the exact action to be taken when a point falls between the inner and the outer limits. This is particularly true if many of the people in a manufacturing plant who are using the $\bar{X}$ and R control charts as a basis for action are not fully clear as to the principles underlying these charts. Inner limits will be exceeded at least 5% of the time as a matter of chance. If a single point just outside the inner limits is to be used as a basis for hunting for trouble there is bound to be unproductive hunting which may tend to destroy confidence in the control charts. Usually in a manufacturing plant so much trouble really exists that it does not pay to hunt for trouble without strong evidence that it is present.

Nevertheless, even though inner limits should not be drawn on most control charts, they can be extremely useful in the sophisticated interpretation of control charts by people who understand control-chart theory. Here the clue to action is given not by a *single* point outside either of the inner limits, but rather by two or more points, both outside the same inner limit. This is really a matter of sizing up extreme runs; it is somewhat comparable to the interpretation of extreme runs on the same side of the central line that was explained in Art. 88. For example, 2 points in succession outside the same inner limit on an $\bar{X}$ chart give even stronger evidence of a shift in process average than a single point outside the outer limit. Two points out of 3 beyond one inner limit, 3 out of 7, or 4 out of 10, may all be considered as appropriate grounds for action.

However, this type of interpretation may be made by the quality control engineer or other qualified individual without confusing matters for his colleagues by having inner limit lines actually drawn on all $\bar{X}$ charts. When a suspicious sequence of points is observed close to a conventional 3-sigma limit, the quality control engineer may imagine an inner limit two-thirds of the distance from the central line to the control limit. Or, if this is too much strain on his imagination, he may draw such a line lightly on the portion of the chart to be studied.

160. The Problem of Misinterpretation of the Relationship between Control-chart Limits and Specification Limits. One source of confusion appears almost universally wherever the control chart for $\bar{X}$ is introduced on production operations. Whenever specifications apply to individual values (as is always true of dimensions and usually true of other quality characteristics), the specification limits tend to be confused with the control-chart limits. This confusion often exists in the minds of shop personnel, inspectors, engineers, and even managers. It leads to a diversity of troubles.

It has already been pointed out in Chap. VI that where the specification tolerances are tighter than the natural tolerances (*i.e.*, than the 3-sigma limits on individual values), some nonconforming product is sure to be made even by a controlled process. A controlled process may also make nonconforming product if the process average is not properly centered with respect to upper and lower specification limits or properly located with respect to a single specification limit. Thus there may be many cases where the control chart shows the process in control and some of the product is bad. If this is not understood, the control chart may give a false assurance that all is well.

If specification limits are drawn on the $\overline{X}$ control chart, there is a natural tendency to compare the subgroup *averages*, plotted on the chart, with the specification limits. This sometimes leads to the false conclusion that whenever an average plots within specification limits, all the product is within specifications.

A misinterpretation opposite to this is also made occasionally. This is to compare measured individual values with the control limits that apply to averages, and to conclude that trouble exists whenever an individual value is outside the limit for averages.

The spread of the control limits for averages is less than the spread of individual values. It is therefore often less than the spread of the specification limits. This condition sometimes leads to the incorrect conclusion that the use of the $\overline{X}$ chart amounts to the use of working tolerances that are closer than the specification tolerances.

The ideal preventive for these various errors is for the people who use the control chart to understand clearly that averages are different from individual values and that control limits mean something entirely different from specification limits. In this book the first illustrations of the $\overline{X}$ chart were deliberately chosen in a way to bring this out. The reader may recall the contrast between Examples 1 and 2. In Example 1 practically all the product was within specification limits even though there were many points out of control. In Example 2 much of the product was defective even though all points were within control limits. Some such illustrations are desirable in any introduction of personnel to the $\overline{X}$ control chart, not only in the short in-plant courses frequently given to production and inspection supervisors but also in presentation of the technique to individuals.

Unless all of the people exposed to $\overline{X}$ charts are familiar with control-chart principles, any specification limits for individual values drawn on such charts may constitute a troublesome source of misunderstanding.

Often the education of personnel to understand principles underlying new techniques seems too slow a job. The remainder of this chapter deals with four adaptations of the $\bar{X}$ control chart that have been devised for the purpose of circumventing these misunderstandings and thus avoiding the immediate urgency for such a program of education.

161. Plotting Subgroup Totals. One scheme that has been used in many plants is to plot on the control chart the sum of the n measurements in each subgroup rather than the average of these measurements. Where totals are plotted, the values on the chart do not appear to shop personnel as if they were comparable with specification limits; hence there is little chance for confusion on this point.

This type of chart is merely a conventional $\bar{X}$ chart with the scale magnified n times. The values for the central line and limits are the $\bar{X}$ chart values multiplied by n. Any conclusions to be drawn from the $\bar{X}$ chart may also be drawn from the chart for totals.

This variation of the $\bar{X}$ chart is particularly useful where a machine operator is using the control chart under definite instructions to leave the machine settings alone as long as a process shows control and to stop production and get help from some definite source (for example, the machine setter or the maintenance department) whenever a point goes out of control.

A minor advantage of the chart for totals is a saving of the arithmetical operation of dividing the total of each subgroup by the subgroup size. A minor limitation is that the method should not be used where the subgroup size is variable.

162. Reject Limits for Averages on $\bar{X}$ Charts. One possible method of showing the relationship between $\bar{X}$ values and the specification limits that apply to individual items is through the use of *reject limits* for averages.[1] If the assumption is made that σ' is known and will not change and that practically all the product will fall within limits of $\bar{X}' \pm 3\sigma'$ (or, for that matter, $\bar{X}' \pm$ any other desired multiple of σ'), it is easy to calculate the highest and lowest values of $\bar{X}'$ that will permit practically all of the product to fall within specification limits. The reject limits for averages are certain control-chart limits that would be appropriate if $\bar{X}'$ should be at each of these computed values. The derivation of these reject limits is explained here. Their application to acceptance inspection is discussed in Chap. XVI.

Figure 42 illustrates the development of such limits. Assume the universe in its highest acceptable position with universe average *exactly* $3\sigma'$ below the upper specification limit. On an $\bar{X}$ chart with subgroup

[1] WINTERHALTER, A. J., Development of Reject Limits for Measurements, *Industrial Quality Control*, vol. 1, No. 4, pp. 12–15, January, 1945; vol. 1, No. 5, pp. 12–13, March, 1945. See also Engineering Data Book, Sec. 29, "Statistical Methods in Quality Control," issued Sept. 22, 1943, Hunter Pressed Steel Co., Lansdale, Pa.

size n, the upper control limit $UCL_{\overline{x}}$ will be $3\sigma'/\sqrt{n}$ above the universe average. This will evidently be the highest possible satisfactory value of the upper control limit and is designated as the Upper Reject Limit for averages, abbreviated as $URL_{\overline{x}}$.

The distance of $URL_{\overline{x}}$ below the upper specification limit for individual values is obviously $3\sigma' - (3\sigma'/\sqrt{n})$. This may be expressed as $[3 - (3/\sqrt{n})]\sigma'$. This factor $[3 - (3/\sqrt{n})]$ is designated as V. Table 25 gives values of V corresponding to values of n from 2 to 25. By a

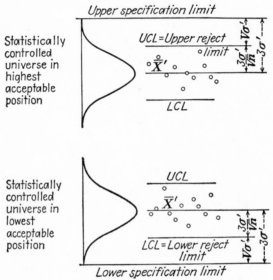

FIG. 42.   Relationship between specification limits, control limits, and reject limits.

similar process of reasoning which assumes the universe in its lowest acceptable position, it may be shown that the Lower Reject Limit for averages, $LRL_{\overline{x}}$, is $V\sigma'$ above the lower specification limit.

If an $\overline{X}$ chart shows a state of statistical control and both control limits fall within the two reject limits, this means that as long as control is maintained all is well; practically all the product will fall within specification limits. If the $UCL_{\overline{x}}$ falls above the $URL_{\overline{x}}$, or if the $LCL_{\overline{x}}$ falls below the $LRL_{\overline{x}}$, the conclusion is that even though control is maintained, some of the product manufactured will fall outside specifications. In this way, limits telling the conformance of individual values with specifications may be placed on the chart for averages.

163. Modified Control Limits. One step beyond the use of reject limits *and* control limits on $\overline{X}$ charts is the use of reject limits *in place of* control limits. Reject limits used in this way have been called *modified control limits*. They have been applied particularly to control of dimensions. Their use is practical only where the spread of the process (frequently estimated as $6\sigma'$) is appreciably less than the difference between the two specification limits $(X_{max} - X_{min})$.

The idea behind the modified control limits is to permit limited shifts in the process average in cases where the difference between the two specification limits is substantially greater than the spread of a controlled process. This is intended to avoid the cost of stopping production to hunt for trouble whenever the shifts in process average are not sufficient

TABLE 25.   VALUES OF V, FACTOR FOR REJECT LIMITS, FOR DIFFERENT VALUES OF n SUBGROUP SIZE

n	V	n	V	n	V
2	0.88	10	2.05	18	2.29
3	1.27	11	2.09	19	2.31
4	1.50	12	2.13	20	2.33
5	1.66	13	2.17	21	2.35
6	1.78	14	2.20	22	2.36
7	1.87	15	2.23	23	2.37
8	1.94	16	2.25	24	2.39
9	2.00	17	2.27	25	2.40

Upper reject limit$_{\bar{x}}$ = X_{max} (upper specification limit) − $V\sigma'$
Lower reject limit$_{\bar{x}}$ = X_{min} (lower specification limit) + $V\sigma'$

$$V = 3 - \frac{3}{\sqrt{n}}$$

to cause the production of defective product. It is as though in Fig. 42 the process were to be allowed to vary from the position marked "highest acceptable position of universe" to that marked "lowest acceptable position."

However in the use of modified control limits a larger margin of safety is sometimes introduced than that given by the assumption that the spread of the process is $\pm 3\sigma'$ from the process average. One British practice is to set such limits at a distance from the specification limits equal to $3.09\sigma' - (1.96\sigma'/\sqrt{n})$. This gives multipliers of σ' of 1.70, 1.97, 2.10, and 2.21 for $n = 2$, 3, 4, and 5, respectively; this contrasts with the more common practice in the United States of using the respective V factors of 0.88, 1.27, 1.50, and 1.66 given in Table 25 for the same subgroup sizes.

Modified control limits seem to have proved particularly useful as applied to intermittent short production runs in machining operations where process dispersion $(6\sigma')$ has been determined from previous runs. The more $(X_{max} - X_{min})$ exceeds $6\sigma'$, the greater the permissible latitude in machine setting. The use of modified control limits may simplify the problem of maintaining machine settings that are good enough for practical purposes.

Nevertheless, where the only limits shown on $\overline{X}$ charts are modified control limits, the users of these charts should recognize that the charts fail to disclose the presence or absence of statistical control in the manufacturing process. Moreover, the protection given by the reject limits depends on a good estimate of σ'; after this estimate has been made, the process dispersion must remain in statistical control. Whenever process dispersion behaves erratically, modified control limits are not appropriate. For this reason, a chart for R should supplement any $\overline{X}$ chart using modified control limits.

164. Charts for Individual Measurements. Where charts for averages are misunderstood by shop personnel, one possible way to avoid this misunderstanding is not to plot averages at all but rather to plot individual measurements. Figures 1a and 3a in Chap. II are charts of this type. Specification limits applying to individual measurements are, of course, properly shown on such charts.

If sampling is by subgroups, as illustrated in Figs. 1a and 3a, universe standard deviation σ' may be estimated from $\overline{R}$. Control limits for individual measurements may then be drawn at $\overline{X} \pm 3\sigma'$. A point outside such limits may be considered as evidence of an assignable cause of variation.

Such a chart may be better than nothing, but it is much inferior to the conventional control chart based on a subgroup size of four or five. It is relatively insensitive to shifts in process average. Unless accompanied by a range chart, it cannot be relied on to show changes in process dispersion. In general it does not give as clear a picture of changes in the process or as quick evidence of assignable causes of variation.

For the reasons cited, in cases where serious difficulties are caused by misunderstandings of the relationship between points and limits on the chart for averages and the specification for individual values and where it seems impracticable to correct these difficulties by better education of personnel in control-chart principles, it is recommended that serious consideration be given either to the use of charts for subgroup totals or to the addition of reject limits to conventional $\overline{X}$ charts. These preserve the advantages of the control chart, many of which are lost by the use of charts that show only individual values.

Problems

72. Tests of tensile strengths of malleable iron castings from four foundries gave the following results:

Foundry	Number of tests	Average tensile strength, psi	Standard deviation
A	54	58,400	1,600
B	60	57,000	1,550
C	71	57,700	1,190
D	49	56,900	2,080

Use the methods explained in Art. 156 to plot $\bar{X}$ and σ charts to judge whether there is clear evidence that the different foundries represent different cause systems. Use simple unweighted averages to determine $\bar{\bar{X}}$ and $\bar{\sigma}$, and base your limits on average subgroup size.

73. Solve Problem 72, computing $\bar{\bar{X}}$ and $\bar{\sigma}$ by the formulas for weighted averages given in Art. 156. Compute separate control limits for each foundry.

74. Explain why, when n is over 25, A_1 is approximately $3/\sqrt{n}$, B_4 and B_2 are approximately $1 + (3/\sqrt{2n})$, and B_3 and B_1 are approximately $1 - (3/\sqrt{2n})$.

75. For purposes of computing control limits in the moving average illustration of Table 22 and Figs. 40 and 41, $\bar{R}$ was assumed as 0.065. From this $\bar{R}$ what would be your estimate of σ'? Assuming $\bar{X}'$ as 0.17, what are 3-sigma limits on individual daily values? If these limits were drawn on Fig. 40a, on what dates would points fall outside control limits? How does this compare with the dates on which points fell outside control limits on the moving range chart, Fig. 41a? How do you explain this relationship?

76. Here are daily analyses of CO_2 as CaO at an intermediate stage in a chemical manufacturing process:

Date	Per cent CO_2 as CaO	Date	Per cent CO_2 as CaO	Date	Per cent CO_2 as CaO
May 1	0.53	14	0.65	27	0.71
2	0.62	15	0.59	28	0.68
3	0.63	16	0.60	29	0.74
4	0.54	17	0.69	30	0.66
5	0.50	18	0.65	31	0.67
6	0.50	19	0.65	June 1	0.67
7	0.51	20	0.67	2	0.68
8	0.53	21	0.71	3	0.72
9	0.56	22	0.78	4	0.70
10	0.64	23	0.82	5	0.67
11	0.57	24	0.82	6	0.69
12	0.56	25	0.88	7	0.68
13	0.55	26	0.82		

Compute 3-day moving averages and moving ranges and plot a chart for each. Base your control limits on an $\bar{X}'$ of 0.66 and an $\bar{R}$ of 0.085, both obtained from past data.

77. Compute the standard deviation of each subgroup in Table 1, Example 1, Chap. II. Plot a control chart for σ. Plot a control chart for $\bar{X}$ with the control limits based on $\bar{\sigma}$. Use conventional 3-sigma control limits for both charts.

78. In Problem 77 figure probability control limits for both charts, using probabilities of 0.001 and 0.999.

79. Assume that probability limits rather than 3-sigma limits were to be used for the data of Example 2, Chap. II. Where would these limits be on the $\bar{X}$ and R charts.

(*a*) If the probability of a point falling outside the limits in sampling from a normal universe were to be 0.002?

(*a*) If this probability were to be 0.01?

(*c*) If this probability were to be 0.05?

80. Using the first 20 subgroups of Table 6, Chap. III, prepare a control chart for subgroup totals.

81. In Example 1, Chap. II, the specified dimension was 0.4037 ± 0.0013 in. Compute a revised $\bar{R}$, eliminating the out-of-control points on the R chart. Estimate σ' from this revised $\bar{R}$. From this estimate of σ' compute the position of reject limits on the chart for averages.

82. In Example 2, Chap. II, the dimension was originally specified as 0.140 ± 0.003 in. Compute the reject limits to be used on an $\bar{X}$ chart when this specification was in effect. What is the practical meaning of reject limits such as these? The specification was later changed to $0.140 \begin{cases} +0.010 \\ -0.015 \end{cases}$. Where would you now put the reject limits? How do they compare with the control limits?

Part Three

OTHER SHEWHART CONTROL CHARTS

CHAPTER IX

SOME FUNDAMENTALS OF THE
THEORY OF PROBABILITY

There are many difficulties and troubles with which a factory management has to contend—dies which wear; bearings that get loose; stock which is undersize, oversize, or dirty; loose fixtures; careless, tired, or untrained employees. For these reasons it would seem that there is no mathematical method which takes into account all these factors. However there is a kind of mathematics which is applicable in just such conditions, and that is the mathematics of probability.—L. T. RADER[1]

165. Probability Has a Mathematical Meaning.[2] The statement that tomorrow will probably be a hot day is perfectly clear and understandable, whether you agree with it or not. So also is the statement that Smith is more likely than Jones to receive a promotion. In general, the word *probability* and its derivative and related words such as *probable, probably, likelihood, likely,* and *chance* are used regularly in everyday speech in a qualitative sense and there is no difficulty in their interpretation.

But consider a statement that the probability is 0.98 that the shear strength of a spot weld will be above 480 lb. if two 0.040-gage test strips of duralumin are welded on Sciaky machine No. 18 provided statistical control is maintained on the welding operation. Or a statement that if a sample of 5 is taken at random from a lot of 50 pieces that contains exactly 3 defectives, the probability is 0.724 that the sample will contain no defective pieces. In such statements, *probability* is used in its quantitative or mathematical sense. It is evident that some special explanation of the meaning of *probability* is necessary before these statements can be understood. A critical consideration will show that the two statements not only call for more explanation but that they need somewhat different explanations.

Two different definitions of *probability* in its mathematical sense may be given. One may be described as the *frequency definition,* the other as the *classical definition.*

[1] RADER, L. T., Putting Quality into Quantity, *American Machinist,* vol. 87, pp. 92–93, Oct. 28, 1943.

[2] The explanation of probability developed in the initial articles of this chapter was considerably influenced by a volume of mimeographed notes on the subject prepared (about 1930) by Paul Coggins and R. I. Wilkinson for use in an out-of-hour course given for engineers of the New York Telephone Company.

166. Definitions of Probability. From the standpoint of its useful applications in industry, probability may be thought of as relative frequency in the long run. This may be phrased somewhat more precisely as follows:

Assume that if a large number of trials be made under the same essential conditions, the ratio of the number of trials in which a certain event happens to the total number of trials will approach a limit as the total number of trials is indefinitely increased. This limit is called the probability that the event will happen under these conditions.

It may be noted that this limit is always a fraction (or decimal fraction), which may vary from 0 to 1. A probability of 0 corresponds to an event that never happens under the described conditions; a probability of 1 corresponds to an event that always happens.

It is because *probability* describes relative frequency in the long run that the concept is so useful in practical affairs. But its use would be severely limited if the only way to estimate any probability were by a long series of experiments. Most mathematical manipulations of probabilities are based on another definition, which may be stated as follows:

*If an event may happen in **a** ways and fail to happen in **b** ways, and all of these ways are mutually exclusive and equally likely to occur, the probability of the event happening is **a**/(**a** + **b**), the ratio of the number of ways favorable to the event to the total number of ways.*

This is called the *classical definition.* It represents the approach to the subject developed by the classical writers on the mathematics of probability, many of whom wrote particularly about probabilities associated with games of chance. Experience shows that where properly used, this definition permits the successful forecasting of relative frequency in the long run without the necessity of a long set of trials prior to each forecast.

The statement in the preceding article about the probability of a given strength for spot welds could only be justified on the basis of a considerable record of measurements of spot-weld strength from Sciaky machine No. 18; it would be impossible to enumerate a number of equally likely ways in which the strength could be above or below 480 lb. On the other hand, the statement about the sample of 5 from the lot of 50 is based on a counting of equally likely ways in which the sample of 5 might contain no defectives or one or more defectives; even though not based on the evidence of actual trials, a statement of this sort may be made with strong confidence that the stated probability is really the relative frequency to be expected in the long run.

Many problems in the mathematics of probability are troublesome because of the difficulty of classifying events into "equally likely" ways of happening or failing to happen. Fortunately, most of the important applications of probability theory in statistical quality control are fairly simple and straightforward.

167. Some Theorems of the Theory of Probability. Three important theorems, developed in books on the mathematics of probability, are here stated and illustrated. They are the theorem of total probabilities, sometimes called *the addition theorem;* the theorem of compound probabilities, sometimes called *the multiplication theorem;* and the theorem of conditional probabilities.

The theorem of total probabilities, or addition theorem, may be stated as follows:

The probability of the occurrence of either one or another of any number of mutually exclusive events is the sum of the probabilities for the separate events.

This is sometimes stated more concisely as

The probability of the occurrence of any event is the sum of the probabilities of its mutually exclusive forms.

Events are mutually exclusive if the occurrence of any one of them makes impossible the simultaneous occurrence of all the others.

As an example, consider the probability that a single drawing from Shewhart's normal bowl (see Table 11, Chap. IV) will give a chip marked 50 or 51. The probability of a chip marked 50 is 5/998. This is obtained from the assumption that each of the 998 chips in the bowl may be considered to be equally likely; of these 998 chips, 5 are marked 50. By similar reasoning from the fact that there are 4 chips marked 51, the probability of a chip marked 51 is 4/998. The probability of either 50 or 51 is the sum of the two probabilities, namely 9/998.

The theorem of compound probabilities, or multiplication theorem may be stated as follows:

If a compound event be made up of a number of separate and independent subevents, and the occurrence of the compound event be the result of each of these subevents happening, the probability of occurrence of the compound event is the product of the probabilities that each of the subevents will happen.

Events are independent if the occurrence of one of the events has no influence on the probability of any of the other events happening.

As an example, consider two successive draws from Shewhart's bowl, with the chip first drawn replaced and the chips stirred before the second drawing. What is the probability that a 50 will be obtained on both draws? The probability of a 50 on the first draw is 5/998. So also is the probability of a 50 on the second draw. The two events are independent. Therefore the probability of both draws giving a 50 is

$$(5/998) \ (5/998) = 25/996{,}004$$

When the events are not independent but the nature of the dependence is known, the theorem of conditional probabilities may be used:

The probability that both of two dependent events will occur is the probability of the first multiplied by the probability that if the first has occurred the second will also happen.

As an example, consider two successive draws from Shewhart's bowl with the chip first drawn not replaced before the second drawing. Under these circumstances, what is the probability that a 50 will be obtained on both draws? The probability of a 50 on the first draw is 5/998. The probability on the second draw is clearly dependent on what chip has been removed from the bowl on the first draw. If a 50 occurs on the first draw, there remain only 4 chips marked 50 in the 997 chips still in the bowl. Thus the probability is 4/997 that if a 50 has been drawn first, another 50 will be obtained on the second draw. The probability of 50 on both drawings is the product of these probabilities, namely $(5/998)(4/997) = 20/995{,}006$.

168. Formula for Combinations. For the solution of many problems in probability it is necessary to know how many different sets of r objects can be chosen from n objects.

For example, consider a lot of 50 pieces from which a sample is to be drawn. How many different ordered sets of 5 can be drawn? (That is, how many sets are possible which differ either in the pieces included or in the order in which the pieces were drawn?) The first draw might be any one of 50; the next, any one of the remaining 49; the next, any one of 48; the next, any one of 47; and the final draw any one of 46. The total number of possible ordered sets is obviously the product of these numbers; this is called the number of *permutations*. The symbol P_5^{50} is read "the number of permutations of 50 things taken 5 at a time." This is

$$P_5^{50} = (50)(49)(48)(47)(46) = 254{,}251{,}200$$

In general, the number of permutations of n things taken r at a time is given by the formula

$$P_r^n = (n)(n-1)(n-2) \cdots (n-r+1) = \frac{n!}{(n-r)!}$$

Here the expression $n!$, read as "factorial n" or "n factorial," is used for the product of the first n integers. By definition, $0! = 1$. From this an expression may be written for the number of permutations of n things taken all at a time.

$$P_n^n = n!$$

Sets without regard to the order of drawing are called *combinations*.

To find the number of different combinations of 5 that may be drawn from a lot of 50, it may first be noted that any one combination of 5 has $5! = (5)(4)(3)(2)(1) = 120$ possible permutations. As each combination includes 120 possible permutations, the total number of combinations can be computed by dividing the total number of permutations by 120.

$$C_5^{50} = \frac{50!}{5!45!} = \frac{(50)(49)(48)(47)(46)}{(5)(4)(3)(2)(1)} = \frac{254,251,200}{120} = 2,118,760$$

In general, the number of combinations of n things taken r at a time is given by the formula

$$C_r^n = \frac{n!}{r!(n-r)!}$$

169. Application of the Combination Formula to Probability Problems. Example 5, Chap. II, gave some probabilities associated with the common sampling acceptance procedure of inspecting 5 articles from each lot of 50. With the use of the combination formula, it is now possible to illustrate how such probabilities are computed.

Consider a lot of 50 articles containing 3 defectives. A sample of 5 is selected at random from the lot. What are the respective probabilities of 0, 1, 2, and 3 defectives occurring in the sample of 5?

The total number of different samples of 5 has already been calculated as 2,118,760. If the sample is selected at random, all these may be considered to be equally likely. To compute the respective probabilities we must find how many of these different possible samples contain exactly 0, 1, 2, and 3 defectives.

Consider a sample containing 0 defectives. Such a sample must come from the 47 good articles. From these articles the number of different possible samples of 5 is

$$C_5^{47} = \frac{47!}{5!42!} = \frac{(47)(46)(45)(44)(43)}{(5)(4)(3)(2)(1)} = 1,533,939$$

A sample containing exactly one defective must include 4 articles from the 47 good ones and 1 article from the 3 bad ones. Thus there are

$$C_4^{47}C_1^3 = \frac{47!3!}{4!43!1!2!} = \frac{(47)(46)(45)(44)}{(4)(2)} = 535,095$$

A sample containing exactly 2 defectives must include 3 articles from the 47 good ones and 2 articles from the 3 bad ones. Of such samples, there are

$$C_3^{47}C_2^3 = \frac{47!3!}{3!44!2!1!} = \frac{(47)(46)(45)}{2} = 48,645$$

A sample containing exactly 3 defectives must include 2 articles from the 47 good ones and all 3 bad articles. There are

$$C_2^{47}C_3^3 = \frac{47!}{2!45!} = \frac{(47)(46)}{2} = 1{,}081$$

The respective probabilities are

$$P_0 = \frac{1{,}533{,}939}{2{,}118{,}760} = 0.72398$$

$$P_1 = \frac{535{,}095}{2{,}118{,}760} = 0.25255$$

$$P_2 = \frac{48{,}645}{2{,}118{,}760} = 0.02296$$

$$P_3 = \frac{1{,}081}{2{,}118{,}760} = 0.00051$$
$$\text{Total} = \overline{1.00000}$$

(Here P_0 means the probability of exactly 0 defectives, P_1 means the probability of exactly 1 defective, etc.)

As the probabilities of all the mutually exclusive alternatives have been computed, their sum must be unity. This check should be made for all such calculations.

170. Use of Logarithms of Factorials. Factorials are very large numbers. For instance $15! = 1{,}307{,}674{,}368{,}000$. In dealing with many problems in probability, it is convenient to use logarithms of factorials such as those given in Table H, Appendix III.*

As an illustration, consider a sampling problem that is discussed at greater length in Chap. XIII. A sample of 170 articles is to be taken from a lot of 1,000 articles. The lot will be accepted if not more than 1 defective article is found in the sample. What is the probability that the lot will be accepted if it contains exactly 20 defectives?

A sample with 0 defectives, or a sample with 1 defective, will result in acceptance of the lot. It is therefore necessary to find the respective probabilities of each of these samples.

The number of different possible samples of 170 articles is C_{170}^{1000}. As the lot contains exactly 20 defectives, it must contain 980 good articles. The number of possible samples consisting entirely of good articles is therefore C_{170}^{980}. The probability of a sample containing 0 defectives is

$$P_0 = \frac{C_{170}^{980}}{C_{170}^{1000}} = \frac{980!170!830!}{170!810!1000!}$$

---

* For factorials of numbers above 1,000, use the first term of Stirling's approximation to the factorial: $n! = n^n e^{-n} \sqrt{2\pi n}$. Here e is 2.71828. See T. C. Fry, "Probability and its Engineering Uses," pp. 103–107, D. Van Nostrand Company, Inc., New York, 1928.

Solving this by logarithms of factorials from Table H,

$$
\begin{array}{llll}
\log & 980! & 2507.6877 & \\
\log & 830! & 2064.2291 & 4571.9168 \\
\hline
\log & 810! & 2005.9477 & \\
\log & 1{,}000! & 2567.6046 & 4573.5523 \\
\hline
\log P_0 & & & 8.3645 - 10 \\
& & P_0 = 0.02315 &
\end{array}
$$

The probability of a sample containing exactly 1 defective is

$$
P_1 = \frac{C_{169}^{980}C_1^{20}}{C_{170}^{1000}} = \frac{980!170!830!20!}{169!811!1000!19!} = \frac{980!830!(170)(20)}{811!1000!}
$$

Solving this by log factorials

$$
\begin{array}{llll}
\log & 980! & 2507.6877 & \\
\log & 830! & 2064.2291 & \\
\log & 170 & 2.2304 & \\
\log & 20 & 1.3010 & 4575.4482 \\
\hline
\log & 811! & 2008.8567 & \\
\log & 1{,}000! & 2567.6046 & 4576.4613 \\
\hline
\log P_1 & & & 8.9869 - 10 \\
& & P_1 = 0.09703 &
\end{array}
$$

The probability of accepting the lot is the sum of the probabilities of a sample containing no defectives and a sample containing 1 defective. This is

$$
P_0 + P_1 = 0.02315 + 0.09703 = 0.12018
$$

Roughly, one lot out of every eight lots that are 2% defective will be passed by this sampling acceptance scheme.

171. Changes in Probabilities Due to Partial Exhaustion of a Lot by a Sample. The problems in the two preceding articles that were solved with the help of the combinatorial formula might also have been solved by computing the probabilities on each draw and applying the theorem of conditional probabilities.

This may be illustrated by again considering the calculation of the probability that a sample of 5 will contain 0 defectives if drawn from a lot of 50 containing 3 defectives. The probability that the first article drawn will be good is $^{47}\!/_{50}$. If the first draw is good, the probability that the second will be good is $^{46}\!/_{49}$. If the first and second are both good, the probability that the third will be good is $^{45}\!/_{48}$ etc. This gives the probability that all 5 are good as

$$
P_0 = \left(\frac{47}{50}\right)\left(\frac{46}{49}\right)\left(\frac{45}{48}\right)\left(\frac{44}{47}\right)\left(\frac{43}{46}\right) = \left(\frac{45}{50}\right)\left(\frac{44}{49}\right)\left(\frac{43}{48}\right) = 0.72398
$$

It is evident that, because each new drawing changes the proportion of good and bad articles in the remaining portion of the lot, the probability changes from draw to draw. This partial exhaustion of the lot by the sample is recognized by the above type of calculation, or by calculations that use the combinatorial formula in the way illustrated in Arts. 169 and 170. However if the lot is large enough compared to the sample, the change in probability from one draw to the next is of negligible importance. Consider a sample of 5 taken from a lot of 5,000 containing 300 defectives. The probability that this sample contains 0 defectives is

$$P_0 = \left(\frac{4700}{5000}\right)\left(\frac{4699}{4999}\right)\left(\frac{4698}{4998}\right)\left(\frac{4697}{4997}\right)\left(\frac{4696}{4996}\right)$$

For all practical purposes, this is $\left(\dfrac{4700}{5000}\right)^5$ or $(0.94)^5$.

Many industrial sampling problems are of this type, in which for practical purposes it is good enough to assume that the probability of a defective article is not affected by the partial exhaustion of a lot by the portion of the sample already drawn. The assumption of a constant probability of a defective from draw to draw in a given lot often greatly simplifies the calculations required to solve practical problems. In many other cases, as in sampling from a continuous stream of product not segregated into lots, this is a correct assumption in principle.

In judging the results of inspection of successive lots or successive days of production, it is desirable to judge whether the observed variations in per cent defective are consistent with an assumption that the probability of a defective is constant. As explained in Chap. X, the control chart for p (fraction defective) provides a test for this purpose. To understand the interpretation of the control chart, it is necessary to understand something of the theory governing cases where the probability is constant that a defect will occur.

172. The Binomial as a Probability Distribution. Probability problems in which the probability of occurrence of an event may be assumed to be constant may be solved by the use of a formula that depends on the familiar binomial theorem. The reader who recalls his algebra will remember that

$$(a + b)^n = a^n + na^{n-1}b + \frac{n(n-1)}{(2)(1)} a^{n-2}b^2$$
$$+ \frac{n(n-1)(n-2)}{(3)(2)(1)} a^{n-3}b^3 + \frac{n(n-1)(n-2)(n-3)}{(4)(3)(2)(1)} a^{n-4}b^4 + \cdots$$

This binomial expansion is the basis of a probability distribution that is of great importance in statistical quality control.

Let p' be the symbol for the constant probability that a particular event will happen. In applications to statistical quality control, this is generally the probability of a defective article.

Let q' be the symbol for the probability that the same event will not happen. In applications to statistical quality control, this is generally the probability of a good (sometimes called an effective) article.

$$\text{As } p' + q' = 1$$
$$q' = 1 - p'$$

As a specific example, let p', the fraction defective in a bulk of articles, be 0.06. Then $q' = 0.94$. Consider the respective probabilities of the various possible numbers of defectives in samples of 5 drawn from this bulk.

By the multiplication theorem, it is obvious that the probability of 0 defectives in a sample of five

$$P_0 = (0.94)(0.94)(0.94)(0.94)(0.94) = (0.94)^5$$

Similarly, the probability of five defectives is

$$P_5 = (0.06)(0.06)(0.06)(0.06)(0.06) = (0.06)^5$$

Consider the probability of exactly 1 defective. This defective might be any one of the 5 articles in the sample. The probability that the first is defective and the other 4 are good is

$$(0.06)(0.94)(0.94)(0.94)(0.94) = (0.94)^4(0.06)$$

The probability that the first is good, the second defective, and the last 3 good is $(0.94)(0.06)(0.94)(0.94)(0.94) = (0.94)^4(0.06)$. Similar statements may be made about the respective probabilities of the third, fourth, and fifth articles being defective with the others good. By the addition theorem, the probability that some one of the articles is defective is the sum of these five separate probabilities

$$P_1 = 5(0.94)^4(0.06)$$

The probability that the first 2 articles are defective and the last 3 good is $(0.06)(0.06)(0.94)(0.94)(0.94) = (0.94)^3(0.06)^2$. The various ways in which exactly 2 of the articles might be defective (D) and the other 3 good (G) may be enumerated as follows:

$$
\begin{array}{ll}
D\,D\,G\,G\,G & G\,D\,G\,D\,G \\
D\,G\,D\,G\,G & G\,D\,G\,G\,D \\
D\,G\,G\,D\,G & G\,G\,D\,D\,G \\
D\,G\,G\,G\,D & G\,G\,D\,G\,D \\
G\,D\,D\,G\,G & G\,G\,G\,D\,D
\end{array}
$$

The probability of each of these is $(0.94)^3(0.06)^2$.

Therefore the probability that some 2 of the 5 articles will be defective is

$$P_2 = 10(0.94)^3(0.06)^2$$

It was not really necessary to enumerate the 10 ways in which exactly 2 of the articles might be defective and the other 3 good. This is evidently the problem of the number of different sets of 2 articles that can be selected from 5, $i.e.$, the number of combinations of 5 things taken 2 at a time.

$$C_2^5 = \frac{5!}{3!2!} = \frac{(5)(4)}{2} = 10$$

Similarly, the coefficient 5 in the expression for P_1 is the number of combinations of 5 things taken 1 at a time, C_1^5.

TABLE 26. ILLUSTRATION OF THE BINOMIAL AS A PROBABILITY FORMULA
(Probability of exactly r occurrences in n trials)

r	General expression	Value when $p' = 0.06$ and $n = 5$
0	$C_0^n q'^{n-0} p'^0 = q'^n$	$(0.94)^5 = 0.7339040224$
1	$C_1^n q'^{n-1} p'^1 = nq'^{n-1}p'$	$5(0.94)^4(0.06) = 0.2342246880$
2	$C_2^n q'^{n-2} p'^2 = \dfrac{n!}{2!(n-2)!} q'^{n-2}p'^2$	$10(0.94)^3(0.06)^2 = 0.0299010240$
3	$C_3^n q'^{n-3} p'^3 = \dfrac{n!}{3!(n-3)!} q'^{n-3}p'^3$	$10(0.94)^2(0.06)^3 = 0.0019085760$
4	$C_4^n q'^{n-4} p'^4 = \dfrac{n!}{4!(n-4)!} q'^{n-4}p'^4$	$5(0.94)(0.06)^4 = 0.0000609120$
5	$C_5^n q'^{n-5} p'^5 = \dfrac{n!}{5!(n-5)!} q'^{n-5}p'^5$	$(0.06)^5 = 0.0000007776$
Total...		$= 1.0000000000$

In general, the probability of exactly r occurrences in n trials of an event that has a constant probability of occurrence p' is

$$C_r^n q'^{n-r} p'^r = \frac{n!}{r!(n-r)!} q'^{n-r}p'^r$$

The above is a generalized term of the binomial expansion, applying to all terms of the binomial. This should be clear from examination of Table 26, which illustrates the binomial as a probability formula.

In the literature of statistics, the binomial as a probability distribution is frequently described as the Point Binomial or as the Bernoulli Distribution.

173. Average and Standard Deviation of the Binomial. If a product is 6% defective ($p' = 0.06$) and many samples of 5 are drawn from this product, it seems obvious that the expected average number of defectives per sample will be $(5)(0.06) = 0.3$. This may be verified in a particular case by a calculation using the binomial distribution of Table 26.

Number of defectives*	Relative frequency, i.e., probability of occurrence	Defectives × relative frequency
0	0.7339040224	0.0000000000
1	0.2342246880	0.2342246880
2	0.0299010240	0.0598020480
3	0.0019085760	0.0057257280
4	0.0000609120	0.0002436480
5	0.0000007776	0.0000038880
Totals.....	1.0000000000	0.3000000000

* Average number of defectives = 0.3/1 = 0.3.

Where many sets of n trials are made of an event with a constant probability of occurrence p', the expected average number of occurrence in the long run is np', i.e., np' is the average of the binomial. Translated into terms of a problem in statistical quality control, if many random samples of size n are taken from a product having a fraction defective p', the expected average number of defectives per sample is np'.

The expression for standard deviation of the frequency distribution that results from the binomial is derived in standard works on mathematical statistics.[1] It is $\sqrt{np'q'} = \sqrt{np'(1 - p')}$.

In the case where n is 5 and p' is 0.06, the standard deviation is $\sqrt{5(0.06)(0.94)} = \sqrt{0.282} = 0.531037$.

The standard deviation given by the formula may be checked by the following calculation from the distribution:

Fraction defective	Number of defectives	Defectives squared	Relative frequency	Relative frequency × defectives squared
0.00	0	0	0.7339040224	0.0000000000
0.20	1	1	0.2342246880	0.2342246880
0.40	2	4	0.0299010240	0.1196040960
0.60	3	9	0.0019085760	0.0171771840
0.80	4	16	0.0000609120	0.0009745920
1 00	5	25	0.0000007776	0.0000194400
Total..				0.3720000000

$$\sigma = \sqrt{0.372 - (0.3)^2} = \sqrt{0.372 - 0.09} = \sqrt{0.282} = 0.531037$$

[1] For example, see W. D. Baten, "Elementary Mathematical Statistics," p. 125, John Wiley & Sons, Inc., New York, 1938.

It is important to distinguish between the average number of occurrences of the event in n trials np' and the relative proportion of occurrence or probability of occurrence p'. In statistical quality control, this is a distinction between average number of defectives in the samples, and the average fraction defective. In any sample, the fraction defective is the number of defectives divided by the sample size n. The standard deviation of the fraction defective is, of course, the standard deviation of the number of defectives, $\sqrt{np'q'}$, divided by the sample size n. This is

$$\sigma_p = \frac{\sqrt{np'q'}}{n} = \sqrt{\frac{p'q'}{n}} = \sqrt{\frac{p'(1 - p')}{n}} = \frac{\sqrt{p'(1 - p')}}{\sqrt{n}}$$

This is an important formula in connection with the control chart for fraction defective.

174. The Binomial as a Basis for Approximate Estimates of Probabilities in Sampling from Finite Lots. The binomial describes the situation that exists when the probability of a defective is constant from draw to draw. As already pointed out, this is never quite true in sampling from finite lots. Nevertheless, the binomial often provides a good enough approximation to serve as a practical basis for judgments about various sampling plans.

In Arts. 172 and 173, the binomial example was carried to many decimal places. This was necessary to illustrate how np' and $\sqrt{np'q'}$ gave exact results for the average and standard deviation of the binomial distribution. However, practical calculations for industrial quality control never require so many decimal places. For the common calculations to judge the quality protection given by alternative sampling plans, three decimal places, or in some instances only two decimal places, are adequate.

Article 169 gave the probabilities of 0, 1, 2, and 3 defectives in drawing samples of 5 from lots of 50 that were 6% defective. Table 26 in Art. 172 gave the probabilities of 0, 1, 2, 3, 4, and 5 defectives in drawing samples of 5 from an infinite lot that was 6% defective. Where these probabilities are expressed only to three decimal places, the differences between them do not seem to be serious.

Defectives	Probabilities from lot of 50	Probabilities from infinite lot
0	0.724	0.734
1	0.252	0.234
2	0.023	0.030
3	0.001	0.002

From the standpoint of practical action based on these probabilities, it may well be true that it is satisfactory to assume that the probabilities that apply to an infinite lot also apply to samples of 5 from finite lots of 50 or more.

Actual calculations by the binomial involving large sample size may be illustrated by computing the probabilities of 0 and 1 defectives in samples of 170 from a large bulk of product that is 2% defective. In this case n is 170 and p' is 0.02, and the first two terms of the binomial (corresponding to 0 and 1) are required.

$$P_0 = (q')^n = (0.98)^{170} = 0.032$$
$$P_1 = n(q')^{n-1}(p') = 170(0.98)^{169}(0.02) = 0.112$$

$\log 0.98 = 9.991226 - 10$		$\log 0.98 = 9.991226 - 10$	
$170 \log 0.98 =$		$169 \log 0.98 = 8.5172$	$- 10$
$\log P_0 \quad = 8.5084 \quad - 10$		$\log 170 = 2.2304$	
$P_0 \quad = 0.032$		$\log 0.02 = 8.3010$	$- 10$
		$\log P_1 \quad = 9.0486$	$- 10$
		$P_1 \quad = 0.112$	

These probabilities of 0.032 and 0.112 in a sample of 170 from an infinite lot may be compared with the probabilities of 0.023 and 0.097 obtained in Art. 170 for samples of the same size from lots of 1,000 containing the same percentage of defectives. In general, the more the lot tends to be exhausted by the sample the greater will be the difference between the correct probabilities and the approximate ones computed by the binomial on the assumption of an infinite lot.

175. Poisson's Approximation to the Binomial. Calculations involving the use of the binomial are often burdensome; this is particularly true if many terms are involved and if n is large. Fortunately, a simple approximation may be obtained to any term of the binomial. This approximation, called *Poisson's Exponential Binomial Limit*, is referred to more briefly in statistical literature as "the Poisson law," "Poisson distribution," or simply as "the Poisson." The larger the value of n and the smaller the value of p', the closer is the Poisson approximation. It is admirably suited to the solution of many problems that arise in industrial quality control. Derivations of the Poisson as a limit of the binomial as n approaches infinity and np' remains constant are given in standard texts on the mathematics of probability.[1]

Table 27 gives a comparison of the corresponding terms of the binomial and Poisson. The binomial terms as stated in Table 26 have been rewritten in a way to emphasize a comparison with the Poisson terms. The Poisson term for the probability of 0 occurrences is $e^{-np'}$. e is

---

[1] For instance, see Fry, *op. cit.*, pp. 214–216.

2.71828+, the base of natural or Naperian logarithms. It will be remembered that np' is the average value of the expected number of occurrences. For ordinary use in discussion of the Poisson throughout this book, c' is used for this average instead of np'.

Once the probability of 0 occurrences has been computed, the calculation of the remaining terms of the Poisson is simple. An examination of the terms as stated in Table 27 shows that the probability of 1 occurrence is np' (or c') times the probability of 0. The probability of 2 is $np'/2$ times the probability of 1. The probability of 3 is $np'/3$ times

TABLE 27. COMPARISON OF CORRESPONDING TERMS OF BINOMIAL AND POISSON FORMULAS

Number of occurrences of event	General expression for probability of exact number of occurrences		Numerical expression for probability when n is 170 and p' is 0.02.	
	Binomial	Poisson	Binomial	Poisson
0	$(q')^n$	$e^{-np'}$	$(.98)^{170}$	$e^{-3.4}$
1	$n(q')^{n-1}(p')$	$np'e^{-np'}$	$170(.98)^{169}(.02)$	$3.4e^{-3.4}$
2	$\dfrac{n(n-1)}{2!}(q')^{n-2}(p')^2$	$\dfrac{(np')^2}{2!}e^{-np'}$	$\dfrac{170!}{2!168!}(.98)^{168}(.02)^2$	$\dfrac{(3.4)^2}{2!}e^{-3.4}$
3	$\dfrac{n(n-1)(n-2)}{3!}(q')^{n-3}(p')^3$	$\dfrac{(np')^3}{3!}e^{-np'}$	$\dfrac{170!}{3!167!}(.98)^{167}(.02)^3$	$\dfrac{(3.4)^3}{3!}e^{-3.4}$
4	$\dfrac{n(n-1)(n-2)(n-3)}{4!}(q')^{n-4}(p')^4$	$\dfrac{(np')^4}{4!}e^{-np'}$	$\dfrac{170!}{4!166!}(.98)^{166}(.02)^4$	$\dfrac{(3.4)^4}{4!}e^{-3.4}$
r	$\dfrac{n!}{r!(n-r)!}(q')^{n-r}(p')^r$	$\dfrac{(np')^r}{r!}e^{-np'}$		

the probability of 2. The probability of 4 is $np'/4$ times the probability of 3. And so on.

In many problems in industrial quality control it is necessary to know the probability of less than a given number of occurrences or more than a given number. This requires a summation of the terms of distributions such as the binomial or Poisson. Such summations are illustrated in Table 28 for a specific numerical example in which n is 170 and p' is 0.02. This table also serves as an illustration of the closeness of agreement between binomial and Poisson where n is large and p' is small.

176. Use of Tables and Diagrams for Solution of Poisson Problems. Molina's tables[1] give individual terms and summation terms of the Poisson formula to six decimal places for values of c' (np') up to 100. Table G in Appendix III of this book gives summation terms to three decimal places. Figure 43, taken from Dodge and Romig,[2] also gives

[1] MOLINA, E. C., "Poisson's Exponential Binomial Limit," D. Van Nostrand Company, Inc., New York, 1942.

[2] DODGE, H. F., and H. G. ROMIG, "Sampling Inspection Tables," Fig. 6, John Wiley & Sons, Inc., New York, 1944.

TABLE 28. COMPARISON OF NUMERICAL VALUES COMPUTED BY BINOMIAL AND POISSON FORMULAS

$n = 170 \qquad p' = 0.02 \qquad np' = 3.4$

Number of occurences of event c	Summation Probability of c or less occurrences		Individual terms* Probability of exactly c occurrences	
	Binomial	Poisson	Binomial	Poisson
0	0.032	0.033	0.032	0.033
1	0.144	0.147	0.112	0.114
2	0.337	0.340	0.193	0.193
3	0.557	0.558	0.220	0.218
4	0.745	0.744	0.188	0.186
5	0.873	0.871	0.128	0.127
6	0.944	0.942	0.071	0.071
7	0.978	0.977	0.034	0.035
8	0.992	0.992	0.014	0.015
9	0.998	0.997	0.006	0.005
10	0.999	0.999	0.001	0.002
11	1.000	1.000	0.001	0.001

* If carried to five decimal places, the individual terms of the Poisson corresponding to 0 and 1 are 0.03337 and 0.11347, respectively. These give summation terms of 0.03337 and 0.14684. If the individual terms are rounded off to 0.033 and 0.113 and the summation terms to 0.967 and 0.853, the individual term 0.113 will not be consistent with the difference of 0.114 between the corresponding summation terms. This illustrates a dilemma that exists in the tabulation of individual terms and summation terms of such distributions; if the individual and summation terms are made consistent with each other, they cannot both always be correct in the final decimal place. In Table 28 the summation terms are all correct in the third decimal place and the individual terms have been made consistent with the summation terms.

summation values; this may be read to two decimal places, with some uncertainty in the second place.

In Table G the values of c' go by intervals of 0.02 from 0 to 0.10, by intervals of 0.05 from 0.10 to 1.00, by intervals of 0.1 from 1.0 to 2.0, by intervals of 0.2 from 2.0 to 8.0, by intervals of 0.5 from 8.0 to 15.0, and by intervals of 1 from 15 to 25. The approximate Poisson distribution corresponding to any value of c' under 25 that is not given in Table G may be obtained by interpolation between the distributions for the two adjacent values of c' that are given in the table. Such an interpolation is illustrated in Table 29, in which c' is 5.28. Each value for 5.28 is assumed to be 0.4 $\left(\text{that is, } \dfrac{5.28 - 5.20}{5.40 - 5.20} \right)$ of the way from the 5.20 value to the 5.40 value. Such a linear interpolation in Table G will generally give values that are either correct or in error by not more than one unit in the third decimal place.

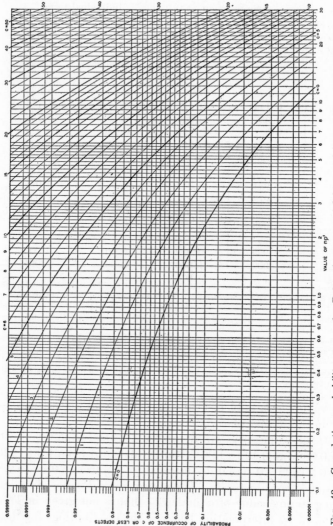

FIG. 43. Cumulative probability curves for Poisson's exponential binomial limit. For determining probability of occurrence of c or less defects in a sample of n pieces selected from an infinite universe in which the fraction defective is p'. (*Reprinted by permission from "Sampling Inspection Tables" by Dodge and Romig, published by John Wiley & Sons, Inc.*)

In addition to illustrating the use of Table G, Table 29 gives values of the Poisson summation as read from Fig. 43. As both Table G and Fig. 43 give only summations of terms, the individual Poisson terms must be obtained by subtracting the adjacent summation terms. This has been done in Table 29.

TABLE 29. ILLUSTRATION OF ESTIMATION OF TERMS OF POISSON BY USE OF TABLES AND DIAGRAMS

$$n = 240 \qquad p' = 0.022 \qquad np' = c' = 5.28$$

	Probability of c or less occurrences			Probability of exactly c occurrences for $c' = 5.28$	Estimates from Fig. 43	
	Summation terms from Table G		Interpolated summation terms for $c' = 5.28$		Summation terms	Individual terms
	for $c' = 5.2$	for $c' = 5.4$				
0	0.006	0.005	0.006	0.006	0.005	0.005
1	0.034	0.029	0.032	0.026	0.03	0.025
2	0.109	0.095	0.103	0.071	0.10	0.07
3	0.238	0.213	0.228	0.125	0.23	0.13
4	0.406	0.373	0.393	0.165	0.39	0.16
5	0.581	0.546	0.567	0.174	0.57	0.18
6	0.732	0.702	0.720	0.153	0.72	0.15
7	0.845	0.822	0.836	0.116	0.83	0.11
8	0.918	0.903	0.912	0.076	0.91	0.08
9	0.960	0.951	0.956	0.044	0.96	0.05
10	0.982	0.977	0.980	0.024	0.98	0.02
11	0.993	0.990	0.992	0.012	0.992	0.012
12	0.997	0.996	0.997	0.005	0.997	0.005
13	0.999	0.999	0.999	0.002	0.999	0.002
14	1.000	1.000	1.000	0.001	0.9996	0.0006

177. The Poisson as a Distribution in Its Own Right. The Poisson can be used to save labor of calculation both in probability problems to which the binomial is directly applicable and in other problems to which the binomial provides a satisfactory approximation. But this is not the limit of usefulness of the Poisson. Certain types of frequency distributions occur in nature, both in industrial quality control work and elsewhere, that are closely fitted by the Poisson. The situations to which it has been shown to be applicable are so numerous and so diversified that the Poisson has sometimes been called the law of small numbers. Some representative examples are shown in Table 30.

Table 30a* is based on 33 years of records for 10 rainfall stations

* GRANT, E. L., Discussion of "Rainfall Intensities and Frequencies," by A. J. Schafmayer and B. E. Grant, *Transactions Am. Soc. C. E.*, vol. 103, p. 388, 1938.

widely scattered throughout the midwestern United States. It gives the number of 10-min. periods in a year having half an inch or more of rainfall. c is the number of such cloudbursts in a station-year; the frequency is the number of station-years having respectively 0, 1, 2, 3, 4, and 5 such excessive rainstorms. The average number of such storms

TABLE 30. EXAMPLES OF DISTRIBUTIONS TO WHICH THE POISSON LAW IS APPLICABLE

(a) Excessive Rainstorms

c	Frequency
0	102
1	114
2	74
3	28
4	10
5	2

(b) Deaths from Kick of a Horse

c	Frequency
0	109
1	65
2	22
3	3
4	1

(c) Lost Articles

c	Frequency
0	169
1	134
2	74
3	32
4	11
5	2
6	0
7	1

(d) Vacancies in the U.S. Supreme Court

c	Frequency
0	59
1	27
2	9
3	1

(e) Calls from Group of 6 Coin-box Telephones

c	Frequency
0	8
1	13
2	20
3	37
4	24
5	20
6	8
7	5
8	2
9	1

(f) Errors in Alignment Found at Aircraft Final Inspection

c	Frequency	c	Frequency
0	0	10	2
1	0	11	5
2	0	12	2
3	1	13	3
4	4	14	1
5	3	15	2
6	6	16	1
7	7	17	0
8	7	18	1
9	5		

per station-year, $\bar{c}$, is 1.2. Table 31 shows the close agreement between the frequencies observed for the 330 station-years and the frequency computed by the Poisson for the same average and the same number of station-years.

Table 30b is the classic example of the Poisson series that has been quoted in many books on probability and statistics. It was compiled by Bortkewitsch, who wrote on the subject of the Poisson law in 1898.

He found from the records of the Prussian army the number of men killed by the kick of a horse in each of 14 cavalry corps in each of 20 successive years, and after discarding the records for 4 corps that were considerably larger than the others, treated the rest as one series of samples. c is the number of Prussians killed in this way in a corps-year. The frequency is the number of corps-years having exactly c cavalrymen killed. This was the first example of the applicability of the Poisson to accident statistics.

TABLE 31. COMPARISON OF OBSERVED FREQUENCIES WITH THEORETICAL FREQUENCIES BY THE POISSON
(Data of Table 30a on excessive rainstorms)

c	Observed frequency in 330 trials	Total number of rainstorms	Summation terms of Poisson, $c' = 1.2$	Individual terms of Poisson, $c' = 1.2$	Expected frequency in 330 trials
0	102	0	0.301	0.301	99
1	114	114	0.663	0.362	119
2	74	148	0.879	0.216	71
3	28	84	0.966	0.087	29
4	10	40	0.992	0.026	9
5	2	10	0.998	0.006	2
6	0	0	1.000	0.002	1
	330	396	. . . . .	1.000	330

$$\bar{c} = {}^{396}\!/_{330} = 1.20$$

Table 30c gives the number of articles turned in per day to the lost and found bureau of a large office building (excluding Sundays and holidays, and June, July, and August, when there might be a considerable reduction in the average population of the building).[1] The frequency is the number of days with exactly c lost articles turned in.

Table 30d shows the vacancies in the United States Supreme Court, either by death or resignation of members, from 1837 to 1932.[2] The frequency is the number of years in which there were exactly c vacancies.

Table 30e shows the number of telephone calls per 5-min. interval from a group of six coin-box telephones in a large railway terminal. The data were taken for the period from noon to 2 P.M. for seven days, not including a Saturday or Sunday. The frequency is the number of 5-min. intervals in which exactly c calls were originated.

Table 30f gives the numbers of errors in alignment discovered by

[1] Tables 30c and 30e are taken from Frances Thorndike, Applications of Poisson's Probability Summation, *The Bell System Technical Journal*, vol. 5, pp. 604–624, October, 1926.

[2] WALLIS, W. A., The Poisson Distribution and the Supreme Court, *Journal of the American Statistical Association*, vol. 31, p. 376, June, 1936.

inspectors at the time of final inspection of an airplane. The frequency is the number of planes for which exactly c such errors were listed on the inspector's "squawk sheet."

At first impression, these six Poisson illustrations may seem to have very little similarity to one another. However, a more critical examination shows they have very definite characteristics in common. In each, a count was made of the number of occurrences of an event which had many opportunities to occur but which was extremely unlikely to occur at any given opportunity. There were many 10-min. periods in a year; it was unlikely any particular one would bring a cloudburst of half an inch or more of rain. There were many contacts between a cavalryman and a horse during a year of history of a cavalry corps; it was unlikely the horse would make a fatal kick at any particular contact. There were many people passing through the large office building during a day; it was unlikely that any one person would find a lost article and turn it in to the lost and found bureau, etc.

In all these cases, there is the concept of the existence of a large n and a small p', even though it may be impossible to assign definite values to either n or p'. Even in cases where it is not impossible to determine definite values of n and p', it may simply be of no advantage to determine n and p' and to calculate a binomial based on them; the Poisson will serve as well.

It will be noted that in all instances an effort has been made to keep constant a quantity that might be called *the area of opportunity for occurrence*. Thus the 4 cavalry corps that were much larger than the other 10 were eliminated from the tabulation of deaths of cavalrymen; the days in which the office building was believed to have a less than normal population were eliminated from the tabulation of articles turned in to the lost and found bureau; the record of calls from the group of coin-box phones was limited to an apparently homogenous 2-hr. period in the middle of the day and Saturdays and Sundays were eliminated.

By similar reasoning, it would not have been appropriate to combine alignment "squawks" observed on two airplanes of different designs.

178. Average and Standard Deviation of the Poisson. The average and standard deviation of the binomial have been stated as np' and $\sqrt{np'(1 - p')}$, respectively.

The Poisson distribution is always derived from a known or assumed average, which may be stated as np' or c'. The Poisson is the limit of the binomial as n approaches infinity and np' remains constant. Under such circumstances, the limit of $(1 - p')$ is obviously 1. Thus the limit of the standard deviation, $\sqrt{np'(1 - p')}$, is $\sqrt{np'}$ or $\sqrt{c'}$.

The Poisson is therefore a distribution for which the standard deviation $\sqrt{c'}$ is always the square root of the average c'.

179. Theory of Extreme Runs. If, in tossing a coin, the probability of a head on one toss is $\frac{1}{2}$, the probability of heads on both of two successive independent tosses is $(\frac{1}{2})^2$. Similarly, the probability of heads on all of seven successive independent tosses is $(\frac{1}{2})^7 = \frac{1}{128}$. As the probability of tails on every toss for 7 tosses is also $\frac{1}{128}$, the probability of a run of either 7 heads or 7 tails in any given set of 7 tosses is

$$\frac{1}{128} + \frac{1}{128} = \frac{1}{64}$$

The *median* of a set of numbers has been defined (Art. 51) as the mid-number, the one so located that half the numbers are above it and the other half below it. If numbers were written on a set of chips, the probability is $\frac{1}{2}$ that a single chip drawn at random would fall above the median. Or if measurements are made on a quality characteristic that is statistically controlled, the probability is $\frac{1}{2}$ that any one measurement will be above the universe median. Whenever a frequency distribution is symmetrical, the median and average (arithmetic mean) are the same. In this case, the probability is $\frac{1}{2}$ that any one measurement will fall above the universe average, or that the average of any subgroup will fall above the universe average. Extreme runs of subgroup averages above or below the universe average are as likely as extreme runs of heads or tails in coin tossing. Thus the probability is $\frac{1}{64}$ that 7 successive subgroup averages will fall on the same side of the universe average.

This type of reasoning is the basis for the rules given in Art. 88, Chap. V, regarding interpretation of extreme runs on a control chart. For example, if the probability is assumed as $\frac{1}{2}$ that any subgroup average will fall above the universe average, the probability that at least 10 out of 11 subgroups would fall on the same side of the universe average can be computed by adding the first two and last two terms of the binomial, $(\frac{1}{2} + \frac{1}{2})^{11}$.

P_{11}, the probability of all 11 above $\qquad = \left(\dfrac{1}{2}\right)^{11} \qquad = \dfrac{1}{2048}$

P_{10}, the probability of exactly 10 above $\qquad = 11\left(\dfrac{1}{2}\right)^{10}\left(\dfrac{1}{2}\right) = \dfrac{11}{2048}$

P_1, the probability of exactly 10 below (1 above) $= 11\left(\dfrac{1}{2}\right)\left(\dfrac{1}{2}\right)^{10} = \dfrac{11}{2048}$

P_0, the probability of all 11 below (0 above) $\qquad = \left(\dfrac{1}{2}\right)^{11} \qquad = \dfrac{1}{2048}$

The probability that 10 or more out of 11 will fall
on the same side of the universe average $\qquad\qquad\qquad = \dfrac{24}{2048}$

$$\frac{24}{2048} = 0.0117, \text{ or approximately } \frac{1}{85}$$

As many distributions of industrial quality characteristics are not symmetrical, it is not strictly correct to state that the probability is always $\frac{1}{64}$ that, with no change in the universe, 7 successive subgroup averages will be on the same side of the universe average, or that the probability is always $\frac{1}{85}$ that at least 10 out of 11 will be on the same side. Just as the control chart limits are best interpreted as rules for action rather than as means of estimating exact probabilities, so also should the extreme runs mentioned in Art. 88 be interpreted in this way.

As pointed out in Art. 88, these runs may be expected to occur as a matter of chance with no change in universe average oftener than would a departure from 3-sigma limits. The relative frequencies of the runs and the out-of-control points may be judged by noting that, assuming a normal universe, the probability of a point outside 3-sigma limits is 0.0027 or about $\frac{1}{380}$. If it were desired to set up rules for extreme runs that were as unlikely as departures from 3-sigma limits, such runs could readily be calculated. For example, 9 points in a row on the same side of the average have a probability of $\frac{1}{256}$; 10 points have a probability of $\frac{1}{512}$.

Significant extreme runs are not necessarily with reference to the central line on the control chart. Article 159 suggested that two points in succession on the same side of a 2-sigma limit constituted an extreme run that was a more significant indication of an assignable cause than a single point outside of 3-sigma limits. This statement may be verified by the following calculations. If the probability of one point *above* the *upper* 2-sigma limit is 0.0228, the probability of two in a row is

$$(0.0228)^2 = 0.00052$$

As the probability of two points in a row *below* the *lower* 2-sigma limit is also 0.00052, the probability of two points in succession outside the *same* 2-sigma limit (either above the upper limit or below the lower limit) is $0.00052 + 0.00052 = 0.00104$, or about $\frac{1}{960}$.*

180. The Normal Curve as an Approximation to the Binomial. One of the several common derivations of the normal curve is as a limit of the binomial distribution as n is increased indefinitely. The greater the value of n, the better the estimate of the binomial that can be made from a normal curve area table such as Table A, Appendix III. It should be recognized, however, that the normal curve is always a symmetrical distribution. The binomial is symmetrical only in the special case where $p' = \frac{1}{2}$. For a given value of n the normal curve gives a better

---

* Probability tests may also be applied to runs in which each value is greater (or less) than the preceding value. For probability tables and a diagram applicable to this type of run, see P. S. Olmstead, Distribution of Sample Arrangements for Runs Up and Down, *Annals of Mathematical Statistics*, vol. 17, pp. 24–33, March, 1946.

approximation when p' is close to $\frac{1}{2}$ than when p' is close to 0 or 1. However, if n is large enough—say in the hundreds or more—the normal curve may be used for a wide range of values of p' and will give an approximation to the binomial that is good enough for practical purposes in many problems in industrial sampling. Where p' is close to 0 or 1, the approximation will be considerably less reliable in the extreme tails of the distribution than near the center of the distribution. The method of using Table A to approximate the binomial is illustrated in the following example:

Samples of 45 are being taken from a stream of product. This product is, on the average, 25% defective in the sense that one-fourth of the product normally fails to conform to a particularly severe specification that is being applied as part of the acceptance procedure. The following two questions are representative of the two types of probability calculations that might be required:

1. What is the probability that a sample of 45 will contain exactly 13 defectives?

2. What is the probability that a sample of 45 will contain 13 or more defectives?

It is evident that the binomial distribution is applicable and that $n = 45$ and $p' = 0.25$. To answer question 1 by calculation from the binomial distribution itself, it must be recognized that $r = 13$.

$$P_{13} = C_r^n q'^{(n-r)} p'^r = \frac{45!}{13!32!} (0.75)^{32}(0.25)^{13} = 0.109$$

The actual calculation of this 0.109 requires the use of logarithms of factorials from Table H, Appendix III, as well as the use of a table of ordinary logarithms. Because this calculation is similar to calculations already illustrated, it is not given here.

To approximate this answer from Table A, it is first necessary to compute the average and standard deviation of the binomial in question.

$$\overline{X}' = np' = 45(0.25) = 11.25$$
$$\sigma' = \sqrt{np'q'} = \sqrt{45(0.25)(0.75)} = 2.905$$

In answering question 1 it must be recognized that the normal distribution is a continuous one, whereas the binomial is discontinuous or—in statistical language—discrete. That is, there can be 12 or 13 or 14 defectives in the sample of 45 but not 12.72 or 13.39. Hence in selecting that portion of the area of the normal curve corresponding to exactly 13 defectives, it is appropriate to take the area from $X = 12.5$ to $X = 13.5$. Each of the limiting values of X must then be expressed as $\overline{X}'$ plus some multiple of σ' (or, if appropriate, as $\overline{X}'$ minus some multiple of σ').

$$13.5 = \bar{X}' + \frac{13.5 - 11.25}{2.905}\sigma' = \bar{X}' + 0.7745\,\sigma'$$

$$12.5 = \bar{X}' + \frac{12.5 - 11.25}{2.905}\sigma' = \bar{X}' + 0.4303\,\sigma'$$

Table A figure corresponding to $\bar{X}' + 0.7745\ \sigma'$ is 0.7807
Table A figure corresponding to $\bar{X}' + 0.4303\ \sigma'$ is 0.6665

Difference 0.1142

This figure, 0.114, is an approximation to the correct figure of 0.109, the probability of exactly 13 defectives under the stated conditions.

A fairly long and tedious calculation is required to find the correct answer to question 2 regarding the probability of 13 or more defectives. It is necessary to calculate 33 terms of the binomial corresponding to values of r from 13 to 45 inclusive and to take the sum of these terms. A somewhat shorter calculation, still fairly long, requires the evaluation of the 13 terms corresponding to values of r from 0 to 12 inclusive, the summation of these terms, and the subtraction of the sum from 1.

In the present instance these long calculations can be avoided by the use of "Applied Mathematics Series No. 6, Tables of the Binomial Probability Distribution," published by the Government Printing Office and available from the Superintendent of Documents, Washington, D. C. This volume, containing 387 large pages, gives to seven decimal places both the individual values and the summation values of the terms of the binomial where n is 49 or less. The values of p' go from 0.01 to 0.50 by intervals of 0.01. The table for $r = 13$ and $n = 45$ gives the correct answer to question 2 as 0.3251992.

The approximate answer that the normal curve gives for question 2 requires only a slight modification of the calculations already made to answer question 1. It has already been pointed out that, as applied to a continuous distribution such as the normal curve, the probability of exactly 13 defectives should be interpreted as meaning the probability of from 12.5 to 13.5 defectives. It follows that the probability of 13 or more defectives should be interpreted to mean the probability of 12.5 or more defectives. It has already been calculated that 0.6665 of a normal distribution having the same $\bar{X}'$ and σ' as this particular binomial will be below 12.5. It follows that the approximate probability of 13 or more defectives is $1 - 0.6665 = 0.3335$.

180a. Deciding on the Method to Be Used for Calculating Probabilities in Industrial Sampling Problems. In the attributes inspection of industrial product, each item either conforms to specifications or fails to conform. Nonconforming items are described as *defectives*. In sampling for acceptance purposes, the decision on acceptance or rejection of the product sampled will commonly depend on the number of defectives in the sample or samples. In judging the merits of any proposed sampling acceptance scheme, it is appropriate to calculate the probabilities of acceptance assuming a number of different percentages of defectives in the product sampled. Some calculations of this type have already been illustrated; many more are given in the chapters on acceptance sampling by attributes.

In one type of problem it is specified that a random sample of size n is to be drawn from a lot of size N containing a specified percentage of defectives. It is desired to find the probability that the sample will contain exactly r defectives or, perhaps, r or more defectives or r or less defectives. In this type of problem, the theoretically correct answer requires consideration of lot size N as well as sample size n. Methods of making such calculations were illustrated in Arts. 169 to 171; probabilities so calculated are described as *hypergeometric* probabilities. As pointed out in Art. 174, in problems of this type it is often good enough for practical purposes to assume that the sample is drawn from an infinite lot rather than from a finite lot and to use the binomial to give an approximation to the desired hypergeometric probabilities.

In another type of problem the random sample of size n is assumed to be drawn from a stream of product containing a specified percentage of defectives. Here the binomial is applicable in principle rather than as an approximation.

For many of the problems involving either hypergeometric probabilities or the binomial, the required calculations may be long and time-consuming. This is particularly true if n is large and probabilities must be calculated for many different possible numbers of defectives in order to solve a problem dealing with "r or more" or "r or less" defectives. In solving such problems it is necessary to decide whether to use an approximate method that saves computational time even though it gives answers that are not quite correct. If some approximate method is to be used, a choice must be made among the various approximate methods.

No simple general rules can be laid down as to when to use approximate methods. It is always a matter of balancing the saving in the time and cost of calculations against the error introduced by the approximation. The following suggestions are merely intended to give some general guidance.

1. In principle, hypergeometric probabilities are required whenever a sample is drawn from a finite lot of stated size N. The decision on whether to compute hypergeometric probabilities or to assume an infinite lot should be influenced by the size of N, by the ratio n/N, and by the number of values of r for which calculations are required. If N is more than 1,000, the fact that log factorials are not available makes the calcu-

lation of such probabilities very time-consuming; where N is small, say 20 or less, it is easy to compute such probabilities even without the aid of logarithms. The smaller the ratio of sample size to lot size, the less the error introduced by assuming that the sample is drawn from an infinite lot. The amount of time saved by an approximation is relatively small if calculations are required for only one or two values of r and much greater if many values of r are involved.

2. Wherever the binomial applies in principle or is considered to give a satisfactory approximation to hypergeometric probabilities, the decision must be made among (a) calculation by the binomial, (b) use of the Poisson as an approximation to the binomial, and (c) use of the normal curve as an approximation to the binomial. For anyone having a copy of the binomial table referred to in Art. 180, it is simple to use correct binomial values if n is 49 or less. Above this value of n, the decision for or against calculation by the binomial depends in part on the number of terms to be evaluated. If many terms are to be evaluated in a "r or more" or "r or less" type of problem, it is practically necessary to use an approximate method.

3. The great timesaver in all such calculations is the Poisson distribution. With a table such as Molina's table or Table G or with a Poisson diagram such as Fig. 43, approximate answers may be obtained very rapidly. This statement applies to calculations of the probability of exactly r defectives as well as to "r or more" or "r or less" defectives. In many industrial sampling problems these approximations are good enough. The larger the n and the smaller the p', the closer the approximate answer will be to the true probability.

4. The normal curve as an approximation to the binomial gives a more rapid answer than the Poisson approximation only when the np' of the problem is greater than the maximum np' in the available Poisson table or diagram. (This maximum is 25 in Table G, 30 in Fig. 43, and 100 in Molina's tables.) The normal curve is somewhat better adapted to rapid calculation of cumulative terms than of individual terms. The larger the n and the nearer the p' to 0.5, the closer the approximate answer will be to the true probability.

181. The Use of Probability in Statistical Tests. Suppose two points occur in a row outside the same 2-sigma limit on a control chart for $\overline{X}$. The question is asked, "Does this indicate that the universe has changed?" As explained in Art. 81, Chap. IV, the mathematical statistician does not give a direct answer to this question. In effect, he says, "On the hypothesis that the universe has not changed,[1] the probability that this

---

[1] The hypothesis that two or more samples come from the same universe is called by mathematical statisticians a "null hypothesis." See R. A. Fisher, "The Design of Experiments," p. 11, Oliver and Boyd, Edinburgh, 1937.

event would have happened is $\frac{1}{960}$. Make up your own mind whether this is so unlikely that you believe the hypothesis is disproved."

In just this way, most tests of statistical significance are based on probability calculations.

181a. Bayes' Theorem. It has seemed to many people that the mathematical statistician should answer the question, "What is the probability that this observed sample came from a given universe?" rather than merely answer the more indirect question, "What is the probability that a given universe would have produced this observed sample?"

It is possible to set up artificial examples in which the mathematical statistician may make unquestionably valid calculations of the respective probabilities that various universes were the source of a given sample. A classic example described by Fry[1] is as follows:

Three identical boxes each contain two coins. It is known that one contains two gold coins (GG), another contains a gold and a silver coin (GS), and another contains two silver coins (SS). A box is selected at random and a coin drawn from it at random. The coin is gold (G). What is the probability that the box selected is GG?

In this problem, we may start with three possible hypotheses regarding the universe; it was either GG, GS, or SS. Before the drawing, each hypothesis was equally likely; the probability of each was $\frac{1}{3}$. These are called the *existence probabilities*. We also can compute the probabilities that each universe would have given the sample that was observed, namely, the drawing of a gold coin. These are called *productive probabilities*. For each hypothesis regarding the universe, the existence probabilities and the productive probabilities may be multiplied together. Bayes' theorem states that the probability that any one hypothesis is correct is a fraction whose numerator is the product of the existence probability and the productive probability for that hypothesis, and whose denominator is the sum of such products for all the possible hypotheses.[2] This may be illustrated as follows:

Hypothesis regarding universe	Existence probability	Productive probability	Product	Probability that hypothesis is correct
GG	$\frac{1}{3}$	1	$\frac{1}{3}$	$\frac{2}{3}$
GS	$\frac{1}{3}$	$\frac{1}{2}$	$\frac{1}{6}$	$\frac{1}{3}$
SS	$\frac{1}{3}$	0	0	0
Total......	1		$\frac{3}{6}$	1

[1] FRY, *op. cit.*, Chap. V.
[2] This is actually Laplace's modification of Bayes' original theorem.

The probabilities that the various hypotheses regarding the universe are correct are called *a posteriori* probabilities or *inverse* probabilities, in contrast with the *a priori* probabilities that the various samples would have been drawn from given universes.

If the statement of the problem is slightly changed, it is possible to show how Bayes' theorem combines the evidence of a sample with the knowledge of the situation which was available before taking the sample. Suppose there are now 10 identical boxes, one containing GG, eight containing GS, and one containing SS. A box is selected at random; the coin drawn from the box is gold. The appropriate calculations of a posteriori probabilities are

Hypothesis regarding universe	Existence probability	Productive probability	Product	Probability that hypothesis is correct
GG	$\frac{1}{10}$	1	$\frac{1}{10}$	$\frac{1}{5}$
GS	$\frac{8}{10}$	$\frac{1}{2}$	$\frac{4}{10}$	$\frac{4}{5}$
SS	$\frac{1}{10}$	0	0	0
Total......	1		$\frac{5}{10}$	1

In this case, even though the drawing of the sample G makes GG seem more likely than it did before we had the sample, the evidence of the sample is not sufficient to overbalance the strong existence probability of GS.

If probabilities of all the various possible universes are really known in advance of sampling, Bayes' theorem provides a valid way of combining this knowledge with the evidence of the sample. However, in most problems in industry there is no way of knowing such existence probabilities. In some cases, there may be a basis for guessing them. But in most cases where Bayes' theorem is used in industry, the assumption is made that the existence probabilities are equal for all possible hypotheses regarding the composition of the universe. Many tables and diagrams for industrial use have been based on this assumption.

This assumption has been severely criticized by many mathematical statisticians on the grounds that it has no reasonable basis whatsoever. That is, there is no more reason for assuming that all universes are equally likely than for making any other assumption about them. The defense usually given for tables and diagrams based on this assumption is that such tables and diagrams apply to situations in which samples are large enough for the productive probabilities to carry the greater weight in the conclusions; in such cases, substantial changes in assumed existence probabilities may make little difference in the calculated a posteriori probabilities of the various universes. In other words, the assumption is defended on the basis that it is good enough for practical purposes even though the people who make it realize it is not correct.

Chapter XV contains references to Simon's well-known I_Q charts[1] and their use in acceptance sampling. These charts are based on Bayes' theorem with the assumption that all possible universes are equally likely. With the exception of this reference, Bayes' theorem and a posteriori probability are not used in this book.

Problems

NOTE: In all of the following problems, use the method that is correct in principle unless the problem statement specifies the use of an approximate method.

83. What is the probability that a single draw from Shewhart's normal bowl will yield a chip marked 29, 30, or 31? See Table 11 (page 76) for the distribution in this bowl. *Ans.* $120/998$.

84. If two successive draws from Shewhart's normal bowl are made with the first chip drawn replaced before the second draw, what is the probability that a 30 will be obtained on both draws? *Ans.* 1,600/996,004.

85. If two successive draws are made with the first chip drawn not replaced before the second draw, what is the probability that a 30 will be obtained on both draws? *Ans.* 1,560/995,006.

86. A sample of 3 is to be selected from a lot of 20 articles. How many different samples are possible? *Ans.* 1,140.

87. A sample of 30 is to be selected from a lot of 200 articles. How many different samples are possible? *Ans.* 4.096×10^{35}.

88. A random sample of 4 is to be selected from a lot of 12 articles, 3 of which are defective. What is the probability that the sample will contain exactly 1 defective? *Ans.* $28/55$.

89. A random sample of 20 is to be selected from a lot of 150 articles, 15 of which are defective. What is the probability that the sample will contain 2 or more defectives? *Ans.* 0.627.

90. What is the probability of getting exactly 3 sixes in a throw of 6 dice? What is the probability of 3 or more sixes? *Ans.* 0.0535; 0.0621.

91. What are the respective probabilities of getting 0, 1, 2, 3, 4, 5, 6, and 7 heads in a toss of 7 coins? Assume the probability of heads in one toss to be $\frac{1}{2}$. *Ans.* $\frac{1}{128}$; $\frac{7}{128}$; $\frac{21}{128}$; $\frac{35}{128}$; $\frac{35}{128}$; $\frac{21}{128}$; $\frac{7}{128}$; $\frac{1}{128}$.

92. A controlled manufacturing process is 0.2% defective. What is the probability of finding 2 or more defectives among 100 pieces? *Ans.* 0.0172.

93. Use the Poisson distribution to obtain an approximate answer to Problem 92. *Ans.* 0.018.

94. A random sample of 25 articles is taken from a stream of product 20% defective. What is the probability that the sample will contain exactly 5 defectives? *Ans.* 0.196.

95. From past records it is estimated that the probability that a flood of 10,000 sec.-ft. or more will occur in any year on a certain stream is $\frac{1}{5}$. What is the probability that such a flood will occur at least once in the next 5 years? *Ans.* 0.672.

96. An acceptance plan calls for the inspection of a sample of 75 articles out of a lot of 1,500. If there are no defectives in the sample, the lot is accepted; otherwise

[1] SIMON, *op. cit.* In appendixes *A* and *B* General Simon explains the basis on which these charts were computed.

it is rejected.   If a lot 1% defective is submitted, what is the probability that it will be accepted?   Solve this using the Poisson as an approximation.   *Ans.* 0.472.

97. An acceptance plan calls for the inspection of a sample of 115 articles out of a lot of 3,000.   If there are 6 or less defectives in the sample, the lot is accepted; with 7 or more it is rejected.   If a lot 5% defective is submitted, what is the probability that it will be rejected?   Solve this using the Poisson as an approximation.

Ans. 0.354.

98. If the probability is 0.033 that a single article will be defective, what are the respective probabilities that a sample of 100 will contain exactly 0, 1, 2, 3, 4, 5, 6, 7, 8, 9, 10, and 11 defectives?   Assume the Poisson is a satisfactory approximation to the binomial in this problem, and solve by interpolation in Table G.

Ans. 0.037; 0.122; 0.201; 0.2205; 0.182; 0.1205; 0.0655; 0.0315; 0.013; 0.0045; 0.002; 0.0005.

99. If the probability is 0.25 that a single article will be defective, what is the probability that a sample of 50 will contain exactly 15 defectives?   *Ans.* 0.089.

100. Using the normal curve as an approximation to the binomial, answer the question in Problem 99.   Also find the approximate probability of 15 or more defectives.   *Ans.* 0.094; 0.257.

101. Using the Poisson as an approximation to the binomial, answer the question in Problem 99.   Also find the approximate probability of 15 or more defectives.

Ans. 0.081; 0.275.

102. Bill proposes the following dice game to Jack.   Jack will throw 5 dice.   If 3 or more of them do not turn up the same face (*i.e.*, 3 or more sixes, 3 or more fives, etc.), Bill wins and Jack will pay him 10 cents.   If 3 or more of the 5 dice do turn up the same face, Jack wins and Bill will pay him 40 cents.   What is the probability that Jack will win?   As the game is proposed, who has the best of the bet?

Ans. 0.213; odds of 4 to 1 are favorable to Jack, as fair odds would be 3.69 to 1.

103. (*a*) How many different hands of 13 cards might you have out of a standard deck of 52 playing cards?   *Ans.* 635,013,560,000.

(*b*) What is the probability of a 13-card hand without an ace, king, queen, or jack?

Ans. 0.00364.

(*c*) What is the probability of a 13-card hand containing all four aces?

Ans. 0.00264.

(*d*) What is the probability of a 13-card hand containing one or more aces?

Ans. 0.696.

104. What is the probability that 5 cards selected at random from a 52-card deck will contain all 4 aces?   That they will contain exactly 3 aces?   Exactly 2?   Exactly 1?   None?   What is the sum of these probabilities?

105. What is the probability that, if there are exactly 4 defectives in a lot of 50, a random sample of 5 will contain all 4 defectives?   That it will contain exactly 3?   Exactly 2?   Exactly 1?   None?   What is the sum of these probabilities?

106. If the probability is 0.08 that a single article is defective, what are the respective probabilities that 0, 1, 2, 3, 4, and 5 articles are defective in a sample of 5?

107. The probabilities computed in Problem 106 constitute a binomial distribution. Compute the average and standard deviation of this binomial, following the pattern given in the calculations in Art. 173.   Compare your computed values with the values given by the formulas np' for the average and $\sqrt{np'q'}$ for the standard deviation.

108. If the probability is 0.015 that a single article will be defective, what are the respective probabilities that a sample of 280 will contain exactly 0, 1, 2, 3, 4, 5, 6, 7, 8, 9, 10, 11, and 12 defectives?   Assume the Poisson is a satisfactory approximation to the binomial in this problem, and solve by using Table G.

109. Make a calculation similar to Table 31 (page 215) to compare observed frequencies of Table 30*b* with theoretical frequencies by the Poisson.

110. Make a calculation similar to Table 31 to compare observed frequencies of Table 30*c* with theoretical frequencies by the Poisson.

111. Article 88 states that where 12 out of 14, 14 out of 17, or 16 out of 20 subgroup averages fall on the same side of the central line on the control chart, there are grounds for suspicion that the universe average has shifted. Assume the probability to be $\frac{1}{2}$ that a subgroup average will fall above the central line. If there has been no shift in universe average, what is the probability of

(*a*) At least 12 out of 14 points on the same side of the central line?

(*b*) At least 14 out of 17 points on the same side of the central line?

(*c*) At least 16 out of 20 points on the same side of the central line?

112. Solve Problem 111 determining the approximate probabilities by the use of Table *A*.

113. In 400 tosses of a coin, the probability is 0.9 that the number of heads will be between what limits? Assume the probability of a head on one toss to be $\frac{1}{2}$. The calculated limits should be equally distant from the average number of heads that would be expected if the 400 tosses were repeated many times. Use the approximate method that seems most appropriate in this case.

114. By a series of tests of a certain type of electrical relay, it has been determined that in approximately 3% of the trials the relay will fail to operate under certain specified conditions. What is the probability that in 10 trials made under these conditions the relay will fail to operate one or more times?

115. It has been suggested that the results of the first draft drawing in 1940 indicate that the capsules were not sufficiently stirred in the bowl from which drawings were made. There were 9,000 capsules, each containing one number between 1 and 9,000. In the first 1,500 capsules drawn, only 45 of the numbers drawn were between 1 and 1,000. Using the binomial as an approximation to the appropriate hypergeometric probabilities and the normal curve as an approximation to the binomial, make some type of statistical test to judge whether it would be reasonable to expect so few numbers between 1 and 1,000 if the capsules had been thoroughly mixed.

116. In a hand of 13 cards drawn from a standard 52-card deck, what is the probability of exactly 10 spades?

117. In a hand of 13 cards drawn from a standard 52-card deck, what is the probability of exactly 6 spades and exactly 4 hearts?

118. A die is thrown 1,200 times; the six comes up only 170 times. What is the approximate probability that a discrepancy as great as 30 from the expected value of 200 would have occurred with an unbiased die? Use the approximate method that seems most appropriate in this case.

119. A lot of 10 articles contains 2 defectives. A random sample of 3 articles is to be selected from this lot. What are the respective probabilities that this random sample will contain no defective, 1 defective, and 2 defectives?

120. One-fifth of the articles in a continuous stream of product are defective. A random sample of 3 articles is to be selected. What are the respective probabilities of 0, 1, 2, and 3 defectives in this sample?

121. A great many random samples of 500 each are to be taken from a process which produces 20% defectives. What would be the expected average number of defectives per sample? What is an upper limit of number of defectives in a sample which, in the long run, you would expect to find exceeded just 1% of the time provided the process continued at 20% defective. Use the approximate method that seems most appropriate in this case.

122. An acceptance procedure calls for taking samples of 100 from very large lots.

If no defectives are found in the sample, the lot is passed. If 2 or more defectives are found, the lot is rejected. If exactly 1 defective is found, a second sample is required. If a lot 0.4% defective is submitted for acceptance, what is the probability that this lot will be accepted on the first sample of 100? What is the probability that the lot will be rejected on the first sample? What is the probability that a second sample will be required? Use the approximate method that seems most appropriate.

123. A 50-year period of rainfall in a certain place shows only 5 years in which the annual rainfall was below 10 in. If you assume from this that there is a constant probability of 0.1 that the rainfall in any given year will be below 10 in., what is the probability that the next 10 years will contain no years with rainfall this low? What is the probability of exactly 1 such year in the next 10?

124. A random sample of 4 is to be selected from a lot of 100 articles containing 6 defectives. What are the respective probabilities that the sample will contain 0, 1, 2, 3, and 4 defectives?

125. A random sample of 4 is to be selected from a stream of product 6% defective. What are the respective probabilities that the sample will contain 0, 1, 2, 3, and 4 defectives?

126. Solve Problem 125 using the Poisson as an approximation.

127. In a bridge game (in which each player has a 13-card hand from a standard 52-card deck) you have 5 hearts and your partner has 2 hearts. What is the probability that the other 6 hearts are divided equally between the two opponents? That they are divided 4 and 2? Five and 1? Six and none?

128. In an $\bar{X}$ chart the central line has been placed at the past grand average $\bar{\bar{X}}$. Four of the next 5 points on the chart fall above the central line. Obviously this is not an extreme run. However, the inspector who plots the points would like to know how often this may be expected to occur if the universe average is really unchanged. Compute for him the probability that at least 4 out of 5 values chosen at random will fall on the same side of the average (*i.e.*, either above or below). Assume the probability of a point above the average is $\frac{1}{2}$.

129. It is known that all of the 5 beads in an urn are either white or black and that they were placed in the urn by drawing at random from a bag containing a very large number of beads of which 90% were white and 10% black. What are the respective probabilities that the 5 beads are 5W-0B, 4W-1B, 3W-2B, and 2W-3B if 2 beads drawn from the urn are both white?

130. Article 159 states that where 2 points out of 3, 3 out of 7, or 4 out of 10 all fall outside the same 2-sigma control limit, this may be considered as evidence of lack of control. Assume that with no change in the universe, the probability is 0.0228 that a single point on the control chart will fall outside a given 2-sigma limit. If there has been no change in the universe, what is the probability of:

(a) At least 2 out of 3 points falling outside the same 2-sigma limit?

(b) At least 3 out of 7 points falling outside the same 2-sigma limit?

(c) At least 4 out of 10 points falling outside the same 2-sigma limit?

131. An urn is known to contain 6 balls, some of which are white and some black. Three balls are drawn and not replaced. Of these 3, 1 is white and 2 are black. On the assumption that all proportions are a priori equally likely, what are the a posteriori probabilities in favor of the urn having originally contained just 1 white ball and 5 black? Two whites and 4 black? Three whites and 3 black? Four whites and 2 black?

CHAPTER X

THE CONTROL CHART FOR
FRACTION DEFECTIVE

Some time ago when we first began to get steamed up about this matter of statistical control, we called on a number of large automotive parts manufacturers with the intention of getting production records from which sample control charts could be plotted. The results were quite startling. In the first place, even the well-managed plants which ordinarily have all kinds of records found that they had no record of the percentage defective by lots. Some information was available, of course, but it was woefully inadequate and could not be used to indicate past experience. The tragic thing about it all is that the executives in these several plants had assured the writer that they had specific data on their quality control and knew exactly the range in process average. In several instances, further investigation revealed that the process average was considerably higher than they had estimated, in fact much higher than permissible.—JOSEPH GESCHELIN[1]

182. Some Practical Limitations of the Control Charts for Variables.

In spite of the advantages of the $\overline{X}$ and R charts, both as powerful instruments for the diagnosis of quality problems and as a means for routine detection of sources of trouble, it is evident that their use is limited to only a small fraction of the quality characteristics specified for manufactured products.

One limitation is that they are charts for *variables*, *i.e.*, for quality characteristics that can be measured and expressed in numbers. Many quality characteristics can be observed only as *attributes*, *i.e.*, by classifying each item inspected into one of two classes, either conforming or nonconforming to the specifications.

Moreover, even for those quality characteristics that can be measured, the indiscriminate use of $\overline{X}$ and R charts would often be totally impracticable, as well as uneconomical. For example, the inspection department in one manufacturing plant had the responsibility for checking over 500,000 dimensions. Although any one of these dimensions could have been measured as a variable and was therefore a possible candidate for $\overline{X}$ and R charts, it is obvious that there could not be 500,000 such charts. No dimension should be chosen for $\overline{X}$ and R charts unless there is an opportunity to save costs—costs of spoilage and rework, inspection costs, costs of excess material—or otherwise to effect quality improvements

---

[1] GESCHELIN, JOSEPH, Statistical Method Points to Process Control by Spotting Variables in Manufacture, *Automotive Industries*, vol. 67, pp. 166–169, Aug. 6, 1932.

that would in some way more than compensate for the costs of taking the measurements, keeping the charts, and analyzing them.

183. A Substitute for $\bar{X}$ and R Charts. Fortunately, there is an alternative type of control chart that may be used. This is the control chart for fraction defective p. It may be applied to quality characteristics that can be observed only as attributes. It may also be applied to quality characteristics that are actually observed as attributes—for example, dimensions checked by go and not-go gages—even though they might have been measured as variables. The cost of collecting data for p charts is likely to be less than the cost of collecting data for $\bar{X}$ and R charts, as the p chart generally uses data already collected for other purposes, whereas the $\bar{X}$ and R charts generally require special measurements for control-chart purposes. The cost of computing and charting may also be less, as one p chart may apply to any number of quality characteristics observed on one article at an inspection station, whereas separate $\bar{X}$ and R charts are necessary for each measured quality characteristic. As long as the result of an inspection is a classification of an article as accepted or rejected, a single p chart may be applied to one quality characteristic or a dozen or a hundred.

As a tool for statistical analysis, the control chart for fraction defective has somewhat the same objective as the $\bar{X}$ and R charts. It discloses the presence of assignable causes of variation, even though it is not as sensitive as the $\bar{X}$ and R chart to the influence of such causes. It is used effectively in the improvement of quality, even though it is much inferior to the $\bar{X}$ and R charts as an instrument for actual diagnosis of causes of trouble.

In addition to this, the control chart for fraction defective provides management with a useful record of quality history. Many managerial decisions need to be based on a knowledge of the quality level currently maintained and on prompt information about changes that occur in the quality level.

Fraction defective, p, may be defined as the ratio of the number of defective articles found in any inspection or series of inspections to the total number of articles actually inspected. Fraction defective is nearly always expressed as a decimal fraction.

Per cent defective is $100p$, *i.e.*, 100 times the fraction defective. For actual calculation of control limits, it is necessary to use the fraction defective. For charting, and for general presentation of results to shop personnel and to management, the fraction defective is generally converted to per cent defective.

In the illustration of the chart for p in Example 3, Chap. II, no explanation was given of how the control limits for a p chart are calculated. This calculation is now explained and illustrated in Example 16.

EXAMPLE 16. ILLUSTRATION OF CALCULATIONS NECESSARY FOR CONTROL CHART FOR FRACTION DEFECTIVE

184. Facts of the Case. This example applies to a 4-month record of daily 100% inspection of a single critical quality characteristic of a part for an electrical device. It is intended chiefly as an illustration of how control limits are calculated with variable production, and of the setting and revision of standard values for fraction defective.

When, after a change in design, the production of this part was started early in June, the daily fraction defective was computed and plotted on a chart. At the end of the month, the average fraction defective $\bar{p}$ was computed. Trial control limits were computed for each point. A standard value of fraction defective p' was then established to apply to future production. During July new control limits were computed and plotted daily based on the number of parts n inspected during the day. A single set of control limits was established for August, based on the estimated average daily production. At the end of August, a revised p' was computed to apply to September, and the control chart was continued during September with this revised value.

185. Calculation of Trial Control Limits. Table 32 shows the number inspected and the number rejected as defective each day during June. The fraction defective each day is the number of parts rejected divided by the number inspected that day. For example, for June 6, $p = 31/3,350 = 0.0092$. The per cent defective is $100p = 0.92\%$.

At the end of the month, the average fraction defective $\bar{p}$ is computed. It should be emphasized that the correct way to calculate $\bar{p}$ is to divide the total number of defectives in the period by the total number of parts inspected during the period. Whenever the subgroup size (in this case, the daily number inspected) is not constant, it is incorrect to average the values of p.

The standard deviation of the fraction defective was given in Art. 173, Chap. IX, as $\sqrt{p'(1-p')/n}$. For the purpose of computing trial control limits, p' is assumed to be the observed average fraction defective $\bar{p}$. The formulas for 3-sigma trial control limits are therefore

$$UCL_p = \bar{p} + 3\sqrt{\frac{\bar{p}(1-\bar{p})}{n}} = \bar{p} + \frac{3\sqrt{\bar{p}(1-\bar{p})}}{\sqrt{n}}$$

$$LCL_p = \bar{p} - 3\sqrt{\frac{\bar{p}(1-\bar{p})}{n}} = \bar{p} - \frac{3\sqrt{\bar{p}(1-\bar{p})}}{\sqrt{n}}$$

The value of $3\sqrt{\bar{p}(1-\bar{p})}$ can be computed once to apply to all calculations of control limits. Because of the value of n changes from day to day, new control limits are computed for each day. The value of $\sqrt{n}$ is computed for each day and divided into $3\sqrt{\bar{p}(1-\bar{p})}$ to get the value of $3\sigma_p$ for the day. This 3-sigma value thus obtained is then added to $\bar{p}$ to get the upper control limit and subtracted from $\bar{p}$ to get the lower control limit.

The daily values of p and the control limits for each day are shown in Fig. 44. In this figure, per cent defective ($100p$) rather than fraction defective, has been plotted. Because per cent defective is more readily understood by both shop and administrative personnel, it is usually desirable for fraction defective to be converted to per cent defective for all plotting.

186. Determination of Standard Value p'. If all the points fall within the trial control limits, the standard value p' may be assumed to be equal to $\bar{p}$.

Here many points fell outside the trial control limits. In such cases, the decision as to the value of p' to be used calls for judgment as to what process average fraction defectives can be maintained in the future, provided the occasional assignable causes of bad quality can be eliminated. An aid to such judgment may be obtained by computing a revised value of $\bar{p}$, eliminating the days on which p fell above the upper control limit.

With these days, June 7, 12, 13, and 22, eliminated, the remaining number of defectives is 290 and the remaining number inspected is 46,399. The revised $\bar{p} = 290/46,399 = 0.0063$.

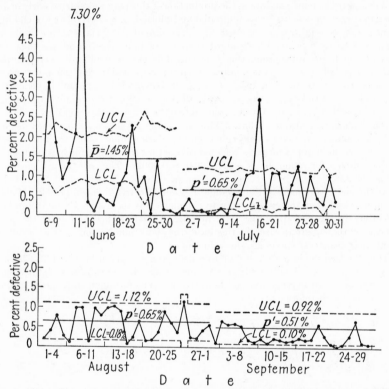

FIG. 44.   Control chart for per cent defective—4 months' production of an electrical device.

After consideration of this and of the previous record on similar parts of slightly different design, it was decided to assume $p' = 0.0065$.

187. Calculation of Control Limits Based on Standard Fraction Defective, p'. Table 33 gives the daily numbers inspected and rejected during July and shows the calculation of control limits based on the standard fraction defective. This calculation appears to be almost identical with that shown in Table 32. The value of p' is used in the calculation of limits in Table 33 wherever $\bar{p}$ was used in Table 32.

The practical difference is that where $\bar{p}$ is used, no control limits can be computed until $\bar{p}$ is known; i.e., not until the end of the period. Where a standard value p' is established in advance, the limits can be computed each day and drawn on the control chart as the day's point is plotted. In this way, the control chart provides a basis for immediate action whenever a point goes outside the control limits.

188. Establishment of Control Limits Based on Expected Average Sub-group Size. Although the correct position of 3-sigma control limits on a p chart depends on subgroup size (in this case, a subgroup is the number of parts inspected each day), the calculation of new limits for each new sub-group consumes some time and effort. Where the variation in subgroup size is not too great (for example, where the maximum and minimum sub-groups are not more than 25% away from the average) it often may be good enough for practical purposes to establish a single set of control limits

TABLE 32.   COMPUTATION OF TRIAL CONTROL LIMITS FOR CONTROL CHART FOR FRACTION DEFECTIVE

(Data on a single quality characteristic of a part of an electrical device)

Date	Number inspected n	Number of defectives	Fraction defective p	$3\sigma = \dfrac{3\sqrt{\bar{p}(1-\bar{p})}}{\sqrt{n}}$	UCL $\bar{p} + 3\sigma$	LCL $\bar{p} - 3\sigma$
June 6	3,350	31	0.0092	0.0062	0.0207	0.0083
7	3,354	113	0.0337	0.0062	0.0207	0.0083
8	1,509	28	0.0185	0.0092	0.0237	0.0053
9	2,190	20	0.0091	0.0077	0.0222	0.0068
11	2,678	35	0.0131	0.0069	0.0214	0.0076
12	3,252	68	0.0209	0.0063	0.0208	0.0082
13	4,641	339	0.0730	0.0053	0.0198	0.0092
14	3,782	12	0.0032	0.0058	0.0203	0.0087
15	2,993	3	0.0010	0.0066	0.0211	0.0079
16	3,382	17	0.0050	0.0062	0.0207	0.0083
18	3,694	14	0.0038	0.0059	0.0204	0.0088
19	3,052	8	0.0026	0.0065	0.0210	0.0080
20	3,477	27	0.0078	0.0061	0.0206	0.0084
21	4,051	44	0.0109	0.0056	0.0201	0.0089
22	3,042	70	0.0230	0.0065	0.0210	0.0080
23	1,623	12	0.0074	0.0089	0.0234	0.0056
25	915	9	0.0098	0.0119	0.0264	0.0026
26	1,644	1	0.0006	0.0087	0.0232	0.0058
27	1,572	22	0.0140	0.0090	0.0235	0.0055
28	1,961	3	0.0015	0.0081	0.0226	0.0064
29	2,440	3	0.0012	0.0073	0.0218	0.0072
30	2,086	1	0.0005	0.0079	0.0224	0.0066
Totals	60,688	880				

$$\bar{p} = \frac{\text{Total number of defectives}}{\text{Total number inspected}} = \frac{880}{60,688} = 0.0145$$

$$3\sqrt{\bar{p}(1-\bar{p})} = 3\sqrt{(0.0145)(0.9855)} = 0.3586$$

based on the expected average subgroup size. In this way, limits may be established at the start of a period (for instance, a month) and projected ahead for the entire period.

At the end of July the situation was reviewed to consider the possibility of doing this. It was decided that daily output was well enough stablized to justify the use of a single set of control limits during August. Average daily production during July had been $61,701/25 = 2,468$. The estimated average daily output during August was 2,600; this was assumed as the value of n for calculation of control limits. As $\bar{p}$ during July had been $393/61,701 = 0.0064$, no change was made in the p' of 0.0065. The calculations for the control limits for August are shown in Table 34.

TABLE 33. COMPUTATION OF DAILY CONTROL LIMITS BASED ON STANDARD VALUE OF FRACTION DEFECTIVE p'

(Data on a single quality characteristic of a part of an electrical device)

Date	Number inspected n	Number of defectives	Fraction defective p	$3\sigma = \dfrac{3\sqrt{p'(1-p')}}{\sqrt{n}}$	UCL $p' + 3\sigma$	LCL $p' - 3\sigma$
July 2	2,228	4	0.0018	0.0051	0.0116	0.0014
3	2,087	9	0.0043	0.0053	0.0118	0.0012
5	2,088	3	0.0014	0.0053	0.0118	0.0012
6	1,746	2	0.0014	0.0058	0.0123	0.0007
7	2,076	1	0.0005	0.0053	0.0118	0.0012
9	2,164	1	0.0005	0.0052	0.0117	0.0013
10	2,855	5	0.0018	0.0045	0.0110	0.0020
11	2,560	5	0.0020	0.0048	0.0113	0.0017
12	2,545	14	0.0055	0.0048	0.0113	0.0017
13	1,874	1	0.0005	0.0056	0.0121	0.0009
14	2,329	24	0.0103	0.0050	0.0115	0.0015
16	2,744	30	0.0109	0.0046	0.0111	0.0019
17	2,619	77	0.0294	0.0047	0.0112	0.0018
18	2,211	5	0.0023	0.0051	0.0116	0.0014
19	1,746	19	0.0109	0.0058	0.0123	0.0007
20	2,628	28	0.0107	0.0047	0.0112	0.0018
21	2,366	5	0.0021	0.0050	0.0115	0.0015
23	2,954	23	0.0078	0.0044	0.0109	0.0021
24	2,586	32	0.0124	0.0047	0.0112	0.0018
25	2,790	8	0.0029	0.0046	0.0111	0.0019
26	2,968	30	0.0101	0.0044	0.0109	0.0021
27	3,100	13	0.0042	0.0043	0.0108	0.0022
28	1,359	4	0.0030	0.0065	0.0130	0.0000
30	3,940	39	0.0099	0.0038	0.0103	0.0027
31	3,138	11	0.0035	0.0043	0.0108	0.0022
Totals	61,701	393				

Standard fraction defective p' is 0.0065
$$3\sqrt{p'(1-p')} = 3\sqrt{(0.0065)(0.9935)} = 0.241$$

Whenever control limits are set in this way on an expected average value of n, any points on the control chart that are either outside the limits or just inside the limits require more critical examination to see whether the limits as drawn really apply to these points. Whenever the subgroup size is larger than the assumed

TABLE 34. RECORD OF DAILY FRACTION DEFECTIVE WITH CONTROL LIMITS COMPUTED ON STANDARD DAILY PRODUCTION AND ON STANDARD VALUE OF FRACTION DEFECTIVE, p'

(Data on a single quality characteristic of a part of an electrical device)

Date	Number inspected n	Number of defectives	Fraction defective p	Date	Number inspected n	Number of defectives	Fraction defective p
Aug. 1*	3,068	6	0.0020	Sept. 1†	2,539	3	0.0012
2	776	3	0.0039	3	2,425	16	0.0066
3	2,086	16	0.0077	4	1,537	9	0.0058
4	3,652	10	0.0027	5	2,852	17	0.0060
6	2,606	3	0.0012	6	2,953	16	0.0054
7	2,159	21	0.0097	7	2,649	5	0.0019
8	2,745	27	0.0098	8	2,835	4	0.0014
9	2,606	3	0.0012	10	2,752	6	0.0022
10	2,159	21	0.0097	11	892	1	0.0011
11	2,745	22	0.0080	12	3,186	7	0.0022
13	3,114	30	0.0096	13	2,646	5	0.0019
14	1,768	18	0.0102	14	2,714	4	0.0015
15	3,208	29	0.0090	15	2,878	5	0.0017
16	2,629	2	0.0008	17	2,384	6	0.0025
17	3,576	9	0.0025	18	2,639	5	0.0019
18	2,262	15	0.0066	19	3,160	7	0.0022
20	3,294	5	0.0015	20	1,895	11	0.0058
21	3,026	5	0.0017	21	4,287	13	0.0030
22	2,713	10	0.0037	22	2,917	3	0.0010
23	2,687	24	0.0089	24	2,479	1	0.0004
24	3,824	23	0.0060	25	1,991	2	0.0010
25	3,265	12	0.0037	26	3,280	10	0.0030
27	1,205	14	0.0116	27	2,195	15	0.0068
28	3,035	7	0.0023	28	2,570	3	0.0012
29	2,793	6	0.0021	29	3,323	3	0.0009
30	3,295	14	0.0042	Totals	65,978	177	
31	3,227	18	0.0056				
Totals	73,523	373					

* For August:

     Estimated average daily production is 2,600

     Standard fraction defective, p', is 0.0065

$$3\sigma = \frac{3\sqrt{p'(1-p')}}{\sqrt{n}} = \frac{3\sqrt{(0.0065)(0.9935)}}{\sqrt{2,600}} = 0.0047$$

     $UCL = p' + 3\sigma = 0.0065 + 0.0047 = 0.0112$

     $LCL = p' - 3\sigma = 0.0065 - 0.0047 = 0.0018$

† For September:

     Estimated average daily production is 2,700

     Standard fraction defective, p', is 0.0051

     $3\sigma = 0.0041$

     $UCL = 0.0051 + 0.0041 = 0.0092$

     $LCL = 0.0051 - 0.0041 = 0.0010$

average value of n, the true limits are inside those drawn. Whenever the subgroup size is smaller, the true limits are outside.

Such a calculation was made for August 27, when p was 0.0116. This is above the upper control limit of 0.0112 which was computed for the assumed daily production of 2,600. A revised upper control limit for this day based on the actual production of 1,205 is 0.0134. The revised limits for this day are indicated on the control chart (Fig. 44); they show that the point was actually not out of control.

189. Further Revision of p'. During August, the average fraction defective $\bar{p}$ was $373/73,523 = 0.0051$. No points fell above the upper control limit. This value, 0.0051, was therefore assumed as p' to apply to September. Control limits for September were based on an estimated average subgroup size of 2,700. (Daily production during August had been $73,523/27 = 2,723$.) Daily values for September with calculated control limits are shown in Table 34 and plotted in Fig. 44.

The process quality during September improved even more. Although only two points fell below the lower control limit during the month, confirmation of the existence of a new better level of quality was given by an extreme run for eleven points—from September 7 to 19—below the central line. For the month, the process average $\bar{p}$ was $177/65,978 = 0.0027$. This justified a further downward revision of p' to 0.0027 for October. The data and the control chart for October are not shown here.

190. The Binomial as a Probability Law That Determines the Fluctuations of Fraction Defective. Suppose 10,000 beads of the same size and density are placed in a container. Of these, 9,500 are white and 500 red. White may be considered to represent good articles, red to represent defective articles. Let samples of 50 beads be drawn at random from this container. If the beads are replaced after each drawing and thoroughly mixed before the next drawing, the theory of probability enables us to calculate the relative frequency in the long run of getting exactly 0, 1, 2, 3, 4, 5, etc. red beads. As explained in Art. 171 and 174, Chap. IX, the binomial gives a very close approximation to these probabilities. If the container held an infinite number of beads, 5% of which were red, the binomial would apply exactly.

Any one sample of beads drawn from the container is a sample from a very large quantity of beads 5% red. As a matter of chance, variations in the number of red beads are inevitable from sample to sample. In a similar way, we may think of a day's production (or other lot) of any manufactured article or part as a sample from a larger quantity with some unknown fraction defective. This unknown universe fraction defective depends upon a complex set of causes influencing the production and inspection operations. As a matter of chance, the fraction defective in the sample may vary considerably. As long as the universe fraction defective remains unchanged, the relative frequencies of various sample fractions defective may be expected to follow the binomial law.

This is the basis for using the formula for standard deviation of the binomial to establish 3-sigma limits on control charts for p. The same general reasoning underlying control limits on the $\bar{X}$ and R chart also applies to the p chart. That is, limits should be placed far enough from the expected average value so that a point outside the limits indicates either that the universe has changed, or that a very unlikely event has happened. If the limits are placed so that the event is unlikely enough, it is safe to act on the assumption that the universe has changed.

If the exact numerical values of the probability of a departure beyond 3-sigma limits were desired, they would have to be computed separately for every value of n and p'. The general statement may be made that they are of the same order of magnitude as the probabilities of a point falling outside 3-sigma limits in drawing from a normal universe. The larger the value of n and the closer p is to 0.5, the closer the fit of the normal curve to the binomial.

Industrial practice in the use of the p chart generally bases control limits either on 3-sigma or some other multiple of sigma. Except for very small subgroups, the calculation of probability limits (such as described for $\bar{X}$, R, and σ charts in Art. 158) for a p chart is too burdensome a job. However, if probability limits are desired, they may be obtained for probability levels of 0.005 and 0.995, and for 0.1 and 0.9, by the use of Simon's I_Q charts.[1]

As in the case of the $\bar{X}$ and R charts, the use of 3-sigma limits rather than narrower or wider limits is a matter of experience as to the economic balance between the cost of hunting for assignable causes when they are absent and the cost of not hunting for them when they are present. Although in most cases 3-sigma limits are best, special cases arise in which the use of narrower limits, such as 2-sigma, is desirable. The need for narrower limits arises out of the use of the p chart as an instrument for executive pressure on quality.

191. Problems Introduced by Variable Subgroup Size. The larger the subgroup, the more likely it is that the fraction defective in the subgroup will be close to the fraction defective of the universe. This obvious general principle is expressed in mathematical terms by the statement that the standard deviation of p, like the standard deviation of $\bar{X}$, varies inversely with $\sqrt{n}$.

For both the $\bar{X}$ chart and the p chart, the appropriate 3-sigma control limits depend on the subgroup size (see Art. 153, Chap. VIII). The practical difference is that because most measurements used for $\bar{X}$ charts are taken for control-chart purposes, it is usually possible to keep subgroup size constant. Most p charts, on the other hand, use data taken for other purposes than the control chart; where subgroups consist of daily or weekly production, the subgroup size is almost certain to vary.

---

[1] SIMON, L. E., "An Engineers' Manual of Statistical Methods," John Wiley & Sons, Inc., New York, 1941, particularly Chaps. III and IV. It should be noted that General Simon uses Q, rather than p, to represent fraction defective.

As a practical matter, whenever subgroup size is expected to vary, a decision must be made as to the way in which control limits are to be shown on the p chart. There are three common solutions to this problem, as follows:

1. Compute new control limits for every subgroup, and show these fluctuating limits on the control chart. This was illustrated in Example 3, Chap. II, and in the first two months of the four months shown in Example 16.

2. Estimate the average subgroup size for the immediate future. Compute one set of limits for this average and draw them on the control chart. Whenever the actual subgroup size is substantially different from this estimated average, separate limits may be computed for individual subgroups. This is particularly necessary if a point for an unusually small subgroup falls outside control limits, or if a point for an unusually large subgroup falls just inside control limits. This scheme was illustrated in the final two months of the period shown in Example 16. Estimates of future average subgroup size must be revised from time to time; where each day's production is one subgroup, it is customary to revise these estimates monthly.

3. Draw several sets of control limits on the chart corresponding to different subgroup sizes. A good plan is to use three sets of limits, one for expected average subgroup size, one close to the expected minimum, and one close to the expected maximum. In Example 16, for instance, limits might have been drawn corresponding to subgroup sizes of 1,000, 2,500, and 4,000. This scheme is not satisfactory unless the data are shown on the same sheet with the control chart, with the figures for each subgroup on the same line with the plotted point for the subgroup, so that the subgroup size may be seen at a glance. Because with this scheme it is not immediately evident from inspection of the chart which points are out of control, it is desirable to use a special symbol to mark out-of-control points. For instance, if a dot were used for each point on the chart, a circle might be drawn around the dot for each point out of control.

192. Simplifying the Computation of Control Limits. The chief objection raised to separate calculation of correct control limits for each subgroup is the time consumed by such calculations. Actually, for any one who can use a slide rule, these calculations should take very little time. With a slide rule, it is not even necessary to compute $\sqrt{n}$ such as was shown in Tables 32 and 33. Once the value of $3\sqrt{p'(1-p')}$ has been computed to apply to all control limits for a given period of time, the division of this each day by $\sqrt{n}$ can be accomplished with a single setting of the slide rule. The precision given by a 10-in. slide rule is entirely satisfactory for calculation of control limits on a p chart.

If limits are to be determined without the use of a slide rule, Table F in Appendix III may be used. This gives upper and lower control limits for a number of per cents defective and subgroup sizes. By interpolation in this table, the values of control limits for any common per cent defective and subgroup size may be found.[1]

Or a diagram may be prepared from which the values of $3\sigma_p$ may be read for any value of n. For any given value of p', the values of $3\sigma_p$ as a function of n plot as a straight line on logarithmic paper.[2] This is illustrated in Fig. 45 which shows such straight lines for the three values of $\bar{p}$ and p' used in Example 16. The curve for any desired value of p' may be obtained by computing $3\sigma_p$ for two values of n, plotting on logarithmic paper the two points so defined and connecting these two points by a straight line. For example, for $p' = 0.0145$ and $n = 900$,

---

[1] For any value of p' or $\bar{p}$ not already given in Table F, a new table may be prepared by interpolation. This computation may be shortened by limiting the new table to the expected range in subgroup size. For example, if such a table had been prepared for upper control limits for a value of $\bar{p}$ of 0.0145 to use in the situation shown in Table 32, it would have been interpolated between the values for 0.014 and 0.016 as follows:

100p	n						
	800	1,000	1,500	2,000	3,000	4,000	5,000
1.40	2.65	2.51	2.31	2.19	2.04	1.96	1.90
1.45	2.72	2.58	2.38	2.25	2.10	2.02	1.96
1.60	2.93	2.79	2.57	2.44	2.29	2.20	2.13

Each value for 1.45 is $\frac{5}{20}$ of the way from the 1.40 value to the 1.60 value.

The upper control limits for the individual days might then be obtained by interpolating in this 1.45 table. For example, the upper control limit for June 6 on which n was 3,350 is interpolated between the values for 3,000 and 4,000. This interpolation gives

$$2.10 - \frac{3,350 - 3,000}{4,000 - 3,000} (2.10 - 2.02) = 2.07$$

Such a linear interpolation in Table F will sometimes result in an error of one or two figures in the final decimal place.

$$3\sigma_p = \frac{3 \sqrt{p'(1 - p')}}{\sqrt{n}}$$

$$\log 3\sigma_p = \log 3 \sqrt{p'(1 - p')} - \tfrac{1}{2} \log n$$

If, for any given value of p', $\log 3\sigma_p$ is plotted on rectangular coordinate paper as a function of $\log n$, it is evident from this equation that the resulting curve will be a straight line with a slope of $-\tfrac{1}{2}$ and an intercept of $\log 3 \sqrt{p'(1 - p')}$. Such a plotting on rectangular coordinate paper is equivalent to plotting $3\sigma_p$ as a function of n on paper having a logarithmic ruling.

$3\sigma_p$ is $0.359/\sqrt{900} = 0.01197$.   For $n = 4,900$,

$$3\sigma_p = 0.359/\sqrt{4,900} = 0.00513$$

These two points may be plotted and connected by a straight line.   The straight lines for all values of p' are parallel to one another.   Thus lines for additional values of p', such as 0.0065, may be added to the diagram by computing the coordinates of a single point and drawing a line through that point parallel to the original line.[1]

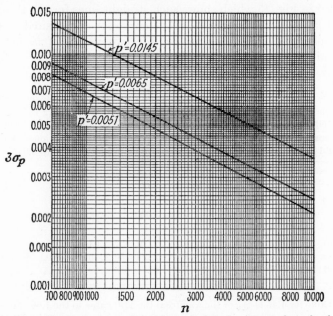

FIG. 45.   A logarithmic chart may be used to calculate $3\sigma_p$ for any desired value of p'.

193. Outline of Necessary Steps in Connection with Control Chart for Fraction Defective.   It is helpful to visualize the decisions and calculations that must be made and the actions which must be taken as occurring in a sequence somewhat as follows: (The numbers of the articles in which each step is discussed are given in parentheses.)

I. Decisions preparatory to the control chart
    A. Determination of the purpose of the chart (194)
    B. Selection of inspection station and quality characteristics to be charted (195–196)
    C. Decisions on the selection of subgroups (197)
    D. Choice between chart for p and chart for np (198)

---

[1] A special purpose slide rule may also be used.   One such rule is the Statistical Quality Control Slide Rule designed by John Howell and manufactured by Pickett & Eckel, Inc., Alhambra, California.   This is a standard log-log-type slide rule that also contains scales for use in calculation of limits on $\bar{X}$, R, σ, and p charts as well as

I. DECISIONS PREPARATORY TO THE CONTROL CHART

194. Determination of the Purpose of the p Chart. As applied to 100% inspection, a control chart for fraction defective may have any or all of the following purposes:

1. To discover the average proportion of defective articles or parts submitted for inspection over a period of time.

2. To bring to the attention of management any changes in this average quality level.

3. To discover those out-of-control high spots that call for action to identify and correct causes of bad quality.

4. To discover those out-of-control low spots that indicate either relaxed inspection standards or erratic causes of quality improvement which might be converted into causes of consistent quality improvement.

5. To suggest places for the use of $\bar{X}$ and R charts to diagnose quality problems.

The p chart as applied to sampling inspection on a lot-by-lot basis may have any or all of the purposes cited for 100% inspection. An additional purpose usually is:

6. To afford a basis for judgment whether successive lots may be considered as representative of a process. This judgment may properly influence the severity of acceptance criteria. This matter is discussed at length in Chap. XV.

---

areas under the normal curve. The Bender Control Limit Calculator, manufactured by the Bender Calculator Company, Anderson, Indiana, is a circular rule designed for calculation of control limits on $\bar{X}$, R, p and c charts.

EXAMPLE 17. AN ILLUSTRATION OF THE SELECTION OF QUALITY CHARACTERISTICS FOR CHARTS FOR FRACTION DEFECTIVE

195. Facts of the Case. In this example, the product manufactured was an automatic pressure switch used to open and close a valve in a gas line in order to maintain gas pressure within given limits. An inspection station was located in the assembly line just before the cover was bolted onto this device. This was not final inspection in the sense that it involved a check of the over-all functioning of the device. However, it was the final chance before the completion of the device to identify a number of defects that would prevent the functioning of a completed pressure switch.

At this inspection station 31 different possible defects might be observed. A *defect* is defined as any failure to conform to specifications. A device with one or more defects is called a *defective*. For purposes of the inspector's record sheet, each defect was designated by its initials or some symbol based on its initials (such as *BL* for broken lead, *DR* for defective receptacle, etc.).

When the *p* chart was first applied at this inspection station, the average proportion defective was around 15%. It was decided to start with 11 *p* charts. A chart was maintained for each of the following nine defects: (1) points off; (2) broken lead; (3) defective receptacle; (4) defective bar; (5) high tube; (6) cracked base; (7) loose bar; (8) close bar; and (9) defective tube. The other 22 of the 31 possible defects were grouped together in a single chart (10) for miscellaneous. In addition, a chart was kept for total per cent defective. The total number of *defectives* recorded from any day's inspection might, of course, be less than the total *defects* observed, as one device containing two or more defects would be classified as only one defective. For this reason, the fraction defective shown on the total chart was generally less than the sum of the fractions defective shown on the 10 constituent charts.

Prompt attention to out-of-control points on some of the charts resulted in a substantial improvement in the average quality. In a short time, "points off" was reduced from 4.5% to 0.5% and "total defectives" reduced from 15% to 9%. After the charts had been in operation for three months, it was decided that separate charts for individual defects could be abandoned except for the three defects which were giving the most trouble. After several more months of work on these defects, the total defectives level was reduced to 3%. At this time all control charts for separate defects were abandoned and only a single control chart for the total fraction defective was maintained.

In the establishment of these control charts, a problem was created by the fact that all rework as well as all new work was inspected at this station. Experience showed that the chances of rejection of a reworked article were considerably greater than the chances of rejection of a new article. There was a tendency on the part of the production department to accumulate rework for several days; then a large number of reworked devices would come to the inspection station on the same day. If these had been included in the inspection record, the days receiving considerable rework would have shown lack of control. Moreover, the average quality level would have appeared to be worse than it really was, because of the inclusion of two or more rejections of the same article. And the number of items inspected would have appeared to be greater than the total production. For these reasons, the maintenance of the control chart made it necessary to put special tags on all rework items and to keep separate inspection records for inspection of rework, which were not included in the control-chart data.

196. Comments on Selection of Inspection Stations and Quality Characteristics to Be Charted. It is a common practice for a p chart to be applied at an inspection station where many different quality characteristics are to be checked. In such cases, a decision must always be made on the question faced in Example 17, *i.e.*, whether to have one control chart or several. A single control chart is the most common solution, with the thought that any investigation of the causes of rejections may look to the supporting data on the inspection record sheet.

Occasionally, however, it will pay to follow the scheme used in Example 17 of separate control charts for certain selected defects. It is nearly always true that different defects are unequal in their influence on costs. Some may be corrected by simple inexpensive rework operations; others require costly rework; others involve the scrapping of the article inspected. It may pay to concentrate attention by means of separate control charts on those defects which are responsible for the greatest costs. A single control chart that includes all defects observed at an inspection station will have its variations (and its showings of lack of control) influenced more by the most common defects than by the most costly ones.

In some cases it may pay to keep separate control charts for spoilage and rework. This may be particularly true in checking dimensions with go and not-go gages, where rejection by the go gage means rework, and rejection by the not-go means spoilage (or vice versa, depending on the dimension to be checked).

Another breakdown for control-chart purposes may be on the basis of the effect of a defect on the functioning of a part or product. The classification into Critical, Major, Minor A, and Minor B defects, discussed in Chap. XV, is an example of this. This breakdown is most common in the case of sampling acceptance plans that use acceptance criteria which depend on the seriousness of a defect.

In all cases, the determination of which inspection stations should employ p charts should be based on a consideration of whether the accomplishment of the purposes outlined in Art. 194 seems likely to have a sufficiently favorable effect on costs to justify the expense of maintaining the chart.

197. Decision on the Selection of Subgroups. As in the case of the Shewhart control chart for variables, in the control chart for fraction defective the most natural basis for selecting rational subgroups is the order in which production takes place.

A common basis for subgrouping is the one illustrated in Examples 3 and 16 in which each subgroup consisted of the items inspected in a day. This is a good basis wherever the inspection operation is an integral part of the production process, so that the order of inspection is substantially the same as the order of production. Sometimes a control chart showing daily per cent defective may be supplemented by charts showing weekly and monthly figures. The daily chart may be used as a basis for current action on the manufacturing process by production supervisors, methods analysts, and operators; the weekly chart may be used by manufacturing executives such as department heads; the monthly chart may be used in quality reports to top management.

Where production is not on a continuous basis, a satisfactory alternative basis of subgrouping may be to consider each production order as one subgroup.

In the sampling inspection of a large lot of purchased articles from a single source, it is often desirable to use the p chart as a test for homogeneity in order to judge whether the sample may be considered to be representative of the entire lot. For example, consider the receipt of a shipment of 100,000 bolts packed in 50 containers each holding 2,000 bolts. Even though the purchaser of the bolts has no way of knowing the order of production, there is a strong likelihood that the bolts have not been thoroughly mixed since production took place. If 50 bolts were taken at random from each box of 2,000, and tested for conformity to specifications, each such sample of 50 would be an appropriate rational subgroup for use in a p chart. If the control chart showed control, the conclusion would be either that (1) the bolts had been well mixed, or (2) although not well mixed, they came from a production process that was in statistical control. Either conclusion would be satisfactory from the standpoint of considering the 2,500 bolts inspected as representative of the lot of 100,000.

In all control charts, rational subgroups should be selected in a way that tends to minimize the chance for variation within any subgroup. A possible assignable cause of variation in any inspection operation is difference in inspectors. This is particularly true in inspection by attributes. In visual inspection, where judgment plays an important part, there is a great chance for differences among inspectors. Even with go and not-go gages, inspectors may differ considerably. If each subgroup is taken in a way to reflect the work of only one inspector, the p chart may sometimes be used as a useful check on inspection standards.

198. Choice between Chart for p and Chart for np. Whenever subgroup size is variable, the control chart must show the fraction defective (or proportion defective) rather than the actual number of defectives. If actual numbers of defectives were plotted, the central line on the chart (as well as the limits) would need to be changed with every change in subgroup size. However if subgroup size is constant, the chart for actual number of defectives may be used. Such a chart is called a chart for np or pn. (The fraction defective p was obtained by dividing the actual number of defectives by the subgroup size n. The actual number of defectives may therefore be represented by np, the quantity which, divided by n, gives p.)

A chart for np may be used for data such as those shown in Table 35. This table gives the results of inspection of a sheet-metal part for an aircraft turbosupercharger skin. The part was inspected after being shaped by means of a drop hammer.

TABLE 35. CALCULATIONS FOR CONTROL CHART FOR NUMBER OF DEFECTIVES, np
(Inspection in drop-hammer department of sheet-metal part)

Production order number	Lot size n	Number of defectives np
1	200	23
2	200	15
3	200	17
4	200	15
5	200	41
6	200	0
7	200	25
8	200	31
9	200	29
10	200	0
11	200	8
12	200	16
Totals.....	2,400	220

$$n\bar{p} = \frac{220}{12} = 18.3$$

$$\bar{p} = \frac{220}{2,400} = 0.0917$$

$$3\sigma_{np} = 3\sqrt{n\bar{p}(1-\bar{p})} = 3\sqrt{(200)(0.0917)(0.9083)} = 12.2$$
$$UCL = n\bar{p} + 3\sigma_{np} = 18.3 + 12.2 = 30.5$$
$$LCL = n\bar{p} - 3\sigma_{np} = 18.3 - 12.2 = 6.1$$

As explained in Art. 173, Chap. IX, the standard deviation of the *number* of occurrences in n trials of an event with a constant probability of occurrence p' (in other words, the standard deviation of the *number* of defectives) is $\sqrt{np'(1-p')}$. The standard deviation of the *proportion* of occurrences (in other words, the *fraction* defective) is $\sqrt{p'(1-p')/n}$. Thus 3-sigma limits on the chart for np are $3\sqrt{np'(1-p')}$ in contrast to the 3-sigma limits of $3\sqrt{p'(1-p')}/\sqrt{n}$ on the chart for p. In Table 35, as no standard value of p' had been established, the average fraction defective $\bar{p}$ is used as the best available estimate of p'.

Figure 46 shows a chart for np for the data of Table 35. If a chart for p were drawn for the same data, it would look exactly like the chart for np except for the graduations on the vertical scale. Each unit on the vertical scale would represent $\frac{1}{200}$ (*i.e.*, $1/n$) as much as it does on the chart for np. It is evident that there is no fundamental difference in the appearance of the np and the p charts or in the information they give.

Where subgroup size is constant, there might be two possible reasons for preferring an np chart to a p chart. One reason is that the np chart saves one calculation for each subgroup, the division of number of defectives by subgroup size to get p. The other reason is that some people may understand the np chart more readily.

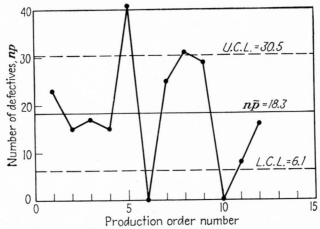

Fig. 46. An np chart shows actual numbers of defectives rather than per cent defective.

However, it often happens that in a manufacturing plant there are many places where, because of variable subgroup size, only a p chart is applicable, and a few places where, because subgroup size is constant, either type of chart may be used. In such cases, the possibility of confusion from having two types of chart might outweigh the slight advantage of the np chart, and it would be better to use the p chart even for constant subgroup size.

199. Decision Regarding Calculation of Control Limits. For any p chart with variable subgroup size, a decision must be made whether to compute new control limits for each subgroup or to adopt one of the less accurate methods described in Art. 191.

In making this decision, it should be recognized that only the separately computed limits are really correct. The objections raised in some manufacturing plants to separately computed limits have been twofold, namely,

(1) the difficulty (and therefore, cost) of their calculation, and (2) the difficulty in explaining to many of the people who see the control charts the reasons why control limits vary from day to day.

The difficulties and costs of separate calculations of control limits for each subgroup tend to be overestimated. As explained in Art. 192, there are a number of ways in which the job of making these computations can be simplified. With proper organization of the calculations, the extra costs of computing separate limits may be negligible.

On the other hand, where the p charts are posted in places available to shop personnel, there are real difficulties in explaining varying control limits. (Sometimes it may be even harder to explain them to the top executives than to the machine operators.) This may be a good reason for establishing one set of limits based on expected average subgroup size, particularly if such limits do not have to be changed frequently and if variations in subgroup size are not so great as to call for numerous calculations of separate limits for individual subgroups (such as the one shown in Fig. 44 for August 27). However, where subgroup sizes vary enough so that numerous variations in limits are inevitable, it may be better practical psychology to have everyone get used to the idea that control limits *always* vary with subgroup size, rather than to have control limits seem to vary in some cases and not in others.

200. Setting Up the Forms for Recording and Charting the Data. Figure 47 illustrates a form used for recording data for a control chart

RECORD SHEET FOR p CHART

Name of product or part ______ Part No. ______
Characteristics measured ______
Inspection station ______ Recorded by ______

Lot No.	Date	Number inspected	No. of defectives	Percent defective	Control limits		Remarks
					Upper	Lower	

FIG. 47. A simple form for p chart data.

for fraction defective. This form contains space for all the information which is essential for preparing the control chart itself.

Often it is desirable that information regarding the particular defects observed be included in a record sheet showing items inspected and numbers of defectives found. Figure 48 illustrates a sampling record form containing columns giving this type of information. This form was used by Allen B. DuMont Laboratories, Incorporated, and is reproduced from an article by C. L. Gartner, Quality Control in Television Receiver Manufacturing, in the November, 1951, issue of *Industrial Quality Control*.

LOT BY LOT SAMPLING RECORD

PART No. 0300/570

DESCRIPTION Cap, Pa, .005 mf 25%

600 V

VENDOR ▇▇▇▇

SAMP. PLAN No. DR-7

SUMMARY PERIOD 3 mos.

DEFECTS IN FIRST SAMPLE: Out of tol. on high side; " " " low; Wrong lead length; Oin holes in wax coating

#	1949 YEAR DATE	REC. REPORT No.	LOT SIZE	FIRST SAMPLE SS₁	DEF.	TOTAL SAMPLE SS₁+SS₂+	TOTAL DEF.	Out of tol. high	" low	Wrong lead length	holes wax					INSPECTOR'S INITIALS	DISPOSITION OF LOT	REMARK No.
1	8/15	0014	1000	35	0											TH	P	
2	8/25	0090	700	35	0											BX	P	
3	9/5	0170	1500	50	1	150	3	1								BX	R	1
4	9/20	0220	1800	50	1	150	2	1								CD	P	
5	10/5	0278	1250	35	1	105	1									TH	P	
6	10/22	0315	1155	35	2			1	1							BK	R	2
7	10/31		7405	240	5			2	1	1	1							3
8																		
9	11-1	0407	1200	35	0											TH	P	
10	11/13	0438	1500	50	0											TH	P	
11	11/29	0500	2100	50	0											BK	P	
12	12/5	0539	2900	50	4			2	2							BK	R	4
13	12/10	0581	3500	75	0											TH	P	
14	12/17	0644	2700	50	0											TH	P	
15	1/8	0773	2005	50	1					1						TH	P	
16	2/1		15905	360	5													3
17																		
18	2/3	0838	1550	50	0											CD	P	
19	2/21	0907	1275	35	0											CD	P	
20	3/5	0982	1475	50	0											TH	P	
21																		
22																		
23																		
24																		
25																		

REMARKS: 1. Returned to vendor
2. Rush- Balance of lot inspected.
3. Entered into summary report.
4. Rejection waived on lead lengths. 100 % electrical inspection of lot.

FIG. 48.　Record of attributes inspection including columns showing different types of defects observed.　(*Reproduced from article by Carl L. Gartner in Industrial Quality Control.*)

The chart itself may be plotted to advantage on coordinate paper with a "profile" type of ruling.

A compact presentation is provided by a combination of data sheet and control chart in one form such as is illustrated in Fig. 49. This particular form shows weekly figures as well as daily figures.

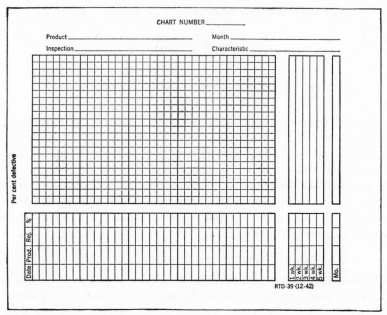

FIG. 49.   This form combines p chart data with a control chart.   (*Courtesy of General Electric Company.*)

II. STARTING THE CONTROL CHART

201. Essential Steps in the Control Chart.   The steps in starting the control chart were illustrated in Example 16.   Briefly stated, they are:

1. Record the data for each subgroup on number inspected and number of defectives.   Any occurrences that might be clues to an explanation of points out of control or to changes in the quality level should be noted on the data sheet as supplementary remarks.

2. Compute p for each subgroup

$$p = \frac{\text{number of defectives in subgroup}}{\text{number inspected in subgroup}} = \frac{np}{n}$$

3. Compute $\bar{p}$, the average fraction defective

$$\bar{p} = \frac{\text{total number of defectives during period}}{\text{total number inspected during period}}$$

Wherever practicable, it is desirable to have data for 25 subgroups before computing $\bar{p}$ and establishing trial control limits.

4. Compute trial control limits for each subgroup.   These are

$$UCL = \bar{p} + \frac{3 \sqrt{\bar{p}(1 - \bar{p})}}{\sqrt{n}}$$

$$LCL = \bar{p} - \frac{3 \sqrt{\bar{p}(1 - \bar{p})}}{\sqrt{n}}$$

5. Plot each point as obtained.   Plot trial control limits as soon as calculated and note whether the process appears to be in control.

It often happens that when the decision is made to use a p chart for any manufacturing operation, data are available for the period immediately past.   If so, the steps just outlined should be applied to this past record.   This permits putting the p chart to work at once as an effective instrument for process control and avoids a period for which no control limits are currently available.

III. CONTINUING THE CONTROL CHART

202. Selecting a Standard Fraction Defective p'.   The p chart is not, as generally used, merely a test for the presence or absence of assignable causes of variation.   It is also a basis for judging whether the quality level is at some desired objective.

In the setting of a standard fraction defective p', the two purposes sometimes seem to be in conflict.   For example, if p' should be set at 0.02 and if the process actually is in statistical control (*i.e.*, there are no assignable causes of variation from subgroup to subgroup) at a substantially higher fraction defective, such as 0.05, the majority of the points on the control chart may fall above the upper control limit.   With the p chart used to establish a standard quality level, points may be expected to fall outside control limits for either of two reasons, (1) the existence of assignable causes of variation, or (2) the existence of a quality level that is different from the assumed standard p'.   This interpretation of the p chart should be kept in mind in the establishment and revision of the standard fraction defective p'.

When a preliminary period has been completed and trial limits have been computed on the basis of $\bar{p}$, the control chart may show any condition from an excellent state of control with all points falling within control limits to an apparently hopeless absence of control with very few points within limits.

If the chart shows control, p' should be assumed equal to $\bar{p}$.   This is generally desirable even though $\bar{p}$ is considered too high a fraction defective to be satisfactory in the long run.   For any standard really to be accepted by production personnel as a basis for action, there needs to be evidence that the standard is attainable.   As illustrated in Example

16, p' may later be reduced as soon as efforts to improve the general quality level have resulted in lower values of $\bar{p}$.

If the chart shows apparently hopeless absence of control, it is generally better to continue the p chart for a time without any control limits (and without any standard value of fraction defective) until the situation can be somewhat improved. For control limits to be respected, there needs to be evidence that it is possible to stay within the control limits most of the time. Until such evidence exists, the drawing of control limits on a p chart can be of little help and may hurt the control-chart program by creating a state of mind antagonistic to control limits.

In most cases, the control chart for the preliminary period will show a condition somewhere between the two extremes of perfect statistical control and complete absence of control. There will be a few points outside control limits, even though the majority fall within limits. This common situation was illustrated in Example 16. In such cases, the best procedure is to eliminate the points above the upper control limit and then to recompute $\bar{p}$. (In Example 16, this revised $\bar{p}$ was 0.0063 in contrast to the original $\bar{p}$ of 0.0145.) Judgment may then be applied to the revised $\bar{p}$ when establishing the standard fraction defective p' to be used in the immediate future.

203. Calculation of Control Limits. Once p' is established, 3-sigma control limits are computed currently from the following formulas:

$$UCL = p' + \frac{3\sqrt{p'(1-p')}}{\sqrt{n}}$$

$$LCL = p' - \frac{3\sqrt{p'(1-p')}}{\sqrt{n}}$$

Where subgroup size is variable, limits should be computed separately for each subgroup unless some plan for approximate limits is adopted such as one of those described in Art. 191 (see also Arts. 188 and 199).

Except in rare instances, it is desirable to standardize on 3-sigma control limits. For comment on the use of narrower limits, see Art. 190.

204. Plotting the Points and Limits. As soon as the data are obtained, points and limits should be plotted promptly on the control chart. Promptness is particularly important where the charts are posted in the shop where they may be seen by operating personnel and foremen.

In charts exhibited in the shop, it is often desirable to omit the lower control limit. It is almost impossible to make clear to some operating people just why a point should be classed as out of control when it refers to quality that is better than the standard.

In the discussion of the $\bar{X}$ and R charts, it was stated that it is generally desirable not to draw lines connecting the points which represent the successive subgroups. The contrary is true in the case of the p chart; a line connecting the points is usually helpful in interpretation of the chart. Such a line assists in the interpretation of trends; this may be almost as important on the p chart as the interpretation of control limits.

205. Interpretation of Lack of Control. There may be erratic changes in the quality level for an occasional subgroup, even though quality is otherwise maintained at the standard fraction defective p'. Such changes are shown by points outside control limits and are evidence of assignable causes of variation.

In most p charts that extend over any considerable length of time, there are also definite sustained shifts of average fraction defective to a new level either better or worse than standard. Both types of shift were illustrated in Example 3. A shift to a better level was illustrated in Example 16. Such departures from the standard fraction defective p' are often evident merely from inspection of the control chart without application of any formal statistical tests. Extreme runs above or below the central line, as well as points outside control limits, may be used to provide tests that supplement observation of the chart. The rules regarding extreme runs that were suggested for $\overline{X}$ charts in Art. 88, Chap. V, are also applicable to the p chart.

For purposes of a statistical test, any consecutive set of subgroups may be combined into a single subgroup. In this way the average fraction defective of a set of subgroups may be tested to see whether it varies by more than 3-sigma from the standard fraction defective.

For instance, the September data in Example 16 might be tested to see whether the observed fraction defective during September, 0.0027, may be explained as a chance variation from a process which has its average at the assumed p' of 0.0051. With all September combined into a single subgroup, the subgroup size n is 65,978 (see Art. 189 and Table 34). The lower control limit corresponding to this subgroup size and to a p' of 0.0051 is computed as follows:

$$LCL = p' - \frac{3\sqrt{p'(1 - p')}}{\sqrt{n}} = 0.0051 - \frac{3\sqrt{(0.0051)(0.9949)}}{\sqrt{65,978}}$$
$$= 0.0051 - 0.0008 = 0.0043$$

It is evident that the September figure of 0.0027 is a long way outside the limits. (The difference of 0.0024 between the p' of 0.0051 and the actual p of 0.0027 is really a 9-sigma difference.) As this makes it clear that a new improved quality level has been established, it is possible to proceed with confidence to set a new value of p'.

206. Periodic Review and Revision of p'. The standard fraction defective should be reviewed from time to time. This might be done at irregular intervals whenever there seems to be enough evidence to justify a change; this plan was illustrated in Example 3, Chap. II. Where many p charts are being used, it is usually better practice to ensure periodic review by establishing a regular review period. In Example 16, this review period was once a month. Where a subgroup consists of one day's production, it may be satisfactory to have a 2 months' review period, with half the charts reviewed each month. Where subgroups consist of production orders or of lots submitted for inspection, the frequency of subgroups will influence the proper length of the review period. This period might then be stated as once every 20 subgroups, once every 40 subgroups, etc.

Whenever there is sustained evidence of an improved quality level, it is a good idea to revise p' downward. This helps to supply an incentive to hold this new and better level. On the other hand, when there is sustained evidence of a poorer quality level, the quality control engineer should be reluctant to revise p' upward. An upward revision should not be made without evidence that changes have taken place, such as tighter specification limits or poorer incoming materials, which seem to make it inevitable that with the same attention to quality as before, the fraction defective will increase. The value of p' should not be increased merely on the basis of a poorer quality level that seems to have resulted from less attention to quality on the part of production personnel.

IV. REPORTS AND ACTIONS BASED ON THE CONTROL CHART

207. Action to Bring a Process into Control at a Satisfactory Level. Experience shows that the mere introduction of a p chart often causes some quality improvement. This improvement may result from the influence of the chart in focusing the attention of production personnel on the quality level and may have no relation to the actual use of the control limits. This influence is most likely to be effective when the chart is new.

In the long run, much of the quality improvement attributable to the use of the p chart will come from concentration of attention on assignable causes of trouble indicated whenever a point on the chart falls above the upper control limit. Such out-of-control points are known as "high spots." Often they are reported to production supervisors and to management in regular forms known as "high spot reports."

Frequently the discovery and correction of assignable causes of poor quality are really technical jobs. In such cases, it may do no good merely to bring pressure on the production foreman by means of a high spot report. The foreman may already know he is in trouble; what he needs is technical help in discovering its causes.

For this reason, any p chart program may need to be reinforced by methods engineers or other technical specialists who are available to give immediate attention to the most urgent high spots. In this connection, it should be emphasized that the only clue given by the p chart as to the *cause* of lack of control is the *time* at which lack of control was observed. This is in contrast to the $\overline{X}$ and R charts which, as pointed out in Chaps. V and VI, are often very effective instruments for the diagnosis of the causes why product fails to meet specifications. The p chart, therefore, may point to the place for effective use of $\overline{X}$ and R charts. This was illustrated in Example 3, Chap. II.

Low spots on the control chart (*i.e.*, points below the lower control limit) call for a different kind of attention from that given to high spots. They sometimes point to faulty inspection and may indicate the necessity of providing better inspection standards or securing better inspectors. In other cases they may be worth examining to find the reasons why quality for one subgroup was so much better than the standard; a knowledge of these reasons may help to bring about more permanent quality improvement.

208. Use of the Control Chart as a Basis for Sampling Acceptance Procedures. No scheme of accepting product on the basis of inspection of samples can ensure that the product not inspected conforms to the specifications. Every sampling acceptance plan implies a willingness to take a chance on accepting *some* defective product. It is good sense to recognize this fact by a conscious decision as to just what per cent defective is acceptable in each case. The practical question then becomes just how great a chance is being taken on accepting product worse than the acceptable quality level. This point is elaborated in Chaps. XIII, XIV, and XV.

The degree of the chance being taken depends in part on whether or not the specified quality characteristics of the product inspected are in statistical control. If control exists at a satisfactory level, adequate quality protection may be obtained with smaller samples and less severe acceptance criteria than would otherwise seem to be necessary. The use of the control chart viewpoint in determining eligibility for reduced inspection is explained in Chap. XV.

209. Review of Design and Specifications in Relation to the Capabilities of a Production Process. The control chart for p may exhibit fairly good control over a period of time, but this control may be at an average fraction defective that is too high to be satisfactory. This suggests that the situation can be improved only by fundamental changes of some sort.

Such a fundamental change might be in the design of the product. For example, a p chart used in the manufacture of an oxygen pressure gage gave an average fraction defective which was too high. It was suggested that this might be corrected by the use of a somewhat heavier Bourdon tube in the gage. When this change in design was made, the average fraction defective was immediately reduced to half of its previous figure.

Or it might be a change in specifications. For instance, a review of the needs of the product might indicate that tolerances were tighter than necessary on certain dimensions.

Or it might be a change in the production process through the substitution of new tooling or new machinery.

These matters may call for joint study of the problem by representatives of design, production, and inspection.

210. Information to Management regarding the Quality Level. The facts obtained for purposes of a p chart constitute information that should always be available to management. But—as suggested in the quotation at the start of this chapter—frequently this information is not available in any form.

The usual difficulty is that although numbers of defectives may have been regularly recorded, no record shows the numbers inspected for each group of defectives. To compare quality levels at different times, it is necessary to know the fractions defective at the various times. Every fraction has a numerator and a denominator. The numerator, number of defectives, is commonly recorded. The denominator, number inspected, is often omitted. One great advantage of the p chart is that it requires the denominator as well as the numerator to be recorded and thus supplies information to management regarding the current quality level and the changes in that level.

In a plant where there are a number of departments, and many control charts for fraction defective are maintained in each department, it may be desirable to prepare charts which in some way summarize all the p charts in each department. Such summary charts may be useful to top executives who would not have time to examine each individual p chart.

211. Special Definition of a Defective for p Chart Purposes. In order to make effective use of the control chart for fraction defective as a help in process control, there must be some defectives in the sample observed. It is obvious that the better the quality, the larger must be the sample in order to find some defectives in the majority of the samples. If only 0.1% of the product is defective, the sample size must be at least 1,000 before there will be an average of one defective per sample. On the other hand if 20% of the product is defective, a sample size of 5 will give an average of one defective per sample. It is evident that with very good quality the p chart is useful in detecting lack of control only if samples are large; with poor quality, the p chart may be useful with small samples.

In some cases where the quality level is good and it is necessary to use inspection by attributes, circumstances require the use of small samples. Here the only way in which a p chart or np chart may be used to advantage is by artificially creating a bad quality level by applying acceptance standards for control-chart purposes which are much more severe than those really imposed by the specifications. That is, there may be established a special severe definition of a "defective" which is used only for purposes of process control by means of the control chart. In this way, the small sample size is not such an obstacle to the use of a control chart based on inspection by attributes.

This scheme has been applied advantageously in certain types of electrical testing and in ballistic testing. In Great Britain it has been applied to dimensional control. Example 18 describes an application taken from British literature.[1]

EXAMPLE 18. PROCESS CONTROL BY np CHART BASED ON GAGE TOLER-ANCES THAT ARE TIGHTER THAN SPECIFICATION TOLERANCES

212. Facts of the Case. This example deals with an internal diameter specified as 1.008 ± 0.0035 in. Actual measurements were made on 100 components. These showed control with an estimated σ' of 0.0011. The following calculations show the relationship between the natural tolerances of the process and the specification tolerances

$$X_{max} - X_{min} = 1.0115 - 1.0045 = 0.0070 \text{ in.}$$
$$6\sigma' = 6(0.0011) = 0.0066 \text{ in.}$$

As the tolerance spread was barely greater than $6\sigma'$, it was evident that the centering of the dimension must be maintained accurately at the nominal dimension of 1.008.

A special quality control gage was made with not-go and go dimensions as 1.00925 and 1.00675, respectively. These limits were at $\bar{X}' \pm 1.14\sigma'$. If the distribution were normal and perfect statistical control were maintained with the dimension centered at its nominal value, approximately 25% of the product would be rejected by this quality control gage, even though substantially all the product would be within specification limits.

Samples of 10 were used with this quality control gage. A variation of the np chart was used. The upper half of this chart showed the number rejected by the not-go gage and the lower half showed the number rejected by the go gage. In accordance with the British practice, warning limits as well as action limits were used on this chart.

Figure 50 shows a comparison of this chart for number of defectives with an $\bar{X}$ chart based on actual measurements of the same components which were gaged with the special go and not-go gage. This applies to a period when the process was out of

---

[1] Quantity Control by Limit Gauging, *Production and Engineering Bulletin*, vol. 3, pp. 433–437, October, 1944. This article also contains other examples and gives general directions for the application of this technique to dimensional control. See also A. E. Mace, The Use of Limit Gages in Process Control, *Industrial Quality Control*, vol. 8, No. 4, pp. 24–31, January, 1952.

control. It will be observed that the lack of control was readily apparent from this np chart, with even more points showing out of control than on the chart for averages.

213. Comment on Example 18. In some manufacturing plants, patrol inspection is carried out with go and not-go gages having tighter tolerances than the gages used for acceptance or rejection of finished product. This may provide a good opportunity for the use of the type of np chart shown in Fig. 50.

The appropriate value of p' for use in setting control limits on this np chart is not necessarily the average value $\bar{p}$ as determined from the work gages. For best results, it is necessary to estimate σ', the universe standard deviation. (In Example 18 this estimate was made by actual measurements on 100 components.) This permits differentiation of circumstances where the centering of a dimension must be closely con-

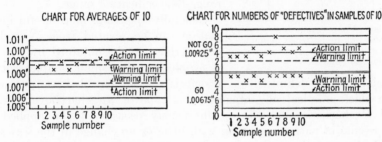

FIG. 50. Comparison of charts for $\overline{X}$ and np for out-of-control period—Example 18. (*Reproduced from Quality Control by Limit Gauging, Production and Engineering Bulletin. October, 1944.*)

trolled from those circumstances where the average value may be permitted to shift.

Figure 51 illustrates the case in which the centering of a process may not shift without producing defective product. If samples of 10 are to be used, the gage limits should be set so that each shaded portion of the area under the frequency curve (representing satisfactory product rejected by the work gage) includes 10 to 15% of the total area under the curve. In this case, if the centering is maintained, the "defectives" observed by the go portion of the work gage will be approximately equal to those observed by the not-go portion of the gage. If the sum of the shaded areas in Fig. 51 is 25% of the area under the frequency curve, p' is 0.125 for the go chart and 0.125 for the not-go chart. If the centering of the process is maintained, the observed $\bar{p}$ values will be practically the same as these p' values.

Figure 52 illustrates the case in which the centering of a process may be allowed to shift through a considerable range. If control-chart limits are to be set to permit this shift, p' should be based on the ratio of each shaded area to the total area under the frequency curve, just as was done in the case illustrated by Fig. 51. However, in Fig. 52 the actual fraction rejected by the work gages might be considerably less than in Fig. 51; *i.e.*, $\bar{p}$ might be less than the value of p' used for establishing control limits.

In Example 18, the tolerance range used for the special quality control gage (0.0025) was about one-third the total range permitted by the specifications (0.0070). This is approximately the best ratio for cases

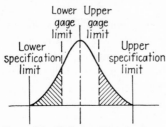

Fig. 51. Relationship between special severe gage limits and specification limits when manufacturing process can just work to specification limits.

of the type illustrated in Fig. 51. For cases such as illustrated in Fig. 52, the tolerance range on the work gage should be a larger fraction of the tolerance range permitted by the specifications; the greater the permissible shift in process average, the greater the best value of work gage range to specification range.

Generally speaking, more useful information can be secured from $\bar{X}$ and R charts than can be obtained by the use of np charts using small samples with a special severe definition of a defective for control-chart purposes. The chief practical advantage of this type of np chart over the $\bar{X}$ and R charts is that the np chart may occasionally be applied to the results of patrol inspection with little or no change in the way this inspection is being carried on. In such circumstances, the np chart may involve lower costs for securing data and a minimum amount of

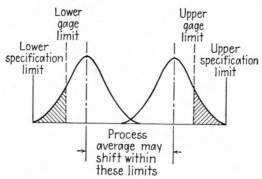

Fig. 52. Relationship between special severe gage limits and specification limits when manufacturing process has a margin to spare.

training of personnel and changing of inspection procedures. Unless these conditions favorable to the np chart are present, the $\bar{X}$ and R charts are usually preferable.

214. Sensitivity of the p Chart. With small samples and reasonably good quality, the fraction defective of a single sample is a very poor indicator of the quality of the product from which a sample is taken.

The larger the sample, the more closely it may be expected to reflect the universe. Consider, for example, samples of various sizes drawn from product that is 2% defective. A sample of 5 will generally be either 0 or 20% defective (that is, it will contain either 0 or 1 defective). A sample of 20 will generally be from 0 to 10% defective. A sample of 100 will generally be from 0 to 6% defective. A sample of 2,000 will generally be from 1.06 to 2.94% defective. A sample of 50,000 will generally be from 1.81 to 2.19% defective. In the preceding statements, "generally" applies to 3-sigma limits.

For this reason, the smaller the subgroup size, the less sensitive is the p chart to changes in the quality level and the less satisfactory it is as an indicator of assignable causes of variation. As pointed out in the three preceding articles, the higher the fraction defective (up to 50%), the better the results obtainable from small samples as indicators of lack of control.

Where it is desirable to use a control chart for a single measurable quality characteristic and a choice must be made between the p chart and the $\bar{X}$ chart, it is important to recognize that the $\bar{X}$ chart requires a much smaller sample to give good results. From a statistical standpoint, variables are much superior to attributes; actual measurements on a few parts are as good as gagings on many parts with go and not-go gages.

215. p Charts Are Not Suitable for All Data on Fraction Defective. Control limits on the p chart are based on the use of the binomial as a probability distribution. As explained in Art. 172, Chap. IX, the binomial assumes a constant probability of occurrence of whatever event is under consideration—in the case of the p chart, a constant probability of occurrence of a defective article or part. If the probability is to be constant from one article to another, each article must be a separate unit independent of the preceding and succeeding articles. With this probability constant, defectives will tend to occur at random rather than in bunches. As long as successive articles continue to be independent of one another and the quality level does not change, practically all the points on the p chart will fall within 3-sigma limits.

In some instances, however, it is obvious from the way in which manufacturing or inspection operations are carried on that successive units measured are not independent of one another. In such cases, most of the points on a conventional p chart may fall outside control limits. Here the control-chart limits tell—quite correctly—a fact that is already evident without the control chart, namely, that the probability of one article being defective is influenced by whether or not the immediately preceding articles were defective. If this fact is already known and it is evident that nothing can be done about it, the information given by the p chart limits is of no practical help. The use of the p chart with conventional limits may even do harm, as it may tend to discredit the control chart in the minds of operating personnel and thus handicap the use of the control chart in other cases where it might really be helpful.

Four representative cases where conventional p charts were unsuitable because of this type of difficulty are described in the following paragraphs:

1. In the manufacture of a certain type of rubber belt, a large mold was used which produced 2,300 belts at one time. Conditions of curing varied throughout the mold; if one belt was defective, it was likely that many of the adjacent belts would be defective.

2. In the manufacture of a certain type of pile floor covering, daily figures were recorded for total yards produced and for total yardage of output which was classified as substandard. In this case an imperfection that caused the classification of product as substandard might persist through many successive yards; defective yards were not independent of one another. Moreover, there was no natural unit of counting the product (no n for the binomial); for instance, feet or meters might have been used as readily as yards.[1]

3. In the sheet-metal inspection booth of a large aircraft factory, records were kept showing daily numbers of parts inspected and numbers rejected. An average of 160,000 parts per day were inspected. Some 1,250 different parts—including practically everything of sheet metal that went into the airplane—were subject to this inspection. Over a period of time the defectives averaged about 3%. Because of the many different parts which passed through this booth, with different cause systems affecting the different parts, it was evident that the probability of a defective could not be constant from part to part. Control limits based on a p' of 0.03 and an n of 160,000 would have been 0.0313 and 0.0287. Actual daily fractions defective varied from about 0.05 to 0.01.

4. In the 100% inspection of detonators in an ammunition plant, inspection was performed in lots of 10,000. The average fraction defective $\bar{p}$ was 0.0223. This gave control limits of 0.0268 and 0.0178. Actual lot fractions defective varied from 0.055 to 0.008 with approximately two-thirds the points falling outside the control limits. A study of the production process made it evident that quite different cause systems were influencing the different lots.[2]

Even though the conventional p chart cannot be used to advantage in situations like these, it may still be desirable to keep a quality record

---

[1] This is described as Example 4 in *American War Standard* Z1.3-1942, "Control Chart Method of Controlling Quality During Production," American Standards Association, New York.

[2] Taken from "Quality Control Lectures," pp. 138–139, Commonwealth of Australia, Ministry of Munitions, Melbourne, 1944.

in the form of a chart that will be available to production supervision and to management. Generally speaking, this may be done to best advantage simply by plotting per cent defective without control limits.

Problems

132. Article 185 states that "because the daily production is not constant, it would be incorrect to average the values of p." Compute the correct value of $\bar{p}$ from the following data:

Lot	Number inspected	Number of defectives	p
1	500	27	0.054
2	50	12	0.240
3	800	12	0.015
4	100	14	0.140
5	150	15	0.100
Total.........	1,600	80	

Compare your correct $\bar{p}$ with the unweighted average value of p. Why do the two differ? Why is the unweighted average value of p an unsatisfactory measure of the process average fraction defective?

133. For a given period, $100p'$ is 2.80. Daily production is expected to vary from 400 to 1,000. Table F, Appendix III, gives values of upper and lower control limits for values of $100p'$ of 2.50 and 3.00, and for subgroups of 400, 500, 600, 800, and 1,000. Interpolate between the values for 2.50 and 3.00 and prepare a table showing upper and lower control limits for subgroup sizes of 400, 500, 600, 800, and 1,000 for a standard per cent defective of 2.80.

134. In your table for a standard per cent defective of 2.80 which you prepared in Problem 133, interpolate to get upper and lower control limits for $n = 450$, 620, and 950.

135. The following table gives the results of daily inspection of galvanized sheets produced in a steel mill.   Compute trial control limits for each day and plot a *p* chart. Compute a revised $\bar{p}$, eliminating the points above the upper control limit.

Date	Number inspected	Number of defectives
May 1	4,892	86
2	10,555	77
3	1,508	3
4	6,857	105
5	8,247	127
6	2,337	14
7	4,078	29
8	5,772	65
9	8,672	137
10	9,632	136
11	9,516	158
12	9,759	123
13	6,013	84
14	10,407	229
15	10,138	102
16	3,832	30
17	4,811	107
18	8,490	109
19	8,994	161
20	12,036	125

136. In the testing of a certain ballistic characteristic of ammunition, it is desired that all values of this quality characteristic fall between 1,680 and 1,800 units.   The quality characteristic has been tested on a variables basis with a sample of 4 taken from each lot. $\bar{X}$ and R charts have been plotted from past samples.   The R chart has shown excellent statistical control with an $\bar{R}$ of 34 units.   The $\bar{X}$ chart has shown a decided lack of statistical control.   This lack of control of $\bar{X}$ is to be expected, as past experience with other ammunition has indicated that it is very difficult to control the centering of the production process with respect to this particular quality characteristic.

It has been determined that it will be considerably more economical to test 16 items on an attributes basis than 4 items on a variables basis.   In this connection it is decided to maintain an *np* chart similar to the right-hand chart in Fig. 50 (page 257). For purposes of this chart it is desired to conduct the go and not-go testing using special severe test limits similar to the upper and lower gage limits shown in Fig. 52 (page 258).   These severe limits are to be established so that the appropriate p' is 0.15 for the "above limits" chart (corresponding to the not-go chart of Fig. 50) and is also 0.15 for the "below limits" chart (corresponding to the go chart of Fig. 50).

(*a*) With specification limits of 1,680 and 1,800 as stated, what should be the values of these special severe test limits?

(b) With 16 items tested in each sample, where should the action limits (3-sigma limits) be placed on the np chart?

137. The following table gives the results of daily inspection of radio transmitting tubes for a particular quality characteristic. Compute trial control limits for each day of this 4-week period and plot a p chart. Compute a revised $\bar{p}$, eliminating the points above the upper control limit.

Date	Number inspected	Number of defectives
Aug. 31	106	4
Sept. 1	122	8
2	29	0
3	0	0
4	36	1
5	66	2
7	162	12
8	18	2
9	138	8
10	36	0
11	189	15
12	162	24
14	33	4
15	51	4
16	69	4
17	123	8
18	108	7
19	142	19
21	36	1
22	141	22
23	15	2
24	213	3
25	84	5
26	117	3

138. The following results were obtained in the 4 weeks immediately following those given in Problem 137. Use as p' the revised value of $\bar{p}$ obtained in Problem 137. Compute daily control limits and plot a p chart. Based on this 4 weeks of record, would you revise the value of p' for use in the following period? If so, what value of p' would you recommend?

Date	Number inspected	Number of defectives
Sept. 28	114	5
29	212	5
30	53	2
Oct. 1	117	5
2	264	14
3	51	0
5	102	2
6	66	2
7	138	2
8	138	11
9	189	8
10	176	1
12	206	6
13	130	4
14	185	5
15	170	5
16	201	5
17	188	5
19	0	0
20	120	1
21	411	5
22	36	0
23	214	10
24	281	15

139. A manufacturer purchases small bolts in cartons that usually contain several thousand bolts. Each shipment consists of a number of cartons. As part of the acceptance procedure for these bolts, 250 bolts are selected at random from each carton and are subjected to visual inspection for certain defects. In a shipment of 10 cartons, the respective percentages of defectives in the samples from each carton are 0, 0, 0.4, 0.8, 0, 2.0, 0.4, 0, 0, and 0.8. Does this shipment of bolts appear to exhibit statistical control with respect to the quality characteristics examined in this inspection?

140. The following table gives the results of daily inspection of a vacuum tube. The standard value of fraction defective p' established at the start of the month was 0.04. The estimated daily average production was 1,600 tubes. Establish a single set of control limits based on these figures and plot a control chart. Compute separate control limits for any points that seem to you to require them. Based on this month of record, what would you recommend as the value of p' to use for the following month?

Date	Number inspected	Number of defectives	Fraction defective
Nov. 2	531	25	0.0471
3	1,393	62	0.0445
4	1,422	61	0.0428
5	1,500	73	0.0487
6	1,250	46	0.0368
7	2,000	58	0.0290
9	685	28	0.0408
10	2,385	89	0.0373
11	2,150	89	0.0414
12	2,150	58	0.0270
13	2,417	115	0.0476
14	2,549	115	0.0451
16	2,331	75	0.0322
17	2,009	81	0.0403
18	2,198	86	0.0392
19	2,271	67	0.0295
20	1,948	41	0.0210
21	2,150	77	0.0358
23	1,700	49	0.0288
24	2,214	68	0.0307
25	2,394	82	0.0343
26	1,197	56	0.0468
27	850	27	0.0318
28	848	30	0.0353
30	850	33	0.0388
Total.........	43,392	1,591	

141. Establish a special severe definition of a defective to apply to the data of Problem 6, Chap. III, using $X_{max} = 410$ and $X_{min} = 390$. Use this for purposes of an np chart similar to the right-hand chart in Fig. 50. In plotting this np chart, use subgroups of 10, combining subgroups 1 and 2, 3 and 4, etc., as given in Problem 6, Chap. III. For example, the first subgroup will have 4 low defectives (namely, 376, 381, 381, and 383) and one high defective (420). Low and high values correspond to the go and not-go values in Fig. 50. Base your control limits on a p' of 0.15 for low values and an equal p' of 0.15 for high values. Plot all the data of Problem 6, Chap. III. (This will give you 22 subgroups of 10 observations each.)

142. The following table gives the data on inspection of rubber belts referred to as the first case in Art. 215. Compute trial control limits and plot an np chart.

Lot number	Number inspected	Number of defectives
1	2300	230
2	2300	435
3	2300	221
4	2300	346
5	2300	230
6	2300	327
7	2300	285
8	2300	311
9	2300	342
10	2300	308
11	2300	456
12	2300	394
13	2300	285
14	2300	331
15	2300	198
16	2300	414
17	2300	131
18	2300	269
19	2300	221
20	2300	407

CHAPTER XI

THE CONTROL CHART FOR DEFECTS

The fundamental difference between engineering with and without statistics boils down to the difference between the use of a scientific method based upon the concept of laws of nature that do not allow for chance or uncertainty and a scientific method based upon the concept of laws of probability as an attribute of nature.—W. A. Shewhart[1]

216. The Place of the c Chart in Statistical Quality Control. The $\bar{X}$ and R control charts may be applied to any quality characteristic that is measurable. The control chart for p may be applied to the results of any inspection that accepts or rejects individual items of product. Thus both these types of chart are broadly useful in any statistical quality control program.

The control chart for defects, generally called the c *chart*, has a much more restricted field of usefulness. In many manufacturing plants there may be no opportunities for its economic use, even though there are dozens of places where $\bar{X}$ and R charts and p charts can be used advantageously.

Nevertheless, there are certain manufacturing and inspection situations in which the c chart is definitely needed. To decide whether or not to use a c chart in any individual case, it is first necessary to determine whether its use is appropriate from the viewpoint of statistical theory. If so, it is then necessary to judge whether the c chart is really the best technique to use for the purpose at hand.

217. Distinction between a Defect and a Defective. As already explained, a *defective* is an article that in some way fails to conform to one or more given specifications. Each instance of the article's lack of conformity to specifications is a *defect*. Every defective contains one or more defects.

The np chart, which was explained in Chap. X, applies to the number of *defectives* in subgroups of constant size. The c chart, which is explained in this chapter, applies to the number of *defects* in subgroups of constant size. In most cases, each subgroup for the c chart consists of a single article; the variable c consists of the number of defects observed in one article. However, it is not necessary that the subgroup for the c chart

[1] Shewhart, W. A., Contribution of Statistics to the Science of Engineering, included in "University of Pennsylvania Bicentennial Conference. Volume on Fluid Mechanics and Statistical Methods," pp. 97–124, University of Pennsylvania Press, Philadelphia, 1941.

be a single article; it is essential only that the subgroup size be constant in the sense that the different subgroups have substantially equal opportunity for the occurrence of defects.

218. Limits for the c Chart Are Based on the Poisson Distribution. Article 177 in Chap. IX explained that Poisson's Exponential Binomial Limit was useful not only as a limit of the binomial but also as a probability distribution in its own right. Table 30 illustrated a number of examples of this. In all these examples, a count was made of the number of occurrences of some event that had many opportunities to occur but that was extremely unlikely to occur at any given opportunity.

In many different kinds of manufactured articles, the opportunities for defects are numerous, even though the chances of a defect occurring in any one spot are small. Whenever this is true, it is correct as a matter of statistical theory to base control limits on the assumption that the Poisson distribution is applicable. The limits on the control chart for c are based on this assumption. Some representative types of defects to which the c chart may be applied are as follows:

1. c is the number of defective rivets in an aircraft wing or fuselage.

2. c is the number of breakdowns at weak spots in insulation in a given length of insulated wire subjected to a specified test voltage.

3. c is the number of surface defects observed in a galvanized sheet or a painted, plated, or enameled surface of a given area.

4. c is the number of "seeds" (small air pockets) observed in a glass bottle.

5. c is the number of imperfections observed in a bolt of cloth.

6. c is the number of surface defects observed in a roll of coated paper or a sheet of photographic film.

219. The Combination of Poisson Distributions. Assume that the average number of surface defects observed in a piece of enameled ware of a certain size is 0.5 and that the frequency of these defects follows the Poisson law. If 1,000 such pieces are examined, the expected frequencies of the various numbers of defects may be determined from Table G, Appendix III, to be as follows:

Number of Defects	Frequency in 1,000 Observations
0	607
1	303
2	76
3	12
4	2
Total...............	1,000

Now assume that the average number of surface defects is 1.5 in another piece of enameled ware having three times the area of the first.

The expected frequencies of various numbers of defects in 1,000 pieces are as follows:

Number of Defects	Frequency in 1,000 Observations
0	223
1	335
2	251
3	125
4	47
5	15
6	3
7	1
Total.............	1,000

Suppose that these two pieces of enameled ware pass the same inspection station and that the results of the inspection are recorded with no identification of whether the defects were observed on the small or the large pieces. If 1,000 pieces of each size pass the station, the expected frequencies in the total of 2,000 will be the sum of the two frequency distributions just given. The average number of surface defects per observed piece will of course be 1.0, the average of 0.5 and 1.5.

However, this combined distribution will not follow the Poisson law. This may be demonstrated by comparing it with the expected frequency distribution of 2,000 observations on a quality characteristic which does follow the Poisson law and which has an average value $\bar{c}$ of 1.0.

Number of defects	Expected frequencies in 2,000 observations	
	1,000 observations with $\bar{c} = 0.5$ and 1,000 observations with $\bar{c} = 1.5$	2,000 observations with $\bar{c} = 1.0$
0	830	736
1	638	736
2	327	368
3	137	122
4	49	30
5	15	6
6	3	2
7	1	0
Totals.....	2,000	2,000

On the other hand, assume that one small and one large piece of enameled ware are fastened together in an assembly. If many such assemblies are made and inspected for surface defects, the average number of defects per assembly will, of course, be 0.5 + 1.5 = 2.0. If the pairing of the small and large pieces is done at random, the frequency distribution of the number of defects in the assemblies will follow the Poisson law. (This statement can be proved mathematically. However, no simple demonstration of it is given here, similar to the demonstration just given that the sum of two Poisson distributions having different averages is not a Poisson.)

These two illustrations show one kind of combination of Poisson distributions that *does not* give a Poisson, and another combination of Poisson distributions that *does* give a Poisson. In general, a frequency distribution *will not* follow the Poisson law if some of the frequencies recorded refer to the number of occurrences of one event that follows the Poisson law, and the remaining frequencies recorded refer to the number of occurrences of another event that also follows the Poisson law but has a different average. But a frequency distribution *will* follow the Poisson law if a count is made of the combined number of occurrences of both events provided the pairing of the two events is at random.

Because the control chart for c uses limits based on the Poisson, the preceding remarks on various ways of combining Poisson distributions have a bearing on industrial quality control. They indicate that if Poisson limits are to be used, care should be taken to keep approximately constant the area of opportunity (see Art. 177) for the occurrence of a defect. However, the c chart need not be restricted to a single type of defect but may be used for the total of many different kinds of defects observed on any unit. This adds another field of usefulness to those listed in Art. 218, namely, a count of the total number of defects of all types in complex assemblies such as aircraft subassemblies, radio receiving sets, machine guns, etc.

220. Probability Limits vs. 3-sigma Limits on Control Charts for c. The standard deviation of the Poisson is $\sqrt{c'}$ (see Art. 178). Thus 3-sigma limits on a c chart are as follows:

$$UCL = c' + 3\sqrt{c'}$$
$$LCL = c' - 3\sqrt{c'}$$

When a standard value of average number of defects per unit, c', is not used, c' may be estimated as equal to the observed average $\bar{c}$. This is always done in the calculation of trial control limits. In this case the control limits are

$$UCL = \bar{c} + 3\sqrt{\bar{c}}$$
$$LCL = \bar{c} - 3\sqrt{\bar{c}}$$

As the Poisson is not a symmetrical distribution, the upper and lower 3-sigma limits do not correspond to equal probabilities of a point on the control chart falling outside limits even though there has been no change in the universe. This fact has been advanced as a reason for the use of probability limits on c charts. The use of 0.995 and 0.005 probability limits has been favored.[1]

The position of limits corresponding either to these probabilities or to any other desired probabilities may readily be determined either from Fig. 43 in Chap. IX or from Table G in Appendix III. The use of this figure and this table is explained in Art. 176, Chap. IX.

The theoretical conditions for the applicability of the Poisson distribution call for the count of the number of occurrences of an event that has an infinite number of opportunities to occur and a very small constant probability of occurrence at each opportunity. (For practical purposes, "infinite" may be interpreted as meaning very large.) As already emphasized, the area of opportunity for occurrence at each count of occurrences must remain constant. However, as pointed out in Art. 219, the count may be of the occurrence of all of several different events, each with its own very large number of opportunities to occur and each with a different small probability of occurrence at every opportunity.

In a large proportion of the applications of the Poisson to industrial quality control (or, for that matter, to all other practical affairs), it is possible to pick minor flaws in the theoretical applicability of the Poisson to the actual situation. It may be evident that the number of opportunities for the occurrence of a defect (or other event being counted) falls far short of being infinite. Or it may be clear that the unknown probability of occurrence of a defect is not quite constant. Or it may not be possible to keep the area of opportunity exactly constant. As long as these are only minor failures to meet the exact conditions of applicability, the results obtained by assuming that the Poisson is applicable are likely to be good enough for practical purposes.

This bears on the question of probability limits versus control limits based on $3\sqrt{\bar{c}}$. When probability limits are used, they are based on the exact Poisson distribution and probabilities are generally stated to three decimal places (such as 0.995 and 0.005). Such a precise statement of probabilities would hardly seem to be justified in the frequent cases where it is evident that the Poisson is roughly applicable but not exactly so.

Slight departures of the actual distribution from the true Poisson usually will cause the standard deviation to be slightly greater than $\sqrt{\bar{c}}$.

---

[1] A diagram on logarithmic paper giving these limits is shown in Control Chart Method of Controlling Quality During Production, *American War Standard* Z1.3, 1942, p. 20, American Standards Association, New York, 1942. Another diagram which shows these limits on rectangular coordinate paper is given in L. E. Simon, "An Engineers' Manual of Statistical Methods," p. 73, John Wiley & Sons, Inc., New York, 1941.

Limits based on 3 $\sqrt{\bar{c}}$ may really be at a little less than 3-sigma. This fact in itself generally does not justify discarding 3 $\sqrt{\bar{c}}$ or 3 $\sqrt{c'}$ as a basis for calculating limits. In some situations to which the c chart is applied, such as records of numbers of defects observed in inspections of complex assemblies, this use of limits a little tighter than 3-sigma may actually be desirable. As pointed out in Chap. IV, the economic basis of any control-chart limits is experience that the procedures used for their computation strike a satisfactory balance between the costs of two kinds of errors, namely, looking for assignable causes when they are really absent, and not looking for them when they are really present.

In general, the c chart limits used in this book are based on 3 $\sqrt{\bar{c}}$ or 3 $\sqrt{c'}$.

EXAMPLE 19. CONTROL CHART FOR DEFECTS PER UNIT

221. Facts of the Case.   Table 36 gives the numbers of errors of alignment observed at final inspection of a certain model of airplane.   Figure 53 gives the control chart

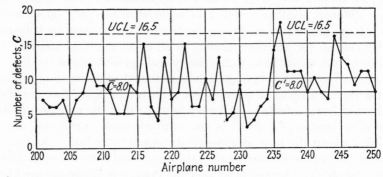

Fig. 53.   Control chart for defects per unit, c.   Data on aircraft alignment defects observed at final inspection.

for these 50 observations.   The defects observed on each airplane constitute one subgroup for this chart.

The total number of alignment defects in the first 25 ships was 200.   The average $\bar{c}$ is $200/25 = 8.0$.   Trial control limits computed from this average are as follows:

$$UCL = \bar{c} + 3\sqrt{\bar{c}} = 8 + 3\sqrt{8} = 16.5$$
$$LCL = \bar{c} - 3\sqrt{\bar{c}} = 8 - 3\sqrt{8} = 0$$

(Whenever calculations give a negative value of the lower control limit of a c chart, that limit is recorded as zero.)

As none of the first 25 points on this chart is outside the trial control limits based on these points, the standard number of defects c' may be taken as equal to $\bar{c}$ and the control chart continued for the following period with a central line of 8.0 and control limits of 16.5 and 0.

One point (airplane No. 236) out of the next 25 is above the upper control limit. The average during this period was $236/25 = 9.44$.   (Even omitting the out-of-control value, the average is 9.08.)   Of the final 16 points corresponding to airplanes 235 to 250, 12 are above the standard c', 3 are exactly at the standard, and only one is

TABLE 36. AIRCRAFT ALIGNMENT DEFECTS OBSERVED AT FINAL INSPECTION

Airplane number	Number of alignment defects	Airplane number	Number of alignment defects
201	7	226	7
202	6	227	13
203	6	228	4
204	7	229	5
205	4	230	9
206	7	231	3
207	8	232	4
208	12	233	6
209	9	234	7
210	9	235	14
211	8	236	18
212	5	237	11
213	5	238	11
214	9	239	11
215	8	240	8
216	15	241	10
217	6	242	8
218	4	243	7
219	13	244	16
220	7	245	13
221	8	246	12
222	15	247	9
223	6	248	11
224	6	249	11
225	10	250	8
Total.........	200	Total.........	236

below. It seems evident that there has been a slight but definite deterioration in quality (or increase in the strictness of inspection) during this period.

222. Comment on Example 19. In a case such as this, the previously established standard value of c' should nearly always be continued despite the evidence of quality deterioration. The principle stated in Art. 206 regarding the p chart also applies to the c chart, namely, that the standard value should not be revised in the direction of poorer quality merely because production personnel seem to be giving less attention to quality. On the other hand, if a definite tightening up of inspection standards had the effect of making quality *seem* poorer, even though it was really no worse than before, an upward revision of c' might be justified.

Many of the comments and suggestions relative to the p chart in

Arts. 205 to 210 obviously apply also to the c chart and do not need to be repeated here. It should be emphasized that extreme runs should be looked for in the c chart, just as in the other control charts. Other significant patterns in the data should also be noted. (This was illustrated by the fatigue patterns shown for the c chart in Example 4, Chap. II.)

223. Conditions Favorable to the Economic Use of the Control Chart for Defects per Unit. The c chart has been used to advantage in four different types of situation, as follows:

1. It has been applied to a count of defects all of which must be eliminated following 100% inspection. In this use, the c chart is primarily an instrument for reducing cost of rework incident to correcting the defects and to a lesser extent for reducing costs of inspection incident to identifying the defects. The chart serves to keep management and production supervisors informed about the current quality level, indicates whether or not the process appears to be in control, and serves as a basis for executive pressure to improve the general quality level and to eliminate out-of-control points. The c chart applied in this way sometimes calls attention to the lack of definite inspection standards or to irregularities in the application of inspection standards. A typical example of this kind of use of the c chart is its application to defects of all types observed in inspection of aircraft subassemblies and final assemblies.

2. Where a certain number of defects per unit are tolerable, even though it is desired to hold their number to a minimum, the c chart may be applied to periodic samples of production. Here the chief objective is the improvement of the quality of outgoing product, leading possibly to fewer rejections by customers' inspection and to a generally better consumer acceptance of the product. Like the application to 100% inspection, this use of the c chart gives management up-to-date information on the quality level and helps to increase uniformity of product by putting pressure on out-of-control points. A typical example of this kind of use is found in a paper mill in which a sample consisting of one roll of coated paper per shift is carefully examined for surface defects.

3. It has been applied for special short studies of the variation of quality of a particular product or manufacturing operation. The 3-day record of defects in welded seams described in Example 4, Chap. II, was an illustration of this type of c chart application.

4. It has been applied to sampling acceptance procedures based on defects per unit. This application is referred to in Chap. XV.

224. Adaptations of the c Chart to Variations in the Area of Opportunity for a Defect. The quantity c is the number of defects observed in some specified inspection. Often this inspection is of a single unit of product, such as an airplane, a radio set, a coil of wire, or a roll of coated paper. In this common case where the subgroup size is unity, c is both the number of defects and the number of defects per unit. As already explained, the units should be alike in size and in the apparent likelihood of the existence of a defect, in order that the area of opportunity for a defect be constant from unit to unit.

However, it is not really necessary that the subgroup be a single unit of product. The unit for control-chart purposes (*i.e.*, the subgroup) may be 10 product units, or 100, or any convenient other number. Total defects for each subgroup may be plotted just as if the subgroup were a single unit of product. As long as the number of product units does not change from subgroup to subgroup, no special problem is created.

Whenever for some reason there is an evident change in the area of opportunity for occurrence of a defect from subgroup to subgroup, the conventional c chart showing total number of defects is not satisfactory. In such cases, if total defects observed in each subgroup were plotted, the central line on the chart as well as the control limits would have to change from one subgroup to another. This would make the chart confusing and hard to read.

A way out of this difficulty is to divide defects c by units n. The quotient c/n is represented by the symbol u. The central line on a u chart will be standard defects per unit u'. Limit lines on such a chart will vary with subgroup size, just as control limits vary with subgroup size on the $\overline{X}$ chart and the p chart. The formulas for control limits on such a chart are

$$UCL = u' + \frac{3\sqrt{u'}}{\sqrt{n}}$$

$$LCL = u' - \frac{3\sqrt{u'}}{\sqrt{n}}$$

These formulas assume that a value has been established for standard defects per unit u'. For trial control limits, this standard value may be estimated as equal to the average number of defects per unit, *i.e.*, the total number of observed defects divided by the total number of units.

Example 20 illustrates the calculations required for this adaptation of the c chart.

EXAMPLE 20. A CONTROL CHART FOR DEFECTS PER UNIT WITH VARIABLE SUBGROUP SIZE

225. Facts of the Case. This is an application to defects observed in aircraft subassembly. The problem of the variable subgroup size was created by the difference in the number of employees on the three shifts. These were roughly in the ratio of 3 on the day shift to 2 on the swing and 1 on the graveyard shift. The number of units assembled in each production center varied from shift to shift in something like this proportion and also showed some variation from day to day.

Table 37 gives the record of the number of defects (which, in this aircraft plant, were picturesquely described as *squawks*) recorded by the inspection department for

TABLE 37. COMPUTATION OF CONTROL-CHART LIMITS FOR DATA ON DEFECTS OBSERVED ON AIRCRAFT SUBASSEMBLIES

Date	Shift	Defects observed on shift c	Units produced n	Defects per unit u	$3\sigma = \dfrac{3\sqrt{u'}}{\sqrt{n}}$	$UCL = u' + 3\sigma$	$LCL = u' - 3\sigma$
June 9	D	13	6.0	2.2	2.2	5.4	1.0
	S	12	4.3	2.8	2.6	5.8	0.6
	G	7	2.9	2.4	3.2	6.4	0.0
11	D	19	5.5	3.5	2.3	5.5	0.9
	S	14	4.4	3.2	2.6	5.8	0.6
	G	9	2.0	4.5	3.8	7.0	0.0
12	D	18	5.5	3.3	2.3	5.5	0.9
	S	13	4.0	3.2	2.7	5.9	0.5
	G	6	2.0	3.0	3.8	7.0	0.0
13	D	24	6.1	3.9	2.2	5.4	1.0
	S	15	4.9	3.1	2.4	5.6	0.8
	G	6	2.9	2.1	3.2	6.4	0.0
14	D	16	6.6	2.4	2.1	5.3	1.1
	S	11	4.1	2.7	2.7	5.9	0.5
	G	20	2.5	8.0	3.4	6.6	0.0
15	D	16	4.3	3.7	2.6	5.8	0.6
	S	29	4.2	6.9	2.6	5.8	0.6
	G	3	2.2	1.4	3.6	6.8	0.0
16	D	21	6.1	3.4	2.2	5.4	1.0
	S	20	4.2	4.8	2.6	5.8	0.6
	G	2	1.8	1.1	4.0	7.2	0.0
17	D	14	2.9	4.8	3.2	6.4	0.0
	S	10	1.9	5.3	3.9	7.1	0.0
	G	3	1.0	3.0	5.4	8.6	0.0
Totals........		321	92.3				

Standard value of defects per unit u' is 3.2

each shift in one production center for a period of 8 days. The number of units produced is also given. In order to measure this production on each shift, the establishment of a system of weighting different assembly operations was required. For example, if one production center carried out operations 251, 252, and 253, it might happen that on one day, because of the irregular flow of parts to the department, the day shift would work chiefly on operations 251 and 252; the swing shift might concentrate on 253.   On another day, this might be reversed.   By giving each operation an appropriate weighting factor, the actual production on the different operations may be converted to an equivalent number of production units, as follows:

Assembly operation number	Weighting factor	Production on assembly operation	Equivalent units produced on shift
251	0.45	6	2.7
252	0.30	8	2.4
253	0.25	4	1.0
	1.00	..	6.1

That is, these operations actually carried out on the shift are judged to be equivalent to carrying out all three of the required assembly operations on 6.1 airplanes.

In Table 37, c, the total defects observed on each shift, is divided by n, the number of equivalent units produced, to get defects per unit, u.   In plotting the value of u on

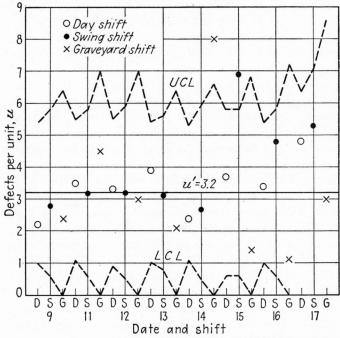

Fig. 54.   Adaptation of c chart to variable subgroup size.   (Data of Table 37.)

the control chart (Fig. 54), a different symbol is used for each shift.   The standard value of defects per unit u' of 3.2 was established by past performance; this is used as the central line on the control chart.   Table 37 shows the calculation of the upper and lower control limits for each subgroup.

226. Comment on Example 20. The comparison in one chart of the performance of the three shifts may improve the general quality level by stimulating competition among the shifts. Moreover, if one shift is out of line with the others, such a chart will make this fact quickly evident to management.

If no consideration had been given to the advantages of combining the shifts on one chart and separate charts had been kept for each shift, the slight variations in subgroup size within each shift from day to day might have been neglected. Each chart might then have been a conventional c chart showing number of defects and having constant limits. Or, if it were desired to express quality in terms of defects per unit, constant limits might have been plotted based on average subgroup size.

The limits for any subgroup on a u chart are simply the appropriate c chart limits divided by the value of n for the particular subgroup. For instance, n was 6.0 for the first subgroup of Table 37. The standard value c' for a chart with this subgroup size would be 19.2, *i.e.*, 3.2 times 6.0. The upper control limit for such a c chart would be

$$19.2 + 3 \sqrt{19.2} = 32.3$$

If 32.3 is divided by n (6.0), the upper control limit of 5.4 for the u chart is obtained.

The points in Fig. 54 have not been connected. If they were to be connected, it would be better to draw separate lines for each shift rather than a single line connecting all the points. If the symbols used for the three shifts differ enough from one another, the chart is more easily read if the points are not connected. A good plan is to use a different color for each shift.

This is one of the many cases where, even though the strict applicability of the Poisson distribution might be questioned by a statistical theorist, the limits based on the Poisson are good enough for practical purposes. The Poisson might be questioned because the equivalent production units depend on the weighting factors adopted for the various assembly operations. Ideally, the weighting factors should be chosen in a way to be proportional to the relative frequency of defects in each of the assembly operations being weighted. Actual weighting, based on some such factor as standard direct labor hours for each operation, may measure this well enough in most instances unless certain of the assembly operations are much more difficult than others.

227. Adaptation of the c Chart to Quality Rating. Some defects are more serious than others. In an over-all picture of quality by departments to be presented to management, there may be an advantage in weighting defects according to some scale that measures their seriousness.

Such a plan has been in use for many years in the Bell Telephone System. The classes of defects used are described by H. F. Dodge, as follows:[1]

Class "A" Defects—Very serious.
Will render unit totally unfit for service.
Will surely cause operating failure of the unit in service which cannot be readily corrected on the job, *e.g.*, open induction coil, transmitter without carbon, etc.
Liable to cause personal injury or property damage.
Class "B" Defects—Serious.
Will probably, but not surely, cause Class *A* operating failure of the unit in service.
Will surely cause trouble of a nature less serious than Class A operating failure, *e.g.*, adjustment failure, operation below standard, etc.
Will surely cause increased maintenance or decreased life.
Class "C" Defects—Moderately serious.
Will possibly cause operating failure of the unit in service.
Likely to cause trouble of a nature less serious than operating failure.
Likely to cause increased maintenance or decreased life.
Major defects of appearance, finish, or workmanship.
Class "D" Defects—Not serious.
Will not cause operating failure of the unit in service.
Minor defects of appearance, finish, or workmanship.

Once such a classification of all defects is established, demerits may then be assigned to each class of defect. Control charts may be plotted for demerits per unit rather than for defects per unit. The reader is referred to Dodge's paper cited in the footnote on this page for the details of this variation of the *c* chart.[2]

228. Use of 3 $\sqrt{c'}$ for Approximate Calculation of Control Limits in Situations Involving the Binomial Distribution. It often happens that a quick calculation of control limits is useful in some situation where no actual control chart has been plotted. If this is needed in any case to which the binomial is applicable as a probability distribution, it is handy to remember that the standard deviation of the Poisson $\sqrt{c'}$ is an approximation to $\sqrt{np'(1 - p')}$. Even though the binomial itself is only an approximation to the correct probability obtainable by the use of combinatorial formulas, 3 $\sqrt{c'}$ often provides a basis for rapid mental arithmetic about control limits that may be good enough for practical purposes.

[1] DODGE, H. F., A Method of Rating Manufactured Product, *The Bell System Technical Journal*, vol. 7, pp. 350–368, April, 1928. This article, which has been reprinted as Bell Telephone Laboratories Reprint B-315, gives clear detailed directions for the use of such a plan based on demerits per unit. In May, 1944, issue of the reprint, demerit weights currently used are stated as Class *A*—100, Class *B*—50, Class *C*—10, and Class *D*—1.

[2] See also D. A. Hill, Control of Complicated Product, *Industrial Quality Control*, vol. 8, no. 4, pp. 18–22, January, 1952.

For example, assume that product submitted under a purchase contract has been 0.4% defective. The question is raised as to what variation in number of defectives may be expected in lots of 1,000. The expected average number of defectives in such lots is obviously 4. As $3\sqrt{4} = 6$, the answer is that defectives might generally be expected to fall between 0 and 10 in lots of 1,000. The occurrence of 11 or more defectives in such a lot would be evidence of an assignable cause of variation.

229. Applicability of c Chart Technique in Fields Other Than Industrial Quality Control. Like all control charts, the c chart gives evidence regarding the quality level, its variability, and the presence or absence of assignable causes of variation. This is useful information as a basis for action in many other fields besides industrial quality control. The universal nature of the Poisson distribution as the law of small numbers makes the c chart technique broadly useful.

For example, it has been applied to accident statistics, both of industrial accidents[1] and of highway accidents. It might also be applied to advantage in the field of epidemiology. In both these fields, action should often be based on evidence of assignable causes of variation, and it is important to note changes in the average value of the variable being studied.

Problems

143. The following table gives the results of inspection of 100-yd. pieces of woolen goods:

Piece number	Number of defects	Piece number	Number of defects	Piece number	Number of defects
1	3	10	8	18	4
2	3	11	4	19	5
3	6	12	10	20	1
4	3	13	5	21	1
5	0	14	5	22	0
6	1	15	5	23	1
7	3	16	4	24	1
8	5	17	3	25	4
9	7				

Find $\bar{c}$, compute trial control limits, and plot a control chart for c. What value of c would you suggest for the following period?

[1] GOODE, H. P., How, Why, When, Where and How Many? A New Approach to Accident Frequency Rates, *Safety Engineering*, vol. 92, July, 1946, pp. 25–26.

HOWELL, J. M. and LEE JOHNSON, Statistical Control of Accidents, *Iron Age*, vol. 158, July 18, 1946, pp. 56–59.

144. The following table gives the numbers of missing rivets noted at aircraft final inspection:

Airplane number	Number of missing rivets	Airplane number	Number of missing rivets	Airplane number	Number of missing rivets
201	8	210	12	218	14
202	16	211	23	219	11
203	14	212	16	220	9
204	19	213	9	221	10
205	11	214	25	222	22
206	15	215	15	223	7
207	8	216	9	224	28
208	11	217	9	225	9
209	21				

Find $\bar{c}$, compute trial control limits, and plot a control chart for c. What value of c would you suggest for the subsequent period?

145. (a) Article 219 gives the expected frequencies in 2,000 observations, 1,000 of which came from a Poisson with $\bar{c} = 0.5$ and 1,000 from a Poisson with $\bar{c} = 1.5$. Find the standard deviation of this distribution.

(b) The $\bar{c}$ of this combined distribution is, of course, 1.0. If random samples were drawn from this distribution for a c chart and control limits were set at 3 $\sqrt{\bar{c}}$ under the mistaken assumption that the distribution was a Poisson, at what multiple of the true standard deviation would they actually be set?

146. Use Table G, Appendix III, to find the expected frequencies of 1,000 observations with $\bar{c}$ of 1.2 and 1,000 observations with $\bar{c}$ of 3.6. Combine these 2,000 into a single frequency distribution. Compare this with the expected frequency distribution of a Poisson of 2,000 observations with a $\bar{c}$ of 2.4.

147. Use Table G, Appendix III, to find 0.995 and 0.005 probability limits for a c chart when $c' = 5.8$. Also when $c' = 12.0$ *Ans.* 12.5, 0.1; 21.3, 3.5.

148. Use Table G, Appendix III, to find 0.95 and 0.05 probability limits for a c chart when $c' = 4.2$. Also when $c' = 9.5$. *Ans.* 7.4, 0.6; 14.4, 4.2.

149. A control chart for defects per unit u uses probability limits corresponding to probabilities of 0.975 and 0.025. The central line on the control chart is at $u' = 2.0$. The limits vary with the value of n. Determine the correct position of these upper and lower control limits when $n = 5$. *Ans.* 3.23, 0.76.

150. Find 0.995 and 0.005 probability limits for a c chart when $c' = 7.5$. Also when $c' = 18.2$.

151. Find 0.975 and 0.025 limits for a c chart when $c' = 2.3$. Also when $c' = 13.5$.

152. A control chart for defects per unit u uses probability limits corresponding to probabilities of 0.95 and 0.05. The central line on the control chart is at $u' = 1.4$. The limits vary with the value of n. Determine the correct position of these upper and lower control limits when $n = 8$.

153. The following tabulation gives defects c observed in an aircraft subassembly operation and shows the number of units produced on each shift during a week. Prepare a control chart similar to Fig. 54. Assume $u' = 4.4$.

Shift	Mon.		Tues.		Wed.		Thurs.		Fri.		Sat.	
	c	n	c	n	c	n	c	n	c	n	c	n
Day.................	19	5	25	5	15	5	29	5	36	4	27	5
Swing...............	20	4	20	4	14	4	9	4	22	3	24	4
Graveyard...........	8	2	7	2	2	2	2	2	4	1	6	2

154. In a manufacturing plant, a sample of a certain product having an enameled finish is taken from the production on each shift and is inspected carefully for minor surface imperfections. The following tabulation gives imperfections c and number inspected n for a 1-week period. No standard value of imperfections per unit has been established. Plot some kind of control chart showing this information in terms of imperfections per unit of product. Discuss the implications of the control chart you have prepared.

Shift	Mon.		Tues.		Wed.		Thurs.		Fri.		Sat.	
	c	n	c	n	c	n	c	n	c	n	c	n
Day.................	16	16	21	27	6	17	18	11	17	27	3	25
Swing...............	4	20	6	34	1	6	9	33	6	21	1	37
Graveyard...........	15	11	16	19	1	22	9	28	5	35	2	17

Part Four

A STATISTICAL APPROACH TO ACCEPTANCE PROCEDURES

CHAPTER XII

SOME STATISTICAL ASPECTS OF TOLERANCES

. . . It looked as if some of the tolerances were assigned much closer than should be necessary, and I started to try to find out how they had been fixed. To accomplish this, on every occasion when I met an engineer I asked him how he decided the tolerances in his branch of the subject; I fear I bored a great many people at this time. I got a variety of answers which sometimes explained things a bit, but often not at all, and though I discussed it with quite a number of men, many of them occupying prominent places in different branches of the profession, I came away with the impression that scarcely any of them were really interested in the subject of tolerances. To exaggerate the picture which I got as the result of my inquiry, I concluded that in designing a new machine the chief engineer drew it freehand with dimensions to the nearest inch, and sent it to the draughtsman to work out the detail to the nearest thousandth, who then gave it to his junior assistant to mark in the tolerances. Instructions were certainly always given that tolerances should be as easy as possible, but only lip service was done to them, and the junior assistant, anxious not to get himself into trouble, would, as a general rule, think of the smallest number he knew and then halve it.—C. G. DARWIN[1]

230. Specification Limits Are Not Always Enforced. A clear statement of the common situation regarding the specification of dimensional tolerances and their enforcement is made by William B. Rice, Director of Statistics and Reports of the Plomb Tool Company. Rice says, in part:[2]

In many machine shops and metal working plants there have grown up over a period of years certain practices with regard to tolerances which can well bear re-examination. The blueprints may call for one tolerance; inspection gages may allow another usually wider tolerance, and the foreman may be even more liberal. Each of the three parties views the operation from a different standpoint. The engineer sees the problem as one of design; the inspector tries to maintain an acceptable quality; the foreman is under pressure to produce in quantity. Much of the spoilage and reworking which cost American industry so much in time, money and man-power arise from a failure to coordinate the viewpoints of the designing, inspection and production departments.

One reason why engineers, foremen and inspectors have different ideas about

[1] DARWIN, C. G., Statistical Control of Production, *Nature*, vol. 149, pp. 573–575, May 23, 1942.

[2] RICE, W. B., Setting Tolerances Scientifically, *Mechanical Engineering*, vol. 66, pp. 801–803, December, 1944.

what tolerances should be permitted is that there are several ways in which inspection can be done. Take as an illustration a half-inch turning on a four-spindle automatic screw machine. If four successive pieces are taken off the same spindle, the diameters of the four turnings will probably vary by less than a thousandth of an inch. If, however, one turning is taken off each spindle, the measurements may vary by as much as two thousandths. Again, suppose that a run of 50,000 turnings has been completed; if a large sample (say 1,000) is taken at random from the entire lot, the difference between the largest and smallest diameters measured may be six or seven thousandths.

Another reason for disagreement is that the dimensions of the work which can actually be produced depend upon many factors. A new machine will hold more closely than an old one; skilled workers can do more accurate work than green hands can; experienced foremen are able to get better results than untried men in supervisory jobs; material, too, has a strong bearing on quality, as have the kind and quantity of tooling, personnel relationships, morale, pay, and a thousand other factors which come and go, fluctuating throughout the process in usually unpredictable fashion.

In general, product or design engineers often seem to do their planning and drafting with reference to somewhat ideal conditions, assuming good machines, well-trained workers and skilled supervision, or else they use reference tables which may tacitly assume such factors. Therefore tolerances on blueprints tend to be conservative and are sometimes actually impossible to meet with any degree of economy in the manufacturing process. Nearly ideal conditions may be attained during some small part of the process, but almost never for any extended period of time.

Production men, on the other hand, knowing from experience that a careless operator, a soft spot in the steel, a slight mis-adjustment of the tools, a loose collet or any one of a multitude of other troubles will cause an automatic to do out-of-tolerance work, are included to ask for more liberal tolerances; if these are not forthcoming they just 'do the best they can.' Unfortunately they do not always stop to figure how they can make that best better. Being human, and under pressure to turn out large volume, they are prone to accept what they have as the best they can get.

The process inspector, caught in the crossfire of these opposing interests, usually has to compromise. The workmen on the floor, with whom the inspector is in daily contact, argue that too strict adherence to blue-print standards will slow down or even stop production, and that another thousandth won't make any difference anyway. The engineering department, more remote but exerting its influence through the blue-print which the inspector sees and uses constantly, calls for certain dimensions to which all pieces must adhere. Who can blame the inspector for letting an occasional out-of-tolerance piece go by under such conditions?

Two dangers arise, however, under such circumstances. First, neither the inspector nor the foreman knows every step in the manufacturing process, hence their judgment as to what can and what cannot be allowed to pass is usually poor. Second, laxity is encouraged which may destroy the validity and nullify the value of inspection. The idea of concrete, objective standards which result in *usable articles economically produced* should be basic to the inspection function. Violating this idea undermines the fundamental purpose of inspection.

231. Some Bad Consequences of Careless Setting of Specification Limits. The quotation at the beginning of this chapter was taken from an address by Dr. C. G. Darwin, Director of the British National Physical Laboratory, given in April, 1942, at a joint meeting of the Institutions of Civil, Mechanical, and Electrical Engineers. These two quotations from Darwin and Rice reflect the fact that specification limits are often set by designers with little or no critical consideration of the various problems involved. In some instances, this may be because designers are too absorbed in other matters to have time to give much attention to tolerances. Lacking time and information, designers feel they are on the safe side by not being too liberal in their tolerances. They often feel that they can count on complaint from production and inspection to tell them of any cases where tolerances turn out to be tighter than can be held by production.

In other instances, the use of unnecessarily tight tolerances may be a deliberate policy on the part of designers. They may be conscious of the difference between the blueprint tolerances and those which actually are enforced. Therefore, in order actually to get what they think they need, these designers tend to specify closer tolerances than they believe are necessary.

As Rice suggests, an unfortunate result of this policy may be the creation of lack of respect for specifications on the part of production and inspection personnel. Sometimes it is critically important that specifications be met. Production and inspection personnel, tending to ease up a bit on any tolerances that are difficult to meet, and not understanding the reasons behind the designer's specifications, may ease up as readily on the critical ones as on those less important.

On the other hand, enforcing tolerances that are really too tight tends to increase costs. Without doubt, this was often true in war production, particularly in the production of parts by small vendors and subcontractors. The lack of any basis for judgment as to what specifications could be relaxed, and the difficulties of effective communication with authorities who might review specifications, led conscientious inspection groups to enforce many specifications of unnecessarily close tolerances. The results of this were often excessive spoilage and rework, high cost, and shortages of needed parts.

232. Statistical Methods May Help in Setting Better Specification Limits. The designer's considerations in establishing any specification limits may be classified into three groups, namely, (1) those related to the service needs of the article or part for which specifications are being written, (2) those related to the capabilities of the production process to produce to any given specification limits, and (3) those related to the means to be used for determining whether the specifications are actually met by the product.

The fundamental basis of all specification limits is, of course, the service need of the part or article. This is not primarily a statistical matter. However, it often happens that the service need can be judged more accurately with the aid of statistical methods. The viewpoint that every quality characteristic is a frequency distribution is always helpful. This is particularly true in matters involving the interrelationships of specification limits. The usefulness of statistics in this respect is illustrated later in this chapter in Examples 21 and 22.

There is no use specifying desired tolerances on any quality characteristic without some prospect that these tolerances can be met. Whenever production methods will not meet the proposed tolerances, this fact needs to be known and considered before such tolerances are adopted. The inability of any process to meet its quality specifications is sure to be responsible for extra costs. These may be costs of spoilage and rework, or of changing to another more expensive production process, or—in the case of dimensional tolerances—costs incident to giving up the idea of interchangeable manufacture and adopting selective fitting of parts. If such costs are to be undertaken, this should be done deliberately after weighing the facts rather than unconsciously because the capabilities of a production process are unknown. One of the major contributions of statistical quality control to design can be in the information the control chart gives about the capacity of a production process to meet any given tolerances. This point is expanded later in this chapter.

The third matter which was stated as relevant in setting specification limits is the means to be used for determining whether the specification limits are actually met. Both Shewhart and Simon have emphasized in their writings[1] the distinction between a design specification, i.e., what is desired, and an acceptance specification, the means of judging whether what is desired is actually obtained. The relevance of the acceptance specification in determining the design specification is not always understood. Both design engineers and inspection executives sometimes say, "It is the designer's job to specify what is needed; it is the inspector's job to devise tests and acceptance procedures to find out whether the designer's specifications have been met; let each stick to his own job."

---

[1] SHEWHART, W. A., "Economic Control of Quality of Manufactured Product," particularly Part V, D. Van Nostrand Company, Inc., New York, 1931.

SHEWHART, W. A (edited by W. E. Deming), "Statistical Method from the Viewpoint of Quality Control," particularly Chap. II, The Graduate School, Department of Agriculture, Washington, 1939.

SIMON, L. E., "An Engineers' Manual of Statistical Methods," particularly Appendix D, John Wiley & Sons, Inc., New York, 1941.

This fails to take into account the fact that, although the designer may not devise tests and acceptance procedures, he should not be indifferent to the tests and acceptance procedures that are to be applied. These constitute useful information for the designer for the same reason that he should know something about the capabilities of the production process; both influence the likelihood of obtaining what is specified. This point is developed throughout the remainder of Part Four of this book.

233. Use of Information from the Control Chart as an Aid in Setting Tolerances. If there is difficulty in producing within existing specification limits, the $\overline{X}$ and R charts provide a method of finding out why. They tell whether a process is in control, and, if so, at what average value and with what dispersion. If a long enough record of controlled production is available, a picture may be obtained of the form of the frequency distribution of the quality characteristic. All this provides a basis for judging whether or not it is possible to meet existing specifications without a fundamental change in the production process. As emphasized in the comments on Example 2, Chap. II, this information should be available in any review of a request for more liberal tolerances.

In setting specification limits on new designs, considerable help may be obtained from $\overline{X}$ and R charts on past production operations similar to those which are to be employed, even though there is no control-chart information directly applicable to the new design. For such past control-chart data to be used effectively, design engineers must understand control-chart principles, and there must be some plan of organization that makes control-chart information readily available to them.

234. Some Common Methods of Interpretation of a Pilot Run as a Basis for Setting Tolerances. In the development of any new design of a manufactured product, it is often possible to improve the design and avoid production difficulties by means of a pilot run. If production methods used on this pilot run are similar to those which are to be used later in actual quantity production, it is good sense to use the pilot run to review the proposed specification limits for the various quality characteristics. In this way it may be possible to anticipate and avoid many situations in which the design tolerances are closer than can be met by the production departments.

The number of units produced in such a pilot run will depend on the costs involved, and might vary from two or three to several thousand. Suppose 40 units are produced, and actual measurements are made on each unit for every quality characteristic for which tolerances have been proposed. What tabulations and calculations are required relative to the measurements on each quality characteristic? How should the measurements be interpreted with regard to the setting of tolerances? Different individuals might answer these questions in different ways.

Without benefit of any statistical analysis, a common answer might be to take the highest and lowest measured values on the pilot run as indicating the upper and lower limits of the production process.

Someone who had been introduced to conventional elementary statistics, including frequency distributions and the normal curve, might reject this simple method as unsatisfactory. Instead he might group the measurements into a frequency distribution and compute the average and standard deviation. He might then compute 3-sigma limits on either side of the average and state that such limits would include practically all the items produced. Or he might even go so far as to make the precise statement that they will include 99.73% of the items produced.

The individual who has been introduced to the Shewhart control chart will be inclined to insist that the order of production of the units in the pilot run of 40 not be lost sight of. He might then divide the measurements into rational subgroups—perhaps 10 subgroups of four. He might then test the figures for control by means of charts for $\overline{X}$ and R or $\overline{X}$ and σ. If no points fall outside control limits, he might estimate σ', either as $\overline{R}/d_2$ or $\bar{\sigma}/c_2$. Then $\overline{\overline{X}} \pm 3\sigma'$ will give him an estimate of upper and lower limits for individual values in a controlled process—the so-called "natural tolerances" of the process. The individual who has made these calculations might state that if control is maintained, practically all the items produced will fall within these estimated natural tolerance limits. Or, as in the case of the frequency distribution analysis, he might go farther and state that 99.73% of the cases will fall within these limits.

235. Errors in Common Interpretations of a Pilot Run. All these methods of interpreting a pilot run miss the point to some extent. The frequency distribution method is likely to be better than taking as the limits merely the upper and lower measured values in the pilot run. The control-chart method is much more realistic than the frequency distribution method, in that it recognizes that there is no basis for an inference that a frequency distribution from an uncontrolled process will repeat itself. But no method of analysis can be found which justifies the positive statements that the process will hold within certain limits.

The justifiable statement is a negative one to the effect that without a fundamental change in the process it will be impossible to hold the process within limits closer than certain specified values. The control-chart method provides the basis for such a statement if the process is in control. If the proposed tolerances are closer than such limits, it is clear that either the tolerance range must be widened, or the process must be changed, or, if 100% inspection is possible, the decision must be made to accept the inevitability of producing some nonconforming product and doing a 100% sorting job of separating good from bad.

Even though no positive statement can be justified that a production process will hold within given limits,[1] a positive decision must be made by the designer regarding the tolerances to be specified. In using the evidence of the pilot run to help him in this decision, he should recognize that even though the natural tolerances as computed from $\overline{X} \pm 3\sigma'$ happen to be within the proposed specification limits, this fact does not *ensure* that these proposed limits can always be met. The estimate of what tolerances actually can be held is partly a matter of statistics and partly a matter of engineering judgment.

The statistical questions involved deal with the reliability of estimates from a limited sample and with the form of the frequency distribution from a controlled process. Not a great deal can be told about the exact shape of a frequency curve from the evidence of a short pilot run, such as one providing only 40 measured values. It would take tens of thousands of values all in control to define the extreme portions of a frequency curve well enough to justify a statement such as one that in the long run 99.73% of the values will fall within certain specified limits. As explained in Part Two of this book, skewed distributions of industrial quality characteristics often have several times 0.27% of the distribution outside one 3-sigma limit even though none of the distribution is outside the other 3-sigma limit.

The questions of engineering judgment involved in estimating what tolerances can be held deal with the difficulties of maintaining statistical control in the light of such matters as expected tool wear, operator variability, variability of incoming materials, and so forth. Any differences between the conditions of the pilot run and those of actual production should also be considered.

---

[1] Wilks has developed a method of predicting from one sample from a process in statistical control the probabilities of extreme values in succeeding samples from the same controlled process. For example, suppose a sample of 100 is taken from a controlled continuous distribution. The probability may be computed by Wilks's method as 0.99 that at least 94% of a second sample of 100 will be greater than the lowest value in the first sample of 100. The probability is 0.99 that at least 95.5% of an infinite sample would be above the lowest value in the first sample of 100. Similarly, the probability is 0.95 that at least 96% of a second sample of 100 will be greater than the lowest value in the first sample, and is 0.95 that 97% of an infinite sample would be greater. Wilks's method does not depend on the form of the universe from which samples are drawn, and can be applied with any desired probabilities. It is developed in the following three articles:

WILKS, S. S., Determination of Sample Sizes for Setting Tolerance Limits, *The Annals of Mathematical Statistics*, vol. 12, pp. 91–96, March, 1941.

WILKS, S. S., Statistical Prediction with Special Reference to the Problem of Tolerance Limits, *The Annals of Mathematical Statistics*, vol. 13, pp. 400–409, December, 1942.

WALD, A., An Extension of Wilks's Method for Setting Tolerance Limits, *The Annals of Mathematical Statistics*, vol. 14, pp. 45–49, March, 1943.

EXAMPLE 21.　ESTABLISHMENT OF TOLERANCE LIMITS BY PILOT RUNS

236. Facts of the Case. Nearly all the product of a company manufacturing electron tubes was sold to one customer. New designs of tubes were continually being developed. In each new design, it was necessary to establish tolerances on the many different measurable quality characteristics of the tube. With regard to many of the electrical characteristics, the usual practice had been for the customer to set specification limits at the design value $\pm 10\%$. It nearly always happened that when the tube got into production there would be difficulty in meeting some of the tolerance limits that had been specified in this way.

After this manufacturer had started to use statistical quality control in connection with production operations, the control chart was applied to the analysis of the pilot runs used in development work on new tubes. This analysis disclosed those electrical characteristics for which the $\pm 10\%$ tolerances seemed likely to cause trouble. It also disclosed other characteristics for which it seemed probable that tolerances could be held much closer than $\pm 10\%$, so that some specified tolerances might be tightened where it was advantageous to do so. On this basis, definite suggestions were made to the customer regarding tolerances for all quality characteristics. These suggestions were usually accepted. As a result, specifications on new designs were better adapted to the capabilities of the production process, the percentage defective was reduced, and increased uniformity was obtained on certain important quality characteristics.

237. Two Statistical Theorems of Great Importance in the Interrelationship of Tolerances. A dimension on an assembled product may be the sum of the dimensions of several parts. Or an electrical resistance

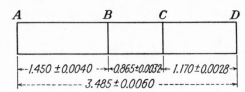

Fig. 55. Dimension AD is built up from the assembly of parts having dimensions AB, BC, and CD.

may be the sum of several electrical resistances of parts. Or a weight may be the sum of a number of weights of parts. In this common situation, what should be the relationship of the tolerances of the parts to the tolerances of the sum? This question may be answered with the aid of a theorem of mathematical statistics that is extremely useful in many problems of quality control. This theorem states that the standard deviation of the sum of any number of independent variables is the square root of the sum of the squares of the standard deviations of the independent variables.

$$\sigma'_{\text{sum}} = \sqrt{(\sigma'_1)^2 + (\sigma'_2)^2 + (\sigma'_3)^2 + \cdots + (\sigma'_n)^2}$$

For example, consider an assembly containing a dimension, AD, which is the sum of the dimensions of parts AB, BC, and CD (see Fig. 55).

Assume that the dimension of each part is statistically controlled with averages and universe standard deviations as follows:

	$\bar{X}'$	σ'
AB	1.450	0.0010
BC	0.865	0.0008
CD	1.170	0.0007

Assume that upper and lower specification limits are at 4-sigma distance from the average. Specifications are then as follows:

	Specification	X_{max}	X_{min}	Tolerance range, $X_{max} - X_{min}$
AB	1.450 ± 0.0040	1.4540	1.4460	0.0080
BC	0.865 ± 0.0032	0.8682	0.8618	0.0064
CD	1.170 ± 0.0028	1.1728	1.1672	0.0056
Total........	....	3.4950	3.4750	0.0200

Someone considering merely the specified tolerances and not the distribution pattern of the dimensions might conclude that the appropriate specification for the over-all dimension AD was 3.485 ± 0.010. This conclusion is incorrect because it fails to recognize the probability aspects of the situation. If the assembly of the parts is at random, large AB parts are just as likely to be assembled with small BC parts as with large ones. If the probability is small of the occurrence of an extreme maximum value of one part, the probability that three parts all having maximum values will be assembled together is very much smaller. The probabilities of all kinds of combinations of parts are reflected in a simple way by the formula for the standard deviation of the sum of independent variables

$$\sigma'_{AD} = \sqrt{(\sigma'_{AB})^2 + (\sigma'_{BC})^2 + (\sigma'_{CD})^2}$$
$$= \sqrt{(0.0010)^2 + (0.0008)^2 + (0.0007)^2} = 0.0015$$

If the specification limits for the sum AD, like the limits for the parts, are placed at 4-sigma distance from the average, the specifications for AD will be 3.485 ± 0.006. This ±0.006 is in sharp contrast with the ±0.010 obtained by simple addition of the allowable maximum and minimum values of the parts.

Some individuals in a manufacturing plant may find it difficult to believe that the laws of chance make the appropriate tolerance range for an assembly less than the sum of the tolerance ranges for the component parts. To convince them, it may be helpful to make an experimental verification of the theorem for the standard deviation of the sum of independent variables. Such an experiment at Westinghouse Electric Corporation is reported by Epstein.[1] Fifty of each of three components of an assembly were drawn at random from storage lots. These were gaged and averages and standard deviations of the dimensions of each component were obtained. The 3-sigma limits on assembled dimensions were then predicted by formula. The components were then selected at random and assembled, and the assemblies were gaged. The 3-sigma limits on the dimensions of the assemblies checked closely with the limits predicted by the use of statistical theory.

Whenever it is reasonable to assume that the tolerance ranges of the parts are proportional to their respective σ' values, such tolerance ranges may be combined by taking the square root of the sum of the squares. Thus

$$(X_{\max} - X_{\min})_{AD}$$
$$= \sqrt{[(X_{\max} - X_{\min})_{AB}]^2 + [(X_{\max} - X_{\min})_{BC}]^2 + [(X_{\max} - X_{\min})_{CD}]^2}$$
$$= \sqrt{(0.0080)^2 + (0.0064)^2 + (0.0056)^2} = 0.012$$

The actual situation in setting tolerance limits is often the reverse of the one just described. Frequently the desired tolerance range is known for the over-all quality characteristic (such as a dimension, electrical resistance, weight, etc.) and the problem is to set tolerance ranges on the component parts that can be expected to produce the desired range on the whole. This may be determined without much difficulty by trial-and-error solution of the formula. However, a direct solution is possible if the standard deviations of the various parts are assumed to be equal. In this case the formula for the standard deviation of the sum of n independent parts becomes

$$(\sigma'_{\text{sum}}) = \sqrt{n(\sigma'_{\text{part}})^2}$$

From this, it is evident that

$$(\sigma'_{\text{part}}) = \sqrt{\frac{(\sigma'_{\text{sum}})^2}{n}}$$

If tolerance ranges are assumed proportional to standard deviations,

$$(X_{\max} - X_{\min})_{\text{part}} = \sqrt{\frac{[(X_{\max} - X_{\min})_{\text{sum}}]^2}{n}}$$

Another useful theorem[2] of mathematical statistics deals with the

[1] EPSTEIN, B., Tolerances in Assemblies, *American Machinist*, vol. 90, no. 1, pp. 119–121, Jan. 3, 1946.

[2] For a simple proof of these two theorems, see BATEN, W. D., "Elementary Mathematical Statistics," pp. 216–218, John Wiley & Sons, Inc., New York, 1938.

standard deviation of the differences between independent variables, which is as follows:

$$\sigma'_{1-2} = \sqrt{(\sigma'_1)^2 + (\sigma'_2)^2}$$

It will be noted that the standard deviation of the difference is the same as the standard deviation of the sum. Example 23 gives an illustration of the use of this difference theorem in a problem involving the interrelationship between nominal dimensions.

A word of caution is called for on the application of these useful theorems to tolerance problems. The theorems assume independence of the variables being added and subtracted. In some assembly operations this independence does not exist. For example, suppose a dimension on an assembled product is the combined thickness of four metal washers. If these washers all come from the same production process and are assembled in the order of production, the thickness of the four washers in any assembly will not be independent of one another unless the process of producing them is in strict statistical control. Otherwise there will be a tendency for thick washers to be assembled together in some assemblies and thin washers assembled together in others. If this tendency exists, the theorem for the standard deviation of the sum of independent variables is not applicable to the problem of setting tolerances on the over-all dimension.

EXAMPLE 22. TOLERANCES AT INTERMEDIATE STAGES IN MANUFACTURING ELECTRICAL CABLE

238. Facts of the Case. The manufacture of armored electrical cable requires a number of operations, such as insulation of wire, spinning strands of insulated wire together, applying various types of insulating and water-resisting coatings, and applying the armored covering. Customers' specifications on dimensions apply only to the finished diameter. However, in order to meet specified tolerances on the finished diameter, it is desirable to set tolerance limits on the diameters after each of the manufacturing operations. Such limits, properly established, should be helpful to the various manufacturing departments. In order that the limits be respected, they should represent a practical goal at each stage of manufacturing, and they should be set in such a way that departure from the intermediate limits really causes difficulty in meeting specifications on the completed product.

In the case where an arbitrary guess is used as the basis for such tolerance limits on intermediate diameters, it is likely that the limits so established will be inconsistent with one another. At one stage in manufacturing, they may be tighter than it is practicable to hold. At another, the manufacturing departments may believe that even though the intermediate tolerances are not met, it will still be possible to make enough corrections in the remaining operations to meet the over-all specification. If the intermediate tolerances have these faults, they may not be respected by the manufacturing departments. If a customer's specified tolerances on final diameter are tight and are enforced, this state of mind on the part of the manufacturing departments may result in a substantial percentage of rejected product.

A rational approach to a consistent set of tolerance limits would require an estimate of the natural tolerances of each operation. For example, if operation 3 increases the diameter from 0.300 to 0.500 in., an $\bar{X}$ control chart might be maintained on which the variable was the increase of diameter produced by operation 3. This would give a basis for estimating $6\sigma'$ for operation 3. The $6\sigma'$ values for the increase in diameter from each of the other operations might be similarly estimated. An analysis of the tolerances should then start with the specification limits on the final diameter and work backwards operation by operation.

TABLE 38. EXAMPLE OF TRIAL COMPUTATION OF TOLERANCE LIMITS AT INTER-
MEDIATE STAGES IN MANUFACTURE OF ELECTRICAL CABLE
(Final diameter specified as 0.750 in. ±0.025)

Operation number	Nominal diameter at completion of operation	Estimated natural tolerance range ($6\sigma'$) of increase in diameter due to operation	Specified tolerance range of diameter at completion of operation $X_{max} - X_{min}$	Computed squared tolerance range	C^2	$E - F$	Computed tolerance range before start of operation $\sqrt{G}$	Computed specification at start of operation
A	B	C	D	E	F	G	H	I
8	0.750	0.016	0.050	0.002500	0.000256	0.002244	0.047	0.710 ± 0.023
7	0.710	0.021	0.047	0.002244	0.000441	0.001803	0.042	0.640 ± 0.021
6	0.640	0.018	0.042	0.001803	0.000324	0.001479	0.038	0.585 ± 0.019
5	0.585	0.007	0.038	0.001479	0.000049	0.001430	0.038	0.550 ± 0.019
4	0.550	0.013	0.038	0.001430	0.000169	0.001261	0.036	0.500 ± 0.018
3	0.500	0.028	0.036	0.001261	0.000784	0.000477	0.022	0.300 ± 0.011
2	0.300	0.016	0.022	0.000477	0.000256	0.000221	0.015	0.100 ± 0.007
1	0.100	0.008	0.015	0.000221	0.000064	0.000157		

This is illustrated in Table 38. The figures used in this table have been modified from an actual case in a way that serves to conceal any confidential information. The calculations in this table start with the assumption that it is desired that the specified tolerance range of 0.050 on the final diameter should represent $6\sigma'$. The tolerance range at the start of the last operation (operation 8) is computed to be consistent with this specification and with the natural tolerance of the final operation (0.016). A similar calculation is made for each preceding operation. The calculations depend on the use of the theorem for the standard deviation of the sum of two variables

$$\sigma'_{sum} = \sqrt{(\sigma'_1)^2 + (\sigma'_2)^2}$$

In this case, σ'_{sum} (the universe standard deviation of the final diameter) and σ'_2 (the universe standard deviation of the last operation) are known or assumed, and it is desired to find a consistent σ' for the diameter just before the final operation. Hence

$$\sigma'_1 = \sqrt{(\sigma'_{sum})^2 - (\sigma'_2)^2}$$

Table 38 is representative of the first of a series of trial calculations for setting the tolerances on the intermediate operations. It uses (column C) an allowance of $6\sigma'$ for each operation from operation 8 to operation 2. This results in a computed tolerance range for operation 1 of 0.015, whereas the $6\sigma'$ tolerance range of operation 1 is 0.008. Thus, if the computed specifications of column I were to be adopted, this would amount to allowing a little over $11\sigma'$ range for operation 1 and only a $6\sigma'$ range for each of the other seven operations. It is evident that a second trial calculation is necessary.

This new calculation might be based on an arbitrary increase of all the column C figures by some selected percentage. In this way each of the eight operations would be treated alike with regard to the increased latitude allowed in the tolerances. Or, if experience indicated that it was difficult to maintain control on two of the operations and easy to maintain control on the other six, the entire increase in latitude of tolerances might be thrown into an increase in the column C figures for the two operations on which control was difficult. Several trial calculations might be required to obtain a satisfactory set of computed specifications. The test of a consistent set is agreement between the computed tolerance range for operation 1 and the figure shown in column C for the estimated natural tolerance range of this operation. Or, stated a little differently, the final computed figure in column G (shown as 0.000157 in Table 38) should be zero.

EXAMPLE 23. AN ILLUSTRATION OF THE STATISTICAL RELATIONSHIP BETWEEN SPECIFIED NOMINAL DIMENSIONS, TOLERANCES, AND FITS AND CLEARANCES

239. Facts of the Case. Many hand tools used by mechanics involve sockets and attachments. Rice describes a study[1] made to determine the difference between the specified nominal dimensions of the socket and the corresponding attachment, and to establish the tolerances for each dimension. He explains, as follows:

"The socket has a square hole into which the end of the attachment fits. There is a ball and spring assembled on the male square (attachment) which catches in a ball check hole in the female square (socket) so that the two tools become a single driving unit. Important dimensions are: On sockets, the inside dimension of the female square; on attachments, the width across the flats and the height of the ball. . . . In actually working out this problem, there were several variables involved, but for the sake of clarity in presentation only the distance across male and female squares will be considered. The type of attachment studied was an extension, a straight metal bar with a male square at one end.

"The first step was to make several hundred random assemblies of finished sockets and extensions to determine what maximum and minimum clearances between male and female squares were necessary for practical use in a mechanic's work. This was done by a field survey. When the effect of ball height and other variables were removed, it was found on the ½-in. drive series that a minimum of 0.004 in. and a maximum of 0.015 in. clearance between male and female squares was required."

Rice explains that this study of consumer requirements was followed by a study of the variability of the dimensions of the sockets and extensions as they were then being produced. Shewhart control charts for variables were maintained on each dimension until a state of control had been reached and the natural tolerances determined. For the extensions (male squares) the average dimension $\bar{X}_M$ was 0.5005 in. The standard deviation σ'_M of this dimension (as estimated from $\bar{R}/d_2$) was 0.0015 in.

[1] Rice, W. B., Setting Tolerances Scientifically, *Mechanical Engineering*, vol. 66, pp. 801–803, December, 1944.

For the sockets (female square) the average dimension $\overline{X}_F$ was 0.5120 in. The standard deviation σ_F' was 0.0010 in. The distribution curves for these two dimensions were approximately normal. This is illustrated graphically in Fig. 56a.

240. Establishing the Nominal Dimensions for Sockets and Extensions. As shown in Fig. 56a, the $3\sigma'$ limits for the individual extensions are 0.496 and 0.505. The $3\sigma'$ limits for sockets are 0.509 and 0.515. If it is assumed that, because the distributions are approximately normal, practically all the values will fall within limits of $\pm 3\sigma'$, it is evident that there will practically never be found an extension and socket with less than the desired clearance of 0.004 in. The maximum extension dimension is 0.505 in. and the minimum socket dimension is 0.509 in.

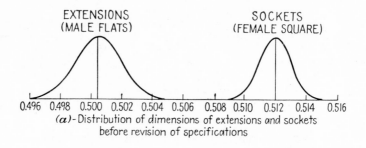

EXTENSIONS
(MALE FLATS)

SOCKETS
(FEMALE SQUARE)

0.496 0.498 0.500 0.502 0.504 0.506 0.508 0.510 0.512 0.514 0.516
(a)- Distribution of dimensions of extensions and sockets
before revision of specifications

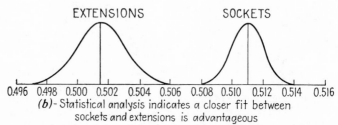

EXTENSIONS

SOCKETS

0.496 0.498 0.500 0.502 0.504 0.506 0.508 0.510 0.512 0.514 0.516
(b)- Statistical analysis indicates a closer fit between
sockets and extensions is advantageous

FIG. 56. Frequency curves representing distribution of dimensions of sockets and extensions—Example 23.

On the other hand, it is clear that occasionally an extension will be paired with a socket with more than the maximum desired clearance of 0.015 in. The minimum extension dimension is 0.496 in., whereas the maximum socket dimension is 0.515 in.

It therefore appears that the existing setting of the nominal dimensions of extensions and sockets at 0.5005 and 0.5120 in., respectively, tends towards fits that are too loose. Generally speaking, the tighter the fit, as long as there is enough clearance for extensions actually to go into sockets, the better satisfied the mechanic will be and the better the reputation of the line of tools. Hence consideration should be given to a possible decrease in the difference between the nominal dimensions.

Rice suggests that the principle governing the decision of how far to go in the change of nominal dimensions may be found in the answer to the question, "What risk does the manufacturer want to take that, somewhere, sometime, a mechanic will pick up a socket and extension with less than 0.004 in. . . . clearance between them?"

The theorem for the standard deviation of the difference of two independent variables may be used advantageously to estimate this risk associated with any given difference between the nominal dimensions.[1]   This standard deviation is

$$\sigma'_{F-M} = \sqrt{(\sigma'_F)^2 + (\sigma'_M)^2} = \sqrt{(0.0010)^2 + (0.0015)^2} = 0.0018$$

The existing average clearance between sockets and extensions is

$$\overline{\overline{X}}_F - \overline{\overline{X}}_M = 0.512 - 0.5005 = 0.0115$$

If, as in this case, both variables are distributed normally, the difference between the variables (*i.e.*, the clearance between sockets and extensions) will also be distributed normally.   From this fact the probabilities may be calculated of a smaller clearance than the minimum desired value of 0.004 and of a larger clearance than the maximum desired value of 0.015.

A clearance of 0.004 is a departure of 0.0075 (*i.e.*, 0.0115 − 0.004) from the average clearance.   This is 0.0075/0.0018 or 4.17 times σ'_{F-M}.   The probability of as great a departure in one direction from the average is so small that it is outside the limits of Table *A*, Appendix III, but may be determined from a six-place table of normal curve areas to be 0.000015.   Thus too tight a fit might be expected about one time in 67,000.

A clearance of 0.015 is a departure of 0.0035 from the average clearance.   This is 1.94 times σ'_{F-M}.   The probability of such a departure is given by Table *A* as 0.0262, or about one time in 38.

Similar calculations for other assumed clearances between average dimensions give the following probabilities of fits that are too tight or too loose:

$\overline{\overline{X}}_F - \overline{\overline{X}}_M$, in.	Probability of smaller clearance than 0.004 in.	Probability of larger clearance than 0.015 in.
0.0115	0.0000+	0.0262
0.011	0.0001−	0.0132
0.0105	0.0002−	0.0062
0.010	0.0004	0.0027
0.0095	0.0011	0.0011
0.009	0.0027	0.0004
0.0085	0.0062	0.0002−
0.008	0.0132	0.0001−
0.0075	0.0262	0.0000+

This type of probability analysis supplies a rational basis for a decision as to the difference between the nominal dimensions.   It is clear that the existing average clearance of 0.0115 should be somewhat reduced.   A reduction of 0.002 to 0.0095 in. gives a probability of 0.0011 (about 1 chance in 900) that a socket and extension selected at random will have a smaller clearance than the desired minimum of 0.004. In deciding whether or not to adopt this average clearance of 0.0095 it is also helpful to observe that if it is adopted, the probability of a clearance of 0.003 in. is 0.0002−, and the probability of a clearance of 0.002 in. is negligible.   All these probabilities are subject to the limitation that they assume statistical control of the production process and a normal distribution of the quality characteristics involved.

If 0.0095 is adopted as the average clearance, it remains to establish the average

[1] From this point on, the analysis presented here differs slightly from that given by Rice.

value of the nominal dimension.   If this were to be 0.511 for the sockets, the nominal dimension of extensions would be 0.5015.   Figure 56b shows the relative positions of the frequency curves if these values are adopted.

If 100% inspection is to be used, the tolerances on extensions should be specified if ±0.045 and on sockets as ±0.030.   For reasons that are subsequently explained, if sampling inspection is to be employed somewhat tighter tolerance limits may be desirable.

241. A Useful Diagram for Dealing with Overlapping Frequency Distributions.   Examples 22 and 23 represent special cases of a common type of problem.   R. W. Hanna and E. C. Varnum of Barber-Colman Company have commented on certain practical aspects of this problem as follows:[1]

It is common practice for many engineers to specify dimensions for mating parts which differ appreciably so that there is essentially no chance of interference, i.e., little chance of getting pairs which will not assemble.   However this method of avoiding interference can result in the equally disturbing problem of extreme looseness of fit.

Consider, too, what happens sometimes when mating parts are delivered to the assembly floor with greatly overlapping distributions.   Under general inspection procedures in many plants both types would be subjected to a 100% screening and the pieces found in the overlapping regions would be removed for correction or scrapping.   In this way the assembly floor is assured of good mating parts but at an unnecessarily high cost in inspection, rework, and scrap.

Figure 57 is a diagram prepared by Hanna and Varnum to determine the probability of interference when two normal distributions overlap.   Their directions for the use of the diagram are as follows:

(1) Divide the larger standard deviation by the smaller; (2) locate this value on the lower scale; (3) subtract the means, or averages; (4) divide this difference by the smaller standard deviation; (5) locate the result of the division in (4) on the vertical scale; (6) find the point which is above the lower scale value and to the right of the vertical scale value; (7) determine the interference risk from the per cent curves passing nearest this point.

If it is desired to assume a given risk of interference, Fig. 57 may be used to determine the distance between the $\overline{X}'$ values that should be specified by the designer.   For example, suppose it is desired to accept a risk of interference of 0.1%.   If the two distributions have equal standard deviations, the distance between the $\overline{X}'$ values should be about $4.5\sigma'$.   If one standard deviation is twice as large as the other, the distance should be about 7 times the smaller standard deviation.

This Hanna-Varnum diagram may be used in place of calculations such as those made in Example 23 for the probability of clearances less

[1] HANNA, R. W., and E. C. VARNUM, Interference Risk When Normal Distributions Overlap, *Industrial Quality Control*, vol. 7, pp. 26–28, September, 1950.

than or more than any stated values. For example, with

$$\overline{\overline{X}}_F - \overline{\overline{X}}_M = 0.0085 \text{ in.}$$

the probability of a smaller clearance than 0.004 in. was computed to be 0.0062. To use Fig. 57 for this calculation, subtract the stated minimum clearance, 0.004 in., from the distance between the average values, 0.0085 in. This difference is 0.0045 in. Compute the ratio of this differ-

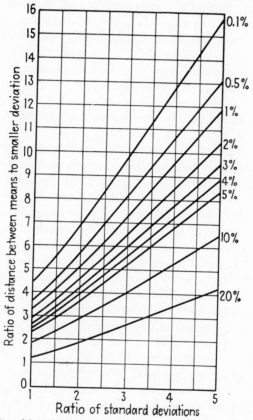

FIG. 57. Probability of interference of two overlapping normal frequency distributions. (*Reproduced from article by R. W. Hanna and E. C. Varnum in September, 1950, issue of Industrial Quality Control.*)

ence to the smaller standard deviation, 0.0010 in. This ratio is 4.5. Enter Fig. 57 using this 4.5 figure in combination with the ratio of the standard deviations, 1.5. The probability falls between the 0.5% and 1.0% lines; interpolation indicates an approximate value of 0.6% (*i.e.*, 0.006).

To illustrate the application of Fig. 57 to the determination of the probability of a fit looser than some stated value, consider the case where $\overline{\overline{X}}_F - \overline{\overline{X}}_M = 0.0115$ in. and it is desired to find the probability of a clearance larger than 0.015 in. Subtract 0.0115 in. from 0.015 in., obtaining a difference of 0.0035 in. The ratio of this difference to the smaller standard deviation, 0.0010 in., is 3.5. For the ratio of standard deviations of 1.5, Fig. 57 shows the probability to fall between the 2% and 3% lines. Interpolation indicates a close check with the probability of 0.0262 computed in Example 23.

242. Precision, Reliability, and Accuracy of Methods of Measurement.[1] The only way in which the value of any quality characteristic—dimensions, hardness, tensile strength, weight, percentage of chemical impurity, etc.—may be determined is by some form of measurement. If measuring devices and those who used them were perfect, it would be possible to make a direct determination of the variability of the true values of the measured quality characteristic. Actually, the measured values reflect errors of measurement as well as variation in the quantity measured.

The phrase *method of measurement* may be thought of as including not only the measuring devices and the procedures specified for their use but also their manipulation by the particular user or users. Any method of measurement of an industrial quality characteristic may be expected to have some pattern of variability. Under favorable conditions this pattern may be observed by repeating a measurement many times on a quality characteristic that remains unchanged. For instance, Fig. 58 shows a frequency distribution obtained from 100 micrometer measurements all on the thickness of the same steel strip.[2] Different methods of measurement will have different patterns of variation.

The *precision* of a method of measurement refers to its variability when used to make repeated measurements under carefully controlled conditions. Where practicable, as in the case referred to in Fig. 58, these repeated measurements should be made on a single quality characteristic of one particular article. Otherwise, as in chemical tests or other destructive tests, they should be made on a homogeneous sample. A numerical measure of precision is the standard deviation of the frequency distribution that would be obtained from such repeated measurements. This may be referred to as $\sigma'_{\text{error of measurement}}$.

The *reliability* of a method of measurement refers to the consistency

[1] The meanings of these three terms are not standardized among writers on errors of measurement. The meanings used here are based on those used by Grant Wernimont in a paper Precision and Accuracy of Test Methods, included in *Special Technical Publication* No. 103—*Symposium on Application of Statistics*, American Society for Testing Materials, Philadelphia, 1950. Regardless of the terminology used, it is important to distinguish among these three concepts.

[2] Taken from "Dimensional Control," p. 19, The Sheffield Corporation, Dayton, 1942.

of its pattern of variation. This may be judged to best advantage by control charts for $\bar{X}$ and R or $\bar{X}$ and σ. For example, the 500 measurements made with a comparator and given on pages 72 to 74 show excellent statistical control. Where repeated measurements show erratic patterns of variation, the method of measurement used is unreliable. Any statement regarding the precision of a method of measurement implies that the method of measurement is reliable.

The *accuracy* of a method of measurement refers to its absence of bias—to the conformity of its results to the true value of the quality characteristic being measured. In an accurate method, the average

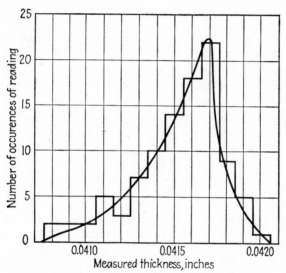

Fig. 58. Frequency distribution of 100 micrometer measurements of the same dimension made by the same experienced inspector. (*Reproduced from "Dimensional Control," published by the Sheffield Corporation.*)

value obtained from a set of measurements should differ from the true value by not more than would be expected as a chance variation in the light of the precision of the particular method. A practical difficulty in judging accuracy is that the only way to find the "true" value is by some other method of measurement. Presumably the method employed to determine the true value should be a method of high precision that is believed to be without bias.

In our initial discussion (pages 6 to 7) of the control chart for variables as applied to an industrial process, it was pointed out that an industrial quality characteristic will have (1) basic variability, (2) consistency of performance, and (3) an average level. This is also true of a method of measurement. It has been pointed out here that *precision* refers to basic variability, *reliability* to consistency, and *accuracy* to average level.

243. Relationship between the Variability of Measured Values and the Precision of the Method of Measurement. The variability observed in measured values of dimensions, hardness, tensile strength, and other quality characteristics of industrial product is due in part to the variability of the product and in part to the variability inherent in the method of measurement. It is helpful to think of a measured value as the sum of two variables, the quantity measured and the error of measurement.

As these two variables are likely to be independent of one another, the formula for the standard deviation of the sum of two independent variables may be used to advantage. For this purpose it might be written

$$\sigma'_{\text{measured value}} = \sqrt{(\sigma'_{\text{true value}})^2 + (\sigma'_{\text{error of measurement}})^2}$$

This formula always supplies a useful point of view toward any problem involving errors of measurement. Its numerical use in solving practical problems depends on obtaining a reliable estimate of the magnitude of the standard deviation of chance errors of measurement.

One possible numerical application of the formula for standard deviation of the sum of two variables is in the determination of tolerance limits that are intended to allow for errors of measurement as well as for fluctuations in the true value of a quality characteristic. Another is in judging the ratio of the variability of true values to the variability of measured values. This latter application is illustrated in Example 24.

EXAMPLE 24. INFLUENCE OF CHANCE ERRORS OF MEASUREMENT ON VARIABILITY OF MEASURED VALUES

244. Facts of the Case. In a chemical plant, the method employed for laboratory analysis of the nonvolatile content of a certain product was not the most precise one possible. It was a rapid and economical method that was considered satisfactory by the laboratory director. Nevertheless, whenever a laboratory analysis showed the product to be outside specification limits, the production department was inclined to place the blame on the lack of precision of the laboratory methods rather than on any fault in the manufacturing operations. For this reason, a change to a more precise method was under consideration.

A determination of the precision of the analytical procedure indicated that the standard deviation of the error of determination was 3.3 units. A control chart on the measured value for the manufactured product supplied an estimate that when the process remained in control σ' was 9.5 units. These values were substituted in the formula given in Art. 242 to estimate the σ' of the true value, as follows:

$$9.5 = \sqrt{(\sigma'_{\text{true value}})^2 + (3.3)^2}$$
$$\sigma'_{\text{true value}} = \sqrt{79.36} = 8.9$$

This indicated that the chance errors inherent in this analytical procedure caused the measured values to be about 7% more variable than they would have been if the analytical procedures had always given perfect results. The adoption of a more precise analytical procedure with a standard deviation of two-thirds the existing one would have reduced the variability of the measured values by about 3%, as shown by the following calculation:

$$\sigma'_{\text{measured value}} = \sqrt{(8.9)^2 + (2.2)^2} = 9.2$$

On the basis of this analysis, it was decided to continue with the less accurate and more economical analytical procedure.

245. Relationship between Specified Tolerance Limits and the Sampling Acceptance Procedures to Be Used. The remaining chapters of Part Four of this book deal with sampling acceptance procedures. In these chapters it is brought out that the selection of a sampling plan should be governed by the associated risks of accepting product with various percentages failing to conform to the design specifications. Any sampling acceptance plan implies a willingness to take a chance on passing some product outside of specification limits.

It is reasonably common for design specifications to contain some margin of safety. That is, they are more severe than the designer really thinks is necessary for the functioning of the product under ordinary circumstances. Where this is the case, product slightly outside of specification limits falls in a twilight zone that will actually be good enough for most purposes. When a designer makes a conscious decision to incorporate a margin of safety into one or more tolerance limits, he is, in effect, making an economic decision. The extent of the margin of safety that is appropriate depends on certain cost factors and requires consideration of the acceptance procedures that are to be used. From a broad viewpoint, the design specification and the acceptance specification may be thought of as two different aspects of a problem in engineering economy. A brief discussion of the economic analysis of this type of problem is given in Chap. XVII, following the presentation of the subject of acceptance sampling.

246. Establishing Manufacturing Tolerances in the Consumer Goods Industries. A situation that is common in many industries is clearly described by Beckwith.[1] He classifies the possible conditions with regard to customer inspection of final product into two groups, namely:

(1) Where the product is not subject to immediate, systematic, and quantitative evaluation of quality and, therefore, is not subject to systematic acceptance and rejection. (2) Where the product is subject to immediate, systematic, and quantitative evaluation of quality and, therefore, is subject to systematic acceptance or rejection.

His comments on the first condition are as follows:

Condition No. 1 has been quite general in the textile industry in the past; *i.e.,* goods are produced, but the consumer, in general, does not make immediate

[1] BECKWITH, O. P., A Fresh Approach to Quality Control, *Textile World,* vol. 94, pp. 79–82, January, 1944.

systematic, and quantitative determination of their conformity to quality standards. Instead, the manufacturer is forced to maintain quality by the customer's longtime, haphazard, qualitative experience with the manufacturer's output. If, through good manufacturing methods, quality (for example, wear life of a fabric) is maintained at a standard level ±10%, it is not likely that increasing uniformity of product to ±5% will be readily discerned by the individual consumer. Therefore, if a manufacturer is enjoying a profitable business with a quality variation of ±10%, the arguments toward adoption of methods and processes designed to give a more uniform production having ±5% variation are somewhat abstract, even though it might prove over a period of years to show savings because of lower claims for defective merchandise. In such situations the need for close control or statistical control of quality is not readily apparent, unless it happens that competitors adopt quality-control techniques which give better products.

Although many such situations exist in textile mills today, there are still cogent arguments for adoption of statistical quality control in these mills. The relationship of each department in a mill to the next one in the manufacturing operation is that of producer and consumer. The picking department produces prepared wool for its consumer, the card room; the card room, for the spinning room; the spinning room for the dyehouse. Even though there may be no testing at these points or systematic attempts to evaluate quality, nevertheless the production of each department is subject to immediate, systematic, and somewhat quantitative evaluation of the product in the next department. If stock is not well picked, the card room will complain and point to higher costs necessary because card speeds must be reduced to process the insufficiently opened and blended stock. If the roving is not well carded, the spinning department complains of allowances that must be made to spinners for their lowered production. Thus, it is seen that even in mills where the need for closely controlling final product quality is not sufficient to induce action by management, closely controlling quality within departments of the mill can be appreciated and the economies effected demonstrated relatively quickly.

This quotation illustrates the way in which the establishment of specification limits on certain quality characteristics at intermediate stages in manufacturing operations may be used to reduce costs and to assist management in controlling the relationship among the various manufacturing departments. It is evident that the only practical basis for such limits is the evidence of past performance in a period in which quality was considered to be satisfactory. Such manufacturing tolerance limits may best be established on the basis of the evidence of control charts. Conformity to the limits may also be determined to best advantage by the use of control charts.

Problems

155. The following 40 readings represent a pilot run on the production of a temperature control device. They give the "on" temperature at which a thermostatically controlled switch operates at a given setting.

Device number	Temperature	Device number	Temperature	Device number	Temperature	Device number	Temperature
1	67.6	11	68.0	21	67.7	31	67.7
2	67.1	12	67.7	22	67.4	32	67.2
3	67.6	13	67.5	23	67.3	33	67.8
4	67.5	14	67.6	24	67.6	34	67.8
5	67.3	15	67.6	25	67.5	35	67.6
6	67.5	16	67.5	26	67.1	36	67.6
7	67.4	17	67.1	27	67.7	37	67.6
8	67.5	18	67.6	28	67.9	38	67.8
9	67.6	19	67.4	29	67.2	39	67.7
10	67.6	20	67.6	30	67.5	40	67.9

Check these for control. Make an estimate of σ'. What conclusions, if any, can you reach regarding the prospect that the process can meet specifications of 67.5 ± 0.5?

156. Make a second trial computation of tolerances for the diameters of the electrical cable discussed in Example 22. Modify Table 38 by using as the natural tolerance range of each operation, a range 10% greater than that given in column C of Table 38. This amounts to $6.6\sigma'$. Interpret this as giving new column C figures of 0.018, 0.023, 0.020, 0.008, 0.014, 0.031, 0.018, and 0.009, respectively. Does this second trial computation give you a satisfactory set of specifications throughout? If not, what would you suggest as the basis for a third trial computation?

157. Suppose it is desired to establish the relationship between nominal dimensions of extensions and sockets on hand tools in a situation similar to Example 23 but involving another size. Assume that a study of consumer requirements indicated a desirable minimum clearance of 0.005 in. and a maximum clearance of 0.018 in. Assume a study of past production showed an average dimension of extensions of 0.7510 with a standard deviation of 0.0018 and an average dimension of sockets of 0.7650 with a standard deviation of 0.0011. Both distributions are statistically controlled and approximately normal.

Compute the respective probabilities of a smaller clearance than the desired minimum and a larger clearance than the desired maximum for average clearances of 0.015, 0.014, 0.013, 0.012, 0.011, and 0.010. Would you recommend any change in the existing average clearance? Explain your reasoning.

158. The standard deviation of the error of measurement of a certain electrical characteristic of a product is determined to be 6 units. The σ' of the measured values under a state of control is 42 units. From this information, what is your estimate of the true σ' of the quality characteristic?

It is believed that the standard deviation of the error of measurement could be cut in half by taking the mean of four measurements on each item of product rather than by taking only one measurement. If this should be done, what reduction would you expect in the σ' of the measured values?

159. Table 11 (page 76) gives the distribution of markings of chips in Shewhart's bowl. Assume these represent the excess over 0.0800 in. of the thicknesses of metal washers measured to the nearest 0.0001 in.; for example, 30 corresponds to a thickness of 0.0830.

The standard deviation σ' of this distribution is approximately 0.0010. Table 12 (pages 79 to 81), in which chips (*i.e.*, washers) are drawn in groups of 4, illustrates the distribution that might be expected if washers were assembled at random in groups of 4. The sum of the four figures in each group, added to 0.3200, gives the thickness of one assembly.

Using the data of Table 12, prepare a frequency distribution of the thicknesses of such assemblies. (Note that the sum of the 4 figures in each group is necessarily 4 times the $\bar{X}$ already computed and shown in the table.) Find the standard deviation of this distribution of 100 assemblies. How does this standard deviation check with the one that would be anticipated by the use of the theorem for the sum of 4 independent variables?

What does this problem suggest to you about the relationship of the theorem for the standard deviation of the average $\bar{X}$ and the theorem for the standard deviation of the sum of a number of independent variables?

160. The following figures were obtained for the "on" temperature of the thermostat on a pilot run of 40 units of a newly designed thermostatically controlled device. These observations have been arranged into subgroups of 4 in the order of production, and $\bar{X}$ and R have been computed for each subgroup.

Subgroup	a	b	c	d	$\bar{X}$	R
1	164	168	167	165	166.0	4
2	165	173	167	175	170.0	10
3	169	171	167	169	169.0	4
4	168	169	172	171	170.0	4
5	170	172	171	169	170.5	3
6	167	168	169	168	168.0	2
7	165	163	165	165	164.5	2
8	170	169	169	170	169.5	1
9	162	167	166	165	165.0	5
10	164	170	171	169	168.5	7

It is desired to establish specification limits of 170 ± 5 for this "on" temperature. It is evident that not all of the thermostats in this pilot run have met these tolerances; moreover several thermostats fell exactly on the specification limits.

You are asked to make a statistical study of the above data to determine whether it seems likely that a production process such as the one used in this pilot run can be expected to meet these tolerances. Discuss this matter as fully as you can, making any calculations that seem to you to be appropriate. Give a definite opinion, in so far as one is justified from the limited number of observations, on the question of whether or not the stated tolerances can be met. If you think they cannot be met, tell why. If you think they can under certain conditions, state the conditions.

161. Two pieces AB and CD are assembled together in a mass production assembly. The average dimension of AB is 3.500 in. This dimension is statistically controlled with a standard deviation of 0.020 in. The average dimension of CD is 2.500 in. This dimension is statistically controlled with a standard deviation of 0.015 in. Both dimensions are normally distributed. The average value of the combined dimension will obviously be 3.500 + 2.500 = 6.000 in. The assembly of the two parts is at random. Compute the approximate value of the probability that an assembly will have a combined dimension in excess of 6.050 in.

162. Ten parties of students in a course in elementary surveying each made two measurements of the length in feet of a given line, with the following results:

Party	Measurement		Discrepancy	Average value
	a	*b*		
A	421.59	421.37	0.22	421.48
B	421.73	421.65	0.08	421.69
C	421.70	422.28	0.58	421.99
D	421.79	421.72	0.07	421.76
E	421.64	421.67	0.03	421.66
F	421.58	421.56	0.02	421.57
G	421.53	421.69	0.16	421.61
H	421.52	421.66	0.14	421.59
I	421.69	421.68	0.01	421.68
J	421.76	421.69	0.07	421.72

The taping methods used by these elementary students called for alignment by eye and estimation of difference of elevation by eye. These methods tend to give a measured distance that is slightly longer than the true distance. An advanced surveying class, using better methods for alignment and finding difference of elevation, made several measurements of this same line; the average of these measurements was 421.58.

What conclusions, if any, can you draw regarding the precision, the reliability, and the accuracy of the measurements made by the elementary class?

163. Two mating parts, *A* and *B*, have dimensions specified as 2.610 in. and 2.615 in., respectively. Control-chart analysis indicates the standard deviations of *A* and *B* to be 0.0012 in. and 0.0015 in., respectively. If the distributions of *A* and *B* are normal and centered about the specified dimensions, and if parts are assembled at random, find the probability of interference between the two distributions. Solve, using Fig. 57. *Ans.* About 0.005.

164. Using the data of Problem 163, make use of Table *A* to compute the probability of a greater clearance than 0.010 in. *Ans.* 0.0047.

165. Control-chart analysis indicates that the standard deviations of the distributions of dimensions of two mating parts, *C* and *D*, are 0.0008 in. and 0.0020 in., respectively. It is desired that the probability of a smaller clearance than 0.002 in. should be 0.005. What distance between the average dimensions of *C* and *D* should be specified by the designer? Assume normal distributions and random assembly, and solve, using Fig. 57. With this distance specified, what is the probability that two parts assembled at random will have a greater clearance than 0.012 in.? *Ans.* 0.0076 in.; 0.02.

166. Two mating parts, *E* and *F*, have an average clearance specified as 0.006 in. Control charts indicate the standard deviations of the dimensions of *E* and *F* to be 0.0010 in. and 0.0030 in., respectively. Use Fig. 57 to find the probability of interference between the two distributions. Assume the distributions to be normal and assembly at random.

167. In Problem 166, what average clearance should be specified in order that the probability of interference would be 0.001?

168. Control charts indicate the standard deviations of the dimensions of two mating parts to have identical values of 0.0012 in. It is desired that the probability of a clearance less than 0.003 in. should be 0.02. What distance between the average values of these dimensions should be specified by the designer? Assume normal distributions and random assembly, and solve, using Fig. 57. If your computed distance is specified, what is the probability that two parts assembled at random will have a greater clearance than 0.009 in.?

CHAPTER XIII

SOME FUNDAMENTAL CONCEPTS
IN ACCEPTANCE SAMPLING

. . . Even where the necessary inspections are not destructive, "inspection fatigue" steps in to prevent one hundred percent inspections from providing one hundred percent insurance of conformance to specification requirements. If you have before you a hand truck containing 15,000 cartridges, and you are given the job of inspecting and gaging them visually one hundred percent, they probably will all look alike to you after you have examined about 9,000 of them, and you won't know whether the discoloration which evidences necessary shoulder anneal, for example, is there on the 9,001st cartridge or not. This is no insult to your intelligence; it is just a plain illustration of experience.

So 100 or 200 or even 500 percent manual inspections are not the answer where large quantities of material are involved, even if the resulting production delays could be tolerated. Mechanical gaging and photoelectric cell gaging are being used in the inspection of ordnance material wherever possible to circumvent inspection fatigue, but even the best of these substitutes have their own margins of error. In other words, it must be recognized that the element of risk just can't be eliminated from quality considerations in mass production, and the real problem is to reduce the chances which must be taken to a minimum without unduly impeding output. Quality control techniques are *built* around limiting such risks to a predetermined degree, and they are thus admirably suited to the problem in hand.—G. D. EDWARDS[1]

247. Importance of Sampling for Acceptance Purposes. Inspection for acceptance purposes is carried out at many stages in manufacturing. There may be inspection of incoming materials and parts, process inspection at various points in the manufacturing operations, final inspection by a manufacturer of his own product, and—ultimately—inspection of the finished product by one or more purchasers.

Much of this acceptance inspection is necessarily on a sampling basis. All acceptance tests that are destructive of the item tested must inevitably be done by sampling. In many other instances sampling inspection is used because the cost of 100% inspection is prohibitive. In still other cases, because of the effect of inspection fatigue involved in 100% inspection, a good sampling inspection plan may actually give better quality assurance than 100% inspection.

[1] EDWARDS, G. D., Quality Control of Munitions—The Modern Ounce of Prevention Applied to Ordnance, *Army Ordnance*, vol. 23, pp. 482–485, November-December, 1942.

248. Common Practices in Acceptance Sampling. When sampling inspection for acceptance purposes is carried out without benefit of formal rules regarding size and frequency of sample, the inspector often uses an informal working rule that is very good from the statistical standpoint. This rule is to permit his current decisions on acceptance to be influenced by his knowledge of the past quality history of the product being sampled. For instance, where the same part or article is purchased from two or more sources, an inspector might check only one or two items in a shipment from a source that he considered reliable but might give critical examination to a shipment from a source that he considered to be unreliable.

Although this is sound as far as it goes, such an informal working system for determining size and frequency of sample and basis of acceptance has obvious limitations. Inspectors' memories of past quality history sometimes may be short and inaccurate. The inspector who keeps in his head the quality history of a number of products may die or resign or be transferred to another job. Or the inspector's confidence in past good quality history may lead him to neglect current inspection and therefore fail to discover when quality has changed for the worse.

These limitations suggest the need of definite working rules regarding size and frequency of sample and basis for acceptance or rejection. But it is not sufficient that such rules merely be *definite*. Many of the definite rules in common use in industry are bad, because they seem to give a promise of quality assurance they cannot fulfill. Example 5 in Chap. II discussed one such common scheme, which on critical analysis turns out to accept product the quality level of which is not appreciably better than the quality level of the product submitted. Often such formal schemes actually give less quality protection than the informal scheme of letting the inspector use his judgment.

Because sampling is a problem involving the laws of chance, the development of good sampling acceptance schemes requires consideration of the mathematics of probability. One reason why many common sampling acceptance plans—for instance, the one described in Example 5—are so bad is that the people who specify them do not realize how little protection they really give. This chapter applies probability mathematics to a determination of the quality protection given by various types of acceptance sampling plans, particularly those based on attributes.

Moreover, bad acceptance sampling procedures are sometimes specified because the people who specify them are not aware that well-planned sampling tables and procedures are readily available for use in attributes inspection. Chapters XIV and XV describe such tables and procedures. Variables acceptance sampling is discussed in Chap. XVI.

249. Some Symbols and Terms Used in Relation to Sampling Acceptance Plans. The probability principles presented in Chap. IX, and the explanation of the control charts for fraction defective and for defects given in Chaps. X and XI, provide the background for a discussion of the evaluation of acceptance plans involving sampling by attributes. In discussing such plans, the following symbols are used:

N = number of pieces in a given lot.

n = number of pieces in a sample.

M = number of defective pieces in a given lot of size N.

m = number of defective pieces in a given sample of size n.

c = acceptance number, the maximum allowable number of defective pieces in a sample of size n*.

p = fraction defective. In a given submitted lot, this is M/N; in a given sample, it is m/n.

p' = true process average fraction defective of a product submitted for inspection.

$\bar{p}$ = average fraction defective in observed samples.

P_a = probability of acceptance. The probability of accepting product meeting some given quality standard is also described as P_c.

P_c = consumer's risk. The probability of rejecting product meeting some given quality standard is referred to as the *producer's risk*, $1 - P_c$.

$p_{0.95}$, $p_{0.50}$, $p_{0.10}$, etc. = fraction defective having a probability of acceptance of 0.95, 0.50, 0.10, etc , under any given acceptance criteria.

250. Lot-by-lot Acceptance, Using Single Sampling by Attributes. In acceptance inspection a defective article is one that fails to conform to specifications in one or more quality characteristics. A common procedure in acceptance sampling is to consider each submitted lot of product separately and to base the decision on acceptance or rejection of the lot on the evidence of one or more samples chosen at random from the lot. When the decision is always made on the evidence of only one sample, the acceptance plan is described as a *single sampling* plan.

Any systematic plan for single sampling requires that three numbers be specified. One is the number of articles N in the lot from which the sample is to be drawn. The second is the number of articles n in the random sample drawn from the lot. The third is the acceptance number c.

This acceptance number is the maximum allowable number of defective articles in the sample. More than c defectives will cause the rejection of the lot. In sampling plans developed without benefit of statistical analysis, c is usually zero. (Often c is specified as zero under the illusion that if the sample is perfect, the lot will be perfect.)

* See footnote on p. 82 in Chap. IV for the justification for the use of the symbol c in a different meaning from those previously employed.

In the discussion that follows, sampling acceptance plans of this type are described by these three numbers. For instance, the sampling plan of Example 5 is specified in this way as $\begin{cases} N = 50 \\ n = 5. \\ c = 0 \end{cases}$ These three numbers may be interpreted as saying: "Take a random sample of 5 from a lot of 50. If the sample contains more than 0 defects, reject the lot; otherwise, accept the lot."

Example 5 examined this plan critically under a particular assumption, namely, that the plan was used for acceptance of product that on the average was 4% defective. The distribution of defectives among the lots was assumed to follow the laws of chance. (This amounted to an assumption either that the production process was statistically controlled or that the product was well mixed before being divided into lots.) Under this assumption, the lots accepted by the plan proved to be 3.6% defective; this modest improvement in product quality was accomplished at the cost of rejecting 18.5% of the submitted lots. After the defective articles found in the rejected lots were eliminated, the average quality of the remainder of the rejected lots was not appreciably worse than the average of the accepted lots. It was evident that this sampling acceptance plan was not a satisfactory one under the assumed conditions.

251. The Operating Characteristic (OC) Curve of an Acceptance Sampling Plan Shows the Ability of the Plan to Distinguish between Good and Bad Lots. In judging various acceptance sampling plans it is desirable to compare their performance over a range of possible quality levels of submitted product. An excellent picture of this performance is given by the *operating characteristic curve*.[1] Such curves are commonly referred to as OC curves.

For any given fraction defective p in a submitted lot, the OC curve shows the probability P_a that such a lot will be accepted by the given sampling plan. Or, stated a little differently, the OC curve shows the long-run percentage of submitted lots that would be accepted if a great many lots of any stated quality were submitted for inspection. Figures 59, 60, and 61 give the OC curves of a number of single sampling plans.

As explained later in Art. 260, in most cases OC curves may also be thought of as showing the probability of accepting lots from a stream of product having a fraction defective p.

---

[1] Most of the terminology of acceptance sampling originated in the Bell Telephone Laboratories in the 1920's, where such curves were called "probability of acceptance curves." The phrase "operating characteristic curve," however, originated in the Ballistic Research Laboratories at Aberdeen Proving Ground, Maryland, just before World War II. It was first used by Col. H. H. Zornig when he was director of that laboratory.

252. Sampling Acceptance Plans with Same Per Cent Samples Give Very Different Quality Protection. A common practice in industry is to specify that the sample inspected shall be some fixed percentage of the lot, such as 1%, 3%, 5%, 10%, or 20%. This specification is generally based on the mistaken idea that the protection given by sampling schemes is constant if the ratio of sample size to lot size is constant. Such specifications are usually associated with an acceptance number of zero.

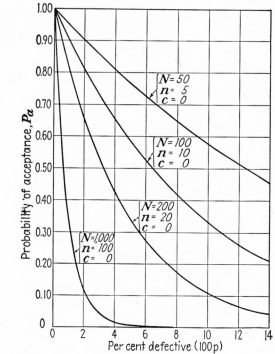

FIG. 59. Comparison of operating characteristic curves for four sampling plans involving 10% samples.

Figure 59 illustrates just how wrong this idea really is. This figure compares the OC curves of four sampling acceptance plans, all of which involve a 10% sample and an acceptance number of zero. The differences in the quality protections provided by these plans are obvious and impressive. They may be emphasized by statements of fact that can be read from the OC curves.

For example, the curves show that lots which are 4% defective will be accepted 81% of the time using a 10% sample from a lot of 50, 65% of the time using a 10% sample from a lot of 100, 42% of the time using a 10% sample from a lot of 200, and less than 2% of the time (actually 1.35%) by a 10% sample from a lot of 1,000, assuming an acceptance number of zero in all cases.   Obviously, a producer making product 4% defective would have a strong motive for trying to have his product inspected in lots of 50 rather than in lots of 1,000.

Or, considered in a slightly different way, the curves show the quality of lot that will be passed 50% of the time by each plan.
$\begin{cases} N = 50 \\ n = 5 \text{ will} \\ c = 0 \end{cases}$

pass a 12% defective lot half the time,
$\begin{cases} N = 100 \\ n = 10 \text{ a 6\% defective lot,} \\ c = 0 \end{cases}$

$\begin{cases} N = 200 \\ n = 20 \text{ a 3\% defective lot, and} \\ c = 0 \end{cases}$
$\begin{cases} N = 1,000 \\ n = 100 \text{ a 0.65\% defective lot.} \\ c = 0 \end{cases}$

These curves are based on computations such as those illustrated in Arts. 169 and 170, Chap. IX.

253. Fixed Sample Size Tends toward Constant Quality Protection. From the standpoint of quality protection, the absolute size of a random sample is much more important than its relative size compared to the size of the lot.   This fact is illustrated by Fig. 60.   This figure shows the OC curves of four different sampling plans all having the same sample size 20 but having lot sizes of 50, 100, 200, and 1,000, respectively.

The three upper curves, in which the sample size varies from 20% to 2% of the lot, show close agreement.   This agreement is in sharp contrast to the great difference among the curves in Fig. 59.   These two figures together emphasize the point that it is the absolute size of the sample rather than its relative size that determines the quality protection given by an acceptance sampling plan.   The story told by these two figures is particularly striking because it contradicts many preconceived notions on the subject of sampling.

The upper curve corresponding to a lot size of 1,000 is practically identical with the OC curve that would be obtained for an infinite lot size.   For example, the probability of acceptance of a 5% defective lot when $N = 1,000$ is 0.355.   When $N = \infty$, the corresponding probability is 0.358.   For a 10% defective lot, the respective probabilities of acceptance are 0.119 and 0.122.   (These figures are obtained using hypergeometric probabilities for the lot of 1,000 and using the binomial for the infinite lot.)   For a given lot fraction defective, the probability of acceptance computed for a finite lot is always less than that computed for an infinite lot because of the recognition of the partial exhaustion of the lot by the sample.

It is evident that unless a sample is a large proportion of the lot, such as the 10%, 20%, and 40% samples in the three lower OC curves of Fig. 60, it will usually be good enough for practical purposes to compute

OC curves as if lot sizes were infinite. Moreover, if the OC curve is viewed as giving probabilities of acceptance of lots from a statistically controlled product having a fraction defective, p, as later discussed in Art. 260, the OC curve computed in this way is correct in principle.

254. No Sampling Plan Can Give Complete Protection against the Acceptance of Defective Product. A practical difficulty in devising an

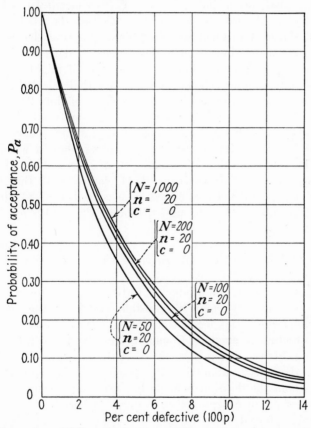

Fig. 60. Comparison of OC curves for four sampling plans involving samples of 20, each with acceptance number of 0.

ideal sampling plan is that it is not possible to change the laws of chance.

All lot-by-lot sampling plans are certain to pass some of the lots containing defective product if such product exists in many of the lots submitted for acceptance. This fact needs to be faced by all who specify and use acceptance sampling.

It follows that the selection of an acceptance sampling plan requires a decision on the risks that the user of the plan is willing to face, all things considered. This is an economic decision that depends on a number of matters discussed in Chap. XVII. In lot-by-lot sampling by attributes, the risks of acceptance of submitted lots containing any stated percentage of defectives are given by the OC curve of the particular sampling plan. It is therefore appropriate to give careful consideration to the OC curve in the selection of a sampling plan. As pointed out in the following discussion of acceptance sampling, the users of sampling plans often find it convenient to concentrate attention on one or two points on the OC curve rather than on the whole curve.

255. OC Curve of an Ideal Sampling Plan. Suppose that it is decided that 2.2% is the maximum tolerable proportion defective in any submitted lots. Once this decision has been made, it might seem that an ideal lot-by-lot sampling scheme would be one that rejected all lots that were worse than 2.2% defective and accepted all lots 2.2% defective or better. The OC curve of such an ideal scheme would be a vertical line at $p = 0.022$. Of course, no such ideal sampling scheme can exist.

It is, however, possible to select a sampling plan in which a 2.2% defective lot has some desired probability of acceptance. If it should be decided that the consumer can take 1 chance in 10 that if a 2.2% defective lot is submitted the lot will be accepted, the OC curve of the selected plan should pass through the point $P_a = 0.10$, $p = 0.022$ (or $100p = 2.2\%$).

Figure 59 shows that the OC curve of the plan $\begin{cases} N = 1,000 \\ n = 100 \\ c = 0 \end{cases}$ passes

through this point. If the product is to be submitted for acceptance in lots of 1,000 articles, this plan is a possible one to give the consumer his desired quality protection against accepting 2.2% defective lots.

256. Conflicting Interests of Consumer and Producer in the Selection of Sampling Plans. There are always two parties to an acceptance procedure, the party submitting the product for acceptance and the party for whom the decision is made regarding acceptance or rejection. In all discussions of acceptance procedures in this book, these parties are concisely referred to as the *producer* and *consumer*. It should be recognized that for many inspection operations the producer and consumer may be part of the same organization; for instance, the producer might be the machine shop and the consumer the assembly department. In a manufacturer's final inspection of his own product, the sales department may be thought of as the consumer. In acceptance inspection of some purchased product, the producer—in the sense used here— may actually be a middleman who had no connection with the original production.

At first impression, it might seem that the producer and consumer should have completely opposite viewpoints toward the selection of sampling plans. The consumer requires protection against the acceptance of too much defective product. The producer, on the other hand, needs to be protected against the rejection of too much good product.

As an example, assume that a consumer selects the plan $\left\{ \begin{array}{l} N = 1{,}000 \\ n = 100 \\ c = 0 \end{array} \right.$

in order to protect himself against accepting lots more than 2.2% defective. As already pointed out, if a lot exactly 2.2% defective should be submitted, there is only 1 chance in 10 of its acceptance. The consumer will have even greater protection if lots of poorer quality are submitted.

This plan, however, gives unsatisfactory protection to the producer who submits product considerably better than 2.2% defective. For instance, the OC curve of Fig. 61 shows that if the producer submits lots 1% defective, 65% of them will be rejected. (The curve says 35% will be accepted; this is subtracted from 100% to get the percentage rejected.) If lots 0.5% defective are submitted, 41% will be rejected. If lots 0.2% defective are submitted, 19% will be rejected. It is evident that the consumer protects himself against accepting product 2.2% defective by rejecting a large proportion of any submitted lots that are of much better quality.

A more critical consideration will show that such substantial rejections of good product in the effort to exclude bad product are not really in the consumer's interest. The consumer is interested in quality. He also is interested in cost. In the long run the costs incident to the rejection of good product tend to be passed on by the producer to the consumer. The consumer may also be interested in having the product now. Any good product that he rejects is not available for his immediate use.

It seems clear that, even from the consumer's viewpoint, it is not sufficient to ask that a sampling plan protect the consumer against the acceptance of lots having a higher percentage of defectives than some maximum tolerable figure.

257. The Acceptance Number Need Not Be Zero. Figures 59 and 60 emphasized the fact that a perfect sample does not ensure a perfect lot. Once this fact is recognized, the objections sometimes raised to permitting some defectives in a sample may be shown to have no logical foundation.

The users of modern acceptance sampling procedures recognize certain psychological advantages of allowing at least one defective in a sample. Moreover, the operating characteristics of plans with acceptance numbers greater than zero are superior to those of comparable plans with acceptance number of zero. For a desired protection against accepting lots containing some stated percentage of defectives, larger acceptance numbers involve larger sample sizes. Plans having larger sample sizes have greater ability to discriminate between satisfactory and unsatisfactory lots.

For example, consider our consumer who wants protection against accepting lots of 2.2% defective or worse and insists that any 2.2% defective lots submitted shall have only a 0.10 probability of acceptance. Assume that product is submitted in lots of 1,000. This consumer's

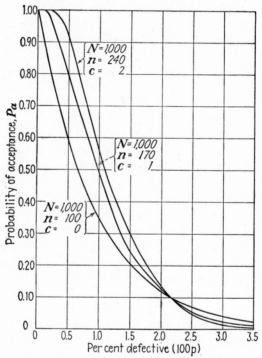

Fig. 61.   OC curves for three sampling plans having a 0.10 probability of acceptance of a 2.2% defective lot.

requirement will be met by using $n = 100$ and $c = 0$, or by using $n = 170$ and $c = 1$, or by using $n = 240$ and $c = 2$, or by various other possible plans.

The OC curves for these three plans are shown in Fig. 61. It will be noted that although all three plans give the consumer equal protection against the acceptance of a 2.2% defective lot, the plans with acceptance numbers of 1 and 2 give the producer much better protection against the rejection of lots that are satisfactory in the sense of being greatly superior to 2.2% defective lots. A few figures read from the three curves serve to emphasize this point.

	$N = 1,000$ $n = 100$ $c = 0$	$N = 1,000$ $n = 170$ $c = 1$	$N = 1,000$ $n = 240$ $c = 2$
Lots 1% defective rejected.....	65%	51%	44%
Lots 0.5% defective rejected....	41%	20%	8%
Lots 0.2% defective rejected....	19%	3%	0%

The plans with the higher acceptance numbers and better OC curves have higher sample sizes for a given lot size. This means more inspection and hence more inspection cost. If, however, as is often the case, the rejection of a lot by sampling inspection means that the lot is to be 100% inspected, the total amount of resulting inspection may actually be less with the higher sample size and acceptance number.

258. Choosing a Sampling Plan to Minimize Total Inspection. The question of minimum total inspection depends on the number of rejected lots that must be detailed (*i.e.*, 100% inspected). This, in turn, depends on the quality level of the product submitted. This point may be illustrated by comparing the total inspection required by the three plans of Fig. 61 under different assumptions as to the quality level of lots submitted.

Assume that 100 lots which are 0.5% defective are submitted for acceptance by each plan:

$$\begin{cases} N = 1,000 \\ n = 100 \\ c = 0 \end{cases}$$
100 articles inspected in 59 accepted lots $= 5,900$
1,000 articles inspected in 41 rejected lots $= 41,000$
Total number of articles inspected in 100 lots $= 46,900$

$$\begin{cases} N = 1,000 \\ n = 170 \\ c = 1 \end{cases}$$
170 articles inspected in 80 accepted lots $= 13,600$
1,000 articles inspected in 20 rejected lots $= 20,000$
Total number of articles inspected in 100 lots $= 33,600$

$$\begin{cases} N = 1,000 \\ n = 240 \\ c = 2 \end{cases}$$
240 articles inspected in 92 accepted lots $= 22,080$
1,000 articles inspected in 8 rejected lots $= 8,000$
Total number of articles inspected in 100 lots $= 30,080$

With the quality level submitted for inspection 0.5% defective, it is evident that the plan $\begin{cases} N = 1,000 \\ n = 240 \\ c = 2 \end{cases}$ requires less total inspection. However, if the quality level submitted should be 0.2% defective, the minimum inspection will be required using $\begin{cases} N = 1,000 \\ n = 170 \\ c = 1 \end{cases}$. This is shown by the following calculation:

$$\begin{cases} N = 1{,}000 \\ n = \quad 100 \\ c = \qquad 0 \end{cases}$$

100 articles inspected in 81 accepted lots   = 8,100

1,000 articles inspected in 19 rejected lots   = 19,000

Total number of articles inspected in 100 lots = 27,100

$$\begin{cases} N = 1{,}000 \\ n = \quad 170 \\ c = \qquad 1 \end{cases}$$

170 articles inspected in 97 accepted lots   = 16,490

1,000 articles inspected in 3 rejected loss   = 3,000

Total number of articles inspected in 100 lots = 19,490

$$\begin{cases} N = 1{,}000 \\ n = \quad 240 \\ c = \qquad 2 \end{cases}$$

240 articles inspected in 100 accepted lots   = 24,000

1,000 articles inspected in 0 rejected lots   =   0

Total number of articles inspected in 100 lots = 24,000

Similar calculations might be made for any assumed quality level of submitted product. Such calculations entered into the calculations of the Dodge-Romig tables, discussed in Chap. XIV, which are based on minimizing the total amount of inspection.

259. Generally Speaking, the Larger the Sample Size, the Steeper the Slope of the OC Curve. It is of interest to compare several plans having different sample sizes and having the same ratio of acceptance number to sample size. Consider the plans $\begin{cases} n = 75, \\ c = 1 \end{cases}$ $\begin{cases} n = 150 \\ c = 2 \end{cases}$, and $\begin{cases} n = 750 \\ c = 10 \end{cases}$. Assume a lot size N of 10,000. This lot size is large enough so that even the largest of these samples is a relatively small fraction of the lot. The OC curves of these three plans are shown in Fig. 62.

Although these three plans each permit 1.33 % (*i.e.*, $\frac{1}{75}$) of the sample to be defective, it is evident that they have quite different OC curves. The larger the sample size, the greater the ability of a sampling plan to discriminate between lots of different qualities. For example, a 3 % defective lot, if submitted, has more than 1 chance in 3 of acceptance if $n = 75$ and $c = 1$ but is practically certain to be rejected if $n = 750$ and $c = 10$. The larger sample which protects the consumer against the acceptance of relatively bad lots also gives the producer better protection against the rejection of relatively good ones. Thus a 0.7 % defective lot has 1 chance in 10 of rejection if $n = 75$ and only 2 chances in 100 of rejection if $n = 750$.

260. Use of Table G for Approximate Calculation of OC Curves of Sampling Plans. If it is assumed that a stream of statistically controlled product with average fraction defective p' is submitted for inspection in lots, a random sample taken from any lot may be thought of as a sample from the entire stream of product. The probability that any sample will lead to acceptance may then properly be computed as if the lot size were infinite. OC curves computed on the assumption of infinite lot size may be interpreted in this way.[1]

As pointed out in Art. 180a (pages 220 to 222) and Art. 253 (pages 316 to 317), when it is desired to find the probability of acceptance of a finite lot containing a stated proportion defective, a close approximation to the correct answer is obtained on the assumption of infinite lot size unless the sample is a substantial fraction of the lot. Hence, even when it is desired to compute an OC curve giving the probabilities of acceptance of *lots* (rather than a stream of product) containing various proportions

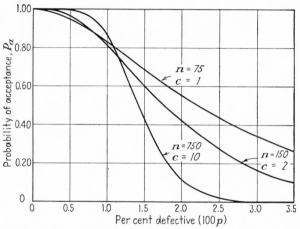

Fig. 62. Comparison of OC curves with different sample sizes, all permitting the same fraction of the sample to be defective.

of defectives, it is usually good enough for practical purposes to compute OC curves as if the lot size were infinite. For reasons explained in Art. 180a, it is usually satisfactory and convenient to compute approximate probabilities of acceptance by use of a Poisson distribution table such as Table G, Appendix III.

Table 39 illustrates the use of Table G in computing the three OC curves shown in Fig. 62. The probabilities of acceptance are read directly from Table G (or interpolated where necessary) as the figures corresponding to c (that is, "c or less") occurrences of the event with an average np'. Table 39 gives all probabilities to three decimal places in order to permit the reader to check his use of Table G. Nevertheless, it should

---

[1] For a more detailed discussion of this viewpoint on OC curves, see W. E. Deming, "Some Theory of Sampling," Chap. 8, John Wiley & Sons, Inc., New York, 1950. See also H. F. Dodge, Administration of a Sampling Inspection Plan, *Industrial Quality Control*, vol. 5, No. 3, pp. 12–19, November, 1948.

be recognized that because of the approximate method used, three decimal places are not really justified.[1]

TABLE 39.   CALCULATION OF APPROXIMATE OC CURVES FOR THREE SAMPLING
PLANS, ASSUMING $N = \infty$

Fraction defective in lot p'	Expected average number of defectives, np', in sample			Probability of acceptance, P_a		
	$n = 75$	$n = 150$	$n = 750$	$\begin{cases} n = 75 \\ c = 1 \end{cases}$	$\begin{cases} n = 150 \\ c = 2 \end{cases}$	$\begin{cases} n = 750 \\ c = 10 \end{cases}$
0.002	0.15	0.30	1.5	0.990	0.996	1.000
0.004	0.30	0.60	3.0	0.963	0.977	1.000
0.006	0.45	0.90	4.5	0.925	0.937	0.993
0.008	0.60	1.20	6.0	0.878	0.879	0.957
0.010	0.75	1.50	7.5	0.827	0.809	0.862
0.012	0.90	1.80	9.0	0.772	0.731	0.706
0.014	1.05	2.10	10.5	0.718	0.650	0.521
0.016	1.20	2.40	12.0	0.663	0.570	0.347
0.018	1.35	2.70	13.5	0.610	0.494	0.211
0.020	1.50	3.00	15.0	0.558	0.423	0.118
0.025	1.875	3.75	18.75	0.441	0.278	0.021
0.030	2.25	4.50	22.5	0.343	0.174	0.003
0.035	2.625	5.25	26.25	0.262	0.106	0.000
0.040	3.00	6.00	.....	0.199	0.062	
0.050	3.75	7.50	.....	0.112	0.020	
0.060	4.50	9.00	.....	0.061	0.006	
0.070	5.25	10.50	.....	0.033	0.002	
0.080	6.00	12.00	.....	0.017	0.001	
0.090	6.75	13.50	.....	0.009	0.000	
0.100	7.50	.....	...	0.004		

261. The Indexing of Acceptance Plans by a Single Point on the OC Curve. Chapters XIV and XV include descriptions of a number of different tables of acceptance sampling plans. Certain tables classify acceptance plans in accordance with a single point on the OC curve.

[1] The approximation of the Poisson to the binomial is, of course, best for the smallest values of p. Hence the OC curves computed, using Table G (or other Poisson tables or diagrams), are more accurate at the upper end than at the lower end. As an example, consider the plan $N = \infty$, $n = 75$, $c = 1$ as applied to product 1% and 5% defective. The correct probabilities of acceptance computed by the binomial are 0.827 and 0.106, respectively. Table 39, computed by the Poisson, shows the approximate values to be 0.827 and 0.112, respectively.

Three points on the OC curve have been given particular importance in the design of systems of sampling plans, namely:

1. The lot (or process) quality for which $P_a = 0.95$. In this book, this quality is referred to as $p_{0.95}$.*

2. The lot (or process) quality for which $P_a = 0.50$. In this book, this is referred to as $p_{0.50}$.†

3. The lot (or process) quality for which $P_a = 0.10$. To be consistent with the preceding symbols, this is referred to as $p_{0.10}$. In the literature of acceptance sampling, this quality is most frequently referred to as the lot tolerance fraction defective; $100p_{0.10}$ is described as the lot tolerance per cent defective (LTPD).[1]

The same acceptance plan may therefore be referred to by several different product quality values, depending on the point of indexing. There are legitimate reasons for this variability in indexing sampling plans. Nevertheless, this has naturally proved to be a source of confusion to some users of acceptance sampling tables. Further comment on this topic is made in the next two chapters.

262. Double Sampling. Single sampling calls for decision on acceptance or rejection of a lot on the basis of the evidence of *one* sample from that lot.

Double sampling involves the possibility of putting off the decision on the lot until a second sample has been taken. A lot may be accepted at once if the first sample is good enough or rejected at once if the first sample is bad enough. If the first sample is neither good enough or bad enough, the decision is based on the evidence of the first and second samples combined. In general, double sampling schemes will involve less total inspection than single sampling for any given quality protection. They also have certain psychological advantages based on the idea of giving a second chance to doubtful lots.

The additional symbols used in connection with double sampling are as follows:

n_1 = number of pieces in the first sample

c_1 = acceptance number for first sample, the maximum number of defectives that will permit the acceptance of the lot on the basis of the first sample

n_2 = number of pieces in the second sample

$n_1 + n_2$ = number of pieces in the two samples combined

c_2 = acceptance number for the two samples combined, the maximum number of defectives that will permit the acceptance of the lot on the basis of the two samples

---

* In the tables developed by the Columbia Statistical Research Group, discussed in Chap. XV, this quality is referred to as the AQL (acceptable quality level).

† This has been referred to by some writers as the "point of control" and by others as the "indifference quality."

[1] More properly, in its original usage by Dodge and Romig, the notion of a tolerance

An example of the use of these symbols to describe a double sampling plan is

$$\begin{cases} N = 1{,}000 \\ n_1 = \quad 36 \\ c_1 = \quad 0 \\ n_2 = \quad 59 \\ c_2 = \quad 3 \end{cases}$$

This may be interpreted as follows:

1. Inspect a first sample of 36 from a lot of 1,000.

2. Accept the lot on the basis of the first sample if the sample contains 0 defectives.

3. Reject the lot on the basis of the first sample if the sample contains more than 3 defectives.

4. Inspect a second sample of 59 if the first sample contains 1, 2, or 3 defectives.

5. Accept the lot on the basis of the combined sample of 95 if the combined sample contains 3 or less defectives.

6. Reject the lot on the basis of the combined sample if the combined sample contains more than 3 defectives.

263. Analysis of a Double Sampling Plan. Figure 63 shows three OC curves involved in the analysis of this double sampling plan.

There are four possibilities for acceptance or rejection of a lot submitted for double sampling, namely,

1. Acceptance after the first sample

2. Rejection after the first sample

3. Acceptance after the second sample

4. Rejection after the second sample

The lowest of the three OC curves in Fig. 63 shows the probability of (1) acceptance after the first sample. This is simply the curve for

$$\begin{cases} N = 1{,}000 \\ n = \quad 36. \\ c = \quad 0 \end{cases}$$ The highest of the three OC curves shows the probability

that the lot will not be rejected after the first sample. It is the curve for

$$\begin{cases} N = 1{,}000 \\ n = \quad 36. \\ c = \quad 3 \end{cases}$$ Both of these limiting curves may be calculated in the

manner already illustrated for the calculation of curves for all single sampling plans. For any given value of per cent defective, the distance

---

per cent defective may be associated with any consumer's risk. For example, the lot quality having a P_a of 0.05 could be described as the lot tolerance per cent defective associated with a consumer's risk of 0.05. However, because the widely used Dodge-Romig tables (described in Chap. XIV) all assume a consumer's risk of 0.10, the term LTPD used without qualification nearly always means $100p_{0.10}$.

between these two curves corresponds to the probability that for a lot of that per cent defective a second sample will be required.

. The middle curve of Fig. 63 is the actual OC curve of the double sampling plan. To compute points for this curve it is necessary to find the probability that if a second sample is taken, the lot will be accepted. The necessary calculations may be illustrated for a single point on the curve corresponding to $p' = 0.010$.

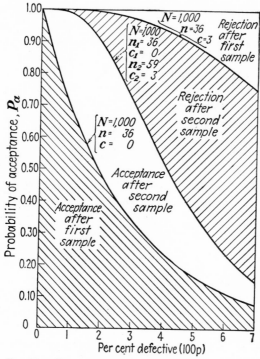

FIG. 63. Characteristics of a double sampling plan.

The lot may be accepted in the following ways:

0 defectives in the first sample
1 defective in first sample followed by 0, 1, or 2 defectives in second sample
2 defectives in first sample followed by 0 or 1 defective in second sample
3 defectives in first sample followed by 0 defectives in second sample

The probability of accepting the lot is the sum of the probabilities of these different ways in which it may be accepted. To compute these, it is first necessary to find the probabilities of 0, 1, 2, and 3 defectives in the first sample of 36.

$$M = p'N = (0.010)(1,000) = 10$$

$$P_0 = \frac{C_n^{N-M}C_0^M}{C_n^N} = \frac{C_{36}^{990}C_0^{10}}{C_{36}^{1,000}} = \frac{990!36!964!}{954!36!1,000!} = 0.692$$

$$P_1 = \frac{C_{n-1}^{N-M}C_1^M}{C_n^N} = \frac{C_{35}^{990}C_1^{10}}{C_{36}^{1,000}} = \frac{990!36!964!(10)}{955!35!1,000!} = 0.261$$

$$P_2 = \frac{C_{n-2}^{N-M}C_2^M}{C_n^N} = \frac{C_{34}^{990}C_2^{10}}{C_{36}^{1,000}} = \frac{990!36!964!(45)}{956!34!1,000!} = 0.043$$

$$P_3 = \frac{C_{n-3}^{N-M}C_3^M}{C_n^N} = \frac{C_{33}^{990}C_3^{10}}{C_{36}^{1,000}} = \frac{990!36!964!(120)}{957!33!1,000!} = 0.004$$

The calculations involving the factorials may be made with the aid of Table H and a table of 4-place logarithms, as illustrated in Chap. IX.

Assume that exactly 1 defective is found in the first sample. The taking of the second sample may, for purposes of calculation, be thought of as a new single sampling plan for the remainder of the lot. It calls for the selection of a sample of 59 (a new n) from the 964 (a new N) articles in the remaining portion of the lot. This remaining portion of the lot contains 9 (a new M) defectives. The new acceptance number, $c, = 2$.

$$P_0 = \frac{C_{59}^{955}C_0^9}{C_{59}^{964}} = \frac{955!59!905!}{896!59!964!} = 0.565$$

$$P_1 = \frac{C_{58}^{955}C_1^9}{C_{59}^{964}} = \frac{955!59!905!(9)}{897!58!964!} = 0.335$$

$$P_2 = \frac{C_{57}^{955}C_2^9}{C_{59}^{964}} = \frac{955!59!905!(36)}{898!57!964!} = 0.086$$

$$\text{Total} \ldots \ldots \ldots \ldots \ldots \ldots \ldots \ldots \ldots \overline{0.986}$$

If exactly 2 defectives are found in the first sample, the probabilities that the second sample will contain 0 or 1 defectives are as follows:

$$P_0 = \frac{C_{59}^{956}C_0^8}{C_{59}^{964}} = \frac{956!59!905!}{897!59!964!} = 0.602$$

$$P_1 = \frac{C_{58}^{956}C_1^8}{C_{59}^{964}} = \frac{956!59!905!(8)}{898!58!964!} = 0.316$$

$$\text{Total} \ldots \ldots \ldots \ldots \ldots \ldots \ldots \ldots \overline{0.918}$$

If exactly 3 defectives are found in the first sample, the probability that the second sample will contain 0 defectives is

$$P_0 = \frac{C_{59}^{957}C_0^7}{C_{59}^{964}} = \frac{957!59!905!}{898!59!964!} = 0.642$$

The probability of acceptance may now be computed, using the theorem of conditional probabilities

0 defectives in first $\qquad\qquad\qquad\qquad\qquad\qquad\quad = 0.692$
1 defective in first, with 0, 1, or 2 in second $= (0.261)(0.986) = 0.257$
2 defectives in first, with 0 or 1 in second $\quad = (0.043)(0.918) = 0.039$
3 defectives in first, with 0 in second $\qquad = (0.004)(0.642) = \underline{0.003}$

Probability of acceptance of a lot 1.0% defective. 0.991

The foregoing time-consuming calculations may be shortened greatly by an approximation. If it is assumed that the binomial is applicable to this sampling problem (in other words, that samples are drawn from an infinite lot) and that the Poisson is a satisfactory approximation to the binomial, Table G may be used.

In using Table G to compute the respective probabilities of results of the first sample, $np' = 36(0.010) = 0.36$. Interpolating in Table G between the values for np' of 0.35 and 0.40, we find

$$P_0 = 0.698$$
$$P_{1 \text{ or less}} = 0.948$$
$$P_1 = 0.948 - 0.698 = 0.250$$
$$P_{2 \text{ or less}} = 0.994$$
$$P_2 = 0.994 - 0.948 = 0.046$$
$$P_{3 \text{ or less}} = 1.000$$
$$P_3 = 1.000 - 0.994 = 0.006$$

If there is 1 defective on the first sample, calculations regarding the second sample should be based on $np' = (59)(9/964) = 0.55$. Table G gives directly

$$P_{2 \text{ or less}} = 0.982$$

If there are 2 defectives on the first sample, $np' = (59)(8/964) = 0.49$. Table G gives

$$P_{1 \text{ or less}} = 0.913$$

And if there are 3 defectives on the first sample,

$$P_0 = 0.648$$

These probabilities may be used to estimate the probability of acceptance, as follows:

0 defectives in first $\qquad\qquad\qquad\qquad\qquad\qquad\quad = 0.698$
1 defective in first, with 0, 1, or 2 in second $= (0.250)(0.982) = 0.246$
2 defectives in first, with 0 or 1 in second $\quad = (0.046)(0.913) = 0.042$
3 defectives in first, with 0 in second $\qquad = (0.006)(0.648) = \underline{0.004}$

Probability of acceptance of a lot 1.0% defective. 0.990

In this case the difference was negligible between the result of theoretically correct calculations and the result obtained by the approximate method using the Poisson and Table G. Although the check between exact and approximate calculations will not usually be as good as this, the OC curve obtained by the use of the Poisson will ordinarily be close enough for all practical purposes.

264. Multiple or Sequential Sampling. Just as double sampling plans may defer the decision on acceptance or rejection until a second sample has been taken, other plans may permit any number of samples before a decision is reached. Plans permitting from three up to an unlimited number of samples are described as *multiple* or *sequential*.[1] Usually multiple or sequential plans can be designed having OC curves closely similar to the OC curve of any given single or double sampling plan. The equivalent multiple plan will generally involve less inspection. The following single, double, and multiple plans (taken from Tables *M*, *N*, and *O* in Appendix III) illustrate a set of matched plans having nearly identical OC curves.

Type of plan	Sample number	Individual sample size	Combined sample size	Acceptance number	Rejection number
Single	1	75	75	2	3
Double	1	50	50	1	4
	2	100	150	3	4
Multiple	1	20	20	*	2
	2	20	40	0	3
	3	20	60	1	3
	4	20	80	2	4
	5	20	100	2	4
	6	20	120	2	4
	7	20	140	3	4

* Acceptance not permitted on first multiple sample.

The foregoing method of describing acceptance sampling plans differs slightly from the one used earlier in this chapter for single and double sampling. It is generally not convenient to use *n* and *c* numbers to describe a multiple plan.

Figure 64 shows the OC curves for these three attributes plans together with the OC curve for a matched plan using variables criteria. The calculation of the OC curve for the multiple plan follows the same pattern already explained for double sampling. The following calculations apply to a single point on the curve, namely, the probability of acceptance of a 2% defective lot. To simplify the calculation, it is assumed that the lot

[1] Generally speaking, these two words seem to be used interchangeably. However, there is some tendency to describe as "pure sequential" those acceptance plans permitting an unlimited number of sample units taken one at a time and to reserve the adjective "multiple" for plans involving a finite number of samples.

size is large enough so that the unsampled portion of the lot will still be substantially 2% defective regardless of the results of past samples. Each multiple sample consists of 20 articles. To use Table G, it should

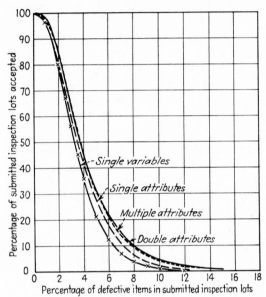

Fig. 64. OC curves for the four matched sampling plans of Arts. 264 and 266.

be noted that $np' = (20)(0.02) = 0.4$. Table G then gives the following useful figures applicable to any sample:

$$P_0 = 0.670$$
$$P_1 = 0.938 - 0.670 = 0.268$$
$$P_2 = 0.992 - 0.938 = 0.054$$
$$P_3 \text{ or more} = 1.000 - 0.992 = 0.008$$

These may be combined by the theorem of conditional probabilities to obtain the following probabilities of acceptance or rejection on each sample:

Sample number	Probability of	
	Acceptance	Rejection
1	0.000	0.062
2	0.449	0.022
3	0.241	0.058
4	0.113	0.010
5	0.000	0.015
6	0.000	0.010
7	0.013	0.007
	0.816	0.184

It will be noted that for 2% defective lots, this particular multiple sampling plan will arrive at a decision with one or two samples (not more than 40 items inspected) more than half the time and will nearly always reach a decision within four samples (with not more than 80 items inspected).

The relative advantages of single, double, and multiple sampling are discussed in Chap. XV.

265. Acceptance Sampling by Variables. Up to this point, all of the discussion in this chapter has dealt with acceptance criteria based on attributes. In plans based on attributes, consideration is given only to the number of articles in a sample conforming or failing to conform to certain design specifications. This conformance or lack of it may relate to a single quality characteristic but usually relates to a number of different quality characteristics.

Acceptance criteria using variables data must be applied to each quality characteristic separately. The characteristic must, of course, be one that can be measured. Acceptance decisions are then based on the actual measured values in the sample rather than on the number of items conforming or failing to conform to the specification limits. Many different types of variables acceptance criteria have been proposed. This general subject is explored in Chap. XVI.

At this stage of our discussion, it seems desirable merely to illustrate one of the simpler types of plans involving variables. This illustration will serve the purpose of emphasizing the point that variables acceptance criteria should be considered as alternatives to attributes criteria in many cases.

266. Computing the OC Curve for a Known-sigma Variables Plan. Many specifications are one-sided. That is, the specification merely states a lower limit L or an upper limit U to apply to individual articles. Perhaps the simplest variables test is one sometimes used with this type of specification in cases where it is believed that the standard deviation of submitted lots will remain fairly constant, that the average $\bar{X}'$ is likely to shift up and down, and that the distribution of the variable is normal.

This test requires taking a sample of size n and measuring the value of the specified quality characteristic for each item of the sample. The item values are averaged to find the $\bar{X}$ of the sample. If this $\bar{X}$ exceeds the lower specification limit L by $k'\sigma'$, the lot is accepted; otherwise it is rejected. (If the limit is an upper one U, $\bar{X}$ must be not more than $U - k'\sigma'$.) The figure for σ' must be estimated from past experience, possibly from a control chart that shows process dispersion to have been in statistical control. The factor k' depends on n and on the desired quality protection; the larger the value of k' for any given n, the more severe the acceptance criteria.

In the literature of variables inspection, such acceptance schemes are described as *known-sigma* plans. In illustrating the necessary calculations for the OC curves of such plans, it may be helpful to use a numerical example. Assume that the specification for a certain product calls for a minimum tensile strength of 20,000 psi (pounds per square inch). $\overline{X}$ and R charts have been maintained on the test results of past samples. All points have fallen within control limits on the R chart; the estimated value of σ' is 1,000 psi. The $\overline{X}$ chart has shown lack of control.

Assume that it is desired to use a variables plan giving quality protection against defectives resulting from a shift in process average comparable with the protection obtainable from the attributes plan $\begin{cases} n = 75 \\ c = 2 \end{cases}$ and from the equivalent double and multiple plans shown on page 330. In their volume on variables acceptance inspection,[1] Bowker and Goode give values of n and k' for known-sigma variables plans that have OC curves corresponding fairly well to many different attributes plans. To match the attributes plan of $\begin{cases} n = 75 \\ c = 2 \end{cases}$, n is given as 16 and k' 1.846. In our particular example, this means that the average tensile strength of a sample of 16 test specimens should be at least

$$20,000 + 1.846(1,000) = 21,846 \text{ psi}$$

It is not possible to compute an OC curve for such an acceptance plan without making some assumption about the frequency distribution of the quality characteristic in question. The OC curve for this plan that is shown in Fig. 64 is based on the assumption of a normal distribution.[2] Figure 65 illustrates the calculation of the probability of acceptance of a 2% defective lot. It shows the frequency distribution in the lot and the frequency distribution of averages of samples of 16 when 2% of the lot falls below the lower specification limit. In this calculation, two questions must be answered. (In the following explanation, $\overline{X}'$ refers to lot average and $\overline{X}$ to the average of a sample of size n.)

1. *What is $\overline{X}'$ for the particular per cent defective?* Consult Table A, Appendix III, to find the value of $(\overline{X}_i - \overline{X}')/\sigma'$ corresponding to an area of 0.0200. Interpolation in this table shows that 2% of a normal distribution falls below the value $\overline{X}' - 2.056\sigma'$. If 2% of the lot falls below the lower specification limit L, then $\overline{X}'$ must be $L + 2.056\sigma'$. Hence as L is 20,000 psi and σ' is 1,000 psi, $\overline{X}' = 22,056$ psi.

2. *With $\overline{X}'$ at this figure, what proportion of the $\overline{X}$ distribution will fall*

---

[1] BOWKER, A. H. and H. P. GOODE, "Sampling Inspection by Variables," McGraw-Hill Book Company, Inc., New York, 1952.

[2] See Art. 331, Chap. XVI, for comment regarding limitations of this assumption

above the minimum allowable value of $\overline{X}$*?* The difference between $\overline{X}'$ and the minimum $\overline{X}$ must be computed. This is $22{,}056 - 21{,}846 = 210$ psi. The standard deviation of $\overline{X}$ must be computed. In this case

$$\sigma_{\overline{X}} = \frac{\sigma'}{\sqrt{n}} = \frac{1{,}000}{\sqrt{16}} = 250 \text{ psi}$$

The value 210 psi is $0.84\sigma_{\overline{X}}$. Table A shows that 0.7995 of a normal distribution is above the value $\overline{X}' - 0.84\sigma$. It follows that the probability of acceptance is 0.7995 or approximately 0.80.

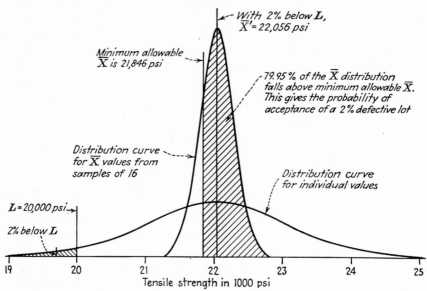

Fig. 65. Diagram illustrating the calculation of the probability of accepting a 2% defective lot under the known-sigma variables plan of Art. 266.

Although the preceding calculation used numerical values of L and σ' for purposes of illustration, the computed probability of acceptance is, of course, independent of these values and depends only on n and k'.

One advantage of variables sampling is the use of smaller sample sizes to obtain the same quality protection against a particular type of trouble. In the preceding example, the variables sample was 16 whereas the attributes single sample was 75. Nevertheless, there are many considerations other than sample size that should enter into the choice between variables and attributes plans. A discussion of this topic is deferred until Chap. XVI, which presents some of the practical problems in connection with the use of variables plans.

The $\overline{X}$ control-chart reject limits discussed on pages 189 to 191 constitute a special case of known-sigma variables acceptance criteria.

However, the V factor given in Table 25 for $n = 16$ is much more severe than the k' factor of 1.846 used in the preceding example. For instance, with a factor of 2.25 the probability of accepting a 2% defective lot is only 0.219.

267. The Average Outgoing Quality Limit. In many instances, the rejection of a lot on the basis of sampling inspection results in 100% inspection of that particular lot. Particularly in the British literature of the subject this is sometimes described as an *acceptance/rectification* scheme. The accepted lots will contain approximately the per cent defective submitted although they will be slightly improved by the elimination of any defectives found in the samples whenever c is one or more. The rejected lots, after screening, will presumably contain no defectives. For any plan, it is possible to compute the maximum possible value of the average per cent defective in the outgoing product. This maximum figure is referred to as the *average outgoing quality limit*, usually abbreviated to AOQL.

TABLE 40. AVERAGE OUTGOING QUALITY FROM $\begin{cases} n = 75 \\ c = 1 \end{cases}$ WHEN USED AS AN ACCEPTANCE/RECTIFICATION PLAN

Per cent defective in submitted lots, $100p'$	Probability of acceptance, P_a	Average per cent defective in accepted product, AOQ
0.2	0.990	0.198
0.4	0.963	0.385
0.6	0.925	0.555
0.8	0.878	0.702
1.0	0.827	0.827
1.2	0.772	0.926
1.4	0.718	1.005
1.6	0.663	1.061
1.8	0.610	1.098
2.0	0.558	1.116
2.1	0.533	1.119
2.2	0.509	1.120
2.3	0.486	1.118
2.4	0.463	1.111
2.5	0.441	1.102
3.0	0.343	1.029
3.5	0.262	0.917
4.0	0.199	0.796
4.5	0.150	0.675
5.0	0.112	0.560

A common type of approximate calculation to determine the AOQL is illustrated in Table 40. This table refers to the plan $\left\{ \begin{array}{l} n = 75 \\ c = 1 \end{array} \right.$, when N is large in comparison with n. The probabilities of acceptance were computed in Table 39 (page 324). The right-hand column gives *average outgoing quality* (AOQ) for each assumed per cent defective in submitted lots. The maximum value of the AOQ is 1.12%, occurring when submitted lots are 2.2% defective. This maximum value is the AOQL. Figure 66 illustrates the variation of AOQ with incoming quality.

The assumptions underlying Table 40 may be explained by examining one particular calculation. Consider incoming lots to be 0.6% defective.

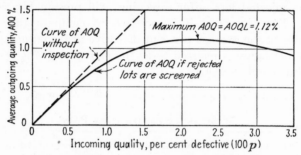

FIG. 66. Average outgoing quality for acceptance/rectification plan $n = 75$ and $c = 1$.

The probability that such lots will be accepted on the basis of the sample is 0.925, or $^{37}\!/_{40}$. In the long run, therefore, only 3 lots out of every 40 lots 0.6% defective will be screened. For every 40 such lots, 37 will be passed containing 0.6% of defectives, and 3 will contain no defectives after screening. The AOQ expressed in per cent defective will therefore be $(P_a)(100p') = (0.925)(0.6\%) = 0.555\%$.

Several simplifying assumptions in the foregoing calculation are as follows:

1. The lot size N is constant. Thus the 3 screened lots may be assumed to be the same size as the 37 unscreened ones.

2. The screening inspection finds all the defectives in the screened lots, and these defectives are removed.

3. The defective articles removed from the screened lots are replaced with good articles. Thus each screened lot contributes N good articles to the final stream of product.

4. The lot size N is large enough in comparison with sample size so that it may be assumed that the removing of any defective articles found in samples from accepted lots will not appreciably change the percentage of defectives in such lots. (Recognition of the elimination of defective items found in the samples from accepted lots will reduce the computed AOQL.)

It should be emphasized that any calculation of average outgoing quality gives the expected quality *in the long run*. As its name implies, the AOQ is an *average*. Over a short period, the outgoing quality may be better or worse than the long-run average. Subject to the limitations of the four simplifying assumptions just stated, any acceptance/rectification plan guarantees that, regardless of the incoming quality submitted, the outgoing quality in the long run will not be worse than the plan's AOQL. This guarantee, however, does not apply to short periods.

268. Some Comments on the Significance of the AOQL. Sampling schemes based on stated AOQL values have gained widespread use in industry. They are used particularly in a manufacturer's inspection of his own product, both in process inspection and in final inspection. They have also been used advantageously in the inspection of lots of purchased product (generally with the purchaser carrying out the screening inspection, where necessary, and by agreement charging the cost thereof to the vendor). Moreover, they have proved well adapted to many circumstances outside of manufacturing, particularly to the checking of clerical work (see Example 25, Chap. XIV).

Nevertheless, as a practical matter the use of lot-by-lot sampling schemes calling for screening of rejected lots is generally confined to circumstances where the great majority of submitted lots are accepted on the basis of the sample. It is evident that such schemes are administratively more complicated than 100% inspection; if many lots are subject to screening, it is likely to be as economical to do 100% inspection in the first place.

Where nearly all the lots are accepted on the basis of the sample, the average outgoing quality will be only slightly better than the average quality in these accepted lots. If submitted lots are badly out of statistical control, so that the screened lots are generally much worse than the unscreened lots, the screening may effect an important improvement in quality. If the submitted product is in good statistical control and few lots are screened, the outgoing quality will not differ greatly from incoming quality. In any event, the AOQ will nearly always be considerably better than the AOQL.

Even though the simplifying assumptions used in the calculation of AOQL's may depart somewhat from actual facts, it follows that this departure is not a matter of great practical importance. Only rarely will the users of schemes based on the AOQL have need to cash in on the guarantee that outgoing quality will not be worse than the computed AOQL.

269. The Role of Acceptance Inspection in Quality Improvement. If product submitted for inspection contains nonconforming articles, neither sampling inspection nor 100% inspection can be counted on to eliminate all of them. It is not possible to inspect quality into a product. The first line of defense against bad product is making the product right in the first place.

Chapter II opened with a quotation from *American War Standard* Z1.3 to the effect that there were two purposes of inspection. One was purpose *A*—action relative to the product being inspected; this has been discussed in the current chapter. The other was purpose *B*—action relative to the production process.

There are two ways in which inspection may serve purpose *B* and assist in the improvement of product quality. One is through pressure exerted by the rejection of product. The other is through the use of information obtained by inspection to help diagnose the causes of trouble.

In the choice among various schemes of acceptance inspection for use in any particular case, an important matter to consider is the prospective contribution of each scheme to quality improvement. This matter is explored further in the next five chapters.

Problems

169. A single sampling plan uses a sample size of 15, and an acceptance number of 1. Using hypergeometric probabilities, compute the respective probabilities of acceptance of lots of 50 articles 2%, 6%, 10%, and 20% defective.
Ans. 1.000; 0.789; 0.524; 0.121.

170. The single sampling plan of Problem 169 is used with a relatively large lot. Use Table *G* to compute the approximate probabilities of acceptance of lots 2%, 6%, 10%, and 20% defective. *Ans.* 0.963; 0.772; 0.558; 0.199.

171. A single sampling plan has $n = 110$ and $c = 3$. The lot size is large in comparison with sample size. Use Table *G* to compute the approximate probabilities of acceptance of lots 0.5%, 1%, 2%, 3%, 4%, 5%, 6%, and 8% defective.
Ans. 0.998; 0.974; 0.819; 0.580; 0.359; 0.202; 0.105; 0.025.

172. Plot the OC curve for the sampling plan of Problem 171. What are the approximate values of lot per cent defective for which probabilities of acceptance are 0.95, 0.50, and 0.10, respectively? *Ans.* 1.2%; 3.3%; 6.1%.

173. A double sampling plan is as follows: (*a*) Select a sample of 2 from a lot of 20. If both articles inspected are good, accept the lot. If both are defective, reject the lot. If 1 is good and 1 defective, take a second sample of one article. (*b*) If the article in the second sample is good, accept the lot. If it is defective, reject the lot.

If a lot 25% defective is submitted, what is the probability of acceptance? Compute this by the method that is theoretically correct rather than by an approximate method. *Ans.* 0.859.

174. In a single sampling plan, $N = 10,000$, $n = 300$, and $c = 1$. This is used with the stipulation that all rejected lots are to be screened. Compute the AOQ if all lots submitted are 0.5% defective. *Ans.* 0.279%.

175. In a double sampling plan, $N = 5,000$, $n_1 = 100$, $c_1 = 0$, $n_2 = 100$, and $c_2 = 1$.

(*a*) Use Table *G* to compute the probability of acceptance of a 1% defective lot.
(*b*) Assume that a lot rejected by this sampling plan will be 100% inspected. What will be the AOQ if the submitted product is 1% defective? (*c*) Considering both

the inspection of samples and inspection of rejected lots, what will be the average number of articles inspected per lot if the submitted product is 1% defective?

Ans. 0.503; 0.503%; 2,549.

176. Specifications require that a certain quality characteristic of a manufactured product have a minimum value of 200 units. This quality characteristic can be tested only by a destructive test. The product is made in batches of several thousand. The past practice regarding acceptance inspection has been to test 4 articles from each batch. If all 4 articles met the quality specification of 200, the batch was accepted. If 2 or more failed, the batch was rejected. If 1 failed, a second sample of 4 was taken; with no failures on the second sample, the batch was accepted; otherwise it was rejected.

(*a*) What is the probability that a batch containing 5% of defectives will be accepted by this procedure?   *Ans.* 0.954.

(*b*) Control charts for $\bar{X}$ and R have been plotted from the first samples. These charts indicate that the range stays in statistical control even though the average shifts from batch to batch. The standard deviation of a batch appears to be 10 units. The suggestion is made that the acceptance decision be based on the average value computed from a single sample of 4, with the batch accepted if the average is 210 or more. Assuming that the standard deviation continues to be at 10 units and assuming a normal distribution of the quality characteristic within a batch, what is the probability of acceptance of a 5% defective lot?   *Ans.* 0.9015.

177. For the single sampling plan $n = 150$, $c = 2$, what are the values of $p_{0.95}$, $p_{0.50}$, and $p_{0.10}$? See Table 39 for probabilities of acceptance.

Ans. 0.55%; 1.8%; 3.6%.

178. Prepare an AOQ curve for the plan of Problem 177, assuming that rejected lots are screened. What is the AOQL?   *Ans.* 0.91%.

179. A multiple sampling plan is as follows:

Sample number	Individual sample size	Combined sample size	Acceptance number	Rejection number
1	5	5	*	2
2	5	10	0	2
3	5	15	0	3
4	5	20	1	3
5	5	25	2	3

* Acceptance not permitted on first sample.

Assuming that lot size is large enough for Table G to be applicable, compute the probability of acceptance of a 10% defective lot.   *Ans.* 0.586.

180. Show the necessary calculations to check the probabilities of acceptance and rejection given on page 331 for the multiple sampling plan given on page 330.

181. At the end of Art. 266 (page 335), the statement is made that with a reject limit factor of 2.25 and an n of 16, the probability of accepting a 2% defective lot is only 0.219. Show the necessary calculations to check this figure.

182. A known-sigma variables plan for a one-sided specification uses $n = 9$ and $k' = 1.466$. Assuming a normal distribution and a correct estimate of sigma, what is the probability of acceptance of a 3.75% defective lot?   *Ans.* 0.827.

183. Prepare an AOQ curve for the single sampling plan $n = 100$, $c = 0$. What is the AOQL?   *Ans.* 0.35%.

184. The lot size N is 2,000 in a certain AOQL inspection procedure.. The desired AOQL of 2.0% can be obtained with any one of three single sampling plans. These are $n = 65$, $c = 2$; $n = 41$, $c = 1$; and $n = 18$, $c = 0$. If a large number of lots 0.3% defective are submitted for acceptance, what will be the average number of units inspected per lot under each of these three sampling plans?

Ans. 67; 55; 121.

185. Make the comparison required in Problem 184, assuming the submitted lots are 1.0% defective.

186. Where destructive testing is involved, a common acceptance procedure is to test one article from a lot, passing the lot if the article is satisfactory and taking a second sample of one if the article fails the test. If the second article also fails, the lot is rejected; if the second article proves satisfactory, the lot is accepted.

Plot the OC curve for this plan, assuming the submitted lot is large enough so that the selection of a defective article on the first sample does not make any appreciable change in the probability of getting a defective article on the second sample. What do you think of the quality protection given by this common plan?

187. A proposed triple sampling plan is as follows: Take a first sample of 2. If both good, accept; if both bad, reject. If 1 good and 1 bad, take a second sample of 2. If both good, accept; if both bad, reject. If 1 good and 1 bad, take a third sample of 2. If both articles in the third sample are good, accept; otherwise reject.

Plot the OC curve of this plan, assuming that the lot is relatively large.

188. In a double sampling plan, $N = 100$, $n_1 = 5$, $c_1 = 0$, $n_2 = 10$, $c_2 = 1$. Using the correct combinatorial formulas, compute the probability that a lot exactly 2% defective will be accepted by this plan.

189. Solve Problem 188 by the use of Table G, assuming that for your purpose the Poisson gives a close enough approximation to the true probabilities.

190. In a certain variables acceptance plan, samples of 4 are tested from each lot. A control chart is plotted with reject limits determined as indicated in Fig. 42 (page 190). If the average of a sample of 4 plots within the reject limits and the range plots inside of the control limits on an R chart, a lot is accepted; otherwise it is rejected.

Assume that after a long period of satisfactory lots, a lot is submitted that is 10% defective. Assume that this lot is normally distributed with a σ' equal to that used in computing the reject limits, but that the average of the lot has shifted to such a high value that the highest 10% of the frequency distribution is above the upper specification limit. What is the probability that this lot will be accepted?

191. Table M, Appendix III, includes the single sampling plan $n = 7$, $c = 1$, for an AQL of 10%. Assuming a lot size of 30 and using hypergeometric probabilities, compute the probabilities of acceptance of lots 10%, 20%, and 30% defective.

192. Use Table G to find the OC curve of the single sampling plan $n = 50$, $c = 3$. Compute the probabilities of acceptance of lots 1%, 2%, 4%, 6%, 8%, 10%, 12%, and 14% defective.

193. For the plan of Problem 192, find the value of lot per cent defective for which the probabilities of acceptance are 0.95, 0.50, and 0.10. Read these values from your OC curve.

194. Plot an AOQ curve for the plan of Problem 192. What is the AOQL?

195. Consider the single sampling plan $n = 150$, $c = 2$. Table 39 gives the probability of acceptance of a 1% defective lot as 0.809. This assumes a very large lot size. Using the correct combinatorial formulas, compute the probability of acceptance of a 1% defective lot when $N = 500$.

196. Use Table G to find the OC curve of the single sampling plan $n = 200$, $c = 5$, assuming N is large in comparison with n. Compute the probabilities of acceptance of lots 0.5%, 1%, 1.5%, 2%, 2.5%, 3%, 4%, and 5% defective.

197. Plot an AOQ curve for the plan of Problem 196. What is the AOQL?

198. For the single sampling plan $n = 750$, $c = 10$, what are the values of $p_{0.95}$, $p_{0.50}$, and $p_{0.10}$? See Table 39 for probabilities of acceptance.

199. A double sampling plan is $n_1 = 25$, $c_1 = 1$, $n_2 = 50$, $c_2 = 3$. Compute the probability of acceptance of a 3.0% defective lot. Assume lot size is large in comparison with sample size.

200. A double sampling plan is $n_1 = 150$, $c_1 = 2$, $n_2 = 300$, $c_2 = 4$. Compute the probability of acceptance of a 1.0% defective lot. Assume lot size is large in comparison with sample size.

201. The following multiple sampling plan involves a maximum of 7 samples of 40 each:

Sample number	Combined sample size	Acceptance number	Rejection number
1	40	*	2
2	80	*	2
3	120	0	2
4	160	0	3
5	200	1	3
6	240	2	4
7	280	4	5

* Acceptance not permitted on first or second sample.

Compute the probability of acceptance of a 0.5% defective lot. Assume lot size is large in comparison with sample size.

202. A known-sigma variables acceptance plan for a one-sided specification uses $n = 10$ and $k' = 1.60$. Compute the probability of acceptance of a 4% defective lot, assuming the frequency distribution in the lot is normal and σ' is estimated correctly.

203. A known-sigma variables acceptance plan for a one-sided specification uses $n = 13$ and $k' = 1.396$. Compute the probability of acceptance of a 3.2% defective lot, assuming the frequency distribution in the lot is normal and σ' is estimated correctly.

204. The lot size N is 2,000 in a certain AOQL inspection procedure. The desired AOQL of 1.0% can be obtained with any one of three single sampling plans. These are $n = 36$, $c = 0$; $n = 80$, $c = 1$; and $n = 130$, $c = 2$. Which plan will involve the minimum total inspection, considering both sampling inspection and screening of rejected lots, if a large number of lots 0.25% defective are submitted for acceptance?

205. Solve Problem 204, assuming submitted lots are 0.50% defective.

206. Solve Problem 204, changing N to 500.

CHAPTER XIV

ACCEPTANCE SAMPLING BY ATTRIBUTES
DODGE-ROMIG TABLES AND PROCEDURES

The question is sometimes asked as to why it is necessary to have so many tables . . . In industry, acceptable quality levels vary and the necessary risks of wrong decisions vary. For each combination of acceptable quality level and risk, a different plan is required; hence the need for many tables. Series of tables that cover nearly all ordinary requirements have been computed and published.—A. C. RICHMOND[1]

270. Two Types of Attributes Sampling Procedure Involving Consideration of the Effect of Screening Rejected Product. The great bulk of acceptance inspection is carried out on an attributes basis, with articles classified into those conforming to specifications and those failing to conform. Attributes inspection is well adapted to the establishment of standard sampling procedures. This chapter deals with two general types of such procedures, as follows:

1. Lot-by-lot procedures aimed at minimizing the total amount of inspection, considering both sampling inspection and screening inspection of rejected lots.

2. Continuous sampling procedures. In these procedures, current inspection results are used to determine whether sampling inspection or screening inspection is to be used for the next articles to be inspected.

The common element in these two types of procedure is that attention is concentrated, in part, on the influence of the provision for using screening inspection whenever the results of sampling inspection are unsatisfactory. As pointed out in Arts. 267 and 268 (pages 335 to 337), the average outgoing quality limit (AOQL) is a useful measure of the quality protection afforded by the combination of the sampling criteria and the screening requirement.

271. Selecting an Acceptance Inspection Scheme. It is explained in Chap. XVII that the choice among various possible plans for acceptance of manufactured product is essentially an economic one. In making a decision regarding acceptance inspection for any particular product, it may be desirable to consider not only various possible schemes of acceptance sampling by attributes but also the alternatives of (1) no inspection at all, (2) 100% inspection, and (3) various possible schemes

---

[1] RICHMOND, A. C., Acceptance Inspection, *Paper* No. 8, Fourth National Convention of American Society for Quality Control, June, 1950.

of acceptance sampling by variables. It is pointed out in Chap. XVII that a satisfactory evaluation of all the pertinent economic factors is often quite difficult. For this reason the choice of an acceptance plan is commonly made on an intuitive basis. Various guides to sound intuition in this matter are discussed in Chap. XIX.

It was pointed out in Chap. XIII that an important element in the selection of an acceptance inspection scheme should be the probable contribution of the scheme to quality improvement. The acceptance sampling schemes described in this chapter and the next have often been strikingly successful in leading to such improvement.

272. Two Useful Volumes of Standard Tables. Anyone responsible for the choice of an acceptance sampling procedure by attributes should have two volumes available for consultation. One of these is the volume "Sampling Inspection Tables" by Dodge and Romig.[1] The other is "Sampling Inspection" prepared by the Statistical Research Group (SRG) of Columbia University.[2] Both of these volumes not only contain extensive tables of acceptance sampling plans for attributes inspection but also contain much useful material on the theory and practice of acceptance sampling.

The Dodge-Romig tables were originally prepared for use within the Bell Telephone System. They were designed primarily to minimize the total amount of inspection, considering both sampling inspection and screening inspection of rejected lots.

Although the SRG's tables were designed originally for the U.S. Navy for use in acceptance/rejection inspection, they may also be used for acceptance/rectification inspection. Further comment on this point is made following the discussion of the Dodge-Romig tables.

273. The Dodge-Romig Tables. The Dodge-Romig volume contains four sets of tables, as follows:

I. Single Sampling Lot Tolerance Tables
II. Double Sampling Lot Tolerance Tables
III. Single Sampling AOQL Tables
IV. Double Sampling AOQL Tables.

Sets I and II apply to the following lot tolerance per cent defectives (assuming Consumer's Risk = 0.10):

0.5%	3.0%	7.0%
1.0%	4.0%	10.0%
2.0%	5.0%	

[1] DODGE, H. F., and H. G. ROMIG, "Sampling Inspection Tables—Single and Double Sampling," John Wiley & Sons, Inc., New York, 1944.
[2] FREEMAN, H. A., MILTON FRIEDMAN, FREDERICK MOSTELLER, and W. A. WALLIS (eds.), "Sampling Inspection," McGraw-Hill Book Company, Inc., New York, 1948.

Sets III and IV apply to the following values of AOQL:

0.1%	1.5%	4.0%
0.25%	2.0%	5.0%
0.5%	2.5%	7.0%
0.75%	3.0%	10.0%
1.0%		

274. Single Sampling Lot Tolerance Tables. Table 41 is representative of Dodge-Romig Set I.

TABLE 41.   EXAMPLE OF DODGE-ROMIG SINGLE SAMPLING LOT TOLERANCE TABLES
Lot Tolerance Per Cent Defective = 5.0%
Consumer's Risk = 0.10
(Reprinted by permission from "Sampling Inspection Tables" by Dodge & Romig, published by John Wiley & Sons, Inc.)

Process Average %	0–.05			.06–.50			.51–1.00			1.01–1.50			1.51–2.00			2.01–2.50		
Lot Size	n	c	AOQL %	n	c	AOQL %	n	c	AOQL %	n	c	AOQL %	n	c	AOQL %	n	c	AOQL %
1–30	All	0	0	All	0	0	All	0	0	All	0	0	All	0	0	All	0	0
31–50	30	0	.49	30	0	.49	30	0	.49	30	0	.49	30	0	.49	30	0	.49
51–100	37	0	.63	37	0	.63	37	0	.63	37	0	.63	37	0	.63	37	0	.63
101–200	40	0	.74	40	0	.74	40	0	.74	40	0	.74	40	0	.74	40	0	.74
201–300	43	0	.74	43	0	.74	70	1	.92	70	1	.92	95	2	.99	95	2	.99
301–400	44	0	.74	44	0	.74	70	1	.99	100	2	1.0	120	3	1.1	145	4	1.1
401–500	45	0	.75	75	1	.95	100	2	1.1	100	2	1.1	125	3	1.2	150	4	1.2
501–600	45	0	.76	75	1	.98	100	2	1.1	125	3	1.2	150	4	1.3	175	5	1.3
601–800	45	0	.77	75	1	1.0	100	2	1.2	130	3	1.2	175	5	1.4	200	6	1.4
801–1000	45	0	.78	75	1	1.0	105	2	1.2	155	4	1.4	180	5	1.4	225	7	1.5
1001–2000	45	0	.80	75	1	1.0	130	3	1.4	180	5	1.6	230	7	1.7	280	9	1.8
2001–3000	75	1	1.1	105	2	1.3	135	3	1.4	210	6	1.7	280	9	1.9	370	13	2.1
3001–4000	75	1	1.1	105	2	1.3	160	4	1.5	210	6	1.7	305	10	2.0	420	15	2.2
4001–5000	75	1	1.1	105	2	1.3	160	4	1.5	235	7	1.8	330	11	2.0	440	16	2.2
5001–7000	75	1	1.1	105	2	1.3	185	5	1.7	260	8	1.9	350	12	2.2	490	18	2.4
7001–10,000	75	1	1.1	105	2	1.3	185	5	1.7	260	8	1.9	380	13	2.2	535	20	2.5
10,001–20,000	75	1	1.1	135	3	1.4	210	6	1.8	285	9	2.0	425	15	2.3	610	23	2.6
20,001–50,000	75	1	1.1	135	3	1.4	235	7	1.9	305	10	2.1	470	17	2.4	700	27	2.7
50,001–100,000	75	1	1.1	160	4	1.6	235	7	1.9	355	12	2.2	515	19	2.5	770	30	2.8

All the sampling plans in this table have the same lot tolerance per cent defective (LTPD) namely, 5.0%. However, the plans have different values of AOQL. The table gives the AOQL figure for each plan.

The table contains six columns, each for a different value of process average per cent defective. The purpose of these different columns is to indicate the plan that involves the minimum total inspection, considering both the inspection of samples and the 100% inspection of rejected lots.

For example, consider the inspection plans indicated in the table for the lot size range from 501 to 600. Six different plans, namely, $\begin{cases} n = 45 \\ c = 0 \end{cases}$, $\begin{cases} n = 75 \\ c = 1 \end{cases}$, $\begin{cases} n = 100 \\ c = 2 \end{cases}$, $\begin{cases} n = 125 \\ c = 3 \end{cases}$, $\begin{cases} n = 150 \\ c = 4 \end{cases}$, and $\begin{cases} n = 175 \\ c = 5 \end{cases}$ all have a lot tolerance fraction defective of 0.05. But, as explained in Art. 258, Chap. XIII, if rejected lots are to be detailed, the total amount of inspection of samples and rejected lots under these plans will depend on the quality level of the product submitted for inspection. Table 41 simply says that this total inspection will be a minimum for $\begin{cases} n = 45 \\ c = 0 \end{cases}$ if the process average is 0-0.05% defective, that it will be a minimum for $\begin{cases} n = 75 \\ c = 1 \end{cases}$ if the process average is 0.06-0.50%, and so forth.

If there is no basis for estimating the process average, the sampling plan should be selected from the right-hand column of the table. This gives the desired quality protection and gives satisfactory lots a better chance of acceptance. Moreover, it collects data more rapidly to permit reliable estimates of the process average.

In the use of these lot tolerance tables, it should be understood that the tables contemplate the screening of rejected lots. However, the tables give the consumer the stated quality protection regardless of any provision for screening. Even though rejected lots are merely returned by the consumer to the producer with no formal provision for screening by anyone, it is reasonable to suppose that the producer will screen these lots. Under such circumstances, the consumer's use of the process average to determine his acceptance criteria may be thought of as aimed at minimizing the total inspection done by industry as a whole, considering both the consumer's sampling inspection and the screening presumably done by the producer.

275. Double Sampling Lot Tolerance Tables. Table 42 is representative of Dodge-Romig Set II.

Some differences between single and double sampling plans are evident from a comparison of Tables 41 and 42. These differences may be brought out to best advantage by comparing any single sampling plan with a double sampling plan for the same lot size and process average that gives the same lot quality protection. For example, consider the plans from Tables 41 and 42 for a lot size of 801–1,000 and a process average of 0.51–1.00% defective:

TABLE 42.   EXAMPLE OF DODGE-ROMIG DOUBLE SAMPLING LOT TOLERANCE TABLES

Lot Tolerance Per Cent Defective = 5.0%

Consumer's Risk = 0.10

(Reprinted by permission from "Sampling Inspection Tables" by Dodge & Romig, published by John Wiley & Sons, Inc.)

Process Average 0–.05

Lot Size	Trial 1 n_1	c_1	Trial 2 n_2	n_1+n_2	c_2	AOQL in %
1–30	All	0	—	—	—	0
31–50	30	0	—	—	—	.49
51–75	38	0	—	—	—	.59
76–100	44	0	21	65	1	.64
101–200	49	0	26	75	1	.84
201–300	50	0	30	80	1	.91
301–400	55	0	30	85	1	.92
401–500	55	0	30	85	1	.93
501–600	55	0	30	85	1	.94
601–800	55	0	35	90	1	.95
801–1000	55	0	65	120	2	.96
1001–2000	55	0	35	90	1	.98
2001–3000	55	0	65	120	2	1.2
3001–4000	55	0	65	120	2	1.2
4001–5000	55	0	65	120	2	1.2
5001–7000	55	0	65	120	2	1.2
7001–10,000	55	0	65	120	2	1.2
10,001–20,000	55	0	65	120	2	1.2
20,001–50,000	55	0	65	120	2	1.2
50,001–100,000	55	0	65	120	2	1.2

Process Average .06–.50

Lot Size	Trial 1 n_1	c_1	Trial 2 n_2	n_1+n_2	c_2	AOQL in %
1–30	All	0	—	—	—	0
31–50	30	0	—	—	—	.49
51–75	38	0	—	—	—	.59
76–100	44	0	21	65	1	.64
101–200	49	0	26	75	1	.84
201–300	50	0	30	80	1	.91
301–400	55	0	55	110	2	1.1
401–500	55	0	55	110	2	1.1
501–600	55	0	60	115	2	1.1
601–800	55	0	65	120	2	1.1
801–1000	55	0	65	120	2	1.1
1001–2000	55	0	95	150	3	1.3
2001–3000	55	0	95	150	3	1.3
3001–4000	55	0	95	150	3	1.3
4001–5000	55	0	95	150	3	1.4
5001–7000	55	0	95	150	3	1.4
7001–10,000	55	0	120	175	4	1.5
10,001–20,000	55	0	120	175	4	1.5
20,001–50,000	55	0	150	205	5	1.7
50,001–100,000	55	0	150	205	5	1.7

Process Average .51–1.00

Lot Size	Trial 1 n_1	c_1	Trial 2 n_2	n_1+n_2	c_2	AOQL in %
1–30	All	0	—	—	—	0
31–50	30	0	—	—	—	.49
51–75	38	0	—	—	—	.59
76–100	44	0	21	65	1	.64
101–200	49	0	26	75	1	.84
201–300	50	0	55	105	2	1.0
301–400	55	0	55	110	2	1.1
401–500	55	0	80	135	3	1.2
501–600	55	0	85	140	3	1.2
601–800	55	0	85	140	3	1.3
801–1000	55	0	115	170	4	1.4
1001–2000	55	0	120	175	4	1.4
2001–3000	55	0	150	205	5	1.5
3001–4000	90	1	140	230	6	1.6
4001–5000	90	1	165	255	7	1.8
5001–7000	90	1	165	255	7	1.8
7001–10,000	90	1	190	280	8	1.9
10,001–20,000	90	1	190	280	8	1.9
20,001–50,000	90	1	215	305	9	2.0
50,001–100,000	90	1	240	330	10	2.1

Process Average 1.01–1.50

Lot Size	Trial 1 n_1	c_1	Trial 2 n_2	n_1+n_2	c_2	AOQL in %
1–30	All	0	—	—	—	0
31–50	30	0	—	—	—	.49
51–75	38	0	—	—	—	.59
76–100	44	0	21	65	1	.64
101–200	49	0	51	100	2	.91
201–300	50	0	55	105	2	1.0
301–400	55	0	80	135	3	1.1
401–500	55	0	105	160	4	1.3
501–600	55	0	110	165	4	1.3
601–800	90	1	125	215	6	1.5
801–1000	90	1	150	240	7	1.5
1001–2000	90	2	185	275	8	1.7
2001–3000	120	2	180	300	9	1.9
3001–4000	120	2	210	330	10	2.0
4001–5000	120	2	255	375	12	2.1
5001–7000	120	2	260	380	12	2.1
7001–10,000	120	2	285	405	13	2.1
10,001–20,000	120	2	310	430	14	2.2
20,001–50,000	120	2	335	455	15	2.2
50,001–100,000	120	2	360	480	16	2.3

Process Average 1.51–2.00

Lot Size	Trial 1 n_1	c_1	Trial 2 n_2	n_1+n_2	c_2	AOQL in %
1–30	All	0	—	—	—	0
31–50	30	0	—	—	—	.49
51–75	38	0	—	—	—	.59
76–100	44	0	21	65	1	.64
101–200	49	0	51	100	2	.91
201–300	50	0	80	130	3	1.1
301–400	55	0	100	155	4	1.2
401–500	85	1	120	205	5	1.2
501–600	85	1	145	230	7	1.4
601–800	90	1	170	260	8	1.5
801–1000	90	1	200	290	9	1.6
1001–2000	120	2	225	345	11	1.9
2001–3000	150	3	270	420	14	2.1
3001–4000	150	3	295	445	15	2.3
4001–5000	150	3	345	495	17	2.3
5001–7000	150	3	370	520	18	2.3
7001–10,000	175	4	370	545	19	2.4
10,001–20,000	175	4	420	595	21	2.4
20,001–50,000	205	5	485	690	25	2.5
50,001–100,000	205	5	555	760	28	2.6

Process Average 2.01–2.50

Lot Size	Trial 1 n_1	c_1	Trial 2 n_2	n_1+n_2	c_2	AOQL in %
1–30	All	0	—	—	—	0
31–50	30	0	—	—	—	.49
51–75	38	0	—	—	—	.59
76–100	44	0	21	65	1	.64
101–200	49	0	51	100	2	.91
201–300	50	0	100	150	4	1.1
301–400	85	1	105	190	6	1.3
401–500	85	1	140	225	7	1.4
501–600	85	1	165	250	8	1.5
601–800	120	2	185	305	10	1.6
801–1000	120	2	210	330	11	1.7
1001–2000	175	4	260	435	15	2.0
2001–3000	205	5	375	580	21	2.3
3001–4000	230	6	420	650	24	2.4
4001–5000	255	7	445	700	26	2.5
5001–7000	255	7	495	750	28	2.6
7001–10,000	280	8	540	820	31	2.7
10,001–20,000	280	8	660	940	36	2.8
20,001–50,000	305	9	745	1050	41	2.9
50,001–100,000	330	10	810	1140	45	3.0

Single Sampling	Double Sampling	
$n = 105$	$n_1 = 55$	$n_2 = 115$
$c = 2$	$c_1 = 0$	$n_1 + n_2 = 170$
		$c_2 = 4$

The first sample in double sampling is smaller than the one sample in single sampling; in this case it is 55 instead of 105. On the other hand, the combined sample in double sampling is larger—170 compared to 105. The relative number of articles inspected in the samples in the two plans evidently depends on the quality of submitted product. If the product sampled is good enough that very few second samples have to be taken, the inspection will be substantially less with the double sampling plan. If many second samples need to be taken, the single sampling will require less sampling inspection. Dodge and Romig give a diagram that compares the inspection under single and double sampling for various lot sizes and ratios of process average to lot tolerance fraction defective.[1] They state that over the portion of the tables most useful in practice, the saving in inspection due to double sampling is usually over 10% and may be as much as 50%.

One characteristic of all the Dodge-Romig double sampling plans is that c_2 is always 1 or more. This means that no lot is ever rejected as a result of only 1 defective.

276. Single Sampling AOQL Tables. Table 43 is representative of Dodge-Romig Set III.

In contrast to Table 41 in which all the single sampling plans had the same lot tolerance per cent defective, all the plans in Table 43 have the same AOQL, namely, 2%. The table gives the lot tolerance per cent defective for each plan. It is of interest to note that the larger the sample size and acceptance number for a given AOQL, the lower the lot tolerance per cent defective.

Like all the Dodge-Romig tables, columns are given for various process averages; the plan in each column is the one which gives the minimum total inspection for the process average at the head of the column. Thus all the plans on any line of the table are alike in quality protection (as measured by the AOQL) and differ only in total amount of inspection required. The remarks in Art. 274 about the selection of a plan where process average is unknown are applicable to this and all other Dodge-Romig tables.

277. Double Sampling AOQL Tables. Table 44 is representative of Dodge-Romig Set IV.

Dodge and Romig point out that the lot tolerance concept was first developed and applied in the Bell Telephone System in 1923. The con-

[1] DODGE and ROMIG, *op. cit.*, Fig. 5, p. 39.

cept of the AOQL was developed and applied in 1927. Thus tables involving both concepts, and involving single and double sampling, have been available within the Bell System for application to all types of inspection for many years. It is significant that Dodge and Romig state that the double sampling AOQL tables, of which Table 44 is an example, have proved the most useful of all the tables.

TABLE 43. EXAMPLE OF DODGE-ROMIG SINGLE SAMPLING AOQL TABLES
Average Outgoing Quality Limit = 2.0%
(Reprinted by permission from "Sampling Inspection Tables" by Dodge & Romig, published by John Wiley & Sons, Inc.)

Process Average %	0–.04			.05–.40			.41–.80			.81–1.20			1.21–1.60			1.61–2.00		
Lot Size	n	c	p_t%	n	c	p_t%	n	c	p_t%	n	c	p_t%	n	c	p_t%	n	c	p_t%
1–15	All	0	—	All	0	—	All	0	—	All	0	—	All	0	—	All	0	—
16–50	14	0	13.6	14	0	13.6	14	0	13.6	14	0	13.6	14	0	13.6	14	0	13.6
51–100	16	0	12.4	16	0	12.4	16	0	12.4	16	0	12.4	16	0	12.4	16	0	12.4
101–200	17	0	12.2	17	0	12.2	17	0	12.2	17	0	12.2	35	1	10.5	35	1	10.5
201–300	17	0	12.3	17	0	12.3	17	0	12.3	37	1	10.2	37	1	10.2	37	1	10.2
301–400	18	0	11.8	18	0	11.8	38	1	10.0	38	1	10.0	38	1	10.0	60	2	8.5
401–500	18	0	11.9	18	0	11.9	39	1	9.8	39	1	9.8	60	2	8.6	60	2	8.6
501–600	18	0	11.9	18	0	11.9	39	1	9.8	39	1	9.8	60	2	8.6	60	2	8.6
601–800	18	0	11.9	40	1	9.6	40	1	9.6	65	2	8.0	65	2	8.0	85	3	7.5
801–1000	18	0	12.0	40	1	9.6	40	1	9.6	65	2	8.1	65	2	8.1	90	3	7.4
1001–2000	18	0	12.0	41	1	9.4	65	2	8.2	65	2	8.2	95	3	7.0	120	4	6.5
2001–3000	18	0	12.0	41	1	9.4	65	2	8.2	95	3	7.0	120	4	6.5	180	6	5.8
3001–4000	18	0	12.0	42	1	9.3	65	2	8.2	95	3	7.0	155	5	6.0	210	7	5.5
4001–5000	18	0	12.0	42	1	9.3	70	2	7.5	125	4	6.4	155	5	6.0	245	8	5.3
5001–7000	18	0	12.0	42	1	9.3	95	3	7.0	125	4	6.4	185	6	5.6	280	9	5.1
7001–10,000	42	1	9.3	70	2	7.5	95	3	7.0	155	5	6.0	220	7	5.4	350	11	4.8
10,001–20,000	42	1	9.3	70	2	7.6	95	3	7.0	190	6	5.6	290	9	4.9	460	14	4.4
20,001–50,000	42	1	9.3	70	2	7.6	125	4	6.4	220	7	5.4	395	12	4.5	720	21	3.9
50,001–100,000	42	1	9.3	95	3	7.0	160	5	5.9	290	9	4.9	505	15	4.2	955	27	3.7

278. Relationship between the Process Average Used in Selecting a Dodge-Romig Sampling Plan and the OC Curve of the Plan Selected. Tables 41 to 44 all have six columns, each corresponding to a stated process average. In general, the greater the process average used in entering any Dodge-Romig table, the larger will be the sample size for any stated lot size. The plans having larger sample sizes have steeper OC curves with resulting better discrimination between lots superior to the quality standard and lots worse than the quality standard. This point is illustrated by Figs. 67 and 68.

TABLE 44. EXAMPLE OF DODGE-ROMIG DOUBLE SAMPLING AOQL TABLES

Average Outgoing Quality Limit = 2.0%

(Reprinted by permission from "Sampling Inspection Tables" by Dodge & Romig, published by John Wiley & Sons, Inc.)

Process Average %	0–04						.05–40						.41–80						.81–1.20						1.21–1.60						1.61–2.00					
Lot Size	n1	c1	n2	n1+n2	c2	pt%	n1	c1	n2	n1+n2	c2	pt%	n1	c1	n2	n1+n2	c2	pt%	n1	c1	n2	n1+n2	c2	pt%	n1	c1	n2	n1+n2	c2	pt%	n1	c1	n2	n1+n2	c2	pt%
1–15	All	0	—	—	—	—	All	0	—	—	—	—	All	0	—	—	—	—	All	0	—	—	—	—	All	0	—	—	—	—	All	0	—	—	—	—
16–50	14	0	—	—	—	13.6	14	0	—	—	—	13.6	14	0	—	—	—	13.6	14	0	—	—	—	13.6	14	0	—	—	—	13.6	14	0	—	—	—	13.6
51–100	21	0	12	33	1	11.7	21	0	12	33	1	11.7	21	0	12	33	1	11.7	21	0	12	33	1	11.7	21	0	12	33	1	11.7	23	0	23	46	2	10.9
101–200	24	0	13	37	1	11.0	24	0	13	37	1	11.0	24	0	13	37	1	11.0	27	0	28	55	2	9.6	27	0	28	55	2	9.6	27	0	28	55	2	9.6
201–300	26	0	15	41	1	10.4	26	0	15	41	1	10.4	29	0	31	60	2	9.1	29	0	31	60	2	9.1	32	0	48	80	3	8.4	32	0	48	80	3	8.4
301–400	26	0	16	42	1	10.3	26	0	16	42	1	10.3	30	0	35	65	2	9.0	33	0	52	85	3	8.2	33	0	52	85	3	8.2	36	0	69	105	3	7.6
401–500	27	0	16	43	1	10.3	30	0	35	65	2	10.3	30	0	35	65	2	9.0	30	0	56	86	3	7.9	36	0	74	110	4	7.5	60	1	90	150	6	7.0
501–600	27	0	16	43	1	10.3	34	0	31	65	2	8.9	35	0	55	90	3	8.9	35	0	55	90	3	7.9	37	0	78	115	4	7.4	65	1	95	160	6	6.8
601–800	27	0	17	44	1	10.2	39	0	31	70	2	8.8	35	0	60	95	3	8.8	38	0	82	120	4	7.7	38	0	82	120	4	7.3	70	1	120	190	7	6.4
801–1000	27	0	17	44	1	10.2	38	0	32	70	2	8.7	36	0	59	95	3	8.7	38	0	87	125	4	7.6	70	1	100	170	6	6.5	70	1	145	215	8	6.2
1001–2000	33	0	37	70	2	8.5	37	0	33	70	2	8.5	37	0	63	100	3	7.5	43	0	112	155	5	7.5	80	1	160	240	8	5.8	110	2	205	315	11	5.5
2001–3000	34	0	41	75	2	8.2	41	0	34	75	2	8.2	41	0	84	125	4	7.7	75	1	115	190	6	6.5	115	2	195	310	10	5.3	160	3	310	470	15	4.7
3001–4000	34	0	41	75	2	8.2	62	0	38	100	3	7.3	41	0	89	130	4	6.9	80	1	140	220	7	5.8	120	2	255	375	12	5.0	235	5	415	650	20	4.3
4001–5000	34	0	41	75	2	8.2	62	0	38	100	3	7.3	42	0	88	130	4	6.9	80	1	175	255	8	5.5	125	2	285	410	13	4.9	275	6	475	750	23	4.2
5001–7000	35	0	40	75	2	8.1	62	0	38	100	3	7.3	44	0	116	160	5	6.4	85	1	205	290	9	5.3	160	3	320	480	14	4.8	280	6	575	855	26	4.1
7001–10,000	35	0	40	75	2	8.1	63	0	37	100	3	7.3	45	0	115	160	5	6.3	85	1	210	295	9	5.2	165	3	335	500	15	4.5	320	7	645	965	29	4.0
10,001–20,000	35	0	40	75	2	8.1	66	0	39	105	3	7.2	45	0	115	160	5	6.3	90	1	260	350	11	5.1	170	3	425	595	18	4.4	395	9	835	1230	37	3.9
20,001–50,000	35	0	40	75	2	8.1	92	0	43	135	4	6.6	47	0	148	195	6	6.0	130	2	300	430	13	4.7	205	4	515	720	22	4.3	480	11	1090	1570	46	3.7
50,001–100,000	35	0	45	80	2	8.0	92	0	43	135	4	6.6	85	1	185	270	8	5.2	135	2	345	480	14	4.5	250	5	615	865	26	4.1	580	13	1460	2040	53	3.5

Figure 67 shows the OC curves for the six double sampling plans given in Table 42 (LTPD = 5%) for the lot size 4,001–5,000. All these curves naturally show that the probability of acceptance of a 5% defective lot is 0.10. At all other points, however, the OC curves differ considerably. The differences are particularly striking at about half the 5% LTPD. Thus a 2.5% defective lot is almost certain to be accepted under the plan corresponding to the process average 2.01–2.50% (curve 6) but has only about a 0.50 probability of acceptance under the plans corresponding to the process averages 0–0.05% and 0.06–0.50% (curves 1 and 2). In

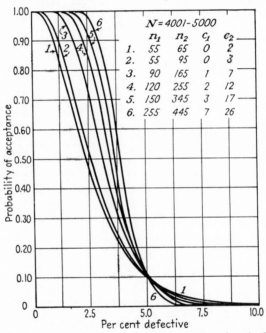

FIG. 67. OC curves for the six Dodge-Romig double sampling plans for LTPD of 5% and lot size 4,001–5,000. (*Reproduced from H. F. Dodge, Administration of a Sampling Inspection Plan, Industrial Quality Control, vol. 4, No. 3, pp. 12–19, November, 1948.*)

general, where submitted lots are as good as the process average used in entering the tables, they are almost certain to be accepted.

Figure 68 shows the OC curves for the six double sampling plans given in Table 44 (AOQL = 2%). A comparison with Fig. 67 may be helpful in emphasizing certain similarities and certain differences between using the LTPD and the AOQL as the quality standard. Just as in the LTPD tables, any lots at the assumed process average or better are almost certain of acceptance. The probability of acceptance of lots at exactly the AOQL value varies from about 0.84 (curve 1) to 0.99 (curve 6). The differences in the right-hand sections of the OC curves reflect different degrees of protection against accepting lots considerably worse than the stated AOQL; these differences are also brought out in Table 44 by the LTPD values given for each sampling plan.

279. Determining the Process Average in Dodge-Romig Inspection. The minimizing of total inspection depends on making a correct estimate of the process average as a basis for the selection of the sampling plan. It follows that in all Dodge-Romig inspection, it is advantageous to

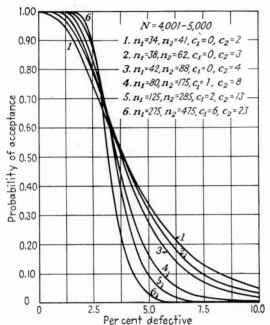

FIG. 68. OC curves for the six Dodge-Romig double sampling plans for AOQL of 2% and lot size 4,001–5,000. (*Reproduced from H. F. Dodge, Administration of a Sampling Inspection Plan, Industrial Quality Control, vol. 4, No. 3, pp. 12–19, November, 1948.*)

make systematic use of the results of sampling inspection to determine the process average.

Two forms that may be used to record this information are illustrated in an article by Keeling and Cisne describing the AOQL double sampling methods used at Western Electric Company.[1] This article has been reproduced as Chap. III in the Dodge-Romig volume. One form (page 60 of Dodge and Romig) records the numbers inspected and numbers of defectives in lot-by-lot samples for a given inspection operation for a week, separating the results of first samples and second samples in double sampling. Columns are provided to show the number of defects of each type observed in first samples.

[1] KEELING, D. B., and L. E. CISNE, Using Double Sampling in a Manufacturing Plant, *Bell System Technical Journal*, vol. 21, pp. 37–50, June, 1942.

Another form (page 61 of Dodge and Romig) contains a weekly summary of the inspection results. One side of the form consists of a control chart for p on which are plotted the weekly percentages of defectives in first samples. Two-sigma limits are used on this chart. Whenever double sampling is used, the process average should be estimated from first samples only. Otherwise the estimate would be too heavily weighted by the samples from the poorer lots.

280. Making Dodge-Romig AOQL Procedures Contribute to Quality Improvement. The record of sampling inspection may contribute in various ways to the improvement of quality. The control chart maintained as part of this record will indicate out-of-control situations and will show quality trends. This gives guidance as to when to hunt for trouble and helps to concentrate executive pressure for improvement in those places where it will be most effective. The lot-by-lot record listing defects in first samples is helpful to anyone engaged in the actual hunting for the sources of trouble.

Moreover, the contribution of the sampling procedure is not limited to the supplying of useful information. The costs of carrying out screening inspection of rejected lots may be used to provide an effective financial incentive to quality improvement. Where producer and consumer are two departments of the same organization, the producer may be required to do all such screening. Or, where this is not practicable, the cost of any screening inspection may be charged against the budget of the producing department. Example 39, Chap. XIX, describes a case in which both of these types of pressure were used.

When a vendor and purchaser are involved, an agreement can be made that whenever lots fail to pass the purchaser's sampling inspection, a stipulated deduction from the price will be made to cover the purchaser's screening costs. Under such circumstances, the AOQL to be used is a matter for prior agreement between vendor and purchaser.

281. Relationship between Lot Size and Sample Size in Dodge-Romig Tables. The Dodge-Romig tables apply to lot sizes from 1 to 100,000 and may be used for any lots that happen to be submitted for acceptance. Where practicable, however, it may be advantageous to establish the size of lots to be submitted for acceptance rather than to take lots as they come. The tables help in making a decision on lot size by showing clearly the disadvantage of small lots as compared with large ones from the viewpoint of the amount of sampling necessary for a given quality protection. For example, the first column of Table 41 calls for a sample size of "All" (i.e., 100%) of a lot of 30 or less, a sample size of 37 (i.e., 37%) of a lot of 100, and a sample size of 45 (i.e., 2.25%) of a lot of 2,000, all for the same quality protection.[1] This emphasizes again the point

---

[1] The only reason the sample size jumps to 75 for lots of 2,001 to 100,000 is that

made in Chap. XIII that it is the absolute size of the sample, much more than its size relative to the lot, which governs the quality protection.

It is evident that wherever possible it is desirable to avoid the very small lot sizes. At the same time it is apparent that the great saving in inspection for a given quality protection consists in taking lots of the order of magnitude of 1,000 rather than the conventional lots of 50 or 100. For example, in Table 41 a reduction from a 37% sample from lots of 100 to a 4.5% sample from lots of 1,000 is a reduction in inspection of 32.5% of the total number of articles submitted in the lots. In contrast, a reduction from a 4.5% sample from lots of 1,000 to a 2.25% sample from lots of 2,000 is a reduction of only 2.25%.

There are several possible practical objections to very large lot sizes such as those from 10,000 to 100,000. One objection is that there are often practical difficulties in bringing such large lots together for inspection purposes; the cost of doing this may more than offset the inspection savings. Another objection is that it is frequently much harder to get a random sample out of a lot of 10,000 than out of a lot of 1,000. Moreover, the adverse effect on producer-consumer relationships of the rejection of very large lots is sometimes serious.

282. A Source for Multiple Sampling AOQL Plans. The SRG volume "Sampling Inspection" referred to on page 343 contains many sets of single, double, and multiple (sequential) sampling plans have nearly identical OC curves. The three matched plans on page 330 are an example.

As these plans were designed primarily for acceptance/rejection inspection, they are discussed at greater length in Chap. XV. The general considerations entering into the choice among single, double, and multiple sampling are also outlined in that chapter.

The discussion here is merely to point out that if multiple sampling is desired in AOQL inspection, "Sampling Inspection" provides a possible source of multiple sampling plans. No such plans may be found in the Dodge-Romig volume, which is restricted to single and double sampling. The SRG volume gives (in Table 15.4, page 165) the AOQL value for each sampling plan that it contains.

The SRG plans were not designed with the objective of minimizing total inspection in acceptance/rectification schemes. In some cases a very rough approximation to this objective in multiple sampling AOQL inspection may be realized by combining the use of the Dodge-Romig tables with the SRG tables. A single sampling plan to meet stated conditions of AOQL, process average, and lot size may be found in the Dodge-

---

$n = 75$ and $c = 1$ gives less total inspection of samples and rejected lots than $n = 45$ and $c = 0$. Even for a lot size of 100,000, the sampling plan $n = 46$ and $c = 0$ gives a 0.10 probability of acceptance for a 5% defective lot.

Romig tables.   The single sampling plan having the same acceptance number and the closest sample size may then be found in the SRG tables. The multiple sampling plan having the OC curve matching this SRG single sampling plan may then be selected.   Where there is a choice between two multiple sampling plans, the one having the AOQL closer to the desired value should be selected.

As an example, suppose it is desired to choose a multiple sampling plan for a 2% AOQL, a 1% process average, and a lot size of 1,000.   For these figures the Dodge-Romig tables specify a single sampling plan with $n = 65$ and $c = 2$ (see Table 43, page 348 of our volume).   The nearest single sampling plans in the SRG tables are $n = 55$ and $c = 2$ (SRG, page 277) and $n = 75$ and $c = 2$ (SRG, page 289).   The AOQL values for the multiple sampling plans corresponding to these single sampling plans are given as 2.5% and 1.9%, respectively.   Hence the multiple sampling plan corresponding to $n = 75$ and $c = 2$ should be selected as coming closer to the stipulated AOQL of 2%.   This multiple sampling plan is the one shown in Chap. XIII on page 330.

If lot quality protection rather than average quality protection in acceptance/rectification should be desired, the Dodge-Romig tables and SRG tables can be used in a similar way to find a multiple sampling plan with a desired LTPD.

283. Dodge's AOQL Plan for Continuous Production—CSP-1. Dodge has developed an acceptance/rectification plan for application to continuous production.   Where production is continuous, the formation of inspection lots for lot-by-lot acceptance is somewhat artificial. Moreover, where conveyor lines are used, it may be impracticable or unduly costly to form inspection lots.   Dodge describes his procedure (referred to as CSP-1) as follows:[1]

(a) At the outset, inspect 100% of the units consecutively as produced and continue such inspection until i units in succession are found clear of defects.

(b) When i units in succession are found clear of defects, discontinue 100% inspection, and inspect only a fraction f of the units, selecting individual sample units one at a time from the flow of product, in such a manner as to assure an unbiased sample.

(c) If a sample unit is found defective, revert immediately to a 100% inspection of succeeding units and continue until again i units in succession are found clear of defects, as in paragraph (a).

Figure 69 gives the necessary information for the selection of such a plan for any desired AOQL.   As an example, suppose the desired AOQL

[1] DODGE, H. F., A Sampling Inspection Plan for Continuous Production, *The Annals of Mathematical Statistics*, vol. 14, pp. 264–279, September, 1943.

DODGE, H. F., Sampling Plans for Continuous Production, *Industrial Quality Control*, vol. 4, No. 3, pp. 5–9, November, 1947.

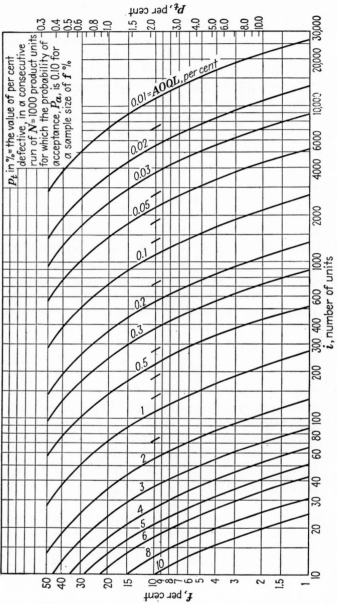

FIG. 69. Curves for determining values of f and i for a given value of AOQL in Dodge's plan for continuous production. *(Reproduced by permission from "A Sampling Inspection Plan for Continuous Production," by H. F. Dodge.)*

is 2%, and it is desired to establish a plan that calls for inspection of 1 piece out of every 20 pieces from the conveyor belt. Then f, the fraction inspected, is $\frac{1}{20}$ or 0.05 or 5%. In Fig. 69, find the value of i corresponding to an f of 5% on the curve for an AOQL of 2%. This $i = 76$. The acceptance plan is then as follows:

1. Inspect all the units consecutively as produced until 76 units in succession are free from defects.

2. As soon as 76 successive units are free from defects, inspect a sample consisting of only one unit out of every twenty. Accept all the product as long as the sample is free from defects.

3. Whenever one of these sample units is found defective, resume 100% inspection until 76 units in succession have again been found free from defects. Then resume sampling inspection.

The 2% AOQL for this plan assumes that defective pieces occur at random. This limitation may be made clear by assuming that after the plan had started and inspection was on a sampling basis, there was introduced into the production process some cause that always made the eighth, ninth, and tenth units out of every 20 defective but did not affect the other units. If the sample units should be regularly spaced, such a condition would not be disclosed by inspecting every twentieth unit. However, this limitation of the AOQL is not of any great practical importance. Such cyclical causes in continuous production are rare; if there is danger that they may exist, the fact is usually evident from the physical circumstances of production. But it should be recognized that this acceptance scheme does not protect against circumstances in which the defectives may be dishonestly manipulated to fall in the intervals between regularly spaced samples.

284. The Dodge-Torrey Modifications of Continuous Sampling Plan 1. H. F. Dodge and Miss M. N. Torrey have developed two modifications of CSP-1. These are referred to as CSP-2 and CSP-3, respectively. They describe CSP-2 as follows:[1]

Plan CSP-2 differs from Plan CSP-1 in that, once sampling inspection is started, 100% inspection is not invoked when each defect is found but is invoked only if a second defect occurs in the next k or less sample units. In other words, if two defects observed during sampling are separated by k or less good inspected units, 100% inspection is invoked. Otherwise sampling is continued.

Although the factor k might conceivably be assigned any value, the only CSP-2 plans prepared for use have been those in which k = i. Table 45 gives values of i in CSP-1 and CSP-2 using 5% and 10% samples

---

[1] DODGE, H. F., and M. N. TORREY, Additional Continuous Sampling Inspection Plans, *Industrial Quality Control*, vol. 7, No. 5, pp. 7–12, March, 1951.

and various AOQL values. These values for CSP-2 were obtained from a graph similar to Fig. 67 given in the Dodge-Torrey article.

Consider the application of CSP-2 when f is 5% and the AOQL is 2%. Table 45 gives $i = 96$. The acceptance plan is then as follows:

1. Inspect all the units consecutively as produced until 96 units in succession are free from defects.

2. As soon as 96 successive units are free from defects, inspect a sample consisting of only 1 out of every 20. Accept all the product as long as the sample is free from defects.

3. If one defective is found in this sampling, continue sampling inspection for the time being. However, if a second sample defective is found within the next 96 samples, resume 100% inspection immediately. Continue 100% inspection until 96 units in succession have been found free from defects. Then resume sampling under the foregoing rules.

TABLE 45. COMPARISON OF VALUES OF i FOR VARIOUS AOQL'S IN CSP-1 AND CSP-2 FOR 5% AND 10% SAMPLING INSPECTION (ASSUMING $i = $ k IN CSP-2)

AOQL, %	$f = 5\%$		$f = 10\%$	
	i in CSP-1	i (= k) in CSP-2	i in CSP-1	i (= k) in CSP-2
0.3	510	650	370	490
0.5	305	390	220	290
1	150	195	108	147
2	76	96	55	72
3	49	64	36	48
4	37	48	27	36
5	29	38	21	29
6	24	31	17	23
8	18	23	13	17
10	14	18	10	14

Plan CSP-3 is a refinement of CSP-2 to provide greater protection against a sudden run of bad quality. When one sample defective is found, the next four units from the production line are inspected. If none of these are defective, the sampling procedure is continued as in CSP-2. If one of the four units is defective, 100% inspection is resumed at once and continued under the rules of CSP-2. In CSP-3, the value of i used for a given f and AOQL is the same as in CSP-2.

285. Further Comments on Continuous Sampling Plans. Various other types of continuous sampling AOQL plans may be developed. Plans by Wald and Wolfowitz and by Girshick start with sampling inspection rather than with 100% inspection.[1] These plans, in effect, give a process credit for such good quality as has been shown in past samples and base the decision regarding the shift from sampling inspection to 100% inspection on cumulative evidence from past samples.

As in all acceptance/rectification schemes, a necessary condition for the successful use of continuous sampling schemes is that the submitted quality should be good enough for most product to be passed without screening. The sampling is intended to give protection against runs of bad quality. If the protection against short runs of bad quality (so-called "spotty" quality) is to be satisfactory, the sample percentage f should not be too low. The relative weakness of small values of f in this respect is brought out by the scale on the right-hand side of Fig. 67 showing values of p_t.

Mention should be made of one practical difference between lot-by-lot acceptance/rectification schemes and most continuous sampling schemes. In lot-by-lot schemes, an unfavorable sample from a lot results in the screening inspection of that particular lot. In continuous sampling, a bad sample calls for the screening of *subsequent* production. In effect, the sample is considered as representative of the production process, and 100% inspection is applied to later articles from the same process. In some instances, where the physical conditions of production permit, a modification of continuous sampling procedures is made to require screening inspection applied to a specified number of units immediately preceding a defective sample.

Incentives to quality improvement may be incorporated into continuous sampling schemes. Dodge comments on this point as follows:[2]

> These plans have been used rather extensively and found most effective when administered in such a way as to provide an incentive to clear faults in process promptly. Such an incentive may be provided, for example, by requiring the production department to perform the necessary 100% inspections when defects are found. To this end, the following administrative procedure has met with good success. A regularly assigned process inspector performs all sampling inspections required; if additional assistance is needed when it becomes necessary to revert to 100% inspection or in performing the initial 100% inspections required, the process inspector notifies the foreman in charge of the production line; the foreman must then immediately assign temporary inspectors who are acceptable to the process inspector and who work under the jurisdiction and

[1] WALD, ABRAHAM, and J. WOLFOWITZ, Sampling Inspection Plans for Continuous Production Which Insure a Prescribed Limit on the Outgoing Quality, *The Annals of Mathematical Statistics*, vol. 16, pp. 30–49, March, 1945.

  GIRSHICK, M. A , Sampling Inspection Plans for Continuous Production, unpublished paper delivered at the meeting of the Institute of Mathematical Statistics, May 10, 1948.

[2] In his 1947 article in *Industrial Quality Control, op. cit.*

supervision of the senior process inspector on the line; when sampling inspection is reinstated the temporary inspectors return to their regular assignments.

286. Acceptance/Rectification Plans Are Applicable to the Checking of Clerical Work and Related Activities. Errors are inevitable in many types of clerical work. For certain types of clerical work and related activities, it is customary to carry out 100% verification. For many other types of clerical work, verification is carried out by sampling. Often there is no particularly rational basis for the type of sampling used, either with respect to the size and frequency of samples or the interpretation of sample results.

In many instances, the techniques of statistical quality control may be applied advantageously in the checking of clerical work. In some instances acceptance/rectification schemes constitute an improvement over 100% verification. This is illustrated in Example 25. In other cases such plans may give better results than the unsystematic sampling plans previously used. Moreover, experience has indicated that—just as in the inspection of manufactured product—the results of sample checks on clerical work may be used to bring about great improvements in the quality of such work.

EXAMPLE 25. APPLICATION OF A DOUBLE SAMPLING AOQL PLAN TO THE CHECKING OF AN ANNUAL MERCHANDISE INVENTORY FOR A DEPARTMENT STORE[1]

287. Facts of the Case. The top management of a large department store considered it necessary that the annual merchandise inventory be as accurate as possible. The need for accuracy existed not only because of the use of the inventory figure for accounting purposes but also because departmental inventory figures were used to provide certain useful information to management. The inventory count was in two parts. The count of reserve (warehouse) stock presented no unusual problems. However, the count of forward (on-the-floor) stock was complicated by the requirement that no merchandise ready for sale should be tied up more than a few hours.

The forward inventory count was carried out by dividing each department of the store into sections and assigning a two-person team to each section. One member of the team called information about the stock from the shelves, tables, bins, etc., and the other entered the items on the inventory sheet. The stock was listed by price, description, quantity, classification within the store, and season letter. This count was carried out under considerable time pressure. In the past, a 100% check had always been made of all work performed in the forward inventory, as it was believed that such a check was necessary for reliable results. This 100% check nearly doubled the cost of the inventory and also nearly doubled the time required.

288. Effective Use of a Double Sampling AOQL Scheme. The management of this store assigned to one individual the job of reviewing various store activities from the point of view of possible economic applications of the techniques of statistical quality control. A likely application seemed to be the substitution of an acceptance/

---

[1] This example is condensed from an unpublished paper by Claude Brinegar describing an application in The Emporium, San Francisco, Calif.

rectification sampling scheme for 100% verification in the checking of forward inventory.

The errors that were presumably corrected in the 100% verification were those within the control of the inventory teams. These were primarily the errors caused by improper calling of the price, quantity, classification, or season letter of the item or by the improper listing of these items by the inventory writer. Fortunately, information about the types, frequency, and severity of errors that had been discovered by the check inventory teams in past years could be obtained by examining the old inventory sheets. No corrections to inventory sheets had ever been permitted by erasure; every correction required calling the inventory supervisor, crossing out the improper entry, and making the corrected entry at the bottom of the sheet. By examining the handwriting of corrected entries, it was possible to tell whether the correction had been made by the original team or by the checking team.

Some 3,000 inventory sheets from the previous year were analyzed. The analysis indicated that a few teams were usually responsible for most of the errors made in any department. A large majority of the teams produced work of quite respectable accuracy. Large errors in price or quantity were infrequent, the most common errors being over or under one unit in physical count, $1 dollar off in price, or listing the wrong season letter. Different types of goods seemed to differ greatly in their liability to inventory error.

As a result of this analysis, an inventory sampling plan was inaugurated for the forthcoming annual inventory. (The 100% double check was maintained in a very few spots, particularly on lines of merchandise where an error in count would prove costly.) The inventory took place during two 4-hr. periods from 6 to 10 P.M. following regular working days. The work of each inventory team was sampled by a "flying inspection squad." If the sample proved satisfactory, the entire night's output of the team was approved. If the sample contained too many errors, the team was immediately notified of the fact and its procedure was closely observed; all of its previous work was checked 100%; subsequent work was sampled again with the possibility of a further 100% check.

In the sampling procedure, three different Dodge-Romig double sampling AOQL plans were used. The plan to be applied to each department was selected on the basis of the analysis of the previous year's inventory sheets, giving weight to the type and value of merchandise and the probable number of inventory entries. In the use of the sampling tables, one line on the inventory sheet (typically representing 10 to 125 items) corresponded to a single manufactured article subject to inspection; any error on the line caused its classification as a defective. However, a line that was correct except for an error in season letter was counted as only one-half a defective; this error affected, not the count or value of merchandise, but only its estimated age distribution.

Sampling plans were selected having OC curves indicating that not more than 20% of the total work would be rejected and reinspected. This decision was an essential part of the planning of the inventory as it determined the number of reinspection teams to be provided. Actually the work of only 10.4% of the teams was rejected, 48 teams out of 462.

All inventory supervisors were instructed to use idle teams in double checking even though the work checked had been approved by the sample check made by one of the flying squads. As a result of this instruction, a fair amount of approved work was double-checked. An analysis of the inventory sheets from all checked work proved that the sampling procedure had really succeeded in separating the inefficient teams from the efficient teams. In almost every case the double checking of approved teams revealed only a bare minimum of errors, one consistent with the AOQL used.

The work of the rejected teams produced additional errors in over 90% of the cases examined.

The auditors and the store executives were well pleased with this application of statistical sampling methods. The scheme was repeated in the inventory of the succeeding year, with minor administrative refinements based on the first year's experience.

289. Further Comments on Applications of Statistical Quality Control to Clerical Work and Related Activities. In general, as already pointed out, acceptance/rectification schemes are particularly suitable if most submitted lots are satisfactory but a small percentage are decidedly unsatisfactory. In manufacturing, it is often true that all submitted lots come from one source; the unsatisfactory lots occur when something has gone wrong with the manufacturing process.

In the sampling inspection of clerical work and related activities, on the other hand, the common situation is that there are many sources for the work being sampled. Although these sources may sometimes be teams, as in Example 25, they frequently are different individuals carrying out the same clerical activity. As in Example 25, it is fairly common for a small percentage of the individuals or teams to make most of the errors.

Example 25 described an activity carried out only once a year. In this instance, the chief purpose of the sampling was to find those teams requiring 100% verification. In contrast, sampling inspection of clerical work carried on day after day usually has several additional objectives, namely:

1. To establish standards of accuracy.
2. To bring effective pressure for improvement in accuracy.
3. To provide a running record of the history of the accuracy of the work being sampled.
4. To identify those sources contributing abnormally high percentages of errors, so that these sources may either be improved or eliminated.

Various types of acceptance/rectification schemes have been used in connection with clerical work. Continuous sampling schemes have been applied successfully to the verification of the work of punched card operators. The Comptroller's Department of the American Telephone & Telegraph Company has developed sequential schemes that have been used on various types of accounting clerical work such as the rating of toll tickets and the posting of daily time reports to a labor distribution summary.[1]

---

[1] American Telephone & Telegraph Company—Comptroller's Department, "Application of Sampling Inspection Plans in the Verification of Clerical Work," issued by the Chief Statistician, American Telephone & Telegraph Company, New York, January, 1947.

In some instances sampling is carried out without any acceptance/rectification scheme. Samples are plotted on control charts, which are analyzed with the objectives that were mentioned on page 241. Examples reported in the literature indicate that striking improvements in accuracy are sometimes made. For example, Dale Lobsinger of United Air Lines reports that, in 5 months, the percentage of errors on certain clerical operations in the Payload Control Office was reduced by 80%.[1] James Ballowe of Alden's, Inc., reports similar spectacular reductions in percentages of errors in many different types of clerical activities in a mail-order plant.[2]

Problems

207. What single sampling acceptance plan should be used for a lot size of 900 and an LTPD of 5% if the process average is estimated as 0.4% defective?
Ans. $n = 75$, $c = 1$.

208. What double sampling plan should be used for the conditions described in Problem 207?   *Ans.* $n_1 = 55$, $c_1 = 0$; $n_2 = 65$, $c_2 = 2$.

209. What single sampling plan should be used for a lot size of 6,000 and an AOQL of 2% if the process average is estimated as 0.6% defective? *Ans.* $n = 95$, $c = 3$.

210. What double sampling plan should be used for the conditions described in Problem 209?   *Ans.* $n_1 = 44$, $c_1 = 0$; $n_2 = 116$, $c_2 = 5$.

211. Determine from Table 43 the single sampling plans for an AOQL of 2%, a process average of 1.0%, and lot sizes of 200, 1,000, and 5,000, respectively. What percentage of the product will be subject to sampling inspection with each lot size?
Ans. 8.5%, 6.5%, 2.5%.

212. In Problem 211, out of 100 submitted lots 1% defective, how many would you expect to be subject to screening inspection for each lot size?   *Ans.* 16, 3, 1.

213. Using the answers in Problems 211 and 212, what will be the total percentage of inspection for each of the three lot sizes, considering both sampling inspection and screening inspection of rejected lots?   *Ans.* 23%, 9%, 3.5%.

214. In Dodge's CSP-1 it is desired to apply sampling inspection to 1 piece out of every 15 and to maintain an AOQL of 2%. What should be the value of i?
Ans. 68.

215. In the Dodge-Torrey CSP-2 it is desired to apply sampling inspection to 1 piece out of every 10 and to maintain an AOQL of 3%. What should be the value of i? Assume $i = k$.   *Ans.* 48.

216. What single sampling plan should be used for a lot size of 2,500 and an LTPD of 5% if the process average is estimated as 0.8% defective?

217. What double sampling plan should be used for the condition described in Problem 216?

218. What single sampling plan should be used for a lot size of 700 and an AOQL of 2% if the process average is estimated as 0.5% defective?

219. What double sampling plan should be used for the situation described in Problem 218?

[1] LOBSINGER, D. L., Air Transportation Finds New and Lucrative Uses for SQC, *Industrial Quality Control*, vol. 6, No 6, pp 76–78, May, 1950.

[2] BALLOWE, J. M., Statistical Quality Control of Clerical and Manual Operations, *Paper* No. 10, Fourth National Convention of American Society for Quality Control, June, 1950.

220. In Dodge's CSP-1 it is desired to apply sampling inspection to 1 piece out of every 8 and to maintain an AOQL of 1 %. What should be the value of i?

221. In the Dodge-Torrey CSP-2 it is desired to apply sampling inspection to 1 piece out of every 20 and to maintain an AOQL of 5 %. Give detailed rules for the operation of this continuous inspection scheme.

222. The ABC Company sells a certain article to the XYZ Company. The purchase agreement stipulates that the product will be submitted in lots of 1,000, that XYZ will inspect under a Dodge-Romig 2 % AOQL single sampling plan, and that ABC will be charged for XYZ's costs in the 100 % inspection of any lots rejected on the basis of the sampling plan. The agreement does not mention the process average to be used in the selection of the sampling plan.

At the start of this contract, XYZ's receiving inspection department used the plan $n = 90$, $c = 3$, taken from the right-hand column of Table 43. Because the initial quality was good and all lots were accepted, XYZ shifted to the left-hand column of the table, using $n = 18$ and $c = 0$ in order to reduce inspection costs. Shortly after this change, a lot was rejected by the sampling plan. This lot was screened by XYZ, and ABC was billed for the cost of the screening.

This lot of 1,000 actually contained 9 defectives. As a lot of 0.9 % defective is substantially better than the 2 % AOQL, the management of ABC wonders whether it should protest this charge. The management also wonders whether it should request a return to the "normal" inspection at the right-hand side of the table instead of the "reduced" inspection at the left-hand side.

Discuss these questions, pointing out the different interests of vendor and purchaser under this type of agreement.

223. Suppose that an agreement such as the one cited in Problem 222 had stated the AOQL (2 %) and the process average column (0.81–1.20) from which the plan was to be selected but had not mentioned lot size. Discuss the question of whether it would have been to ABC's interest to submit product in large or small lots. What are the relative interests of vendor and purchaser in the selection of lot size under this type of agreement?

224. A vendor inspects his own product under a Dodge-Romig 2 % AOQL plan, screening all rejected lots before shipment. The lot size is 1,000, and the assumed process average is 1 %.

The purchaser inspects the same lots under a Dodge-Romig 5 % LTPD plan, returning all rejected lots to the vendor. The plan used is taken from the process average column headed "0.51–1.00."

(a) What is the probability that a 2 % defective lot will pass both the vendor's and the purchaser's inspection?

(b) What is the probability that a 2 % defective lot will pass the vendor's inspection and be rejected by the purchaser's?

225. Answer questions (a) and (b) in Problem 224 with respect to a 5 % defective lot.

CHAPTER XV

ACCEPTANCE SAMPLING BY ATTRIBUTES—
TABLES AND PROCEDURES BASED ON
ACCEPTABLE QUALITY LEVEL

Determination of the acceptable-quality level is a matter of comparative judgment. It is a matter of weighing the seriousness of varying departures from desired levels; of knowing what process averages are being or can be attained by the several available producers of the material in question; of evaluating the possibilities and costs of improving some or all of these process averages, including any increased wastage of scarce materials which will result from higher rejections, etc.; of knowing how much of the material is required and how much can be produced at the several process averages by the manufacturers who are available or can be made available; of setting off these factors one against the other, and making up one's mind.—G. D. EDWARDS[1]

290. Some Reasons for Acceptance Sampling Procedures That Do Not Give Consideration to Screening Inspection of Rejected Product. The acceptance inspection procedures described in the preceding chapter all gave consideration to the effect of a formal provision for screening inspection whenever the results of sampling inspection were sufficiently unfavorable. In the AOQL plans, the enforcement of the quality standard was dependent, in part, on this provision for screening inspection.

Where the producer and consumer are different organizations, dealing at arm's length, there may be good reasons why the consumer is unwilling to base his acceptance procedures on the assumption that rejected lots will be screened. He may consider it impracticable or inadvisable to carry out this screening himself, and he may not be willing to rely on any such inspection carried out by the producer.

Screening inspection by the consumer (either of all the product or of rejected lots) may be impracticable because it is unduly costly, or because he does not have sufficient inspection facilities or personnel, or for other reasons. Even though practicable, he may deem it inadvisable. If the consumer undertakes screening inspection, he may, as a consequence, find himself doing inspection that should really have been done by the producer. Moreover, the pressure for quality improvement exerted

---

[1] EDWARDS, G. D., Quality Control of Munitions—The Modern Ounce of Prevention Applied to Ordnance, *Army Ordnance*, vol. 23, pp. 482–485, November–December, 1942.

by outright rejection of one or more entire lots is much stronger than the pressure exerted by the rejection of individual articles classified as defective by a consumer's 100% inspection.

291. Two Limitations of Acceptance Sampling. The presentation of basic concepts of acceptance sampling in Chap. XIII made it clear that sampling plans cannot:

1. Assure 100% perfection (in the sense of conformance of all the product to specifications).

2. Separate the relatively better lots from the relatively poorer lots in a product that is statistically controlled.

It follows from (1) that any well-thought-out scheme calls for a decision as to the quality level that is acceptable. It follows from (2) that, in dealing with a statistically controlled process, the best that can be done in acceptance/rejection sampling is to devise a scheme that will either accept the process or reject it; *i.e.*, the scheme should accept nearly all the submitted lots if the quality level of the process is at the acceptable level or better and should reject a substantial fraction of the lots if the quality is worse than the acceptable level.

292. Military Standard 105A May Be Used to Illustrate the Various Matters for Consideration in Specifying Acceptance/Rejection Procedures. Much of this chapter is devoted to a discussion of the acceptance sampling schemes that have been used by the armed services of the United States. Particular attention is given to the most recent of these schemes, Military Standard 105A, adopted by the U.S. Department of Defense in September, 1950.[1] This is subsequently referred to as MIL-STD-105A.

The earlier military standards differed from MIL-STD-105A in a number of respects; there will doubtless be later standards that also differ. Industrial schemes adapted from the various military standards have differed from them in many details. Nevertheless, the general problems common to all acceptance/rejection sampling schemes based on attributes can be discussed to best advantage in terms of some one example. MIL-STD-105A is a good example to use, particularly because of its importance in the United States in connection with the government purchase of many billions of dollars' worth of manufactured goods of all sorts.

293. Historical Development of Military Acceptance/Rejection Procedures in the United States. The first branch of the armed services to use statistical acceptance sampling was the Ordnance Department of the Army. The Ordnance tables and procedures were developed in 1942 by a group under direction of distinguished engineers from the Bell

---

[1] MIL-STD-105A, "Sampling Procedures and Tables for Inspection by Attributes," Superintendent of Documents, Government Printing Office, Washington, D.C., 1950.

Telephone Laboratories. With some changes and extensions, these became the Army Service Forces tables developed by the same group.[1] These tables permitted single and double sampling, with double sampling preferred wherever practicable. Several of the Army Service Forces tables were included in the first edition of this book.[2]

Statistical sampling tables and procedures developed for the Navy by the Statistical Research Group of Columbia University were first issued in 1945. The general pattern of these tables and procedures was similar to that used by the Army Service Forces. However, sequential sampling schemes were made available, and there were other important points of difference. After the unification of the armed services, these Navy tables were adopted by the Department of Defense early in 1949 as JAN (Joint Army Navy) Standard 105. These tables were made available for widespread industrial use through the publication of the SRG's volume "Sampling Inspection," mentioned in Chap. XIV.

MIL-STD-105A superseded JAN-STD-105 in September 1950. Although there were no changes in the underlying pattern of the procedures that had been used in the earlier standards, there were again many important changes in detail.[3]

294. Some Decisions Made for Military Acceptance Procedures. In introducing the subject of inspection based on the acceptable quality level, the points of similarity among the various military procedures are of greater interest than the points of difference. Many decisions were made for the original Army Ordnance procedures in 1942 that not only have remained unchanged in subsequent military procedures but also have greatly influenced sampling procedures in industry. Some of these decisions were as follows:

1. In order to establish acceptance criteria for any particular product, it is first necessary to decide on the quality level that is considered accept-

[1] G. D. Edwards, Director of Quality Assurance of the Bell Telephone Laboratories, H. F. Dodge, H. G. Romig, and G. R. Gause, then of Army Ordnance, all played an important part in developing these tables.

[2] A different set of tables involving sequential sampling was used in the latter part of World War II by the Army Quartermaster Corps. See N. L. Enrick, The U.S. Army Quartermaster Corps' Use of Sequential Sampling Inspection, *Industrial Quality Control*, vol. 2, pp. 12–14, March, 1946.

[3] For a statement of the main points of difference among the successive military acceptance procedures, see S. J. Lorber and E. L. Grant, A Comparison of Military Standard 105A with the 1944 Army Service Forces Sampling Procedures and Tables and with JAN-Standard 105, *Industrial Quality Control*, vol. 8, No. 1, pp. 27–29, July, 1951. For a more complete discussion of the same matter, see a 50-page report by the same authors and the same title. This latter report is issued by the Applied Mathematics and Statistics Laboratory, Stanford University, Stanford, California, as Technical Report No. 2, April 1, 1951. It may be requested from Statistics Branch, Office of Naval Research, U.S. Navy Department, Washington, D.C.

able as a process average. In attributes sampling this acceptable quality level (AQL) is expressed as a per cent defective.

2. In the absence of unsatisfactory quality history or other reasons for misgivings about the quality of submitted product, the acceptance criteria should be selected with the objective of protecting the producer against the rejection of submitted lots from a process that is at the AQL value or better.

3. Such acceptance criteria will generally give the consumer unsatisfactory protection against accepting lots that are moderately worse (sometimes considerably worse) than the AQL. For this reason, more severe acceptance criteria designed to protect the consumer must be used whenever the quality history is unsatisfactory or when there are other good reasons for being suspicious about quality. This concept of *tightened inspection* as an alternative to *normal inspection* is at the heart of the statistical sampling procedures in all of the military standards. It is an essential part of any acceptance/rejection procedures where the acceptance criteria are chosen to protect the producer under "normal" conditions.

4. The acceptance criteria for serious defects should be more severe than for trivial defects. In other words, relatively low AQL values should be used for those types of defects which would have serious consequences and relatively high AQL values for those defects which are of little importance. The provision for a *classification of defects* exists in all of the military standards.

5. Economies for the consumer can be realized by permitting *reduced inspection* when the quality history is good enough. This permits the concentration of attention of inspectors on those products where attention seems to be needed most.

6. The relationship between lot size and sample size should recognize the greater difficulty of obtaining random samples from large lots and the more serious consequences of a wrong decision on acceptance or rejection of a large lot. For this reason, the relationship between lot size and sample size is perhaps based more on empirical grounds than on any considerations arising from the mathematics of probability.

295. The Master Tables from MIL-STD-105A Are Included in Appendix III. The essential tables from MIL-STD-105A are designated as follows in Appendix III:

Table *K*. Conversion of a Specified AQL to an AQL Value Used in MIL-STD-105A
Table *L*. Sample Size Code Letters
Table *M*. Master Table for Normal and Tightened Inspection (Single Sampling)
Table *N*. Master Table for Normal and Tightened Inspection (Double Sampling)
Table *O*. Master Table for Normal and Tightened Inspection (Multiple Sampling)
Table *P*. Highest Process Average Permitting Continuance of Normal Inspection
Table *Q*. Process Average Needed to Become Eligible for Reduced Inspection
Table *R*. Master Table for Reduced Inspection

296. The Selection of a Sampling Plan for Normal Inspection in MIL-STD-105A. Tables M, N, and O give acceptance criteria in terms of sample sizes and acceptance and rejection numbers. To determine the acceptance criteria in any particular instance, it is necessary to know (1) AQL), (2) lot size, (3) inspection level, and (4) whether single, double, or multiple sampling is to be used. To illustrate the use of the tables, consider a particular case in which AQL is 2.0%, lot size is 5,000, and inspection level II and single sampling are to be used.

The AQL values in MIL-STD-105A may be interpreted either as per cent defective or as defects per hundred units depending on whether acceptance criteria are to be based on the number of *defectives* observed in a sample or on the number of *defects*. All AQL values above 10.0 are to be interpreted as defects per hundred units. Acceptance criteria based on defects are discussed near the end of this chapter (Art. 316). All of the discussion up to that point refers to the more common acceptance criteria based on numbers of defectives and to AQL values stated as per cent defective.

All but one of the AQL values in Tables M to R are multiples of the numbers 1, 1.5, 2.5, 4.0, and 6.5. (The one exception is 0.035%. This figure, next to the lowest in the AQL scale, provides a single AQL class rather than two classes that would be 0.025% and 0.040%.) These numbers are roughly in a geometric progression and correspond to systems of "preferred numbers" in common use for other industrial purposes.

Whenever an AQL is specified that does not coincide with one of these AQL values, it is necessary to consult Table K to find the AQL to use in the acceptance tables. In our example, the AQL is specified as 2.0%. This falls in the range 1.65–2.79% in Table K, which states that an AQL of 2.5% should be used to determine acceptance criteria.

Next it is necessary to consult Table L to find the sample size code letter. In our example, this letter is M, corresponding to the lot size of 5,000 and to inspection level II. Further comment on the matter of sample size code letters and inspection levels is made in Art. 299.

The single sampling table, Table M, is now entered with the AQL of 2.5% and the sample size code letter M. This gives the sample size as 225 and the acceptance number as 11. The rejection number is stated as 12. In all single sampling plans, of course, the rejection number is 1 more than the acceptance number.

297. Some Difficulties in the Way of a Formalized Allowance for a Percentage of Defectives. The general notion of the acceptable quality level (AQL) as the "maximum per cent defective which can be considered satisfactory as a process average" was initiated with Army Ordnance

acceptance procedures in 1942.   H. R. Bellinson has made the following
interesting comments regarding the difficulties of introducing this
concept:[1]

[A] unique feature in the Army Sampling Tables . . . was the concept of
acceptable quality level.   It was a concept that had to be introduced because the
policy of the Ordnance Department, the policy of all the government purchasing
agencies at that time, was that here was a contract; here were drawings and
specifications; the contractor agrees to manufacture that way; we pay if it is
that way and if it not that way we don't buy it; the material must be perfect.
Unfortunately, you can't develop a sampling plan for attributes on the basis
of accepting only perfect material.   You just can't ensure perfect material with
attributes and sampling.   We had to say that we will accept a certain fraction
defective; make that as small as you please, but there had to be a fraction.   That
may sound as though we proposed to degrade quality, but the fact was that the
proportion defective being accepted under the methods of inspection then in use
was much larger than anything we proposed.

There were difficulties selling that concept, obviously, and difficulties of
different types, depending on whom you talked to.   The engineering department,
for example, was concerned about accepting any defects whatever.   The engineers were convinced on the theory that these defects, and they were largely
dimensional, followed a distribution law which was presumably the well-known
single-peaked affair.   Therefore, if the per cent defective was small enough,
that is, if the area on the tail outside our drawing limit was very small, then the
tail couldn't go very far out, and the actual degree of defectiveness in accepted
material would be extremely small.

That is a sound engineering argument because every engineer puts a factor
of safety in his designs.   If the degree of defectiveness is small, the engineer is
quite willing to permit it.   I am not quite sure that the theory is correct.   I
suspect that under the conditions which we met, that is, where material is presented for acceptance after inspection by the contractor, the distribution is not a
monotonic[2] function.   However, we never got into trouble on that score.

The fiscal department had a different point of view.   The fiscal department's
point of view was that the government had a contract to pay for 100% perfect
material and they simply didn't like the idea of paying the contractor for that
one per cent of material which was not perfect.   However, after we had gotten
together and written an explanation of acceptable quality in which we were able
to prove that the proposed inspection plan was much more economical to the
government than the former methods of inspection, they gave us their blessing.

[1] "Acceptance Sampling—A Symposium," American Statistical Association,
Washington, D.C., 1950.   Bellinson's quoted remarks are on pages 46 and 47.   They
were part of a prepared discussion of two papers on "Acceptance Sampling by Attributes" by Paul Peach and E. G. Olds.   The symposium was held at the first postwar
meeting of the American Statistical Association at Cleveland, Ohio, Jan. 27, 1946.
[2] A monotonic frequency curve is one in which the frequencies decline continuously
on both sides of the mode.—Author.

The legal department had still another point of view. The legal department was not concerned with the fact we were going to accept a few bad ones; the legal department was concerned with the fact we were going to reject a lot of good ones. Because, you see, if we put in acceptance and rejection plans, we would accept lots one per cent defective; but if we find a lot that is 2% defective, we reject that, even though that lot is 98% perfect. The legal department said that we had no right to reject any individual piece which was without defects. That argument was settled by changing specifications.

298. Probabilities of Acceptance of Lots Having AQL Per Cent Defective under the Various Military Standards. The original Army Ordnance (and Army Service Forces) tables contained the following definition of AQL: "The acceptable quality level is the maximum per cent defective which can be considered satisfactory as a process average."

The definition of AQL in the Navy tables (JAN-STD-105) was as follows: "Percentage of defective items in an inspection lot such that the sampling plan will result in the acceptance of 95% of submitted inspection lots containing that percentage of defective items." Substantially the same definition was used in the SRG volume "Sampling Inspection."

The definition of AQL in MIL-STD-105A is as follows: "The acceptable quality level is a nominal value expressed in terms of percent defective or defects per hundred units, whichever is applicable, specified for a given group of defects of a product."

In all of the military standards, the acceptance criteria under normal inspection were chosen to protect the producer against the rejection of product that met the stated quality standard. However, the producer's risk that such product would be rejected has not been the same in all standards and for all sample sizes.

In the Army Ordnance tables, the minimum single sample size was 75 with corresponding double sample sizes of $n_1 = 50$ and $n_2 = 100$. (These were used for the minimum lot size class of 500 to 799.) For acceptance plans using these sample sizes or using the next few sample size classes, the aimed-at probability of acceptance of lots at AQL value was 0.95. For the largest sample sizes it was about 0.99. In other words, the producer's risk that an AQL lot would be rejected varied from 0.05 to 0.01 depending on lot size. In the defects-per-unit portion of the Army Service Forces tables, the probabilities of acceptance were in the region of the 0.80's for the smaller sample sizes.

As indicated in the quoted definition of AQL from the Navy tables, the aimed-at probability of acceptance of lots at stated AQL value was 0.95 throughout the entire tables.

In MIL-STD-105A the probabilities of acceptance of lots at AQL per cent defective vary from about 0.80 for the smallest sample sizes to about 0.998 for the largest. Figure 70 illustrates this variation by showing the OC curves for four of the MIL-STD-105A single sampling plans having a stated AQL of 1%. Sample sizes are 15, 75, 225, and 750, respectively. For the two intermediate sample sizes the probability of acceptance of a 1% defective lot is fairly close to the 0.95 figure previously mentioned.

It is evident, therefore, that the tables in MIL-STD-105A are similar to the Army Ordnance and Army Service Forces tables and differ from

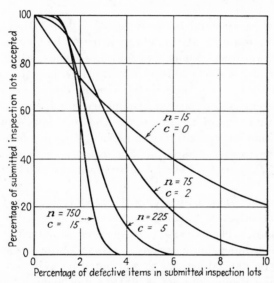

FIG. 70. OC curves for four plans from MIL-STD-105A having a stated AQL of 1%.

other widely used sampling tables in that they are not indexed in a uniform manner on the basis of a particular point on the OC curve of each plan or on the basis of some figure that may be derived from the OC curve. Other tables are classified on the basis of the lot quality for which probability of acceptance is 0.95, 0.50, or 0.10 or on the basis of the AOQL.

Even though this deliberate variability in indexing may be a source of confusion to some users of the tables, there are sound reasons for varying the probabilities of acceptance of lots at the quality standard in the way illustrated by MIL-STD-105A. These reasons are based on the points that (1) large samples are used for large lots and small samples for small lots and (2) large samples result in steeper OC curves with consequent better ability to discriminate between good and bad lots. Consider, for example, the four plans illustrated in Fig. 70.

The lot sizes for these single sampling plans (assuming inspection level II), samples sizes, and acceptance numbers are as follows:

N	n	c
66–110	15	0
501–800	75	2
3,201–8,000	225	5
110,001–550,000	750	15

In spite of the noncommittal definition of AQL in MIL-STD-105A, the 1% AQL for these four plans should presumably be viewed as a quality standard common to the plans. For a lot of 100 exactly 1% defective, $P_a = 0.85$. For a lot of 200,000 exactly 1% defective, $P_a = 0.995$. The producer submitting the large lot is much more certain of acceptance of any submitted lot meeting the quality standard. The consumer, however, has an even greater advantage when he samples from the large lot, as he has much better protection against accepting lots considerably worse than the quality standard. For instance, with a submitted lot 3% defective, P_a is 0.61 for the lot of 100 but is only 0.06 for the lot of 200,000.

There is another reason for giving the producer submitting large lots greater protection against chance rejections of lots meeting the stated quality standard. The adverse consequences of outright rejections of large lots are so much more serious. The producer who has to screen a rejected lot of 200,000 articles is confronted by quite an undertaking. The occasional screening of a lot of 100 is a much simpler matter.

299. Sample Sizes and Inspection Levels in the Military Standards. As stated on page 367, all of the military tables have established a somewhat empirical relationship between lot size and sample size. It is true, of course, that unless a sample is a substantial fraction of its lot, the OC curve of the sampling plan is practically independent of lot size, depending almost entirely on sample size and acceptance number. Nevertheless, computed OC curves always assume random sampling. The use of larger samples for larger lots recognizes that it is relatively difficult to get a small random sample from a very large lot. Moreover, large samples with their steeper OC curves give better discrimination between good and bad lots; the larger the lot size, the more important this discrimination is likely to be.[1]

---

[1] For an extended comment on the relationship between lot size and sample size, see H. A. FREEMAN, MILTON FRIEDMAN, FREDERICK MOSTELLER, and W. A. WALLIS (eds.), "Sampling Inspection," pp. 171–177, McGraw-Hill Book Company, Inc., New York, 1948.

It should be emphasized that although the absolute sample size increases with lot size in the military standards, the relative sample size decreases. In the illustration in the preceding article, for example, a sample of 15 is 15% of a lot of 100, whereas a sample of 750 is only 0.375% of a lot of 200,000.

The Army Ordnance and Army Service Forces tables specified definite single and double sample sizes for each lot size. The Navy tables (available with some extensions in the SRG volume "Sampling Inspection") initiated the idea of inspection levels and sample size code letters. Five inspection levels, designated I, II, III, IV, and V, had sample sizes approximately in the ratio 1, 1.5, 2, 3, and 4. For most lot sizes, the single and double sample sizes in level III agreed fairly closely with those in the Ordnance tables.

The system of inspection levels and sample size code letters has been continued in MIL-STD-105A with the number of levels reduced to three, designated I, II, and III. Sample sizes in level II correspond in a general way to those in the Ordnance tables and in level III of the Navy tables. MIL-STD-105A states that "unless otherwise specified by the Government, inspection level II shall be used." However, levels I and III (roughly corresponding to Navy levels I and V for a number of lot sizes) are available where conditions seem to dictate smaller or larger sample sizes than customary.

Article 296 illustrated the use of Table L, Appendix III, to determine the sample size code letter from the lot size and inspection level. The code letter then establishes the sample size, single, double, or multiple, as the case may be.

300. Criteria for Shifting to Tightened Inspection and Requalification for Normal Inspection in MIL-STD-105A. In acceptance/rejection procedures that make use of normal and tightened inspection, it is customary for normal inspection to be used for the first lots submitted.[1] In effect, the producer is given the benefit of the doubt; if his lots meet the stated quality standard, there is little chance that they will be rejected.

Because normal inspection will accept nearly all lots submitted that are at the AQL value, it will also accept a high percentage of any lots submitted that are moderately worse than the AQL. (The exact protection against such lots is, of course, given by the OC curve, the steepness of which is greatly influenced by sample size.) The consumer's protection against continuing to accept such lots if they are submitted depends on having rules requiring a shift to more severe acceptance

[1] However, MIL-STD-105A states that "the Government shall, in its sole discretion, determine whether to use normal, tightened, or reduced inspection at the start of a contract."

criteria whenever there is good evidence that the process quality is worse than the AQL.

In establishing rules governing this shift from normal to tightened inspection, it is customary to continue to give the producer the benefit of the doubt. The process average is estimated from the results of sampling inspection.[1] In double and multiple sampling, only first samples should be used in this estimate, as the estimated process average would otherwise be unduly weighted by samples from the poorer lots. If the estimated process average is equal to or less than the AQL, no question is raised about a shift to tightened inspection. If the estimated process average exceeds the AQL, a shift to tightened inspection is not required unless the excess is so great that it is not explainable as a chance fluctuation in sampling from a process having exactly the AQL per cent defective.

Table P, Appendix III, gives the highest process averages permitting continuance of normal inspection in MIL-STD-105A. The figures in Table P are 3-sigma limits above the stated AQL values and are comparable with the upper control limits for p charts given in the first half of Table F. The use of Table P is illustrated by the following example:

Assume single sampling, an AQL of 1.5%, submitted lots of 1,000, and inspection level II. Under normal inspection the sample size is 110, and the acceptance number is 4. Assume the numbers of defectives in the samples of 110 from the first 10 lots submitted are as follows: 2, 1, 4, 3, 2, 4, 0, 1, 6, 3. The estimated process average is the total number of defectives in these samples divided by the total number of items inspected in the samples; $26 \div 1,100 = 0.0236$, or 2.36%. Table P indicates that for the AQL of 1.5% and for 1,100 sample units included in the average, the estimated process average must exceed 2.56% in order to force a shift to tightened inspection. Therefore, normal inspection is continued.

Because this estimated average is so close to the limit, a new calculation is appropriate after each new sample. Assume the following results:

Lot number	Number of defectives in sample	Total units in process average estimate	Total defectives in process average estimate	Estimated process average	Limit from Table P
11	1	1,210	27	2.23%	2.56%
12	4	1,320	31	2.35%	2.48%
13	3	1,430	34	2.38%	2.48%
14	4	1,540	38	2.47%	2.42%

[1] For a comprehensive discussion of the technical problems of estimating process average, see FREEMAN, FRIEDMAN, MOSTELLER, and WALLIS, *op. cit.*, pp. 115–120.

After lot 14, therefore, it is necessary to shift from normal inspection to tightened inspection; the estimated process average, 2.47%, now exceeds the 2.42% limit from Table P.[1]

In order to requalify for normal inspection in MIL-STD-105A, the estimated process average must be equal to or less than the AQL. Tightened inspection must therefore be continued until the estimated process average (computed perhaps from the 10 most recent samples) falls to 1.5%.

301. Acceptance Criteria under Tightened Inspection in MIL-STD-105A. In MIL-STD-105A the lot size and inspection level determine the sample size code letter in tightened inspection just as in normal inspection. The type of sampling, single, double, or multiple, used in normal inspection is continued in tightened inspection. The change from normal to tightened inspection is, in general, simply a change in acceptance or rejection numbers. The same tables, M, N, and O, used for normal inspection are used for tightened inspection.

The acceptance criteria in tightened inspection are found by reading from the AQL values given at the bottom of Tables M, N, and O. As may be seen from these tables, this is invariably a shift of one column to the left in the table. The acceptance criteria for a given AQL class under tightened inspection are the same as the acceptance criteria for the next lower AQL class under normal inspection. If the AQL is 1.5%, for example, tightened inspection uses the same acceptance criteria that would be used for an AQL of 1.0% under normal inspection.

In the example described in Art. 300, the sample size under tightened inspection would continue to be 110, and the acceptance number would be reduced from 4 to 3.

302. General Comment on Tightened Inspection in Acceptance/Rejection Plans. In any acceptance/rejection scheme where acceptance criteria are chosen to protect the producer against rejection of lots meeting the quality standard, some provision for tightened inspection is necessary to protect the consumer against accepting a continued series of lots that fail to meet the standard. Two questions necessarily arise in providing for tightened inspection:

1. What should be the rules for shifting between normal and tightened inspection?

2. How tight is it desired that tightened inspection should be?

[1] MIL-STD-105A states that "the Government shall estimate the process average by an arithmetic mean computed from the results of its sampling inspection of the preceding 10 lots or such other quantity of production as the Government shall designate." In this instance, if the most recent 10 lots should be used, the estimated process average would fall barely short of the figure requiring the shift. With the figures as given, however, it seems more reasonable that the consumer (Government) should designate that the process average should be computed from the full 14 lots.

These questions have been answered somewhat differently in each of the military standards and still differently in some industrial schemes based on the AQL. In answering the questions, it should always be kept in mind that one of the ways in which provision for tightened inspection can protect the consumer is by giving the producer a powerful incentive to submit product meeting the quality standard. This incentive exists even though tightened inspection is never actually used. That is, the threat of more severe acceptance criteria if the quality history is bad provides a stimulus to the submission of good quality.

In setting up rules for the shift between normal and tightened inspection, there are advantages in permitting inspection supervisors to use some discretion, particularly where they can be trusted to use good judgment and where there are no legal and administrative obstacles to allowing discretion. Consider, for example, producers A and B, each subjected to the normal sampling plan $n = 110$, $c = 4$, based on an AQL of 1.5%. Both have estimated process averages of 2.5% after 20 lots, each based on 55 defective articles found in 2,200 examined. Producer A has shown good statistical control, with the variation from sample to sample such as might be expected in random sampling from a process 2.5% defective. In contrast, producer B had 40 defectives in the samples from 2 lots and only 15 defectives in the samples from the other 18 lots. It is evident that the consumer has been receiving satisfactory protection against producer B under normal inspection; the out-of-control bad lots have been bad enough to be rejected, and the process average of the other lots has been only about half the 1.5% AQL. Hence normal inspection might reasonably be continued for producer B. On the other hand, the quality record to date suggests that the lots submitted by producer A are nearly all about 2.5% defective. The OC curve of the normal inspection plan shows that 85% of such lots will be accepted. Tightened inspection is therefore needed to give the consumer a satisfactory defense against producer A through the rejection of enough lots to force the producer to improve his process average.

The question of the relative severity of the acceptance criteria in tightened inspection as compared with normal inspection is a fairly complicated matter. Answers to this question have typically been governed more by administrative considerations than by statistical ones. The rule for tightened inspection in MIL-STD-105A is a case in point. Administrative simplicity is gained by the rule of always shifting one AQL class in going from normal to tightened inspection. Any simple rule such as this one inevitably makes the relative tightness of tightened inspection vary considerably throughout the range of the tables. The acceptance criteria in tightened inspection in MIL-STD-105A tend to be more lenient than those in the earlier military standards. In the

Navy tables the shift was two AQL classes. In the Army Service Forces tables it was from one to four AQL classes depending on the AQL; in fact, it was based on shifting to a plan having an AOQL equal to the stated AQL, a feature lost in subsequent schemes.

If acceptance criteria under tightened inspection were to be made consistent for different sample sizes and AQL values in any acceptance program, it would presumably be necessary to decide on an aimed-at probability of acceptance of lots just meeting the quality standard—or perhaps of lots at some multiple of the quality standard. A reasonable protection to the consumer might be given if P_a were close to 0.50 for lots just meeting the quality standard. This really involves the viewpoint discussed later in this chapter in connection with the Philips Standard Sampling System. Generally speaking, the acceptance criteria in tightened inspection in MIL-STD-105A are somewhat more lenient than this.

303. Tightened Inspection Gives the Consumer Some Protection against the Effect of Flinching.[1] In the use of acceptance plans having large samples and an acceptance number greater than 0, inspectors sometimes are reluctant to call the defect that requires the taking of a second sample or the rejection of a lot. For example, consider the double sampling plan, $n_1 = 100$, $c_1 = 3$, $n_2 = 200$, $c_2 = 7$. (This is the plan in MIL-STD-105A for sample size code letter L and an AQL of 1.5%.) If 3 defectives were found in the first 60 articles examined, the inspector might pass all doubtful articles in the remaining 40 rather than call the defect that necessitated a second sample of 200 articles. This would be more likely to happen with visual defects on which there is considerable room for inspector's judgment. However, it might even happen in the gaging of dimensions with go and not-go gages, if the inspector should force the gage a little harder in borderline cases.

The existence of this situation is nearly always evident from the inspection record. A record showing nearly all the lots accepted, with most of the acceptances based on the maximum number of defectives permissible, usually is evidence that inspectors have acted in this way. For instance, with $n_1 = 100$ and $c_1 = 3$, the observed defectives in 20 first samples might be: 3, 3, 2, 3, 3, 3, 1, 4, 3, 3, 1, 3, 5, 2, 0, 3, 3, 3, 3, 2.

The use of the process average to determine the severity of acceptance criteria provides some safeguard against the continued acceptance of many lots as a result of this type of situation. With the figures cited in the preceding paragraph, the process average is $53/2,000 = 0.0265$, or 2.65%. As this is worse than the 2.31% permitted by Table P,

---

[1] For an excellent discussion of flinching and similar problems related to accuracy of inspectors, see J. M. Juran (ed.), "Quality Control Handbook," pp. 216–233, McGraw-Hill Book Company, Inc., New York, 1951. Note particularly Figs. 6 to 11.

tightened inspection must be used on subsequent samples.   Under the tightened criteria of MIL-STD-105A, $c_1 = 2$ and $c_2 = 5$.

304. Criteria for Qualification and Loss of Qualification for Reduced Inspection in MIL-STD-105A.   Generally speaking, eligibility for reduced inspection should be based on recent quality history indicating quality considerably better than the quality standard.   Moreover, it should seem likely that the product to be inspected under reduced inspection is being produced under the same conditions that gave rise to the recent good quality history.

MIL-STD-105A permits reduced inspection under the following three conditions:

1. The preceding 10 lots have been inspected under normal inspection with no rejections.

2. The estimated process average is below the limit shown in Table Q, Appendix III.   This limit has been computed in the same way as a 3-sigma lower limit on a p chart, assuming p' as the AQL.

3. Production is at a steady rate.

MIL-STD-105A requires that normal inspection be reinstated if any one of the following conditions occurs under reduced inspection:

1. A lot is rejected.

2. The estimated process average exceeds the AQL.

3. Production becomes irregular or delayed.

4. The Government deems that normal inspection should be reinstated.

Presumably the final condition is intended to apply to the case where there are good reasons for suspicion of change in the production process, even though production is not irregular or delayed.

305. Acceptance Criteria under Reduced Inspection in MIL-STD-105A.   Table R, Appendix III, gives sample sizes and acceptance and rejection numbers under reduced inspection in MIL-STD-105A.   In this standard all reduced inspection uses single sampling.   Sample sizes are generally one-fifth of the single sample sizes under normal inspection. Table R is entered using the same sample size code letter that was used under normal inspection.

For example, with code letter K and a 1.5% AQL, the single sampling criteria under normal inspection were $n = 110$, $c = 4$.   Table R shows the corresponding criteria under reduced inspection as $n = 22$, $c = 2$.

Figure 71 compares the OC curves for tightened, normal, and reduced inspection for code letter K, 1.5% AQL, single sampling, in MIL-STD-105A.   It is evident that under reduced inspection an occasional bad lot has a much greater chance of acceptance than the same lot would have under normal inspection.   The ability of a sampling plan to discriminate between good and bad lots depends to a large measure on the absolute size of the sample.   The consumer is, of course, protected against accepting a succession of marginal lots by the various criteria governing continued eligibility for reduced inspection.

Where double sampling has been used in normal inspection, the single sample size in reduced inspection in MIL-STD-105A represents about a 70% reduction below the first sample size in normal double sampling. With multiple sampling in normal inspection, the percentage of reduction depends on the AQL and on the submitted quality. Assume the submitted quality is very good so that acceptance under normal inspection would occur on the earliest sample permitted. For the lower AQL

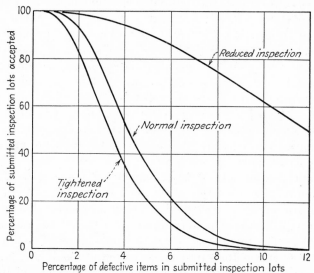

Fig. 71. OC curves for tightened, normal, and reduced inspection plans, code letter K and 1.5% AQL, single sampling, MIL-STD-105A.

values where at least two samples must be inspected before acceptance, the reduction is then 50% or more. For those higher AQL values where acceptance could occur on the first sample, the reduction then varies from 0 to 30%.

306. General Comments on Reduced Inspection in Acceptance/Rejection Plans. A provision for reduced inspection is not a necessary part of an acceptance/rejection plan. Nevertheless, such a provision is based on a principle that is economically sound. This principle is to concentrate inspection attention on those products and quality characteristics where the quality history is doubtful and to give less attention where the quality history is very good.[1]

---

[1] Substantial inspection economies may sometimes be realized by applying reduced inspection to certain individual quality characteristics having good records even though the entire class of characteristics subject to given acceptance criteria (for

The consumer's savings in inspection costs under reduced inspection are apparent. The producer's advantages are not quite so obvious. However, because the acceptance criteria in reduced inspection are not so stringent, the producer receives added protection against lot rejection. The producer may also have a real sense of accomplishment in having qualified for reduced inspection. Hence, from the consumer's viewpoint, the provisions for reduced inspection in any acceptance program may provide a useful nonfinancial incentive to the producer to improve his quality.

The acceptance criteria in reduced inspection have differed greatly among the different military standards. In the Navy tables, the same type of inspection, single, double, or multiple, that had been used in normal inspection was also used in reduced inspection, and the same master tables were used. In reduced inspection, the sample size code letter was shifted two letters toward the start of the alphabet. The reduction in sample size (typically about 50%) was less than in MIL-STD-105A, and the consumer had correspondingly greater protection against accepting an occasional bad lot. Generally speaking, the acceptance criteria in reduced inspection in MIL-STD-105A are more lenient than in the earlier military standards.

307. Single, Double, and Multiple Sampling Plans in MIL-STD-105A. The acceptance criteria in MIL-STD-105A are established by the AQL, the sample size code letter, and the type of sampling. For most code letters and AQL's, three types of sampling, single, double, and multiple, are available. The three types for each combination of AQL and code letter have OC curves that are as nearly identical as it was practicable to make them. Hence the probability of acceptance of a lot of any stated quality is practically independent of the choice among single, double, and multiple sampling. The official pamphlet describing the standard[1] gives OC curves for all single sampling plans with the statement that "curves for double and multiple sampling are essentially equivalent." The double and multiple sampling plans may be determined from Tables N and O in Appendix III in the manner already illustrated for the selection of a single sampling plan from Table M.

Many of the matched sets of acceptance plans are identical with those in the earlier Army Service Forces and Navy tables, particularly for

example, all Major defects) does not qualify for reduction. For recommended criteria for reduction on individual quality characteristics, see G. J. LIEBERMAN, "Reduced Inspection for Characteristics with Infrequent Defects." This was issued by the Applied Mathematics and Statistics Laboratory, Stanford University, Stanford California, as Technical Report No. 5, October 1, 1951. It may be requested from Statistics Branch, Office of Naval Research, U.S. Navy Department, Washington, D.C.

[1] MIL-STD-105A, *op. cit.*

intermediate sample sizes and AQL values. "Sampling Inspection" gives (in three colors) the OC curves for these and all other sets of its matched acceptance plans.[1]

In all of the military standards, the second sample is twice as large as the first. Among other things, this relationship is aimed at administrative simplicity rather than at minimum amount of inspection. The first sample size in double sampling is usually about two-thirds of the single sample size for the same code letter. This also is an empirical relationship aimed in part at uniformity.

The multiple sampling plans in MIL-STD-105A provide for from four to nine samples, with the number of samples tending to increase with sample size. Seven is the most common number. For any given code letter, all individual samples in multiple sampling are the same size. The individual sample size may be from about two-fifths to one-fifth of the corresponding single sample size. The smallest ratios are those where the sample size is largest; the median ratio is slightly more than $\frac{1}{4}$.

308. Curtailment of Sampling Inspection in Double and Multiple Sampling. First samples in double and multiple sampling are used to estimate the process average. Because of the importance of the process average in influencing the acceptance criteria, it is essential that inspection of the entire first sample be completed even though the rejection number is reached before the end of the sample. The same reasoning applies to single sampling; the full single sample should always be inspected.

When the rejection number is reached in the second sample in double sampling, it is customary to discontinue inspection. For example, assume that inspection is under the double sampling plan $n_1 = 100$, $c_1 = 3$, $n_2 = 200$, $c_2 = 7$. On the first sample, 6 defectives are found. This requires a second sample. Suppose that 2 more defectives are found in the fifteenth and twenty-fourth articles inspected in the second sample. As the rejection number of 8 has been reached, no further inspection is needed. In this instance, curtailment saves inspecting 176 units that would have been examined if the full second sample of 200 had been inspected.

In a similar way it is common to curtail multiple inspection whenever a rejection number is reached on any sample after the first. Whenever submitted product is bad enough for there to be numerous lot rejections, curtailment may make a substantial decrease in inspection. It is particularly desirable in double sampling because of the relatively large size of the second sample.

309. Comparing the Amount of Sampling Inspection in Single, Double, and Multiple Sampling. In the common use of acceptance sampling,

[1] FREEMAN, FRIEDMAN, MOSTELLER, and WALLIS, *op. cit.*

the quality of most submitted product is likely to be better than the quality standard; where double sampling is used, nearly all lots are accepted on the first sample. Under these conditions double sampling requires considerably less inspection than single sampling. At the other extreme, where submitted quality is bad enough for nearly all lots to be rejected on the first sample, the average sample size in double sampling is again less than in single sampling. For intermediate values of submitted quality where many second samples are taken, double sampling requires more inspection than the single sampling plan having a matched OC curve.

Multiple sampling generally requires smaller average sample sizes than double sampling, and double sampling smaller than single sampling,

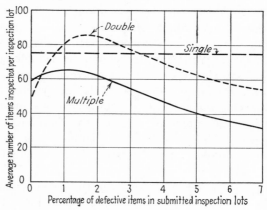

Fig. 72. Average amount of inspection under single, double, and multiple sampling, MIL-STD-105A, code letter J, with AQL of 0.65%.

in cases where the three types of plans have matched OC curves. In some cases the saving in inspection with multiple sampling is large; in other cases it is relatively small. This point is illustrated by Figs. 72 and 73. Each figure compares the average number of sample units inspected under a matched set of single, double, and multiple sampling plans as a function of the quality of submitted lots. These figures are reproduced from "Sampling Inspection."[1] They apply to two sets of matched plans originally developed by the SRG for the Navy; these sets of plans are also used in MIL-STD-105A.

The set of plans compared in Fig. 72 may be found in Tables M, N, and O, Appendix III, for code letter J and for normal inspection with an AQL of 0.65%. They are used for an AQL of 1.0% in tightened inspection. The plans in Fig. 73 are for code letter O and for an AQL

[1] *Ibid.*, p. 95.

of 1.5% in normal inspection.   They are used for an AQL of 2.5% in tightened inspection.

With the small AQL and the small sample size for the multiple plan in Fig. 72, acceptance is not permitted until three samples have been examined. Where submitted quality meets the quality standard (the usual situation), double and multiple sampling offer only a moderate saving in amount of inspection as compared with the single sampling plan of Fig. 72.

In contrast, multiple sampling has the possibility of large savings in the amount of inspection with the plans of Fig. 73.   For instance, if submitted lots are 0.75% defective (half the AQL), nearly all lots will be accepted either on the first multiple sample of 100 or on the second sample of 100; the average sample size (155) will be only slightly more than one-third of the single sample size of 450 and only slightly over half the first sample of 300 in double sampling.

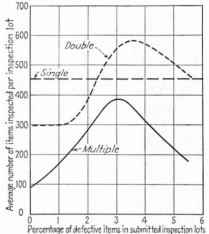

FIG. 73.   Average amount of inspection under single, double, and multiple sampling, MIL-STD-105A, code letter O, with AQL of 1.5%.

Generally speaking, in comparing the amount of inspection in single, double, and multiple sampling in the matched plans of MIL-STD-105A or of "Sampling Inspection," the conditions most favorable to multiple sampling are large sample sizes and high AQL's. Where acceptance is not permitted until the second or third multiple sample, the advantage of multiple sampling is relatively less.

Figures 72 and 73 assume that, because of the need to use sample results in estimating the process average, the entire single sample is always inspected.   For the same reason, they assume that first samples in double and multiple sampling are fully inspected but that the inspection of later samples is curtailed as soon as a decision can be reached.[1]

Comparisons of the available matched sets of single, double, and multiple plans may give too unfavorable an impression of the relative average

---

[1] This assumes curtailment with lot acceptance as well as with rejection.   For example, if six more defectives must be found to reject on the second sample and only five uninspected articles remain in the sample, inspection can be discontinued.   This type of curtailment is less common than curtailment with lot rejection and has a relatively small influence on average sample size.

sample sizes that might be realized under double sampling if some of the administrative simplicity of the military tables could be sacrificed. It is not essential that the second sample in double sampling be twice as large as the first or that the first sample be two-thirds of the corresponding single sample size. (For example, these simple relationships do not exist in the Dodge-Romig tables.) Moreover, double sampling plans with more favorable curves of average sample size may be devised if the rejection number on the first sample is made smaller than the rejection number on the second sample. Such plans have been discussed by various writers but seem to have had little or no use in actual inspection. The use of the same rejection number for first and second samples has the advantage of administrative simplicity. Moreover, the saving in average inspection from having a smaller rejection number on the first sample would apply chiefly when many of the submitted lots failed to meet the quality standard; in the more common case where most lots are accepted on the first sample, little saving would be possible.

310. Choosing between Single, Double, and Multiple Sampling.[1] It sometimes happens that double and multiple sampling are impracticable. There may be physical reasons why only one sample can be drawn from a lot, or it may not be feasible to provide for the variable inspection load associated with double and multiple sampling. Under such circumstances, it is necessary to use single sampling. More often, however, there is opportunity for choice. In deciding among these three types of sampling, consideration should be given to a number of factors in addition to the expected differences in average amount of inspection. Some of these factors are as follows:

1. *The psychological advantages of double sampling.* Two such advantages have played an important part in decisions to adopt double sampling. One is that borderline lots are given a "second chance" to be accepted. The other is that no lot is rejected because of a single defective article.

There is no doubt that the idea of giving a lot a second chance has a definite appeal to practical inspectors. It seems more convincing to say that a lot was rejected after *two* samples than to say that it was rejected on the evidence of a single sample.

Where lots are large, there is often a strong objection by the producer to the rejection of an entire lot on the basis of a single defective article found in a sample. Because in the usual double sampling plans c_2 is never less than 1, no lot can be rejected under them without finding at least 2 defectives in the samples from the lot.

[1] For comparisons in tabular form of relative advantages of the three types of sampling, see JURAN, *op. cit.*, p. 433, and FREEMAN, FRIEDMAN, MOSTELLER, and WALLIS, *op. cit.*, p. 96,

These psychological advantages of double sampling apply also to multiple sampling. However, it is questionable whether the appeal of the third, fourth, or fifth chance adds anything to the appeal of the second chance.

2. *The expected differences in costs of administration.* These costs tend to be highest for multiple sampling and lowest for single sampling. The more complicated the acceptance plan, the greater the attention required from inspection supervisors. Moreover, the variability of inspection load in multiple sampling and double sampling introduces extra difficulties into the scheduling of inspectors' time. In those cases where double and multiple sampling can make relatively small savings in average amount of inspection (as in Fig. 72), the more complicated plans may actually increase total inspection cost.

3. *The difficulty of training inspectors to use double and multiple sam-. pling correctly.* This difficulty seems to vary with the quality of the inspectors and perhaps with other matters. In some plants where inspectors have made frequent bad errors in interpreting instructions on double or multiple sampling, quality control engineers refuse to specify anything but single sampling. In many other plants, double sampling has been used successfully for many years. In still other plants, no serious troubles are reported in securing correct use of sampling procedures as complicated as item-by-item sequential plans.

Sometimes special devices are designed to make it easier for inspectors to use the more complicated schemes correctly. J. W. Enell, writing in "Quality Control Handbook,"[1] illustrates a storage board designed to simplify multiple sampling. A board similar to Enell's is shown in Fig. 74. This board is designed for the acceptance plan given in Table *O*, Appendix III, for code letter H and an AQL of 6.5%. In the figure, a circle represents a good article, and a cross represents a bad article. The sample shown in Fig. 74 resulted in lot rejection when a total of 8 defectives were found in the first 39 articles inspected.

4. *The need for quick and reliable estimates of process average as a basis for decision between normal, tightened, and reduced inspection.* In schemes such as MIL-STD-105A and its predecessors, a producer submitting product moderately worse than the AQL may continue on normal inspection until the estimated process average exceeds some figure such as is given in Table *P* for the 3-sigma limit above the stated AQL. The process average is estimated from the full single samples or from the first samples in double and multiple sampling. The signal for the tightened inspection needed to protect the consumer will come sooner with single sampling than with double; it may be long delayed with multiple sampling. This provides a reason for using single sampling in the early

[1] JURAN, *op. cit.,* p. 435.

stages of a contract even though a change to double or multiple sampling is made after there is satisfactory evidence regarding the process average.

5. *The availability of inspection personnel and facilities.* This should properly be an important factor in the choice of the type of sampling in a number of instances.

One extreme example of this influence may be cited from the experience of the inspection department of a certain government agency. The inspectors employed by this agency typically did sampling inspection in the plants of several different producers during the course of a week, using public transportation to go to and from each plant. The length of the visit to each plant was controlled by bus schedules and train

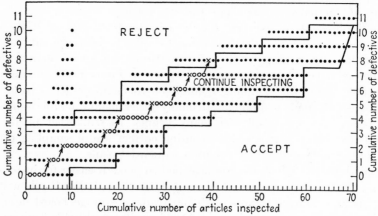

FIG. 74. Storage board for multiple sampling. This is applicable to plan given in MIL-STD-105A for code letter H and AQL of 6.5%.

schedules. With multiple sampling, an inspector generally finished his work some time before it was necessary to leave a plant. Under single sampling, his time at a plant was more likely to be fully occupied. It was therefore decided to change from multiple to single sampling. This change did not increase cost, and, because of the larger single sample size, it gave much better current information regarding process quality.

Similar cases may exist in industrial plants where it is desired to keep an inspection force intact throughout a temporary period of reduced inspection activity.

The opposite extreme exists when the need for inspection personnel and facilities is rapidly increasing. Such a period would seem to be an appropriate one in which to introduce double or multiple sampling, particularly in those spots where such plans seem likely to make large reductions in the average inspection per lot. The alternative to reducing average inspection per lot is the hiring and training of new inspectors (presumably less competent than the old ones) and the making of investments in additional inspection facilities.

311. Classification of Defects. Unless trivial defects are to be given the same weight as serious ones in acceptance decisions, a classification of defects is essential in any acceptance/rejection scheme. MIL-STD-105A contains the following statements under this heading:

Method or classifying defects. A classification of defects is the enumeration of possible defects of the unit of product classified according to their importance. A defect is any deviation of the unit of product from requirements of the specifications, drawings, purchase descriptions, and any changes thereto in the contract or order. Defects shall normally be grouped into one or more of the following classes, however the Government reserves the right to group defects into other classes.

Critical defects. A critical defect is one that judgment and experience indicate could result in hazardous or unsafe conditions for individuals using or maintaining the product; or, for major end item units of product, such as ships, aircraft, or tanks, a defect that could prevent performance of their tactical function.

Major defects. A major defect is a defect, other than critical, that could result in failure, or materially reduce the usability of product for its intended purpose.

Minor defects. A minor defect is one that does not materially reduce the usability of the unit of product for its intended purpose, or is a departure from established standards having no significant bearing on the effective use or operation of the unit.

Product may be subject to 100% inspection by the consumer for critical defects. For many different types of product, there are no defects classifiable as critical; all are either major or minor. It is fairly common to divide minor defects into two groups depending on their relative importance. The more important minors may be designated Minor A; the less important ones, Minor B.

312. An Illustration of the Use of a Classification of Defects in Acceptance Sampling. Assume that the classification of defects for certain bolts includes 5 defects classified as Major, 11 classified as Minor A, and 8 classified as Minor B. Bolts are to be inspected in lots of 20,000 under MIL-STD-105A. Double sampling and inspection level II are to be used. The AQL is 1.0% for Majors, 4.0% for Minor A, and 6.5% for Minor B.

The sample size code letter N is determined by the lot size and inspection level. In this case $n_1 = 200$, and $n_2 = 400$. The acceptance numbers in normal inspection are:

	Major	Minor A	Minor B
c_1	4	12	18
c_2	9	35	66

A first sample of 200 will be drawn from the lot. This sample is inspected separately for each class of defects. The numbers of defects found are as follows:

Major—3

Minor A—15

Minor B—7

The lot is therefore passed for Major and Minor B defects on the basis of the first sample. A second sample of 400 must be drawn and inspected only for Minor A defects. If not more than 20 additional items containing such defects are found, the lot is passed. If 21 or more are found, the lot is rejected for Minor A defects.

In general, it is economical and convenient to inspect the same sample for all classes of defects. However, the acceptance criteria are applied separately for each class. A lot is rejected if it fails to meet the acceptance criteria for one or more classes.[1]

313. The Formation of Inspection Lots.[2] In sampling acceptance inspection, an inspection lot is a group of articles accepted or rejected on the basis of one or more samples. An inspection lot is not necessarily identical with a production lot, a purchase lot, or a lot for other purposes.

Many practical matters such as rate of production and availability of storage space necessarily influence the formation of inspection lots. From the point of view of getting the best results from acceptance sampling, two rules should govern decisions on this matter, namely:

1. Within each lot, the factors that seem likely to cause marked variability in product quality should be as nearly constant as practicable. This may include such matters as sources of raw materials, machines, operators, and time of production.

2. Subject to the limitation of the foregoing rule, inspection lots should be as large as possible.

The desire to have each lot come from a homogeneous source obviously conflicts with the desire ṯo have large lots. Practical decisions usually call for a compromise between these two objectives.

The reason for the requirement of homogeneity should be evident. If most lots are relatively good and a few are relatively bad, sampling inspection can discriminate among lots and the quality of the product

---

[1] In some instances it may be considered necessary to apply one set of acceptance criteria to an entire group of quality characteristics even though sampling takes place at two or more independent inspection stations with different characteristics inspected at each station. For a discussion of this problem, see G. J. LIEBERMAN, "Multistage Inspection Schemes." This was issued by the Applied Mathematics and Statistics Laboratory, Stanford University, Stanford California, as Technical Report No. 4, May 31, 1951. It may be requested from Statistics Branch, Office of Naval Research, U.S. Navy Department, Washington, D.C.

[2] For a more complete discussion of this important topic, see FREEMAN, FRIEDMAN, MOSTELLER, and WALLIS, *op. cit.*, pp. 40–43, 87–90.

accepted can be much better than the average quality submitted. On the other hand, if there is a good deal of mixing of product from various sources, the percentage of defectives may not vary greatly from lot to lot; in this case the average quality of lots accepted will not be appreciably better than the average quality submitted. Where lot formation is close to production, both in time and place, there is a minimum of opportunity for mixing of product among inspection lots.

The reason for the requirement of making lots as large as possible should also be clear. It is the absolute size of the sample that governs its ability to discriminate between good and bad lots. Large lots permit larger samples than do small lots. Moreover, inspection cost will be less with large lots because samples are a smaller fraction of the lot.

314. Randomness in Acceptance Sampling. The probability calculations underlying statistical acceptance sampling assume that samples are drawn at random. That is, each article in a lot is assumed to have an equal chance to be selected in the sample.

Often there are practical difficulties in the way of random selection of a sample. The items in an inspection lot cannot be stirred like a bowl of chips as each item is drawn for the sample. In many instances, the best that can be done in drawing a sample is to avoid any obvious type of bias. For instance, if items are packed in layers, it is clearly not sensible to draw the sample entirely from the top layers.

If it is practicable to assign a different number to each item in a lot, chance devices can be used to determine the items to select. Rather than draw chips from a bowl or cards from a pack, it may be quicker and more satisfactory to make use of published tables of random numbers to choose the items for the sample.[1]

In large lots, the difficulties of random selection may be so great that it is advisable to adopt proportional (stratified) sampling. In the volume "Sampling Inspection" the Statistical Research Group makes the following suggestions for this type of sampling:[2]

1. Draw proportional samples. According to this rule, inspection lots should, wherever possible, be divided into sublots on the basis of factors that are likely to lead to variation in the quality of the product. . . . From each sublot into which the inspection lot is divided a subsample should be selected. The size of the subsample from each sublot should be proportional to the size of that sublot.

2. Draw sample items from all parts of each sublot of the inspection lot.

3. Draw sample items blind.

[1] See JURAN, *op. cit.*, pp. 420–421. For tables of random numbers, see KENDALL and SMITH, "Tracts for Computers, No. 24," Cambridge University Press, London, 1939, and FISHER and YATES, "Statistical Tables for Biological, Agricultural, and Medical Research," Oliver & Boyd, Ltd., Edinburgh and London, 1938.

[2] FREEMAN, FRIEDMAN, MOSTELLER, and WALLIS, *op. cit.*, pp. 48–52.

Such a stratified sample is, of course, different from a random sample. In taking many such stratified samples from a given lot, the average number of defectives will be the same as if samples were drawn at random, but the variation in number of defectives from sample to sample will be less. The result is that the OC curve for any given acceptance criteria will be steeper under stratified sampling than under random sampling. Lots substantially better than those at $p_{0.50}$ (for example, lots at stated AQL values in most acceptance/rejection schemes) will have a somewhat greater chance of acceptance than indicated by the OC curve for random sampling; lots substantially worse than those at $p_{0.50}$ will have a somewhat smaller chance of acceptance. OC curves under stratified sampling cannot be calculated without making an assumption as to the variation of quality from sublot to sublot. Investigations by the Statistical Research Group indicate that for practical situations likely to arise in industrial sampling, the use of stratified samples will seldom make much change from the OC curve computed for random sampling.

315. Problems Arising out of Resubmission of Rejected Lots. Whenever rejected lots are returned to the producer, the resubmission of these lots for another sampling inspection creates certain problems.

One problem deals with the influence of these lots on the computed process average. Presumably when a producer receives a rejected lot, he gives it 100% inspection and resubmits it for acceptance. If this 100% inspection is really effective, rejected lots on their second submission should be better than lots submitted the first time. If the samples from the rejected lots were included in calculations of the process average, this would tend to make the computed process average better than the true process average of submitted first lots. As the real protection to the consumer against accepting quality worse than the acceptable level depends on the use of the process average to determine the acceptance criteria, it is important that all resubmitted lots be identified as such, and that the samples from resubmitted lots be excluded in calculations of process average.

Another problem exists if reliance is placed on an AOQL which is computed on the assumption that the producer removes all defective articles from rejected lots. If this assumption is to be relied on, more severe acceptance criteria should be applied to resubmitted lots and practically no defectives should be permitted in the samples from these lots.

However, the most serious problem is that created when rejected lots are resubmitted unchanged in the hope that the defectives will be missed in the sampling inspection of the resubmitted lots. A simple probability calculation shows the seriousness of this difficulty.

Assume the probability of acceptance of a lot of given quality is 0.80. This will not only be the probability of its acceptance on the first submission but also on any subsequent submission. The probability of acceptance with a maximum of two resubmissions is as follows:

Probability of acceptance on first submission $\qquad$ = 0.80
Probability of rejection on first submission followed by acceptance on second
submission = (0.20)(0.80) $\qquad$ = 0.16
Probability of rejection on first and second submissions followed by acceptance
on third submission = (0.20)(0.20)(0.80) $\qquad$ = 0.03

Probability of acceptance with not more than three submissions $\qquad$ = 0.99

A possible defense against this is for the consumer somehow to police the handling of resubmitted lots. MIL-STD-105A contains the following stipulation: "When the supplier elects to resubmit a rejected lot the supplier shall first inspect the rejected lot, repair or remove all defectives, and then present the units as a resubmitted lot."

Where resubmitted lots can be identified even though their handling cannot be policed, it is sensible to apply tightened acceptance criteria to such lots. Where resubmitted lots cannot be identified, the consumer's only defense arises through the influence of the rejected lots on the process average and through the use of tightened inspection whenever the process average is unsatisfactory.

316. Acceptance Based on Numbers of Defects. A defective article is an article containing one or more defects. In our discussion up to this point, acceptance decisions have been based on the numbers of defectives contained in a sample. Decisions on lot acceptance or rejection have not been influenced by the number of defects observed in each defective article. The sampled article with eight defects has had the same influence on lot acceptance as the sampled article with only one defect; each has counted as a single defective.

Under certain conditions, it may be more reasonable to base acceptance decisions on defects rather than on defectives. For instance, some defects might be tolerable in a bolt of cloth, but it might be desired to limit the average defects per bolt in a shipment of bolts of cloth. In general, the field of application of acceptance based on defects is similar to the field for the c chart discussed in Chap. XI. With acceptance based on defects, AQL values, OC curves, etc., are interpreted in terms of defects per hundred units rather than as per cent defective.

The entire MIL-STD-105A may be used for inspection based on defects as well as for inspection based on defectives. In general, the only changes necessary are to substitute the word *defects* wherever *defectives* is used and to interpret AQL's as defects per hundred units. All AQL values from 15 to 1,000 (*i.e.*, from 0.15 to 10 defects per unit) in this standard are required to be interpreted as defects per hundred units; all inspection using these AQL's must be based on defects rather than on defectives. Only single sampling is used for this particular range of AQL's. The acceptance criteria are given in Table *M*, Appendix III. Normal, tightened, and reduced inspection are used just as in acceptance based on numbers of defectives.

The Army Service Forces tables contained separate tables for inspection based on defects per unit.[1] In addition to limiting the number of defects in a sample, the acceptance criteria in these tables also included a *spottiness limit, L*, which was specified for each AQL. Any inspected unit with more than *L* defects was referred to as a *spotty* unit. For smaller sample sizes, one spotty unit would cause lot rejection regardless of the quality of the rest of the sample. For the larger sample sizes, not more than one spotty unit was permitted. This spottiness concept was not included in MIL-STD-105A.

317. Selecting an Acceptance Plan for Isolated Lots. Schemes having provision for normal and tightened inspection are designed primarily for a continuing relationship between consumer and producer. In such schemes the quality standard (AQL) may appropriately be a value of per cent defective that is the highest figure satisfactory as a process average. Such a quality standard is enforced through the over-all acceptance procedure rather than merely by the lot-by-lot acceptance criteria. The requirement for a systematic record of process average plays a major part in the enforcement of the quality standard. Whenever samples indicate that the process average is worse than the quality standard, the consumer can exert pressure for quality improvement. The threat of tightened inspection helps to make this pressure more effective. Where the over-all procedure is relied on to enforce the quality standard, it is appropriate that the lot-by-lot acceptance criteria used in normal inspection should give the producer the benefit of the doubt, with a small probability that a lot meeting the quality standard will be rejected and a substantial probability that a lot moderately worse will be accepted.

Where lots are isolated or infrequent, there is usually little chance to use the over-all acceptance procedure to develop pressure for the submission of good quality. If the consumer uses acceptance sampling for an isolated lot, his protection depends largely on the operating characteristic of the sampling plan used for the particular lot. The consumer dealing with isolated lots needs to take a good look at the OC curve of his proposed sampling plan to judge whether it gives him adequate protection. Generally speaking, if he wants protection against lots

[1] Two of these tables, applicable to single sampling, were reproduced in the first edition of this book, pp. 404–409. With the spottiness criteria omitted, the defects-per-unit tables were used in some cases for per cent defective inspection for smaller lot sizes.

worse than some stated quality standard, his protection will be insufficient if he selects normal acceptance criteria from one of the common tables indexed under the AQL by entering the table with his desired quality standard as the AQL.

Before choosing an acceptance plan for an isolated lot, a decision is needed as to just how severe the acceptance criteria should be. This decision might be stated in terms of an aimed-at probability of acceptance of a lot just meeting the quality standard. Conceivably this could be 0.10; if so, Dodge-Romig LTPD tables could be used. However, if $P_a = 0.10$ for a lot just meeting the quality standard, the producer is penalized because lots considerably better than this standard will have large probabilities of rejection.[1] In many cases a reasonable compromise between the interests of producer and consumer is to aim at a P_a of 0.50 for lots just at the quality standard. This involves a concentration of attention on the "indifference quality" or "point of control."

318. Establishing Acceptance Criteria with the Quality Standard at $p_{0.50}$**.** The quality $p_{0.50}$, for any lot-by-lot acceptance criteria, is the lot quality having a probability of acceptance of 0.50. In a series of articles in *Philips Technical Review*, H. C. Hamaker and his associates, J. J. M. Taudin Chabot and F. G. Willemze, have explained an approach to acceptance sampling that makes use of $p_{0.50}$ as the quality standard.[2] In these articles, $p_{0.50}$ is referred to as the *point of control*.

---

[1] Severe acceptance criteria are not unfair to the producer if the consumer is willing to screen any lot he does not accept. When the consumer is willing to screen some isolated lots, a three-decision scheme suggested by Professor Henry P. Goode will sometimes be advantageous. This procedure calls for acceptance when the sample is good enough, rejection when it is bad enough, and screening when the sample is of intermediate quality. For example, consider the requirement of a sample of 300 with the sampled lot accepted if this sample contains 0 defectives, rejected if it contains 4 or more defectives, and screened if it contains 1, 2, or 3 defectives. Under this plan the probability that a 1% defective lot will be accepted without screening is only 0.05, and the probability that a 0.4% defective lot will be rejected is only 0.05. Any required screening will occur chiefly with submitted lots that fall between 0.4% and 1% defective. For tables that may be used for this three-decision scheme and for a discussion of problems peculiar to isolated lots, see E. L. GRANT and G. J. LIEBERMAN, "The Problem of the Isolated Lot." This was issued by the Applied Mathematics and Statistics Laboratory, Stanford University, Stanford, California as Technical Report No. 9, 1953. It may be requested from Statistics Branch, Office of Naval Research, U.S. Navy Department, Washington, D.C.

[2] HAMAKER, H. C . Lot Inspection by Sampling, *Philips Technical Review*, vol. 11, pp. 176–182, December, 1949.

HAMAKER, H. C., The Theory of Sampling Inspection Plans, *Philips Technical Review*, vol. 11, pp. 260–270, March, 1950.

HAMAKER, H. C., J. J. M. TAUDIN CHABOT, and F. G. WILLEMZE, The Practical Application of Sampling Inspection Plans and Tables, *Philips Technical Review*, vol. 11, pp. 362–370, June, 1950.

It is easy to devise homemade single sampling acceptance criteria for any desired $p_{0.50}$, using the following approximate formula:[1]

$$n = \frac{c + 0.67}{p_{0.50}}$$

Suppose that lots 2.5% defective or better are considered to be acceptable but that it is desired to reject lots that are any worse. With this quality standard, we wish to find a set of single sampling plans for which a lot 2.5% defective will have a P_a of 0.50. Assume values of the acceptance number c from 0 up to any desired number, and solve the foregoing formula for sample size n, using $p_{0.50}$ as 0.025. The resulting family of acceptance plans is as follows:

c	n	c	n	c	n
0	27	4	187	8	347
1	67	5	227	9	387
2	107	6	267	10	427
3	147	7	307	11	467

Although the OC curves of these 12 single sampling plans all pass fairly closely through the one point $P_a = 0.50$, $p = 0.025$, the plans having the larger sample size give better discrimination between lots that are somewhat better than 2.5% defective and lots that are somewhat worse. This point is illustrated by Fig. 75, which compares the plans with sample sizes of 67, 267, and 467, which have acceptance numbers of 1, 6, and 11, respectively. A choice among the various plans requires balancing the extra inspection costs of larger samples against the advantage of better assurance that a lot meeting the quality standard will be accepted and one failing to meet it will be rejected.

Table 46 reproduces the standard sampling system developed by Hamaker and his associates and used in the Philips works in Holland. This compact table, with acceptance plans classified by the point of control $p_{0.50}$, has apparently been used both for incoming inspection and for inspection of certain finished product. It involves a number of interesting points of difference from the military standards used in the United States and from industrial tables patterned on these standards. Some of these differences are:

1. Because acceptance criteria are chosen so that the producer and consumer split the risk of wrong decisions on lots better or worse than

---

[1] This relationship was first pointed out by G. A. Campbell writing in the *Bell System Technical Journal* in 1923. It assumes lot size is large enough in proportion to sample size for the Poisson distribution to give a satisfactory approximation to the OC curve.

the quality standard, the acceptance criteria do not depend on the process average and the concepts of normal and tightened inspection are not used.

2. Single sampling is specified for all lots up to 1,000; double sampling is used for all lots above that figure.

3. In most of the double sampling plans, c_2 has been made 5 times c_1. Although the various military double sampling tables do not have a fixed ratio of c_2/c_1, the ratios found in these tables are generally appreciably less than $\frac{5}{1}$. As compared with these plans, the Philips plans

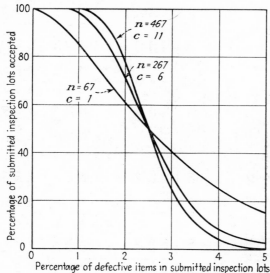

Fig. 75. OC curves for three single sampling plans having a $p_{0.50}$ of 2.5%.

tend to have smaller values of c_1 for the same $p_{0.50}$, with a correspondingly greater chance that bad lots will be rejected on the first sample.

4. For a given lot size, the sample size decreases as the allowable per cent defective increases. This is in sharp contrast to MIL-STD-105A and its predecessors, in which (for a given inspection level) the sample size is determined by lot size and is independent of the AQL.

319. Comment on the Relationship between Acceptance Number, Sample Size, and $p_{0.50}$. A view commonly held by producers is that if the consumer is willing to tolerate a stated percentage of defectives in the lot, he should be willing to tolerate the same percentage in the sample. For instance, if he is willing to accept lots 2.5% defective, he should be satisfied with acceptance criteria no more severe than $n = 40$ and $c = 1$, or $n = 80$ and $c = 2$, or in general $n = 40c$. This view is expressed particularly with regard to acceptance criteria for isolated lots or for tightened inspection in schemes involving normal and tightened inspection.

TABLE 46. PHILIPS STANDARD SAMPLING SYSTEM

Single sampling

Lot size	0.25% n	0.25% c	0.5% n	0.5% c	1% n	1% c	2% n	2% c	3% n	3% c	5% n	5% c	7% n	7% c	10% n	10% c
20–50	A	—	A	—	A	—	30	0	20	0	13	0	10	0	7	0
51–100	A	—	A	—	60	0	30	0	20	0	13	0	10	0	7	0
101–200	A	—	100	0	60	0	35	0	55	1	35	1	25	1	17	1
201–500	175	0	100	0	135	1	75	1	55	1	35	1	40	2	25	2
501–1,000	225	0	225	1	150	1	85	1	85	2	55	2	55	3	35	3

Double sampling

Lot size	0.25% n_1	0.25% c_1	0.25% c_2	0.5% n_1	0.5% c_1	0.5% c_2	1% n_1	1% c_1	1% c_2	2% n_1	2% c_1	2% c_2	3% n_1	3% c_1	3% c_2	5% n_1	5% c_1	5% c_2	7% n_1	7% c_1	7% c_2	10% n_1	10% c_1	10% c_2
1,001–2,000	330	0	1	150	0	1	110	0	2	55	0	2	45	0	3	25	0	3	30	1	5	22	1	5
2,001–5,000	425	0	2	200	0	2	135	0	3	70	0	3	70	1	5	45	1	5	55	2	10	40	2	10
5,001–10,000	525	0	3	260	0	3	220	1	5	110	1	5	125	2	10	75	2	10	75	3	15	55	3	15
10,000–20,000	875	1	5	440	1	5	380	2	10	190	2	10	180	3	15	110	3	15	100	4	20	70	4	20
20,000–50,000	1,500	2	10	750	2	10	540	3	15	270	3	15	240	4	20	140	4	20	120	5	25	85	5	25
50,000–100,000	2,200	3	15	1,100	3	15	700	4	20	390	4	20	290	5	25	175	5	25	145	6	30	105	6	30

A means inspect entire lot.
Second sample $n_2 = 2n_1$.

The difficulty with this view is that it concentrates attention on the *acceptance* number to the exclusion of the *rejection* number. If $n = 40$ and $c = 1$, lots are accepted if the sample is 2.5% defective but cannot be rejected unless the sample is at least 5% defective. Of course the larger the sample, the smaller the disparity between the acceptance percentage and the rejection percentage.

The value of $p_{0.50}$ for $n = 40$ and $c = 1$ may be calculated as follows:

$$p_{0.50} = \frac{c + 0.67}{n} = \frac{1.67}{40} = 0.0418, \text{ or } 4.18\%$$

It was shown on page 394 that with $c = 1$, n should be 67 for $p_{0.50}$ to be 2.5%.

Generally speaking, where samples are relatively small and percentages of defectives are relatively low, samples tend to give a too favorable impression of a lot somewhat more often than an impression that is too unfavorable. For example, consider the following distribution of probabilities of various numbers of defectives in drawing samples of 40 from a large lot 2.5% defective, as estimated from Table *G*:

Number of defectives in sample	Percentage of defectives in sample	Probability of occurrence
0	0.0	0.368
1	2.5	0.368
2	5.0	0.184
3	7.5	0.061
4	10.0	0.015
5	12.5	0.003
6	15.0	0.001

The average number of defectives in a great many samples of 40 from lots 2.5% defective will of course be 1, *i.e.*, 2.5% of defectives. For this to be the average, however, 0 defectives must occur once for every time there are 2 defectives, twice for every time there are 3, three times for every time there are 4, and so on. Thus the probability of 0 defectives is 0.368, whereas the probability of 2 or more is only 0.264.

320. Estimating the Lot Quality from the Sample Quality. In industrial acceptance sampling, the practical question is nearly always what to do with the lot. A decision must be made to accept a lot or reject it or perhaps to screen it. Definite criteria are established to settle such decisions. In most industrial sampling, the estimation of lot quality from sample quality is likely to be viewed merely as an academic question.

In some instances, however, particularly in dealing with isolated lots and in borderline cases, it may be desired to have an idea of the probabilities of various possible values of quality of a sampled lot.

If it is desired to estimate from a given sample by attributes the probability that the true lot quality is within given limits, such an estimate requires the use of Bayes's theorem and *a posteriori* probabilities (see Art. 181, Chap. IX). A solution of this problem was made by General Simon, who has presented this solution in compact form in his I_Q charts.[1] These charts are based on the assumption that prior to sampling, all fractions defective were equally likely (see Art. 181 for comments regarding this assumption). The five charts apply to probabilities of 0.995, 0.9, 0.5, 0.1, and 0.005. For instance, with any given sample size (up to 500) from an infinite or very large lot and with any given number of observed defectives in the sample, the probability is 0.995 that the true fraction defective in the lot is less than a value that may be read from the 0.995 chart.

An illustration of the numerical information given by these charts may help the reader to decide whether they will be useful in dealing with his particular problems. Assume a sample of 240 from a very large lot contains exactly 2 defectives. The charts give the probability as 0.995 that the true fraction defective is below 0.038, and as 0.005 that it is less than 0.0014. In other words, it is a fairly safe estimate (with a 0.99 probability) that the true fraction defective of the lot is between 0.038 and 0.0014. The charts give the probability as 0.9 that the true fraction defective is less than 0.022 and as 0.1 that it is less than 0.0046. In other words, there are four chances out of five that the true fraction defective is between 0.022 and 0.0046. The 0.5 chart gives the estimated lot fraction defective as 0.011. This contrasts with the sample fraction defective of $\frac{2}{240} = 0.0083$.

A contrast is afforded by the probabilities for a sample half as big with half as many defectives. Assume a sample of 120 has exactly 1 defective. The probability is 0.99 that the true fraction defective is between 0.06 and 0.0009, and 0.8 that it is between 0.032 and 0.0043. The estimated lot fraction defective is 0.014. All these probabilities depend on the assumption underlying the charts, namely, that prior to sampling, one fraction defective is as likely as another.

---

[1] These charts, $5\frac{1}{2}$ by $7\frac{1}{2}$ in., are inserted in a pocket in the back of "An Engineers' Manual of Statistical Methods." However, if any considerable use of these charts is to be made, it is desirable to purchase them enlarged to $7\frac{1}{2}$ by 11 in. L. E. SIMON, "Enlarged I_Q Charts," John Wiley & Sons, Inc., New York, 1941.

The symbol I_Q designates the incomplete beta-function ratio. A mathematical discussion of the use of this ratio is given in Appendix B of General Simon's book.

321. Devising Your Own Attributes Acceptance Procedure. The majority of statistical acceptance schemes used by industrial concerns seem to be based on published tables such as the Dodge-Romig tables and the SRG's tables given in "Sampling Inspection." Frequently some modifications or adaptations are made to fit particular conditions. For internal use, the published tables are often too extensive; it is desirable to put sampling plans for shop use into a fairly compact form.[1]

Sometimes instead of needing a set of plans to be used through a range of lot sizes and quality standards, it is merely desired to choose acceptance criteria to fit a particular set of conditions. Here again, the published tables can be very helpful. By examining a volume such as "Sampling Inspection" which contains OC curves for all plans given, it is usually possible to select an acceptance plan to meet any stated requirements. Another good source of multiple plans is a set of tables developed by F. J. Anscombe of the Statistical Laboratory of Cambridge University.[2]

Example 26 illustrates the design of a pure sequential plan to meet particular specifications.

EXAMPLE 26. AN ITEM-BY-ITEM SEQUENTIAL ACCEPTANCE PLAN

322. Design of a Sequential Plan Having an OC Curve Passing through Two Designated Points. A certain product is subject to lot-by-lot acceptance or rejection on the basis of a destructive test applied to a sample. The conditions of the test are considerably more severe than it is expected will be encountered in practice. All items tested are damaged to the point where they are of no further use. In order to keep the number of items tested to a minimum consistent with the desired quality protection, it is decided to design an item-by-item sequential plan.

Such a plan may be designed so that the OC curve passes through any two points desired. In this instance, the desired points are $P_a = 0.95$, $p = 0.10$, and $P_a = 0.20$, $p = 0.30$. Because of the margin of safety in the test procedure, it is believed that lots are satisfactory when not more than 10 % of the items would fail if subjected to this test; with a P_a of 0.95, the producer takes only 1 chance in 20 that such lots will be rejected. From the consumer's viewpoint, there is to be 1 chance in 5 of acceptance of a lot in which 30 % of the items would fail this test.

In the symbols commonly used in the mathematics of sequential sampling, these desired points on the OC curve are represented by $p_1 = 0.10$, $\alpha = 0.05$, $p_2 = 0.30$, $\beta = 0.20$. The symbol α represents $1 - P_a$ for a lot of quality p_1; the symbol β is P_a

---

[1] For examples of such compact presentations developed for industrial use, see JURAN, *op. cit.*, pp. 490–493, and A. V. FEIGENBAUM, "Quality Control," pp. 203 and 206, McGraw-Hill Book Company, Inc., New York, 1951.

[2] ANSCOMBE, F. J., Tables of Sequential Inspection Schemes to Control Fraction Defective, *Journal of the Royal Statistical Society,* vol. 112, part 2, pp. 180–206, 1949.

for a lot of quality p_2. Figure 76 gives a graphical representation of an item-by-item sequential plan. The plan is fully defined by the equation of the acceptance line, $d_2 = sn + h_2$, and the rejection line, $d_1 = sn - h_1$. To compute s, the slope of these

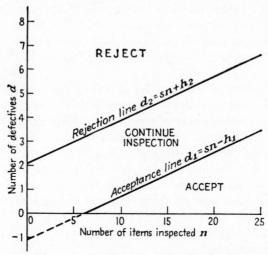

FIG. 76. Graphical representation of an item-by-item sequential plan.

lines, and h_1 and h_2, the intercepts, certain auxiliary symbols, g_1, g_2, a, and b, are used. The necessary computations are as follows:

$$g_1 = \log \frac{p_1}{p_2} = \log \frac{0.30}{0.10} = 0.4771$$

$$g_2 = \log \frac{1 - p_1}{1 - p_2} = \log \frac{0.90}{0.70} = 0.1091$$

$$a = \log \frac{1 - \beta}{\alpha} = \log \frac{0.80}{0.05} = 1.2041$$

$$b = \log \frac{1 - \alpha}{\beta} = \log \frac{0.95}{0.20} = 0.6767$$

$$h_1 = \frac{b}{g_1 + g_2} = \frac{0.6767}{0.5862} = 1.154$$

$$h_2 = \frac{a}{g_1 + g_2} = \frac{1.2041}{0.5862} = 2.054$$

$$s = \frac{g_2}{g_1 + g_2} = \frac{0.1091}{0.5862} = 0.186$$

This gives the following equations:

Rejection line: $\qquad\qquad d_2 = 0.186n + 2.054$
Acceptance line: $\qquad\qquad d_1 = 0.186n - 1.154$

For practical use, these lines should be converted into an item-by-item table of acceptance and rejection numbers. Computed values of d_1 and d_2 are generally not whole numbers. In the following tabulation of acceptance and rejection numbers up to $n = 24$, the rejection number is the next whole number above d_2, and the acceptance number is the next whole number below d_1.

n	Acceptance number	Rejection number	n	Acceptance number	Rejection number	n	Acceptance number	Rejection number
1	*	†	9	0	4	17	2	6
2	*	†	10	0	4	18	2	6
3	*	3	11	0	5	19	2	6
4	*	3	12	1	5	20	2	6
5	*	3	13	1	5	21	2	6
6	*	4	14	1	5	22	2	7
7	0	4	15	1	5	23	3	7
8	0	4	16	1	6	24	3	7

* Acceptance requires a sample of at least 7 items.

† Rejection requires a sample of at least 3 items.

The purpose of adopting such an item-by-item scheme is to reduce the average amount of inspection below the amount that would obtain with a multiple scheme giving about the same quality protection. However, it is usually advisable to fix some upper limit to the size of n; otherwise, an occasional borderline lot might conceivably require the indefinite continuation of sampling.[1]

Five points on the OC curve of an item-by-item sequential plan can be found without difficulty. Two of these are the points used in designing the plan. Two more points are established by the knowledge that when $p = 0$, $P_a = 1.00$ and when $p = 1$, $P_a = 0$. A fifth point is fixed by the relationship that when $p = s$, $P_a = h_2/(h_1 + h_2)$. For the sequential plan just computed, when $p = 0.186$, $P_a = 2.054/3.208 = 0.64$.

A sufficiently good OC curve often can be sketched from these five points. For an explanation of the more complicated calculations of additional points on the OC curve, the reader is referred to the basic source material on sequential analysis.[2]

323. A Systematic Record of Quality History Is an Important Aspect of Statistical Acceptance Procedures.

As pointed out at the start of Chap. XIII, when acceptance procedures are on an informal basis it is frequently recognized that a common-sense principle is to base the severity of acceptance criteria on the quality history of the product being sampled. The formal methods outlined in the current chapter substitute a systematic way of doing this for an informal and unsystematic way. In this systematic procedure, a written record of quality history takes the place of the inspector's memory.

[1] When an upper limit is placed on n, the acceptance criterion at this maximum value of n must be specified. Some users of item-by-item sequential plans accept all lots that have not been rejected at this maximum sample size; others reject all that have not been accepted.

It should be recognized that a maximum value for n changes the OC curve from that contemplated in the calculations to design an item-by-item sequential plan.

[2] WALD, ABRAHAM, "Sequential Analysis," John Wiley & Sons, Inc., New York, 1947.

Statistical Research Group, Columbia University, "Sequential Analysis of Statistical Data: Applications," Columbia University Press, New York, 1945.

This written record should preferably be set up in a way to provide the answers to two questions, namely, What is the quality level? Is the process in control? Figure 77 illustrates a possible form for such a record which combines a control chart with the data on inspection of first samples.[1] The scale for the control chart shown on the right may readily be adapted to any quality level by changing the value of a division on the chart.

Such quality records of sampling inspection are useful even though the final acceptance criteria do not depend on the quality level. They often bring out surprising differences between the quality levels of differ-

CONTROL CHART AND DATA SHEET FOR SAMPLING ACCEPTANCE INSPECTION

Vendor							Article purchased								
Inspection procedure							Acceptable quality level								
Remarks															

Date	Lot size	First sample		Percent defective in first sample	Second sample		Action on lot	Control chart for first samples							
		Number insp'd	Defectives		Number insp'd	Defectives									

FIG. 77. Form that combines record of sampling inspection with control chart for per cent defective.

ent vendors—differences that sometimes were not even suspected before a record was kept (see Art. 11, Chap. I, for a statement of the experience of Bell Aircraft Corporation). In this way they may bring about a decision not to do business with a vendor submitting unacceptable quality; such a decision has an effect similar to the adoption of tightened acceptance criteria that reject the majority of his lots.

Problems

226. In acceptance sampling under MIL-STD-105A, single sampling is to be used with inspection level II, an AQL of 4%, and a lot size of 2,500. What are acceptance criteria under (a) normal, (b) tightened, and (c) reduced inspection?

Ans. (a) $n = 150$, $c = 11$; (b) $n = 150$, $c = 8$; (c) $n = 30$, $c = 5$.

[1] See H. F. DODGE and H. G. ROMIG, "Sampling Inspection Tables," pp. 60–61, John Wiley & Sons, Inc., New York, 1944, for two forms used by the Western Electric Company for a record of statistical sampling inspection. Many forms used by other manufacturers have been adapted from these Western Electric forms.

227. In Problem 226, use Table G to compute the approximate probability of acceptance of a 4% defective lot under normal, tightened, and reduced inspection.

Ans. 0.980; 0.847; 0.998.

228. In acceptance sampling under MIL-STD-105A, double sampling is to be used with inspection level II, an AQL of 0.65%, and a lot size of 750. What are acceptance criteria under (a) normal, (b) tightened, and (c) reduced inspection?

Ans. (a) $n_1 = 50$, $c_1 = 0$, $n_2 = 100$, $c_2 = 2$; (b) $n_1 = 75$, $c_1 = 0$, $n_2 = 150$, $c_2 = 2$; (c) $n = 15$, $c = 1$.

229. In Problem 228, use Table G to compute the approximate probability of acceptance of an 0.8% defective lot under normal, tightened, and reduced inspection. In computing probabilities of acceptance on the second sample, consider the effect of the result of the first sample on the per cent defective in the remainder of the lot.

Ans. 0.93; 0.82; 0.99.

230. In acceptance sampling under MIL-STD-105A, multiple sampling is to be used with inspection level I, an AQL of 6.5%, and a lot size of 10,000. Give the individual sample size, the number of samples, and the acceptance and rejection numbers for successive samples under normal inspection.

Ans. 50; 8; 3-10, 8-15, 13-19, 18-24, 23-30, 28-35, 33-40, 40-41.

231. In acceptance sampling under MIL-STD-105A, double sampling is specified with a stated AQL of 0.20%. Lot size is 1,000, and inspection level is II. What are the acceptance criteria under (a) normal, (b) tightened, and (c) reduced inspection?

Ans. (a) $n_1 = 100$, $c_1 = 0$, $n_2 = 200$, $c_2 = 2$; (b) $n = 75$, $c = 0$; (c) $n = 30$, $c = 1$.

232. In acceptance sampling with MIL-STD-105A, the AQL is given as 100 defects per 100 units (*i.e.*, 1 defect per unit). Lot size is 4,000, and inspection level is I. What are the acceptance criteria under (a) normal, (b) tightened, and (c) reduced inspection?

Ans. (a) $n = 110$, $c = 135$; (b) $n = 150$, $c = 123$; (c) $n = 22$, $c = 31$.

233. In the acceptance plan of Problem 226, the first 10 lots are sampled under normal inspection. The number of defectives found are 6, 15, 9, 8, 3, 10, 11, 7, 6, and 11, respectively. Make the necessary calculations to determine whether or not a shift to tightened inspection is required.

Ans. As the estimated process average, 5.73%, exceeds 5.50%, tightened inspection is necessary.

234. The tightened inspection criteria of Problem 226 are being used. The numbers of defectives observed in the past 10 samples have been 12, 7, 5, 6, 3, 11, 8, 2, 5, and 7, respectively. Make the necessary calculations to determine whether normal inspection shall be reinstated.

Ans. As the estimated process average, 4.40%, exceeds 4.00%, tightened inspection must be continued.

235. In normal inspection with the acceptance plan of Problem 228, no defectives have been found in the first samples from the first 20 lots. Is it permissible to initiate reduced inspection?

Ans. No, as the 1,000 units included in the estimated process average of 0.00% are insufficient to initiate reduced inspection with an AQL of 0.65%.

236. Normal inspection is used for the conditions described in Problem 232. What is the highest number of defects that may be found in the samples from the first 10 lots that will permit qualification for reduced inspection? *Ans.* 1,004.

237. Reduced inspection has been initiated under the conditions described in Problem 228. The numbers of defectives observed in samples from 15 lots are 0, 0, 0, 0, 0, 0, 0, 0, 0, 1, 0, 0, 0, and 1, respectively. May reduced inspection be continued?

Ans. No, as the estimated process average of 0.89% exceeds the AQL of 0.65%.

238. Single sampling with an AQL of 1.0% is being used with acceptance criteria determined by MIL-STD-105A. Use Table G to compute approximate probabilities of acceptance of a lot at exactly AQL value under normal inspection with sample size code letters I, M, and P, respectively.   *Ans.* 0.910; 0.972; 0.996.

239. For the conditions of Problem 238, compute the respective probabilities of acceptance of lots (a) at AQL value and (b) at twice AQL value, assuming tightened inspection is in force.   *Ans.* (a) 0.827, 0.922, 0.920; (b) 0.558, 0.532, 0.185.

240. For a $p_{0.50}$ of 1.5 %, what should be the single sample sizes corresponding to acceptance numbers of 0, 1, 2, 5, and 10, respectively?
        Ans. 45; 111; 178; 378; 711.

241. For comparison with the results in Problem 240, what single sample sizes in MIL-STD-105A correspond to acceptance numbers of 0, 1, 2, 5, and 10, respectively, under tightened inspection for an AQL of 1.5 %?   *Ans.* 15; 50; 75; 225; 450.

242. What are the values of $p_{0.50}$ under the five plans computed in Problem 241 for tightened inspection with an AQL of 1.5 %?
        Ans. 4.47 %; 3.34 %; 3.56 %; 2.52 %; 2.37 %.

243. Under MIL-STD-105A, select a double sampling plan for normal inspection with a lot size of 750, inspection level II, and an AQL of 4.0 %.

244. Put 30 colored beads and 720 white beads into a container. Each colored bead represents a defective, and each white bead represents a good article. The contents of the container represent lots that are 4 % defective. Using the double sampling procedure of Problem 243, take 20 samples from this. Take a second sample only when required. Determine whether each lot is accepted or rejected. Use the first samples from the 20 lots to estimate the process average. Determine from this process average whether to continue with normal inspection or to shift to tightened or reduced inspection.

245. Carry out the sampling described in Problem 244, using 45 colored beads and 705 white beads.

246. Carry out the sampling described in Problem 244, using 15 colored beads and 735 white beads.

247. For the conditions described in Problem 243, what are the acceptance criteria under tightened and reduced inspection?

248. In acceptance sampling under MIL-STD-105A, multiple sampling is to be used with inspection level I, a stated AQL of 2.0 %, and a lot size of 1,500. Determine the acceptance criteria under (a) normal, (b) tightened, and (c) reduced inspection.

249. In acceptance sampling under MIL-STD-105A, single sampling is to be used with inspection level I, an AQL of 2.5 %, and a lot size of 200. What are acceptance criteria under (a) normal, (b) tightened, and (c) reduced inspection?

250. In acceptance sampling under MIL-STD-105A, single sampling is to be used with inspection level III, an AQL of 0.30 %, and a lot size of 500. What are acceptance criteria under (a) normal, (b) tightened, and (c) reduced inspection?

251. In acceptance .sampling under MIL-STD-105A, the AQL is given as 150 defects per 100 units. Lot size is 80, and inspection level is II. What are the acceptance criteria under (a) normal, (b) tightened, and (c) reduced inspection?

252. In acceptance sampling under MIL-STD-105A, single sampling is to be used with inspection level II, an AQL of 1.0 %, and a lot size of 25,000. What are acceptance criteria under (a) normal, (b) tightened, and (c) reduced inspection?

253. In Problem 252, use Table G to compute the approximate probability of acceptance of a 1 % defective lot under normal, tightened, and reduced inspection.

254. Answer the questions in Problem 252 for double sampling.

255. Answer the questions in Problem 252 for multiple sampling.

256. In double sampling inspection under MIL-STD-105A, using an AQL of 0.65 %

and sample size code letter N, $n_1 = 200$, $c_1 = 3$, $n_2 = 400$, and $c_2 = 7$. The numbers of defectives in the first sample from the first 10 lots were as follows: 2, 1, 4, 0, 0, 1, 3, 3, 7, 0. The third lot was accepted with only 3 defectives in the second sample. The ninth lot was rejected when a defective was found in the first 10 articles inspected in the second sample. Show the necessary calculations to determine whether or not a shift to tightened inspection is required.

257. Multiple sampling is conducted under MIL-STD-105A using an AQL of 1.5 % and code letter J. How many lots must show perfect samples before a shift to reduced inspection will be permitted? (Note that where acceptance is not permitted on the first multiple sample, the results of the first two multiple samples may properly be considered in judging whether or not the process average is good enough for a shift to reduced inspection.) If this excellent quality continues, what percentage of saving in number of items inspected per lot will be made under reduced inspection?

258. In normal single sampling under MIL-STD-105A, the AQL is 2.5 %, and the sample size code letter is H. In the samples from the first 20 lots, only 6 defectives have been found and no lots rejected. Does this qualify for reduced inspection? If not, what is the least number of additional lots that must be inspected before qualification is possible? What will be the acceptance criteria under reduced inspection?

259. Single sampling with an AQL of 1.5 % is being used with acceptance criteria determined by MIL-STD-105A. Use Table G to compute approximate probabilities of acceptance of a lot at exactly AQL value under normal inspection with sample size code letters E, J, and O, respectively.

260. For the conditions of Problem 259, compute respective probabilities of acceptance of lots (*a*) at AQL value and (*b*) at three times the AQL value, assuming tightened inspection is in force.

261. For a $p_{0.50}$ of 0.65 %, what should be the single sample sizes corresponding to acceptance numbers of 0, 1, 3, 5, and 8, respectively?

262. For comparison with the results in Problem 261, what single sample sizes in MIL-STD-105A correspond to acceptance numbers of 0, 1, 3, 5, and 8, respectively, under tightened inspection for an AQL of 0.65 %? What are the respective values of $p_{0.50}$ for these five sampling plans?

263. Select from Table 46 (page 396) the sampling plan for a point of control $p_{0.50}$ of 5 % and a lot size of 300. Under what AQL is this plan listed in MIL-STD-105A?

264. Compute (*a*) the LTPD, $p_{0.10}$, and (*b*) the AOQL for the sampling plan of Problem 263.

265. In normal double sampling under MIL-STD-105A, using an AQL of 0.40 % and sample size code letter M, $n_1 = 150$, $c_1 = 2$, $n_2 = 300$, $c_2 = 4$. The inspection record for the samples from the first 10 lots submitted by vendor A is: Defectives in first sample—2, 4, 2, 1, 2, 2, 1, 2, 0, 2. The second lot was rejected when a fifth defective was found after inspecting 80 articles in the second sample. The other lots were accepted.

(*a*) What general conclusion is suggested by this type of acceptance inspection record under double sampling?

(*b*) Is a shift to tightened inspection required at this point?

(*c*) What are the acceptance criteria to be used in tightened inspection?

266. The same normal plan mentioned in Problem 265 is also to be used for vendor B. Suppose the first 10 lots submitted by vendor B are each exactly 0.8 % defective. This is somewhat worse than the AQL of 0.4 %. What is the approximate probability that the process average estimated from the first 10 samples will turn out to be bad enough to force a shift to tightened inspection?

267. A vendor inspects his own product, using the Philips Standard Sampling System, screening all rejected lots before shipment. The lot size is 1,000, and the point of control used is 1 %.

The purchaser inspects the same lots, using normal single sampling inspection under MIL-STD-105A, with inspection level II and an AQL of 1.0 %.

(a) What is the probability that a 1 % defective lot will pass both the vendor's and the purchaser's sampling inspection?

(b) What is the probability that a 1 % defective lot will pass the vendor's sampling inspection and be rejected by the purchaser's?

268. Answer questions (a) and (b) in Problem 267 with respect to a 3 % defective lot.

269. A vendor inspects his own product, using a Dodge-Romig single sampling 1 % AOQL plan, screening all rejected lots before shipment. $N = 2,000$, $n = 130$, and $c = 2$.

The purchaser inspects the same lots, using normal single sampling inspection under MIL-STD-105A, with inspection level II and an AQL of 1.0 %.

(a) What is the probability that a 1 % defective lot will pass both the vendor's and the purchaser's sampling inspection?

(b) What is the probability that a 1 % defective lot will pass the vendor's sampling inspection and be rejected by the purchaser's?

270. Answer questions (a) and (b) in Problem 269 with respect to a 3 % defective lot.

271. Sketch a design for a multiple sampling board similar to Fig. 74 to be used for the MIL-STD-105A plan given for code letter G and an AQL of 6.5 %.

272. A manufacturing plant is experiencing difficulty with the quality of parts received from several vendors. Because these parts are urgently needed, it has been suggested that each lot received should be given a sampling inspection to determine whether it is more than 5 % defective. If the sampling inspection shows it to be not more than 5 % defective, a lot will be purchased and given 100 % inspection; otherwise it will be returned to the vendor. This suggestion has been referred to you by the works manager. He agrees that he is willing that lots not more than 5 % defective shall be accepted and detailed but asks whether you can recommend a satisfactory scheme for sampling inspection of incoming lots to determine which lots are to be accepted.

Write a report to the works manager making definite recommendations. In this report point out the limitations, from the probability or statistical viewpoint, of the scheme you recommend. (Lot sizes submitted vary from 100 to 10,000). Point out any alternative schemes that deserve consideration by the works manager and explain their advantages and disadvantages. In making your report, note that the original proposal was that all *accepted* lots shall be 100 % inspected (not all rejected lots as in an AOQL scheme).

273. Determine the equations of the rejection and acceptance lines for an item-by-item sequential plan in which $p_{0.90} = 0.05$ and $p_{0.20} = 0.15$.

$Ans.$ $d_2 = 0.092n + 1.719$; $d_1 = 0.092n - 1.243$.

274. Plot an approximate OC curve for the sequential plan of Problem 273. Prepare an item-by-item table of acceptance and rejection numbers for values of n from 1 to 50. In this table, make the rejection number the next whole number above d_2 and the acceptance number the next whole number below d_1.

275. Determine the equations of the rejection and acceptance lines for an item-by-item sequential plan in which $p_{0.95} = 0.05$ and $p_{0.10} = 0.15$. Compute the respective acceptance and rejection numbers where n is 20, 40, 60, 80, and 100. In this calculation make the rejection number the next whole number above d_2 and the acceptance number the next whole number below d_1.

CHAPTER XVI

ACCEPTANCE SAMPLING BY VARIABLES

I have never yet seen an inspection problem which would not benefit from the point of view that the product to be inspected was a frequency distribution.—G. D. Edwards

324. Some Advantages and Limitations of Acceptance Sampling by Variables. Most acceptance sampling is by attributes and will doubtless continue to be so. Nevertheless, the growth of knowledge of statistical quality control techniques has led to a considerable increase in the industrial use of acceptance sampling by variables. It seems likely that this tendency will continue.

One obvious limitation on the use of variables criteria in acceptance sampling is the fact that many quality characteristics are observable only as attributes. Where this is true, sampling by variables is out of the question. Nevertheless, it often turns out to be possible to devise methods of measurement in cases where at first glance it seems that inspection must be by attributes.

For those quality characteristics that can be measured, it is usually true that the cost of inspection per item is less by attributes than by variables. Often this is due to the greater economy of inspection methods using the go–not-go principle. Moreover, clerical costs are usually less with attributes inspection; it is less expensive to record merely the conformance or nonconformance to specifications than to record an actual measured value and to make computations using that value.

Perhaps the most serious limitation on the use of sampling by variables is the fact that acceptance criteria must be applied separately to each quality characteristic. This tends to increase the cost of acceptance inspection. For example, if 20 quality characteristics of a product are to be examined at a given inspection station, a single set of attributes sampling criteria can be applied to the acceptance decision. In contrast, if each characteristic is subject to variables inspection, 20 different sets of variables criteria must be used.

An additional limitation on certain types of variables criteria exists in that the computed protection against various percentages of defectives depends on an assumption regarding the form of the underlying frequency distribution of the quality characteristic. This limitation is discussed in Art. 331.

In spite of the foregoing limitations, acceptance sampling by variables is often preferable to acceptance sampling by attributes, particularly for those quality characteristics which are the source of troubles. Possibly only 2 of the 20 characteristics mentioned in the preceding paragraph may turn out to be troublesome. If so, it may be that variables criteria can be applied profitably to these even though attributes criteria are used for the remaining 18.

The great advantage of the use of acceptance sampling by variables is that more information is obtained about the quality characteristic in question. This may lead to a number of desirable results, as follows:

1. For a given sample size, better quality protection may usually be obtained with variables criteria than with attributes. Or, stated a little differently, for a given quality protection against various possible percentages of defectives (as reflected in the OC curve) smaller samples may be used with variables than with attributes.

2. The extent of conformance or nonconformance to the desired value of a quality characteristic is given weight where variables criteria are used. This may be important wherever there is a margin of safety in the design specifications or a twilight zone of values of the quality characteristic between clearly satisfactory and clearly unsatisfactory.

3. Variables information usually gives a better basis for guidance toward quality improvement.

4. Variables information may provide a better basis for giving weight to quality history in acceptance decisions.

5. Errors of measurement are more likely to be disclosed with variables information.

325. Some Different Types of Acceptance Criteria Involving Variables. There are many different ways in which the actual measured values of quality characteristics in a sample can be used to influence decisions on acceptance of submitted product. The following general classification of types of variables criteria is intended to provide a convenient basis for discussion of the subject:

1. Criteria in which the decision on acceptance or rejection of a lot is based on the sample average alone. Plans using such criteria may be referred to as *known-sigma plans*.

2. Criteria in which the decision is based on the sample average in combination with a measure of sample dispersion. Such plans may be referred to as *unknown-sigma plans*.

3. Criteria in which the decision depends in some way on the frequency distribution of the sample. The Shainin Lot Plot is an example of this type of plan.

4. Criteria for acceptance or rejection of a process or of a series of lots based on the evidence of a control chart for variables.

Each of these types of criteria will be discussed with reference to the common type of design specification in which specification limits apply to individual items of product. Near the end of the chapter there is a brief discussion of variables criteria where specification limits apply to lot *averages*.

Sometimes there are legal or other reasons why variables criteria should not be used for lot rejection even though such criteria are appropriate for lot acceptance. This condition may lead to some combination of variables and attributes criteria. This topic is examined following the discussion of known-sigma and unknown-sigma plans.

326. The Bowker-Goode Collection of Factors for Known-sigma Plans. Article 266 (pages 332 to 335) illustrated a particular variables acceptance plan. The specification for minimum tensile strength of a certain product was 20,000 psi. This specification applied to individual items. The variables acceptance plan called for testing 16 items from a lot and computing the average tensile strength of this sample. If this average was 21,846 psi or more, the lot was accepted; otherwise it was rejected. Article 266 explained the calculation of the OC curve of this plan on the assumption that the lot standard deviation was 1,000 psi and the distribution was normal.

This plan is representative of the known-sigma type of variables acceptance plans designed to provide protection against stated percentages of defectives. Where a one-sided design specification states a lower limit L on individual values, the known-sigma criterion for sample average $\bar{X}$ is

$$\bar{X} \geq L + k'\sigma'$$

Where a one-sided specification states an upper limit U, the known-sigma acceptance criterion for sample average is

$$\bar{X} \leq U - k'\sigma'$$

The sample size n and the factor k' may be selected to give any desired quality protection as indicated by the OC curve of the plan chosen. Bowker and Goode[1] give values of n and k' for known-sigma single sampling plans that give approximately the same quality protection as each of the numerous attributes plans in the Columbia Statistical Research Group's volume "Sampling Inspection."[2]

The values of k' given by Bowker and Goode for values of n from 5

[1] BOWKER, A. H., and H. P. GOODE, "Sampling Inspection by Variables," McGraw-Hill Book Company, Inc., New York, 1952.

[2] FREEMAN, H. A., MILTON FRIEDMAN, FREDERICK MOSTELLER, and W. A. WALLIS (eds.), "Sampling Inspection," McGraw-Hill Book Company, Inc., New York, 1948.

to 16 are reproduced in the first two columns of Table S, Appendix III. The third column of this table gives the value of $p_{0.95}$ for each plan. The fourth column of the table gives the value of $p_{0.10}$. The two right-hand columns of Table S give single sampling attributes plans; the OC curves of these attributes plans have been matched as closely as possible by the variables plans given on the same line of the table, subject to limitations imposed by the decision that each attributes sample size code letter would be matched by one variables sample size applicable to the full range of AQL's.

These values of n and k' in the first two columns of Table S apply to one-sided specifications. The OC curves for these plans assume a normal distribution as illustrated in the calculation in Art. 266.

327. Known-sigma Plans for Two-sided Specifications. Where both an upper limit U and a lower limit L are specified for the quality characteristic and the distribution is normal, the ability of a process to make product meeting specifications depends on the relationship between $(U - L)$ and the spread of the process, often assumed as $6\sigma'$. It also depends on the centering of the process. This point was brought out by Figs. 24, 25, and 26 in Chap. VI and in the accompanying discussion (pages 139 to 142).

In the situation illustrated in Fig. 24 (page 140), where $(U - L)$ is substantially greater than the spread of the process—say $7.5\sigma'$ or more—and the distribution in a lot is normal, both specification limits will not be exceeded in a single lot. It follows that where a known-sigma plan is used with such relatively loose tolerances, the OC curve of the plan can be computed as if the specification were one-sided in the way illustrated in Art. 266. For such loose tolerances, n and k' values from the two left-hand columns of Table S may be used; the $p_{0.95}$ and $p_{0.10}$ figures will be as shown in this table. The only difference in the acceptance criterion from the case of the one-sided specification is that there are now two limits on the permissible value of the sample average; $\overline{X}$ may not exceed $U - k'\sigma'$ and may not fall below $L + k'\sigma'$.

The matter is more complicated in the cases illustrated in Figs. 25 and 26 (pages 141 to 142), where the tolerances are tight in relation to the process capability. Here some defectives are sure to be produced. For instance, with a normal distribution there will be 0.27% defective even when $(U - L) = 6\sigma'$. The minimum percentage of defectives will occur when the process is centered midway between U and L. With this centering and such tight tolerances, some defectives will be produced above the upper specification limit and others below the lower limit. It follows that in calculating the OC curve for a known-sigma variables acceptance plan for a two-sided specification with tight tolerances, it is necessary to compute percentages of defectives in both tails of the frequency distribution. Except for this need of considering both tails of the distribution, such calculations follow the lines explained in Art. 266.

Bowker and Goode give values of n and a coefficient designated as $k'*$ for known-sigma variables plans for two-sided specifications assuming a normal distribution. These plans are to be used where the tolerances are tight in reference to process capability. With these plans, $\bar{X}$ may not exceed $U - k'*\sigma'$ or fall below $L + k'*\sigma'$. Like the other types of variables plans in the Bowker-Goode volume, a plan is provided to match the OC curve of each of the attributes plans in "Sampling Inspection." Some of these values of n and $k'*$ are reproduced in Table S, Appendix III.

328. The Use of a Known-sigma Plan Involves the Question of the Value of Sigma and Its Stability. In the industrial use of $\bar{X}$ and R charts, it is a common experience for the R chart to show a state of control over long periods of time even though $\bar{X}$ occasionally goes out of control. This is evidence that the centering of the process shifts but that its dispersion does not change. This condition was pictured in graphs (a), (b), and (c) in Fig. 18 (page 111). As the theory underlying known-sigma plans assumes this condition, their use should be limited to cases where there is evidence that process dispersion is stable. Such evidence may be obtained from control charts for R or σ. Such control charts may also provide the necessary estimate of σ', either as $\bar{R}/d_2$ or as $\bar{\sigma}/c_2$.

The values of σ' used in such plans require frequent review. If σ' is underestimated, the quality protection to the consumer will be less than that assumed. On the other hand, if σ' is overestimated, the producer will be penalized through the imposition of tighter acceptance criteria than were intended.[1]

329. Unknown-sigma Plans. Where there is no satisfactory basis for estimating σ' prior to the submission of a lot, acceptance plans may be devised in which the acceptance criteria make use of some measure of sample dispersion. The Bowker-Goode volume contains many such unknown-sigma plans having OC curves matched to those of the attributes plans given in "Sampling Inspection." Like the known-sigma plans, they assume a normal distribution of the quality characteristic. The factors for some of the single sampling plans (those involving sample sizes from 7 to 35) are reproduced in the fifth and sixth columns of Table S, Appendix III. These factors apply to one-sided specifications.

Although the theory underlying these unknown-sigma plans is beyond the scope of this book, the use of the factors may be illustrated by the following example:

A design specification states a minimum allowable tensile strength L

---

[1] See BOWKER and GOODE, *op. cit.*, Table 6.2, for an indication of the influence on the OC curve of an error in the estimate of σ'.

of 20,000 psi for a certain product.   No basis exists for an estimate of σ'.   It is desired to use an unknown-sigma plan giving approximately the same protection as the attributes plan $n = 30$, $c = 1$.   Table S shows two plans giving this protection, one with $n = 7$ and $k = 1.449$, the other with $n = 10$ and $k = 1.562$.   Assume that the first of these plans is selected.

The acceptance criterion is as follows:

$$\bar{X} \geqq L + ks$$

where s is to be computed for each sample by the following formula:[1]

$$s = \sqrt{\frac{\Sigma(X - \bar{X})^2}{n - 1}}$$

Table 47 gives the tensile strengths of a sample of seven test specimens together with the necessary calculations to find s.

TABLE 47.   CALCULATION OF s FOR UNKNOWN-SIGMA ACCEPTANCE PLAN

X (tensile strength in 100 psi)	$(X - \bar{X})$	$(X - \bar{X})^2$
223	$-\ 6$	36
252	$+23$	529
216	-13	169
239	$+10$	100
225	$-\ 4$	16
238	$+\ 9$	81
210	-19	361
1,603	....	1,292

$$\bar{X} = \frac{1,603}{7} = 229$$

$$s = \sqrt{\frac{1,292}{6}} = 14.67$$

The calculation to determine acceptance or rejection is

$$L + ks = 200 + 1.449(14.67) = 221.2$$

[1] Defined in this way, s is an estimate of universe standard deviation σ'.   We may think of this estimate as an alternative to the estimate obtainable from σ/c_2.   In many books dealing with statistical matters, s, so defined, is referred to as sample standard deviation.   This difference in the meaning attached to the phrase *standard deviation* is a possible source of confusion to readers of statistical literature.   The definition in this book of sample standard deviation σ as $\sqrt{\Sigma(X - \bar{X})^2/n}$ corresponds to the most common practice in quality control literature in the United States and agrees with the standards of the American Standards Association, American Society for Testing Materials, and American Society for Quality Control.

The foregoing figures are in units of 100 psi.

As the $\overline{X}$ of 229 exceeds 221.2, the lot is accepted.

Where an upper specification limit U is involved, the acceptance criterion is

$$\overline{X} \leqq U - ks$$

Bowker and Goode give OC curves for all of the single sampling unknown-sigma plans for one-sided specifications that are included in their volume. These OC curves are based on the assumption of a normal distribution. Factors (not reproduced in this book) are also given for double sampling plans and for unknown-sigma plans for two-sided specifications. The Bowker-Goode volume also gives various methods of shortening the calculation of acceptance criteria.

Table T, Appendix III, gives a set of unknown-sigma and known-sigma plans for one-sided specifications. These were developed under Dr. Bowker's direction by the Applied Mathematics and Statistics Laboratory of Stanford University subsequent to the publication of the Bowker-Goode volume.[1]

Table T gives values of $100p_{0.95}$, $100p_{0.50}$, and $100p_{0.10}$ for many unknown-sigma plans having values of n from 5 to 50 and values of k from 0.6 to 3.0. These three points on each OC curve permit the user to make a rough plotting of the entire OC curve of any desired plan. If, for a given sample size n, a value of k is to be selected corresponding to certain stipulated quality protection, it is advantageous to use the values from Table T to plot curves that show how $p_{0.95}$, $p_{0.50}$, and $p_{0.10}$ vary with k. These curves may then be read to determine the approximate k value for any desired $p_{0.95}$, $p_{0.50}$, or $p_{0.10}$.

330. Acceptance Procedures by Variables May Follow Patterns Similar to Those Developed for Acceptance by Attributes. A collection of variables sampling plans such as the one given by Bowker and Goode may be integrated into a set of over-all procedures for acceptance inspection. Just as in attributes sampling, provision may be made for normal, tightened, and reduced inspection. Where variables criteria are applied to quality characteristics for which 100% attributes inspection is practicable, such as dimensions, hardness, or electrical resistance, acceptance/

---

[1] They are reproduced by permission from more extensive tables in W. G. IRESON, "Sampling Tables for Inspection by Variables." This was issued by the Applied Mathematics and Statistics Laboratory, Stanford University, Stanford, California, as Technical Report No. 7, 1952. The Ireson report also contains tables applicable to two-sided unknown-sigma plans. For a discussion of theory applicable to such two-sided plans, see GEORGE RESNIKOFF, "A New Two-sided Region for Sampling by Variables," Technical Report No. 8. These reports may be requested from Statistics Branch, Office of Naval Research, U.S. Navy Department, Washington, D.C.

rectification schemes are possible and the AOQL can be determined for each plan.

In attributes procedures such as MIL-STD-105A, reduced inspection plans have much flatter OC curves than the corresponding normal plans, with the result that the consumer has much less protection against accepting an occasional bad lot if one is submitted. In variables procedures, on the other hand, a substantial reduction in the amount of inspection can be obtained with no reduction in consumer protection whenever the data on process dispersion justify a shift from an unknown-sigma to a known-sigma plan. For example, Table S gives known-sigma plans with a sample size of 16 that have substantially the same OC curves as the matched unknown-sigma plans with a sample size of 35.

Table T also gives the sample size for a known-sigma plan matching the OC curve of each unknown-sigma plan under the restriction that the k' and k factors in the matching plans are the same. In choosing the matching known-sigma plan, values of sample size were rounded to the next higher integer. It will be noted that the change from unknown-sigma to known-sigma is responsible for a large saving in sample size in those plans having the highest values of k and k' (the tightest plans) and a relatively small saving in sample size for the plans having the lowest values of k and k'.

331. Comment on the Assumption of a Normal Distribution in Known-sigma and Unknown-sigma Plans. The frequency distribution of many industrial quality characteristics is roughly normal. This is particularly so where the product comes from a single source and is produced within a short period of time. For this reason, the assumption of a normal distribution is good enough for practical purposes in many instances. This assumption is most likely to be a reasonable one where inspection lots are formed close to the point of production, so that the chance for the mixing of product having different frequency distributions is held to a minimum.

Nevertheless, even though inspection lots have been produced under apparently homogeneous conditions, it is always well to view the assumption of normality with a somewhat critical eye, investigating to see whether conditions exist that are likely to cause serious departure from a normal distribution. Sometimes the underlying frequency distribution is skewed, or it may be symmetrical but either peaked or flat-topped. The percentages in the extreme tails of such distributions may differ considerably from those obtaining under a normal distribution, and the protection against stated percentages of defectives given by variables acceptance criteria may be either greater or less than the protection indicated by OC curves computed on the assumption of normality.

One important departure from normality exists when a producer has given 100% screening inspection by attributes to a lot prior to its variables sampling inspection by the consumer. In such a case the frequency distribution in the screened lot may be truncated; one or both of the tails of the distribution may have been removed. With such truncated distributions, the variables criteria based on the assumption of normality may indicate that a lot should be rejected even though the actual nonnormal distribution in the lot may contain no defectives.

332. Acceptance/Rejection Plans May Be Devised to Accept on Variables Criteria but to Reject Only on Attributes Criteria. Two objections are sometimes raised to the use of either known-sigma or unknown-sigma plans for lot rejection. One objection relates to the point just mentioned that, for certain nonnormal distributions, the variables criteria may occasionally lead to the rejection of a lot containing no defectives.

The other objection relates to the obvious legal and psychological difficulties incident to rejecting a lot on the basis of a sample even though no defectives have been found in the sample. Consider, for example, the known-sigma plan of Art. 266 in which the design specification stated that the minimum tensile strength of an individual item must be 20,000 psi, whereas the acceptance specification stated that the minimum $\bar{X}$ for a sample of 16 must be 21,846 psi. It is quite possible for a sample to fail this acceptance specification without any of the individual tensile strengths falling below 20,000 psi.[1]

These objections are sometimes met by devising double sampling plans in which variables criteria are applied to a first sample. When these criteria do not lead to acceptance, a second larger sample is taken and the final decision on acceptance or rejection is based on attributes criteria. A number of acceptance plans of this type are described in the Bowker-Goode volume.[2]

333. Using Plotted Frequency Distributions in Acceptance Sampling. In the technical language of inspection, an article is *defective* if it fails to conform to specifications. A slight departure beyond specification limits makes the article defective; so, also, does a large departure beyond the limits. This definition of a defective gives no weight to the extent of the nonconformity to specifications.

Nevertheless, the extent of nonconformity may be a matter of great

---

[1] A possible way to avoid this particular type of objection is to incorporate the acceptance specification as an additional requirement in the design specification. Thus two separate requirements may be made, one that individual values should be at least 20,000, and the other that averages of samples of 16 should be at least 21,846.

[2] See also A. H. BOWKER, "Mixed Variables—Attributes Acceptance Sampling Plans." This was issued by the Applied Mathematics and Statistics Laboratory, Stanford University, Stanford, California, as Technical Report No. 10, 1952. It may be requested from Statistics Branch, Office of Naval Research, U.S. Navy Department, Washington, D.C.

practical importance. Consider any measurable quality characteristic on which the designer has specified upper and lower limits. There frequently is a twilight zone of values just outside one or both specification limits within which it is satisfactory to accept a moderate percentage of "defective" articles.

In many manufacturing plants, it is common for some purchased lots to be rejected initially under the regular acceptance procedures and then finally to be accepted under some sort of material-review procedure. Sometimes there is a highly formalized procedure involving a material-review board; in other cases material review may be quite an informal matter, involving a decision by some one individual. In any event, the extent of nonconformity to specifications is usually given consideration in material-review decisions. Extra costs maybe avoided and interruptions of production may be prevented by using material-review procedures to accept a product that is good enough for the purpose at hand, even though it is technically nonconforming to specifications.

Where sample frequency distributions for certain quality characteristics are plotted as part of the regular acceptance procedures, one objective usually is the provision of a more rational basis for material review. The frequency distribution is a great aid to judgment on the question of the extent of nonconformity to specifications.

Moreover, the frequency distribution has the advantage that it may disclose certain common types of departure from normality, such as skewed distributions, bimodal distributions, distributions with cut-off points, and distributions containing strays at some distance from the main distribution. The larger the sample, the better the chance to recognize such non-normal distributions when they occur, and the less the danger that a sample really taken from a normal distribution will give a false indication of non-normality.

Example 27 illustrates a common type of use of a frequency distribution on an informal basis with a good deal of judgment permitted in the acceptance decision. The Shainin Lot Plot plan explained in Art. 335 illustrates a more systematic approach to the analysis of a frequency distribution to guide decisions on acceptance or rejection.

EXAMPLE 27.   ACCEPTANCE DECISIONS BASED ON PLOTTED FREQUENCY DISTRIBUTIONS

334. Facts of the Case. An electrical manufacturer purchased mica insulators from a number of different vendors. Shipments generally consisted of lots of 8,000 to 10,000 pieces. All vendors seemed to have some difficulty in meeting the dimensional specification on thickness.

The acceptance procedure involved measuring the thicknesses of a sample of 200 from each lot and plotting the frequency distribution on a tally sheet similar to the one shown in Fig. 6 (page 44). The decision on acceptance or rejection was made by the quality control engineer after examining this tally sheet. No formal written criteria were established to govern this decision. Weight was given to the form of the frequency distribution, the number of items outside of specification limits, and the extent to which the nonconforming items failed to meet specifications. Consideration in the acceptance decision was also given to the number of items of this product in stock at the particular moment and the hazard that returning a lot to the vendor might interfere with production schedules.

335. The Shainin Lot Plot Method. This plan, also known as the Hamilton Standard Lot Plot Method, was developed by Dorian Shainin, Chief Inspector, Hamilton Standard Division, United Aircraft Corporation. A full description of this method is given in an article in the July, 1950, issue of *Industrial Quality Control*.[1] Some later refinements are explained in an article included in "Quality Control Conference Papers 1951."[2] In the following discussion these are referred to as the 1950 article and the 1951 article, respectively.

Since its first public presentation in 1947, the Lot Plot method has been used by many industrial companies. In his 1951 article, Shainin lists 45 companies in 25 different industries that have made use of this method. The following brief discussion explains the general characteristics of the method but does not aim to reproduce the full directions for its use that are given in Shainin's 1950 article. (Reproduction of the entire 1950 article would require about 50 book-sized pages.)

In the Lot Plot method, the sample size always is 50. In the Hamilton Standard usage, random numbers are used in drawing the sample to ensure randomness in its selection. Figure 78 shows the 1951 version of the Lot Plot form. A check on the cell width used in the left-hand column of the form is obtained from the first 5 articles measured; if possible, twice the range of this set of 5 values should be from 7 to 16 cells.

The sample is divided into 10 groups of 5 articles each for the purpose of recording the measured values in the Lot Plot form. For each article in the first group, the figure 1 is entered in the appropriate cell. For example, Fig. 78 indicates that the 5 measured values in the first group fell in the cells 254–253, 254–253, 253–252, 252–251, and 251–250. For each article in the second group, the figure 2 is entered in the appropriate cell, and so on. As each group of 5 is entered, the range of the group in cell units is entered in the "Range" column near the right-hand side of the form.

---

[1] SHAININ, DORIAN, The Hamilton Standard Lot Plot Method of Acceptance Sampling by Variables, *Industrial Quality Control*, vol. 7, No. 1, pp. 15–34, July, 1950.

[2] SHAININ, DORIAN, Recent Lot Plot Experiences around the Country, included in "Quality Control Conference Papers 1951," pp. 31–41, American Society for Quality Control, New York, 1951. This article also appears in the March, 1952, issue of *Industrial Quality Control*.

When the 50 measured values have been recorded, the next step is to compute the $\bar{X}$ of the sample and to estimate the 3σ value of the lot from the $\bar{R}$ of the 10 groups of 5 in the sample. In his 1951 article, Shainin explains the short-cut method used for computing $\bar{X}$ as follows:

a. Cut out the column of plus and minus line values from a blank Lot Plot form.

b. Place this column to cover the line values on the Lot Plot so that the zero cell falls opposite the mode or longest horizontal row of entries.

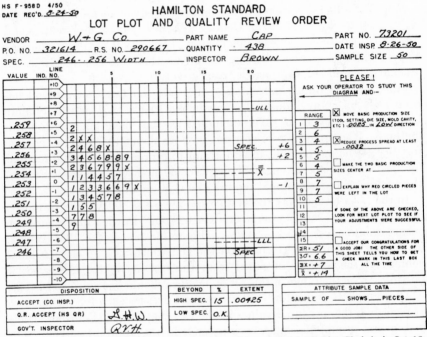

FIG. 78. Example of Lot Plot form. (*Reproduced from article by Dorian Shainin in Oct. 12, 1950, issue of The Iron Age.*)

c. Note whether the $+1$ or -1 cell contains the most readings.

d. Compare the quantities in these two cells by moving the cut column of paper horizontally to the right until the smaller of the two compared rows is just covered.

e. Count the remaining uncovered squares in the partially covered cell row, multiply this count by the cell sign and value, and enter the result at the extreme right side of the grid in that cell row.

f. Repeat using the $+2$ and -2 cells, and continue until only the zero cell remains.

g. Total the results algebraically and enter the answer opposite "Totals" in the lower right hand section of the Plot.

h. Multiply this answer by 2 and point off 2 decimal places to the left.

i. Enter this result in the ($\overline{\overline{X}}=$) space.

j. Point off from the middle of the mode or peak cell row the portion of a cell found by step i, in the direction corresponding to the sign of the i value, and draw a horizontal line labeled $\overline{\overline{X}}$.

The 3σ value needed to estimate the position of the lot limits is computed as $1.3\bar{R}$. (Actually $3\bar{R}/d_2 = 1.29\bar{R}$ when n is 5; the 1.3 factor is used for ease of calculation.) As there are 10 values of R, it is merely necessary to add the R's and point over one decimal place to find $\bar{R}$; 0.3 of $\bar{R}$ is then added to find 3σ.

In Fig. 78, $\overline{X}$ (in cell units) is 0.14, and 3σ (also in cell units) is 6.6. The lot limits, designated *ULL* and *LLL*, are drawn at a distance of 3σ on either side of $\overline{X}$. In Fig. 78 it is evident that the spread of the process is somewhat greater than the spread of the specifications, and that the process is not centered midway between the specification limits.

The key figures to guide the quality review are those contained in the box in the center near the bottom of the Lot Plot form. This box gives an estimate of the extent to which the extreme values of the lot fall beyond the specification limits. The computed 3-sigma lot limits supply the basis for this estimate. The box also contains an estimate of the percentage of the lot beyond each specification limit. This latter estimate is made from a diagram based on a normal-curve-area table (such as Table *A*, Appendix III).

Shainin has classified typical Lot Plots into eleven types, as shown in Fig. 79. The frequency distribution in Fig. 78 gives no grounds for suspicion of non-normality and is therefore treated as if the lot were normal. The rules for interpretation of non-normal appearing Lot Plots are not reproduced here. Much of Shainin's 1950 article deals with detailed instructions for handling the various types of non-normal Lot Plots. For a number of the types, special rules are required for estimating lot limits; examples of this are skewed Lot Plots (for example, type 5), Lot Plots indicating screening or cutoff points (for example, type 6), and bimodal Lot Plots (for example, type 7). Where lot limits fall outside of specification limits, the rules for action are influenced by the type of Lot Plot. In certain instances, doubtful Lot Plots lead to the use of AOQL attributes inspection. Special rules are given for the treatment of lots in which the Plots indicate strays (type 11).

The plotted frequency distributions in the Lot Plot method often provide a good diagnosis for quality troubles and thus lead to quality improvement. A copy of the Lot Plot form is always sent to the vendor. It will be noted that the right-hand side of the form permits the inspector to check one of several types of comments regarding quality, filling in the necessary blanks when there are quality troubles. The reverse

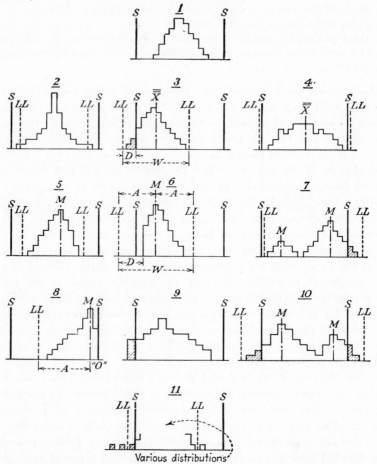

Various distributions

S = specification limit; LL = lot limit   O = zero, "full indicator reading"
X̄ = average of subgroup averages; M = mode A = distance in cells from mode to lot
    limit
D = distance in cells from specific limit or cut-off point, as case may be, to lot limit
W = base width, or distance in cells from one limit to the other

FIG. 79.   Eleven different types of Lot Plots. (*Reproduced from* "*The Hamilton Standard Lot Plot Method of Acceptance Sampling by Variables,*" *by Dorian Shainin, Industrial Quality Control, July,* 1950.)

side of the Lot Plot form contains concise directions for a Sum and Range chart.

In his 1950 article Shainin makes the following comment on this topic of vendor's quality improvement:

The initial use of Lot Plots will probably reveal only a few specifications running as well as the Type 1 situation—a normal shaped distribution included well within the specification limits [Fig. 78].   If such is the case and it is surprising to your organization, you should realize that by the use of proper cell widths, of a really representative or random sample, and by the elimination of flinching on the part of the inspector, you now have a picture of the condition of the lot that corresponds to the revelations brought to your eye by a microscope of the surface of an object.

The correct use by the supplier of Shewhart type control charts, of course, will bring specification after specification into line to give the inspector Type 1 Lot Plots. It is our experience, and that of several other concerns, that sending a copy of each Lot Plot to the supplier of the material also often results in an increasing frequency of Type 1 situations. By far the majority of our Plots are now of this type.

A number of brief case histories of quality improvement are given in Shainin's 1951 article.

336. Use of Variables Control Charts as a Basis for Acceptance Decisions. Although process control is the most common purpose of control charts for $\overline{X}$, R, and σ, such charts may also be used for acceptance purposes. Several different types of use of such charts need to be recognized.

1. The use of reject limits or modified control limits on $\overline{X}$ charts.

2. The use of control charts for identification of grand lots with acceptance decisions made for each grand lot.

3. The use of control charts for acceptance or rejection of a production process.

337. Reject Limits and Modified Control Limits. These types of control chart limits were discussed in Chap. VIII (pages 189 to 192). Their use for acceptance purposes may be on a lot-by-lot basis with each point on the $\overline{X}$ chart corresponding to a submitted lot.

Because both reject limits and modified control limits assume a known value of σ', they are really special cases under the general classification of known-sigma plans. Their OC curves may be calculated in the way explained in Art. 266 (pages 332 to 335). The general comments on known-sigma plans made earlier in this chapter are applicable to reject limits and modified control limits. However, a comparison between the V factors for reject limits given in Table 25 (page 191) and the k' factors in the known-sigma columns of Table S, Appendix III, will show that the V factors represent tighter acceptance criteria than most of the k' factors in Table S. The British factors for modified control limits given on page 191 are even tighter than the V factors.

Frequently the use of reject limits or modified control limits will be supplemented by some type of attributes inspection. For instance, 100% inspection by attributes may take place whenever a point on the control chart fails to fall within limits. This is, in effect, a combined variables-attributes acceptance/rectification scheme for which an AOQL may be calculated.

338. Use of Control Charts to Identify Grand Lots. In a brilliant paper,[1] Gen. Leslie E. Simon suggests a concept of a lot which is useful for many practical purposes. His definition is "a lot is an aggregation of articles which are essentially alike." He defines "essentially alike" as meaning "that small subgroups of sample items taken from the lot in arbitrary order will respond to the Shewhart criterion of control."

Example 28 illustrates the application of this concept to acceptance. The control chart in Fig. 80 makes it evident that there were two different grand lots. The average for the first grand lot fell within the specifications; the average for the second grand lot fell outside. Each grand

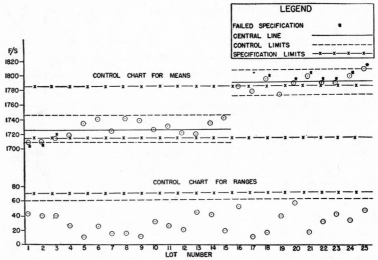

Fig. 80. Control chart illustrating two different grand lots (data of Table 48). *Reproduced from " The Industrial Lot and Its Sampling Implications," by Gen. L. E. Simon.*)

lot should properly have had a single acceptance/rejection decision applicable to the entire grand lot.

Where this concept is used, it is necessary to put off the decision on acceptance or rejection of a sub-lot until the entire grand lot has been identified. This postponement of an acceptance decision is sometimes referred to as *deferred sentencing.*

EXAMPLE 28. GRAND LOTS ARE IDENTIFIED BY CONTROL CHARTS FOR $\bar{X}$ AND R

339. Facts of the Case. General Simon gives an excellent example of the way in which a control chart may show the existence of grand lots, and how the neglect of

[1] SIMON, L. E., The Industrial Lot and Its Sampling Implications, *Journal of the Franklin Institute*, vol. 237, pp. 359–370, May, 1944.

grand lots in acceptance criteria may lead to accepting and rejecting the wrong lots. Table 48 and Fig. 80 are taken from his paper.[1]

Muzzle velocities were determined for samples of 5 from 25 consecutive lots from a manufacturer of complete rounds of ammunition.   Table 48 gives the average $\bar{X}$ and the range R from these samples.   The specifications for lot acceptance or rejection

TABLE 48.   AVERAGES AND RANGES OF MUZZLE VELOCITY FOR SAMPLES OF 5 TAKEN FROM 25 CONSECUTIVE LOTS OF AMMUNITION

Lot	Average muzzle velocity, ft./sec.	Range, ft./sec.
1*	1710	42
2*	1711	40
3*	1713	39
4	1718	26
5	1735	10
6	1739	25
7	1723	14
8	1741	15
9	1738	11
10	1725	31
11	1731	25
12	1721	19
13	1719	43
14	1735	39
15	1741	17
16	1783	51
17	1777	9
18*	1794	15
19	1773	37
20*	1789	54
21*	1798	15
22*	1789	29
23*	1788	39
24*	1799	30
25*	1807	44

were based on the values of average and range (rather than on individual values). $\bar{X}_{max}$ was 1,785 ft. per sec.; $\bar{X}_{min}$ was 1,715; the maximum allowable sample range was 70.   The lots rejected by this specification are marked with an asterisk (*).

Figure 80 shows $\bar{X}$ and R control charts for these data.   General Simon's comments on the conclusions from these charts are as follows:

"It is quite evident that the first 15 lots are of essentially the same quality, and none should have been rejected.   Those which were rejected (or retested until they

[1] *Ibid.*   General Simon states that the data in Table 48 have been altered in scale only, so as to reveal no actual military information.

passed) represent merely so much economic loss. However, near or between Lots 15 and 16 a change occurred. If the specification criteria are really important, all the Lots 16 through 25 (not just part of them) should have been rejected. Thus, it is all too evident that Lots 1 through 15 constitute the real lot (called the grand lot) in the sense that they are *an aggregation of articles which are essentially alike.* In a like manner Lots 16 through 25 constitute another real lot, but a lot which should not pass the specification."

340. Control Charts Used to Accept a Process. The evidence given by a control chart that a process is in control at a satisfactory level and with satisfactory dispersion may be used as a basis for acceptance without the application of lot-by-lot criteria either by variables or attributes. At such time as the control chart shows lack of control—even though no defective product is found in the small control chart sample—lot-by-lot criteria involving larger sample sizes may then be initiated. An example of this is the acceptance procedure for steel castings developed in the Ordnance Department of the U.S. Army. It is reproduced here by permission of the Chief of Ordnance.

STANDARD INSPECTION PROCEDURES
Procedure XI: Inspection of Steel Castings for Acceptance.
Scope

1. This Plan permits a reduction in the amount of tension and cold bend testing required for the acceptance of steel castings, without loss of confidence in their quality. It also provides an improved method of evaluating this quality.

2. The Plan must be applied individually to each class of steel castings produced by a single facility. If a facility is using more than one type of melting process, the plan must be applied separately to each class of castings from each such process.

Eligibility for Reduced Testing

3. Normal testing, as referred to herein, is the character and quantity of testing required by the Specification for the steel castings in question. In order to determine eligibility for a reduction in the amount of testing below that specified as normal, quality control charts shall be constructed for averages and ranges of both yield point and elongation. Averages and ranges shall be determined from the test results obtained for each group of four successive lots of castings. (Notes Paragraph 3.)

4. After averages and ranges have been plotted for ten consecutive groups (forty lots), control limits and central lines for averages, and control limits for ranges, shall be computed and plotted on the charts for yield point and for elongation. (Notes Paragraph 4.)

5. Initial eligibility for reduced testing is established when:

> (a) none of the forty points plotted under paragraph four (ten for yield point averages, ten for yield point ranges, ten for elongation averages, and ten for elongation ranges) is outside its control limits, and

(b) neither lower control limit for averages (yield point or elongation) is below the Specification minimum, and

(c) none of the forty lots involved shall have been rejected (Notes Paragraph 5c), and

(d) not more than two "original" cold bend test failures have occurred in these forty lots, nor more than one such failure in the last ten of these lots (Notes Paragraph 3).

If initial eligibility is not established by the first ten consecutive groups for which results are plotted under paragraph 4, plotting of results shall be continued until ten consecutive groups (forty lots) are obtained for which the requirements of 5a, 5b, 5c, and 5d are met, thus establishing initial eligibility for reduced testing. In computing control limits for the purposes of 5a and 5b, data for only the last ten consecutive groups (forty lots) shall be used.

Inspection under Reduced Testing

6. As soon as initial eligibility for reduced testing has been established:

(a) Only one tension test and only one cold bend test (when required) shall be made for every three successive lots, except that where batch type heat-treatment furnaces holding more than three lots at a time are used, only one test per heat-treatment batch may be required at the discretion of the Ordnance District. Each tension test shall include measurements of tensile strength, yield point, elongation, and reduction of area.

(b) Averages and ranges for yield point and elongation shall continue to be determined for each group of four successive tests, and shall be plotted on the control charts. Control limits for averages and ranges shall be computed from cumulative results. (Notes Paragraph 6b.)

(c) The yield point and elongation values from individual tests shall be plotted on the control charts for averages, along with the average values for groups of four consecutive tests. Control limits for individual test results shall be plotted twice as far from the central line for averages as are the control limits for averages of groups of four.

(d) If an individual test value for yield point or elongation falls below both the Specification minimum and the corresponding lower control limit for individuals, or if an individual test value for tensile strength or reduction of area falls below its Specification minimum, a companion specimen shall be tested for all four characteristics (yield point, elongation, tensile strength, and reduction of area). Each test value thus obtained shall be averaged with its corresponding value from the original specimen, to obtain a "verification value" for each of the four characteristics. (Notes Paragraph 6d.)

7. Reduced testing shall continue, and all current lots may be accepted without awaiting the results of tests, so long as:

(a) all average values plotted under paragraph 6b, fall above their lower control limits, and all range values so plotted fall below their upper control limits; and

(b) no "verification value" for any characteristic, obtained as a result of the provisions of paragraph 6d, is less than the Specification minimum; and

(c) no change is made in raw materials or the manufacturing process which, in the opinion of the Resident Inspector of Ordnance, may have an undesirable effect upon the physical properties of the castings; and

(d) no control chart shows ten consecutive averages which fall either all above, or all below, the central line;

(e) no recomputed lower control limit for averages falls below the Specification minimum; and

(f) not more than one "original" cold bend test failure has occurred in the last ten tests (Notes Paragraph 3).

Loss of Eligibility for Reduced Testing

8. Upon failure to meet any of the conditions of paragraph 7, eligibility for reduced testing is lost, and normal testing as required by the Specification must be resumed, unless the requirements for initial eligibility are met by the last ten groups tested. In the latter event, reduced testing shall continue (Notes Paragraph 8).

9. In case eligibility for reduced testing is lost because of a failure to meet requirements 7a, 7b, or 7c, it is re-established if, for the next four succeeding groups (sixteen consecutive lots), all of the requirements of 7a, 7c, 7d, 7e, and 7f are met. Reduced testing may then be resumed. (Notes Paragraph 9.)

10. If eligibility for reduced testing has not been re-established under the provisions of paragraph 9, or if eligibility is lost because of a failure to meet requirements 7d, 7e, or 7f, reduced testing may be resumed whenever the more exacting requirements of initial eligibility have again been met. (Notes Paragraph 8.)

11. All lots from which specimens have been tested, and which have subsequently been re-heat treated, shall be subject to retest under the provisions of the Specification. No retest results from such lots shall be included in data from which control charts are plotted for the purposes of this Plan.

Notes

Paragraph 3

When more than one specimen from a lot is subjected to tension tests, or when more than one specimen is cold-bend-tested, only the results of the first or "original" test shall be used in each case in applying the requirements of this Plan; except that if a test specimen proves defective, as defined in applicable Specifications, all test results from that specimen shall be disregarded and the results from a replacement specimen shall be used instead.

Test results shall be grouped in the sequence obtained. Testing sequence shall conform as closely as possible to the sequence of manufacture.

Averages and ranges shall be computed to the same number of significant figures to which test results are regularly reported. The range is determined by subtracting the smallest value in each group of four from the largest value.

Paragraph 4.

Upper control limit for averages: $\overline{\overline{X}} + 0.729\overline{R}$
Lower control limit for averages: $\overline{\overline{X}} - 0.729\overline{R}$
Upper control limit for ranges: $2.282\overline{R}$
Lower control limit for ranges: Zero

where $\overline{\overline{X}}$ is the average of the group averages (central line), and $\overline{R}$ is the average of the ranges.

Paragraph 5c.

A lot which has been tested for acceptance and failed shall be considered rejected when withdrawn by the facility from further acceptance testing, or when it is apparent to the Resident Inspector of Ordnance that it cannot successfully pass the required tests.

Paragraph 6b.

All control limits determined for initial eligibility purposes shall be projected ahead and shall apply to the first ten points plotted after reduced inspection becomes effective. When the results for these next ten points become available, they shall be used, together with those used in determining the previous limits, to compute new control limits which shall in turn be projected to cover the next ten points. This process shall be repeated until the control limits are based upon the results from fifty groups (two hundred lots). Thereafter, all projected control limits shall be based upon the most recent fifty groups only.

If an average value or a range value for any group falls outside the control limits in effect at the time that value is plotted, no data from that group shall be included in future control limit recomputations for either averages or ranges, and no such groups shall be counted in accumulating points by tens for control limit recomputations.

Paragraph 6d.

In computing averages and ranges for a group of four lots from one or more of which a companion specimen has been tested, all test results from companion specimens shall be disregarded and results obtained from original specimens only shall be used.

Paragraph 8.

In reapplying the initial eligibility requirements, new control limits must be computed using only the results obtained from the last ten groups (forty lots) plotted. If all requirements of paragraph 5 are met by these ten groups with respect to these new limits, eligibility for reduced testing is established. The new limits shall then be projected ahead and applied to all points for the next succeeding ten groups. The procedure described in the notes on paragraph 6b shall be continued thereafter.

Paragraph 9.

In re-establishing eligibility on the basis of test results from the next four succeeding groups, the control limits in effect immediately before eligibility was lost shall apply; except that if the procedure described in the notes on paragraph 6b requires recomputation of these limits at any time, such recomputation shall be made and the recomputed limits will then apply.

This type of approach may be particularly advantageous in establishing eligibility for reduced testing in cases where testing is unusually costly or testing facilities are limited. Acceptance procedures of this type were developed during World War II for the ballistic testing of armor plate and ammunition with substantial savings in costs of tests and with important resulting improvements in quality. Shortly after the initiation of this program, G. D. Edwards commented on these acceptance procedures as follows:[1]

The quality-control inspection plan now in effect on armor plate already has reduced by approximately one-half the total amount of ballistic testing necessary by Ordnance Department proving grounds, and further reductions are being made constantly as additional manufacturers become eligible for reduced testing. The saving in plate destroyed by test has been substantial—in fact it was this potential saving which provided the original incentive for inauguration of the plan. But the time saving for proof facilities and personnel also has been important as has even the reduction in the number of proof projectiles required. A less tangible but perhaps equally important effect of the plan has been an evident tendency on the part of several manufacturers to improve the ballistic properties of their plate as a result of the better understanding which they now have of the factors by which its quality is judged. . . .

Quality control also is being applied in the ballistic testing of armor-piercing shot under a plan which effects a substantial saving in shot, proof time, and armor plate consumed. With one type of shot, for example, the reduction in rounds fired is seventy-five to eighty percent.

In contrast, acceptance specifications involving costly destructive testing often are written with complete disregard of statistical considerations. Unfortunately, the type of acceptance procedure described in Example 29 is much too common.

EXAMPLE 29. AN UNSATISFACTORY ACCEPTANCE SPECIFICATION

341. Facts of the Case. The production of a certain complicated mechanism under a government contract was about 300 per day. Specifications called for acceptance or rejection of these mechanisms in lots of 100. The chief difficulty in

[1] EDWARDS, G. D., Quality Control of Munitions—The Modern Ounce of Prevention Applied to Ordnance, *Army Ordnance*, vol. 23, pp. 482–485, November–December, 1942. This quotation is from an article written only a few months after the control-chart acceptance program started. The savings during the two and a half years of war following the writing of the article were even more striking than appeared possible during the first few months.

securing acceptance of all product was in connection with an accelerated life test. This test required continuous operation of the mechanism for 60 hr. A certain specified operating characteristic of the mechanism was measured at the end of 60 hr.; a failure of this characteristic to fall above a given limit constituted a failure of the life test.

The acceptance specification required that each 100 mechanisms coming off the production line should be identified as one lot. A single mechanism was selected at random from the lot of 100 and given the life test. Each lot was stored and its identity maintained until the 60-hr. test was completed. If this sample of one passed the test, the lot of 100 was accepted. If the sample of one failed the test, the remaining 99 mechanisms in the lot were disassembled, checked, reassembled, and submitted for a new test. The occasional rejection of a lot proved to be a costly matter, not only from the standpoint of the operations performed on the rejected mechanisms but also because of the interruption to regular production.

342. Comment on Acceptance Procedures Involving Destructive Tests of Small Samples. About the only good thing that can be said about the acceptance procedure in Example 29 is that, by making things unpleasant for the producer whenever a lot was rejected, it brought pressure on him to improve his product. (However, note that it did not give him any help as to how to make the improvement.) In no other way did it give the consumer any real protection against defective product.

The truth of this statement is evident if it is recognized that the quality characteristic that was tested at the end of the 60 hr. was—like all other measurable quality characteristics of manufactured product—really a frequency distribution. The fact that some of the mechanisms tested failed to meet specifications might indicate various possible conditions.

One possible condition was that the product was in statistical control with respect to the quality characteristic but that the frequency distribution was located in a way that part of its area was below the specification limit. For instance, 10% of the distribution might be below the limit. If this were true, there would be little difference between the lots of 100. On the average, one lot in 10 would be rejected by taking a sample of one out of each lot, but the rejected lots would not differ appreciably from the accepted lots. With this condition, the reworking of the rejected lots would be of no value.

Another possible condition was that the product was not in statistical control. The frequency distribution might at some times be located so that all the product met specifications; at other times, different fractions of it would be defective. In the unlikely event that all lots were either 100% good or 100% defective, the sample of one would tell the good lots from the defective ones. Otherwise, this sample has little power to discriminate. Even a lot 50% bad would have an even chance of being accepted. A lot would have to be 90% bad before the probability of its acceptance would be as low as 0.10.

If control charts for $\overline{X}$ and R had been used, this unsatisfactory acceptance procedure might have been greatly improved. The three mechanisms tested from the daily production of 300 would have provided a daily subgroup of three. If the control charts had shown control with a substantial fraction defective, this would have made it evident that for satisfactory results it was necessary either to make a fundamental change in the process, change the specification limit, or reject all the product. On the other hand, if the control charts had shown the product to be satisfactory most of the time, with occasional out-of-control bad lots, the out-of-control lots might have been rejected. Their identification might have given useful clues for process improvement.

The following general comments relate to acceptance procedures whenever it is imperative that samples be very small because tests are destructive or otherwise costly:

1. Most specifications either state or imply that *all* product must fall within (or above or below) given limits for each specified quality characteristic. *It is impossible to enforce* 100% *conformity to such specifications by sampling.* If the test for the quality characteristic is destructive of the article tested, a 100% test would destroy all the product. Another case where 100% testing is impossible is where the product is continuous with respect to the specified quality characteristic, rather than made up of pieces that can be separately tested. Thus many specifications are written in a way which, for practical purposes, makes them unenforceable.

2. Where each lot is accepted or rejected solely because a small sample from that lot either conforms or does not conform to specifications, the acceptance procedure is really unable to distinguish between good and bad lots. Such an acceptance procedure not only gives poor quality protection; it also fails to provide much helpful information regarding the capabilities of the process to meet the specifications.

3. The $\overline{X}$ and R (or $\overline{X}$ and σ) charts, on the other hand, give a great deal of information about the capabilities of the process. They tell whether the current lot and those which preceded it seem to be essentially alike—whether, from the quality viewpoint, there is one process or many different processes. If there is one process (*i.e.*, if statistical control exists) the charts tell the centering of that process and its dispersion. These are matters that need to be known in judging whether the design specifications are being met.

4. *For the $\overline{X}$ and R (or $\overline{X}$ and σ) charts to give satisfactory evidence regarding statistical control, it is necessary to preserve the order of production,* and other information pertinent to establishing rational subgroups. A manufacturer inspecting his own product can do this. So can the government, if it is a purchaser conducting its inspection in a manufacturing

plant. In most vendor-purchaser relationships, however, the purchaser has no way of knowing the order of production.

This need for preserving the basis for rational subgrouping provides a reason for acceptance inspection carried on close to the point of production. One good way of doing this is possible whenever a purchaser has confidence in the vendor; the purchaser may accept on the basis of the vendor's control chart supplemented by occasional tests made by the purchaser. In other cases, where there are a number of purchasers receiving product from a single vendor, an impartial agency may be admitted to the vendor's plant to conduct tests for all purchasers.

5. Any acceptance procedure based on the viewpoint that each lot is unique is certain to fall short of providing the best quality assurance. In order to get satisfactory evidence from small samples, it is necessary to combine lots into a grand lot wherever justifiable. As pointed out in the quotation from General Simon, this calls for the use of the Shewhart control chart as an essential part of the acceptance procedure.

6. Wherever practicable, there is an advantage in allowing some room for judgment in the interpretation of the control chart for acceptance purposes. This statement assumes that someone competent to have judgment is available with sufficient time really to examine the evidence of the chart.

7. Anything that improves quality simplifies the problems of acceptance inspection. In the long run, the greatest contribution of the $\bar{X}$ and R charts to acceptance usually turns out to be their contribution to quality improvement.

8. Because of the common practice of including a margin of safety in design specifications, product not conforming to design specifications is not necessarily unsatisfactory for the purpose intended. This calls for consideration of the size of this margin of safety in making a decision on the acceptance procedure. Sometimes the required quality protection can be obtained with greater economy if the margin of safety is changed. The economic aspects of this matter are discussed briefly in Chap. XVII.

343. Allowance for Sampling Error in Variables Acceptance Tests When Specification Limits Apply to Averages. All of the foregoing discussion of acceptance sampling in Chaps. XIII to XVI has assumed that specification limits apply to individual articles. In some instances, however, specifications may apply to lot averages even though tests are made on individual articles within a lot. Examples of specifications of this type are minimum requirements for average bursting strength in a lot of fiberboard or for average warpwise breaking strength in a lot of cloth and maximum requirements for average moisture content in soap or in food products.

Where this type of specification exists, attributes inspection is impossible. In lot-by-lot acceptance by variables, it is necessary to measure the value of the quality characteristic in each item of a sample, to compute the sample average, and to compare this sample average with the specification requirements for lot average. In this situation, the simplest type of acceptance specification is to require rejection of a lot unless the sample average satisfies the specification for lot average. For example, assume the average warpwise breaking strength in a lot of a certain type of cloth is specified as not less than 200 lb. per in. A sample of four is tested from the lot. If the sample average is 200 or more, the lot is accepted; if it is less than 200, the lot is rejected.

This simple acceptance rule splits the risk of a wrong decision between producer and consumer; the variables sample is as likely to misrepresent a lot too favorably as to misrepresent it too unfavorably. However, this splitting of the risk may be unfair to the producer, particularly if his quality history is satisfactory. It may be more reasonable to use an acceptance rule that protects the producer against sampling errors that might cause the rejection of satisfactory lots.

Specification limits applicable to lot averages are fairly common for certain types of product purchased by the Quartermaster Corps of the U.S. Army. In an article in *Industrial Quality Control*, David H. Schwartz and Paul Kaufman of the Quartermaster Inspection Service describe two tests that have been developed to protect the producer against such lot rejections by making an allowance for possible sampling errors.[1] One test, the U-test, is, in effect, a known-sigma test for a one-sided specification; the other, the Q-test, is, in effect, an unknown-sigma test for a one-sided specification. In both tests, the lot dispersion is described in terms of *lot range*, defined as $6\sigma'$. In the Q-test, sample range is used as the measure of sample dispersion. The U and Q factors are shown in Table 49, reproduced from the Schwartz-Kaufman article.

Where the U-test is used, a lot is accepted unless the sample average fails to meet the specification on lot average by more than the product of the U-factor and the known lot range. Consider the specification of 200 lb. per in. for average warpwise breaking strength of cloth. Past experience indicates a σ' of 5 lb. per in. This gives a lot range ($6\sigma'$) of 30 lb. per in. Four pieces tested from a lot have strengths of 204, 199, 195, and 192. The average of the sample is 197.5 lb. per in.

This is 2.5 below the specification limit. Table 49 gives a U-factor of 0.125. Hence the allowable departure is $(0.125)(30) = 3.75$. As the actual departure is less than that allowable, the lot is accepted.

[1] SCHWARTZ, D. H., and PAUL KAUFMAN, Determining Conformance with Requirements for Lot Average, *Industrial Quality Control*, vol. 7, No. 5, pp. 18–21, March, 1951.

The Q-test may be illustrated by application to the same data, assuming that no prior information is available for estimation of the lot range. With this test, the allowable departure is the product of the Q-factor and the sample range. With the above data, this product is $(0.46)(12) = 5.52$. As the actual departure is 2.5, the lot is accepted.

TABLE 49. U AND Q FACTORS FOR SCHWARTZ-KAUFMAN TESTS

Sample sizes	U Factor	Q Factor
2	0.160	1.50
3	0.138	0.69
4	0.125	0.46
5	0.118	0.37
6–7	0.113	0.32
8–9	0.107	0.26
10–11	0.100	0.22
12–13	0.093	0.19
14–17	0.083	0.16
18–22	0.073	0.13

In the July 1951 issue of *Industrial Quality Control* Schwartz and Kaufman give corrected OC curves for both tests for the various sample sizes. With these U- and Q-factors, the probability of acceptance of a lot having an average at exactly the specification limit varies from about 0.90 for a sample of 2 to about 0.98 for a sample of 20. Of course the larger samples have much steeper OC curves and therefore give the consumer better protection against accepting lots having averages very far from the specification limit. For a given sample size, the U-test gives better consumer protection against bad lots than does the Q-test. The U-test should therefore be preferred whenever there is a satisfactory basis for estimating σ'.

Schwartz and Kaufman make the following remarks regarding the circumstances under which such allowances for sampling error should be made:

The U and Q tests provide margins for sampling error to be used in weighing the *tentative* assumption that the lot average is really satisfactory. Evidence may be available, however, that this tentative assumption should *not* be considered in the first place. For example, the average moisture content of a sample of a prepared spaghetti product is found to be 13% instead of 12% (the maximum allowable lot average). In addition, it is known that in the preparation of this particular batch, the temperature of the mixture was permitted to fall below the boiling point for an unknown period of time. Under such circumstances, it may well be expected that the moisture content of the finished product would be too high, and the unsatisfactory sample average would *not* be explained away as mere sampling error.

After all, there are always two possibilities: either the average of the lot as a whole is really satisfactory, or it is really unsatisfactory. Every available morsel of engineering knowledge should be used in deciding which of these two assumptions is the more likely before applying the U or Q test. An allowance should *not* be made on a lot whose sample average is non-conforming if there is prior evidence that the lot average actually is unsatisfactory. Frequently, however, such prior evidence is unavailable. As a rule of thumb, it is therefore suggested that an allowance be made on the current lot unless it is the third time in a row that the sample average has been outside of the specified lot average limit. The chance of unjustly refusing an allowance under this rule will not exceed one out of eight (*i.e.*, $\frac{1}{2} \times \frac{1}{2} \times \frac{1}{2}$).

This discussion is not meant to discourage the reader from applying the U or Q test, but to point out that good judgment is needed in deciding *when* the tests are applicable. If there is no prior indication that the current lot is unsatisfactory, then an allowance for sampling error *should* be made. A lot should be presumed "innocent" until proven "guilty" beyond a reasonable doubt.

344. Some Statistical Aspects of Proof Testing. Where, because testing is destructive, only a small sample can be tested, a possible alternative is the application of some load short of destruction of 100% of the product. Some advantages and limitations of such proof tests are brought out in the following comments by J. J. Taylor relative to routine tests of ceramic insulators:[1]

Ceramic parts may be inspected visually, sometimes with the aid of penetrating fluids; or aurally by "ringing out" methods. Attention has been given also to X-Ray examination and to non-destructive tests involving supersonic response. Many tests are, however, potentially destructive and would produce failure if increased sufficiently in severity. Dielectric soundness is checked by high frequency or 60 cycle flashover on ceramic parts and assembled units. For certain specialized types of insulators, impulse tests are routine procedure. Routine mechanical tests of assemblies are made at a load level about half the rated ultimate strength and are followed by a dielectric test.

Since routine tests for both dielectric and mechanical strength are potentially destructive, some compromise is necessary between tests too mild to eliminate defectives and those severe enough to damage an appreciable portion of specimens near the minimum end of the distribution pattern.

Mechanical tests at half the rated strength are not intended to cut off the minimum end of the distribution curve. They are used to give assurance against defectives with potential characteristics far below the minimum level of expectancy.

[1] TAYLOR, J. J., Statistical Methods Applied to Insulator Development and Manufacture, *Transactions American Institute of Electrical Engineers*, vol. 64, pp. 495–499, July, 1945.

It cannot safely be assumed that high levels of routine test guarantee quality. Such tests may be particularly undesirable on a product manufactured with good factory control but with no great margin in average strength. In Figure 81, two distribution curves are shown that have the same probability of failure at or below the specified minimum level. If both groups of product are proof-tested to eliminate units lying below the minimum line, and if the test is harmful to units only slightly stronger than the proof load, then it is likely that such testing will be detrimental to design (*a*) and beneficial to design (*b*). In the first case it damages more units than it eliminates and in the other case it eliminates more units than it damages.

It is probable that no amount of proof testing, however drastic, can select from carelessly manufactured material a finished batch as dependable as one

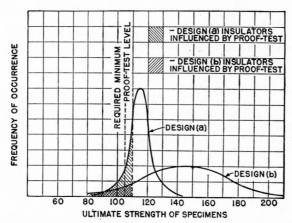

Fig. 81.   Proof testing in relation to strength distribution.

made in the first instance with good technical control and given routine tests at reasonable levels. This view implies, in specifications, emphasis on consistency of tested characteristics; a carefully drawn sampling plan; a cumulative record of test history so that past experience can be of real value in interpreting the results of samples under immediate review.

It should be noted also that some product characteristics cannot be given routine tests that will check them. Line and station insulators are designed and design-tested to withstand electrical surges of great severity, but so far it has not been practical to surge test at these extreme levels in routine fashion. Even if it were possible it might be proved an undesirable practice because of the damaging nature of the tests. In such instances reliance must be placed on methods of quality control which give high-probability assurance that the required characteristic is present.

Problems

276. The minimum temperature of operation for a certain device is specified as 180°. A known-sigma variables acceptance plan with a sample size of 9 is to be used. The desired value of $100p_{0.10}$ is 4.0%. From Table *S*, find k'. If σ' is 6°, will a lot be accepted when the sample items have operating temperatures of 197, 188, 184, 205, 201, 190, 195, 193, and 199? *Ans.* $k' = 2.178$; yes, because $194.7 > 193.1$.

277. From Table S find the n and k of the unknown-sigma plan having its OC curve agreeing most closely with that of the known-sigma plan selected in Problem 276.
Ans. $n = 16$, $k = 2.018$.

278. In the absence of reliable information on σ', the unknown-sigma plan of Problem 277 is to be used for acceptance of the product mentioned in Problem 276. Will a lot be accepted when the sample items have operating temperatures of 202, 195, 191, 198, 178, 185, 194, 191, 192, 188, 203, 197, 197, 190, 189, and 182?
Ans. No, because $192.0 < 193.7$.

279. Assume that the specification in Problem 276 applies to lot averages and that the minimum allowable lot average is 198°. Would the sample in Problem 276 be accepted on the basis of a Schwartz-Kaufman U-test?
Ans. Yes, because $194.7 > 194.15$.

280. In Problem 279, would the lot be accepted on the basis of a Q-test, assuming lot range is unknown? *Ans.* Yes, because $194.7 > 192.5$.

281. The specification for electrical resistance of a certain electrical component is 650.0 ± 30.0 ohms. From Table S find n and k'^* for a known-sigma plan for a two-sided specification that will have an OC curve similar to that of the single sampling attributes plan $n = 55$, $c = 2$. If σ' is 11.5 ohms, within what limits must the $\bar{X}$ of a sample fall for a lot to be accepted?
Ans. $n = 10$, $k'^* = 1.742$; $\bar{X}$ must be between 640.0 and 660.0.

282. With the σ' and the specification in Problem 281, what is the minimum percentage of defectives possible in any lot? *Ans.* 0.9%.

283. With the acceptance plan selected in Problem 281, what is the probability of acceptance of a 2% defective lot? *Ans.* 0.85.

284. Select n and k' for a known-sigma variables plan for a one-sided specification so that the OC curve of the plan will be similar to that of the single sampling attributes plan $n = 15$, $c = 2$. With this plan what will be the probability of acceptance of a 5% defective lot?

285. The specified minimum yield point for certain steel castings is 55,000 psi. Five castings are tested from each lot. A known-sigma variables plan is to be used for which $100p_{0.95} = 1.20\%$. The estimated σ' is 3,000 psi. Make the necessary test to determine whether a lot will be accepted if the yield points of the sample specimens are 62,500; 60,500; 68,000; 59,000; and 65,500.

286. What unknown-sigma variables plan will have an OC curve agreeing most closely with the known-sigma plan selected in Problem 285?

287. The minimum requirement on the weight of the contents of a certain container is 120.0 oz. It is desired that a 2% defective lot have a probability of acceptance of 0.95. The unknown-sigma plan, $n = 13$, $k = 1.472$, is selected. The measured weights in a certain sample of 13 are 122.0, 121.5, 121.9, 120.2, 123.1, 119.7, 120.5, 120.7, 121.3, 121.1, 122.3, 120.9, and 120.4. Make the necessary calculations to determine whether this lot will be accepted.

288. The specification for moisture content of a certain food product states that the average moisture content in a lot must not exceed 14.0%. A sample of four from a certain lot gives the following percentages of moisture: 13.6, 14.5, 14.9, 13.8. If σ' is assumed to be 0.4%, will this lot be passed by a Schwartz-Kaufman U-test?

289. In Problem 288, assume no information is available regarding σ'. Will the lot pass a Q-test?

290. The specification on a certain dimension of a manufactured part is 1.7030 ± 0.0030 in. In a Lot Plot for this dimension, the first three digits of the measured values for all 50 items are 1.70. The final two digits are those given in Table 12 (page. 79), for the first 50 drawings from the Shewhart bowl, in the order stated. Prepare the Lot Plot, assuming cell boundaries of 32.5, 36.5, 40.5, etc. Compute the upper and lower lot limits by the method described in the explanation of the Lot Plot plan. Draw these limits on your Lot Plot.

291. Follow the directions for Problem 290, using the Shewhart bowl drawings 201–250 as shown on page 80.

292. A sample of 50 cans of tomatoes is taken from a large lot. The drained weights of contents of these cans are to be shown on a Lot Plot. Assume that these 50 weights are the first 50 figures in Table 6 (page 43), in the order given. Prepare a Lot Plot, assuming cell boundaries as 20.25, 20.75, 21.25, etc. Compute lot limits, and draw them on your Lot Plot.

293. Follow the directions for Problem 292, using the last 50 measured weights in Table 6 (page 43).

294. In order to gain an impression of the way in which sample size influences the OC curves of unknown-sigma variables plans for a given value of k, use Table T to plot approximate OC curves of four plans all having a k of 2.0 and having values of n of 5, 10, 25, and 50, respectively. What general comment can you make about the effect of increased sample size?

295. It is desired to use an unknown-sigma variables plan having a value of $100p_{0.95}$ of approximately 1.50%. Table T gives plans of $n = 5$, $k = 1.2$; $n = 20$, $k = 1.6$; and $n = 50$, $k = 1.8$ that are close to meeting this requirement. Plot the approximate OC curves of these three plans. Comment on the effect of increasing the sample size in this instance.

296. The initial lots of a certain product are to be accepted or rejected on the basis of a destructive test of a sample of 5 items. An unknown-sigma variables test is to be used. It is desired that if a 4.0% defective lot is submitted, its probability of acceptance shall be 0.50. Use the information in Table T to plot a curve showing the relationship between k and $p_{0.50}$ for a sample size of 5. What is the approximate value of k that should be used for this test? Plot curves to estimate $p_{0.95}$ and $p_{0.10}$ for this k. Plot the approximate OC curve of this acceptance plan.

297. Table T indicates that the matching known-sigma plan having its k' equal to the k of Problem 296 should have a sample size of 2. Compute the probabilities of acceptance of lots 0.1%, 4.0%, and 20% defective, respectively, of lots from a normal distribution under this known-sigma plan.

Part Five
MAKING STATISTICAL QUALITY CONTROL WORK

CHAPTER XVII

SOME COST ASPECTS
OF QUALITY DECISIONS

Without quality control you, as a producer or purchaser, are in the same position as the man who bets on a horse race—with one exception, the odds are not posted. Statistical quality control will give you the odds on which you wish to place your money, your manpower, your tools, and your materials. It will tell you at what level and with what variation you are operating and, more important, it will tell you *when* your process, tools, or materials change from that level and range of variability. . . . Possibly most important of all will be the change in outlook on your purchases or production, and the inspection of both. The dazzling light which statistical quality control throws on everything surrounding the characteristic being examined many times reveals startling facts, sometimes good, sometimes bad. You will be shocked out of your complacency. Your philosophy will change for the better. Variability will be recognized as a natural inherent characteristic of your production or, if you are buying, of the incoming material.—FRANK M. STEADMAN[1]

345. Problems of Business Alternatives Are Problems in Economy. Decisions of many sorts are always being called for in the management of any productive enterprise. All decisions are between alternatives— either express or implied. In business enterprises operated for profit, the real basis of a choice between alternatives is the prospective effect of each alternative on the costs and revenues of the business. Where technical considerations are involved in the alternatives, a study comparing specific money estimates of the differences between the alternatives as well as other estimated differences not readily expressible in money terms is called an *engineering economy study*.

Engineering economy studies dealing with quality matters are often more difficult than studies dealing with such matters as proposed investments in industrial assets. This is primarily because of the difficulty of expressing in money terms the probable effect of particular quality decisions. In some manufacturing plants, this difficulty may be due in part to the fact that the accounts of the enterprise do not identify certain types of costs, such as costs of spoilage and rework, in any satisfactory way. Nevertheless, to a large extent the difficulty is an inherent one in quality decisions; certain elements in such decisions are extremely hard to measure in money terms.

[1] STEADMAN, F. M. Quality Control Posts Mill-production Odds, *Textile World*, vol. 94, p. 63, July, 1944.

Perhaps for this reason, most quality decisions seem to be made on an intuitive basis without any conscious attempt to evaluate the elements of each decision in the only units that can make all the elements commensurable, namely, in money units. Intuition may be a good enough guide in many circumstances, but it may occasionally prove to be a very costly one. Moreover, it is common to find that different individuals in an organization will reach opposite conclusions on quality matters whenever the basis for such decisions depends entirely on intuition.

The brief discussion in the remainder of this chapter is intended to suggest the controlling elements in certain types of quality decisions. A recognition of these elements should be helpful in improving the rational basis for quality decisions even in the numerous cases where a money evaluation of all of the elements in a particular decision turns out to be impracticable.

346. Three General Classes of Costs Entering into Economy Studies Involving Quality of Conformance. In using the word quality, it is necessary to recognize the distinction between quality of design and quality of conformance. In the sense that a Lincoln is considered to be a better quality automobile than a Ford, or a Cadillac a better quality one than a Chevrolet, the word *quality* is used in the sense of quality of design. The designers of the higher priced automobiles have included certain more costly features aimed to secure greater comfort, better appearance, better performance, etc.

In the sense used in this chapter, quality of conformance relates to whether or not the quality characteristics of a product correspond to those really needed to secure the results intended by the designer. Used in this sense, margins of safety written into design specifications are often aimed chiefly at securing quality of conformance. Where such margins of safety are used with this objective, design specifications and acceptance specifications are properly viewed as interrelated matters.

Decisions involving quality of conformance may relate to the amount and type of inspection, to production methods and objectives, and to margins of safety used in design specifications. In making economy studies to guide such decisions, it is helpful to divide the costs influenced by the decisions into three general classes. These may be somewhat loosely referred to as (1) production costs, (2) acceptance costs, and (3) unsatisfactory-product costs.

In this usage, the expression *production costs* is intended to refer to those costs involved in the production of the article under consideration. Different design specifications may require different materials, different labor skills, different amounts of labor time, and different machines. For example, increased strength requirements for a part may change the material to be used; closer required tolerances on dimensions may call for the use of newer or different machines. This general class of costs properly includes *spoilage costs, i.e.,* the production expenses on all product discarded as not meeting specifications minus any receipts from the disposal of this discarded product. It also includes *rework costs* necessary to make product acceptable and screening costs, if any, on rejected lots.

The *acceptance costs* include not only testing and inspection costs but also the costs of administering the acceptance program.

The expression *unsatisfactory-product costs* is intended to refer to those costs resulting from the acceptance of product that turns out to be unsatisfactory for the purpose intended. In this sense the word *cost* should be interpreted as including a reduction in revenue as well as an increase in expense. It should be recognized that some or all of the product that is technically defective in the sense of failing to meet design specifications is not necessarily unsatisfactory for the purpose intended whenever the common practice is followed of including a margin of safety in the specifications. This distinction between product that is really unsatisfactory and product that is satisfactory even though nonconforming to specifications is an important one in any discussion of the economics of quality decisions.

Of these three classes of costs affected by quality decisions, unsatisfactory-product costs are inherently the most difficult to evaluate. Doubtless the greatest difficulty occurs in the consumers' goods industries, where the product goes to a great many different customers who make no formal acceptance tests. It is hard to predict the consequences to the manufacturer of consumers' goods when some stated percentage of his product fails to give satisfactory service to its purchasers, and it is even more difficult to place a money value on these consequences. Where the consumers' product carries a guarantee, past customer service costs can be used as a guide to judgment and changes in these costs can be carefully watched and related to changes in design specifications and in inspection and acceptance procedures.

The most favorable circumstances exist for securing reliable information on unsatisfactory-product costs when all of the product goes to one user. This user may be another department in the producer's organization, or it may be a single purchaser who is responsible for the design specification.

347. Reasons for Margins of Safety in Design Specifications. In specifying a quality characteristic such as a dimension, strength, resistance, etc., there will often be a twilight zone of uncertainty within which the product will be satisfactory under most conditions of use but not under all conceivable conditions. Design specifications may be drawn in a way that classifies as defective all articles falling in this twilight zone.

Moreover, designers often seem to believe that they cannot secure the quality characteristics that are really needed without requiring a margin of safety. This common practice has not been changed by the advent of statistical quality control techniques in industry. Some reasons for continuing to require a margin of safety are clearly stated by Wyatt H. Lewis, as follows:[1]

1. Acceptance sampling plans, although they may guarantee a long range average quality level of no worse than say 2% defective, may accept occasional lots with as much as 8% defective. Such a high per cent defective may cause dislocation of manufacturing operations at considerable cost due to lost time, excessive rework, special handling to make up for delays, etc.

2. Even a control chart using actual measurements may not detect slight shifts in the $\bar{X}$ or σ values for a matter of several samples and you might be in trouble before you realized it.

3. The vendor may have a process operating in control but there are times when causes arise to disturb the state of control. In such cases the margin of safety is very handy for acceptance of material on the basis of deviation from the specification in order to keep assembly lines going and to avoid sending operators home and cancelling orders. The cost of the latter cannot be ignored.

4. Laboratory instruments and inspection gages, although given periodic checks, sometimes drift and such drift is not detected until the next periodic check.

5. There is also the human element to consider: lack of experience, acceptance of borderline cases, etc.

In many industrial plants, it is a fairly common experience for parts first to be rejected by the inspection department because they fail to conform to specifications and later to be accepted by a plant salvage committee or material review board primarily on the grounds that their lack of conformity falls within the margin of safety included in the specifications.

348. Some Economic Aspects of Decisions on the Amount and Type of Inspection. Sometimes it is economical to do no inspection at all, sometimes 100% inspection is the most economical, and sometimes sampling inspection of one type or another is better than either. The objective should be to select that amount and type of inspection that will minimize the sum of the production costs, acceptance costs, and unsatisfactory-product costs influenced by the decision regarding inspection. Once this viewpoint has been adopted, certain conditions are evident that are favorable, respectively, to no inspection, to 100% inspection, and to sampling inspection.

---

[1] Lewis, W. H., Discussion of E. L. Grant, The Economic Relationship between Design and Acceptance Specifications, "Special Technical Publication No. 103, Symposium on Application of Statistics," American Society for Testing Materials, Philadelphia, Pa., 1950.

Where submitted product is consistently satisfactory for the purpose intended, it is likely to be most economical to have no inspection whatever. In this case, there are no unsatisfactory-product costs to be reduced by inspection. Neither do there appear to be production costs such as spoilage and rework to be reduced through diagnosis by control charts or through the pressure for process improvement exerted when product is rejected. Sometimes, however, as in the case of overfill of containers, concealed opportunities may exist for reducing production costs; such opportunities might be disclosed by variables sampling inspection using control charts.

Low unsatisfactory-product costs per unit of such product may also make it economical to do no inspection whatever. For example, where unsatisfactory product is readily discovered and eliminated in a subsequent production operation, it may be cheaper to tolerate a moderate percentage of such product than to eliminate it by inspection.

Where submitted product is consistent in quality but nearly always contains a substantial percentage of unsatisfactory product, 100% inspection may be the most economical alternative. Here the choice is likely to be between 100% inspection and no inspection for acceptance purposes; with a statistically controlled product, sampling inspection cannot be expected to separate the relatively good lots from the relatively bad ones. The higher the percentage of unsatisfactory product submitted and the higher the unsatisfactory-product cost per unit of such product, the more favorable the conditions for 100% inspection as compared with no inspection. The higher the unit cost of inspection and the less the effectiveness of 100% inspection in eliminating unsatisfactory product, the more favorable the conditions for no inspection.

In making economy studies regarding the amount and type of inspection, it should be recognized that sampling inspection schemes may possibly reduce unsatisfactory-product costs in two ways. One way is by the rejection or rectification of the relatively bad lots of product, thereby making the proportion of unsatisfactory product approved less than the proportion submitted. The other way is by reducing the proportion of unsatisfactory product submitted; sampling inspection may improve product quality through diagnosis of causes of quality troubles and through the exertion of effective pressure for process improvement. This improvement of product quality may also reduce production costs, particularly costs of spoilage and rework.

If this possible contribution of sampling inspection to the improvement of product quality is neglected, the following general statement may be made: The economic field for sampling inspection is where submitted product is usually good enough for no inspection to be more economical than 100% inspection and where submitted product is occasionally bad enough for 100% inspection to be more economical than no inspection.

The preceding verbal statements in this article regarding circumstances favorable to different types of inspection may be made somewhat clearer by some numerical illustrations. Examples 30 and 31 supply such illustrations. Example 30 describes a case in which the assumed facts are so simple as to be rather unrealistic. Example 31 is intended to introduce some more realistic complications.

EXAMPLE 30.   COMPARISON OF 100% INSPECTION WITH NO INSPECTION

349. Facts of the Case. A certain part is made in lots that are typically about 0.5% defective. All these defectives might be eliminated by a 100% inspection. If no inspection of this part is made prior to its use in an assembled product, the defective parts will be discovered in a 100% final test of this assembled product and can then be replaced. No margin of safety has been included in the design specification; all parts that are defective in the technical sense of failing to meet the design specification are also unsatisfactory in the sense that they will prevent proper functioning of the assembled product.

Inspection cost for screening inspection is estimated as $0.015 per unit. Unsatisfactory-product cost is $2 per unit of such product. Annual need is for 99,500 parts; because of the 0.5% of defectives this requires production of 100,000. Comparison of those annual costs influenced by the choice between no inspection and 100% inspection is as follows:

	No inspection	100% inspection
Production cost...................	Not affected	Not affected
Acceptance cost...................	$0	$1,500
Unsatisfactory-product cost.........	1,000	0
Total........................	$1,000	$1,500

Under the stated conditions, it is more economical to remove the defective parts from the assembled final product than to screen the parts to prevent the defectives from reaching the final product.

EXAMPLE 31.   COMPARISON OF 100% INSPECTION, AOQL SAMPLING INSPECTION, AND NO INSPECTION

350. Facts of the Case. A certain part is made in lots of 2,000. These lots commonly average about 1.0% defective. Because of a margin of safety in the design specification, unsatisfactory parts constitute only 0.2% of a lot containing 1% of parts failing to conform to design specifications. This process is not in good statistical control. About one-tenth of the lots average about 5% defective; such lots contain 1.4% of unsatisfactory product. It is desired to compare the economy of (1) 100% inspection, (2) the Dodge-Romig 2% single sampling AOQL plan $n = 65$ and $c = 2$, and (3) no inspection.

In this comparison it is assumed that because of inspection fatigue, 100% inspection will remove only 90% of the unsatisfactory parts. It is also assumed that inspection will find all defective parts submitted in samples and in screened rejected lots under the AOQL plan. Inspection will cost $0.015 per unit under 100% inspection and, because of the variability of inspection load and the more complicated job of supervision, $0.02 under the AOQL plan. Any unsatisfactory part entering the assembly department will be finally discovered and eliminated at an average cost of $3 per part. Annual production of this part is 100,000, *i.e.*, 50 lots of 2,000 each.

To estimate the inspection cost and unsatisfactory-product cost for the AOQL plan, it is necessary to compute the average number of items inspected per lot and the average number of unsatisfactory parts per lot passed on to assembly. Using Table G to estimate values of P_a, these calculations are:

For 1% defective product (90% of the lots)

$np' = (65)(0.01) = 0.65$
$P_a = 0.972$ ˙
Av. items inspected per lot $= 0.972(65) + 0.028(2,000) = 119$
Av. unsatisfactory parts passed $= (0.972)(0.2\%) = 0.194\%$, or 3.88 per lot

For 5% defective product (10% of the lots)

$np' = (65)(0.05) = 3.25$
$P_a = 0.370$
Av. items inspected per lot $= 0.370(65) + 0.630\ (2,000) = 1,284$
Av. unsatisfactory parts passed $= (0.370)(1.4\%) = 0.518\%$, or 10.36 per lot

For all product

Av. items inspected per lot $= 0.9(119) + 0.1(1,284) = 236$
Av. unsatisfactory parts passed per lot $= 0.9(3.88) + 0.1(10.36) = 4.53$

A comparison of the sum of inspection costs and unsatisfactory-product costs for the three inspection plans is as follows:

100% Inspection

Inspection cost...................................... $(100,000)($0.015) = \$1,500$
Unsatisfactory-product cost
           $90,000(0.002)(0.1)(\$3) + 10,000(0.014)(0.1)(\$3) =$ 96

Total... $1,596

AOQL Sampling Inspection

Inspection cost.................................... $50(236)($0.02) = \$ \ 236$
Unsatisfactory-product cost............................ $50(4.53)($3) =$ 680

Total.. $ \ 916$

No Inspection

Inspection cost.. $ \ 0$
Unsatisfactory-product cost....... $90,000(0.002)($3) + 10,000(0.014)($3) =$ 960

Total... $ \ 960$

An engineering economy study involves a comparison of money figures (costs and revenues) influenced by a choice among alternative courses of action. It finally concludes with a decision that some one of the alternatives is to be adopted (or recommended for adoption).   Between the tabulation of the money figures and the decision, two questions often need to be reviewed.[1]

The first question deals with any prospective differences among the alternatives that have not been reduced to money terms.   All prospective differences are relevant in the choice among the alternatives.   The second question deals with the way in which the relative advantages of the various alternatives will be influenced by changes from the particular circumstances assumed as a basis for the money comparison.

In the money comparison of the totals of inspection costs and unsatisfactory-product costs, one cost aspect not evaluated was the possibility of a difference in production costs.   Experience indicates that AOQL schemes often do exert effective pressure for quality improvement, particularly in cases where the screening of rejected lots is charged against the production department.   This favors the AOQL plan, as it is quite likely that in the long run this plan would result in more quality improvement than would occur either with 100 % inspection or with no inspection; spoilage costs may therefore be less if AOQL sampling is used.

Another prospective difference among the alternatives relates to the handling of those parts that are satisfactory for use in the assembled product even though technically defective in the sense of not meeting design specifications.   Under the alternative of no inspection, such parts will be used in the final product with no particular extra costs involved.   Under 100 % inspection and AOQL inspection, there will be extra costs, either for the replacement or reworking of all such parts rejected by inspection or for their ultimate acceptance for use in the assembled product through some procedure for material review.

In considering possible changes from the circumstances assumed in the money comparison, it is desirable to see how costs would be affected if submitted quality should be considerably worse than assumed and also if it should be considerably better. A review of this question is definitely favorable to the AOQL sampling scheme. Under no inspection, there is no upper limit to unsatisfactory-product cost if quality gets bad enough, whereas both the AOQL scheme and 100 % inspection definitely limit such costs.   At the other extreme, considering the sum of inspection costs and unsatisfactory-product costs, a great improvement in quality can make little saving in the costs under 100 % inspection, whereas substantial cost savings from quality improvement are possible both under the AOQL scheme and under no inspection.

All things considered, it seems clear that it is better to adopt the AOQL plan than to use either 100 % inspection or no inspection.

351. Further Comment on Decisions on the Amount and Type of Inspection.

Sometimes it is desired to compute the average percentage of unsatisfactory product at which 100% inspection will just break even with sampling inspection.   If submitted quality is better than this figure most of the time, the economic choice is then between sampling inspection and no inspection.

Under the simple conditions assumed in Example 30, acceptance costs may be equated to unsatisfactory-product cost to compute this break-even figure, as follows:

[1] For a more complete discussion of the ideas presented in this paragraph, see E. L. GRANT, "Principles of Engineering Economy," 3d ed., The Ronald Press Company, New York, 1950, particularly Chaps. 1, 2, and 11.

(Inspection cost per unit)(units of product)
= (unsatisfactory-product cost per unit of such product)(units of product)(average fraction unsatisfactory)

Av. fraction unsatisfactory at break-even point

$$= \frac{\text{inspection cost per unit}}{\text{unsatisfactory-product cost per unit of unsatisfactory product}}$$

For the data of Example 30, this break-even point is

$$\frac{\$0.015}{\$2} = 0.0075$$

or 0.75%.

In Example 30 it was stated that no margin of safety existed in the design specification. Hence this break-even point of 0.75% may be interpreted in per cent defective as well as per cent of unsatisfactory product. In the more usual case where a margin of safety exists, a break-even point expressed in per cent defective is obtained by multiplying by a factor equal to the expected ratio of defectives to unsatisfactory items. Further correction to such a computed break-even point must be made whenever it is believed that 100% inspection will not remove all of the unsatisfactory items.

Perhaps most readers of Example 31 will feel that the assumed facts sound rather complicated. Nevertheless, the complications introduced there are present in many actual situations. Still other complications not illustrated in this example are common in practice. One such complication is the need to consider many different possible sampling acceptance schemes rather than a single one. Another complication is the difficulty, already referred to, of placing a money value on unsatisfactory product where such product goes to customers. Still another complication is the difficulty existing whenever acceptance decisions relate to purchased product. In an economy study to determine acceptance criteria for purchased product, the relevant "production costs" are the payments to the vendor. It should be recognized that in any price negotiations, these payments are likely to depend on the vendor's production costs, which in turn are influenced by the design specifications (which presumably include a margin of safety aimed at quality protection) and by the severity of the purchaser's acceptance criteria.

Even though many practical situations are so complicated that a formal comparison of costs seems out of the question, the point of view that has been illustrated in Examples 30 and 31 should be a useful guide to judgment. It is suggested that the following points should be kept in mind in making decisions on the amount and type of inspection:

1. No economic comparison of alternative plans for acceptance inspection is possible without making assumptions regarding the quality of

the product submitted for acceptance. The conclusions of any economy study will depend on these assumptions.

2. In general, as the level of submitted quality is improved and as its consistency is improved, it becomes economical to use acceptance schemes involving less inspection. This is one of the reasons for keeping a record of quality history and for making periodic reviews of acceptance procedures in the light of that history.

3. In any proposal for a change in acceptance procedures, it is insufficient to consider merely the expected change in acceptance costs. Attention should also be given to the probable influence of the proposed change on production costs and on unsatisfactory-product costs.

4. The most important point favorable to certain acceptance sampling schemes is their prospective contribution to the improvement of submitted quality, in some cases through diagnosis of quality troubles and in others through effective pressure for quality improvement. This improvement of quality decreases production costs by reducing the cost of spoilage and rework. It also tends to decrease unsatisfactory-product costs. In the long run it permits a reduction in acceptance costs.

352. Will It Pay to Use a Control Chart for Variables? The greatest opportunities for cost reduction from statistical quality control often arise out of applications of the Shewhart control chart for variables. These savings are sometimes spectacular. They come from many sources—from reduction in cost of spoilage and rework, from reduction in inspection cost, from better control over the quality of purchased product, from the use of more economical materials or methods due to their greater reliability under statistical control, from better decisions on proposed investments in plant and machinery.

On the other hand, each control chart for variables involves some costs. The measurements of the variable must be made and recorded. Clerical labor is required for plotting the charts and computing the averages and limits. The time of people who have good technical ability is required for interpreting charts as a basis for action. Trouble shooting based on the evidence of the charts may sometimes be a costly matter.

Each set of $\bar{X}$ and R charts may be thought of as a gamble that the resulting savings will be greater than the cost of keeping the charts. In the introduction of the control chart for variables in any mass-production industry, experience indicates that from the over-all viewpoint this gamble almost amounts to betting on a sure thing; there are certain to be *some* opportunities for substantial cost savings. However, there are bound to be many quality characteristics for which $\bar{X}$ and R charts will not pay their way.

Before applying $\bar{X}$ and R charts to any given quality characteristic, it is seldom possible to be *certain* that the resulting cost savings will more than pay for the charts. It is, however, often possible to eliminate many quality characteristics from consideration by observing that sufficient opportunities for cost savings do not seem to exist, and to observe that for other quality characteristics there seem to be excellent opportunities for savings. This calls for an examination of costs that might be reduced, such as spoilage, rework, and inspection costs, and for a consideration of the possibilities of using the control-chart information as a basis for changes in design, specifications, or manufacturing methods.

Sometimes the question of whether it is a good gamble to use $\bar{X}$ and R charts for a given quality characteristic cannot be answered without the evidence of the charts themselves. Fortunately this is not a serious obstacle, as the cost of maintaining charts for a short period usually is small. It is always possible to discontinue control charts whenever it is clear that they are no longer justified.

Example 32 deals with the question of whether prospective savings in spoilage and rework will justify the expense of a control chart. Example 33 illustrates possible economies in the control of product weight when a control chart is used. Example 34 deals with a decision as to whether it is likely to be worth while to use a control chart for this purpose.

Example 35 illustrates the use of a large margin of safety to provide a desired quality protection. This example is followed by a general discussion of the economic aspects of such margins of safety.

EXAMPLE 32. ANALYSIS OF SPOILAGE REPORTS

353. Facts of the Case. In the introduction of statistical quality control in one manufacturing plant, many p charts were initiated. In most cases, these charts made use of inspection records that already were maintained for 100% inspection by attributes. The p charts indicated the quality level of various parts and products, and the presence or absence of statistical control. In this way, they suggested possible places for the use of $\bar{X}$ and R charts to diagnose the causes of trouble.

The chances of reducing costs by reducing the amount of spoilage and rework on any given part or product depend on the percentage defective, on the subdivision of defectives into spoilage and rework, on the unit cost of a spoiled part or product and on the average rework cost, and on the prospective future production of the part or product.

From the standpoint of possible $\bar{X}$ and R chart applications, it was evidently necessary to break down the defectives by reasons for rejection and to note particularly those defectives which resulted from failure to meet specifications on some quality characteristic that might readily be measured (such as dimension, weight, resistance, tensile strength, etc.). For rejections due to each such characteristic, defective work reports or other cost records should be examined to estimate the average net cost of a spoiled unit (usually the manufacturing costs up to the point of spoilage minus scrap value of the unit) and average rework cost.

In manufacturing operations on a job that has a definite forseeable termination and that is unlikely to be repeated, the possible saving from elimination of spoilage and rework is limited by the total amount still to be produced. For instance, assume 20,000 units are still to be produced on a given job. Past spoilage due to failure to meet specifications on a certain dimension has averaged 2%; rework has averaged 4%. The net cost of a spoiled unit is $5, and the average rework cost is $0.30. The total possible saving from the complete elimination of spoilage and rework from all remaining product is therefore

$$
\begin{array}{lll}
\text{Spoilage}\ldots\ldots\ldots & 20,000(\$5)(0.02) & = \$2,000 \\
\text{Rework}\ldots\ldots\ldots & 20,000(\$0.30)(0.04) = & 240 \\
\hline
\text{Total}\ldots\ldots\ldots\ldots\ldots\ldots\ldots\ldots\ldots & & \$2,240
\end{array}
$$

This estimate neglects the fact that anything learned in trouble shooting on this particular job may also prove helpful in reducing spoilage and rework on other similar operations.

Where manufacturing operations on the given product are expected to continue for an indefinite period, it is desirable to estimate expected annual production. The maximum possible annual saving from complete elimination of spoilage and rework may then be estimated.

Such estimates guide the selection of quality characteristics for the application of $\bar{X}$ and R charts so that each chart has definite possibilities for substantial cost savings.

EXAMPLE 33. CONTROL OF PRODUCT WEIGHT

354. Facts of the Case. Figure 82, taken from an article by O. P. Beckwith,[1] illustrates the effect of successive changes in a textile manufacturing operation. The

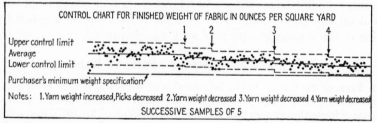

Fig. 82. $\bar{X}$ chart illustrating the effect of successive changes working closer to a minimum specification limit on weight—Example 33. (*Reproduced from article by O. P. Beckwith in Textile World*).

purchase specification for this fabric stated that the average weight in ounces per square yard of a sample of five from a lot of material should not be less than a stated value. As time went on, it proved possible to work closer and closer to this specification limit with safety.

The first section of the chart shows a few points close to the specification minimum, even though there was a relatively high average value. At this time the operation was not in statistical control. Moreover, trouble was experienced with yarn strength. Beckwith explains the successive changes as follows:

"In the first change the weight of the yarn was increased, which, under the particular conditions of manufacture, made a more uniform yarn. At the same time the yarn-weight increase was compensated for by a decrease in fabric picks per inch. Meanwhile considerable investigation of the spinning process showed how yarn could be

[1] BECKWITH, O. P., A Fresh Approach to Quality Control, *Textile World*, vol. 94, pp. 79–81, January, 1944.

spun at required strength and uniformity, but at reduced weight. The yarn weights were therefore lowered progressively, as is reflected by the third, fourth, and fifth changes in limits."

Because the specification applied to *averages* of samples of five rather than to individual values, it was appropriate to show the specification limit on this $\bar{X}$ chart.

EXAMPLE 34. POSSIBLE REDUCTION IN OVERFILL OF CONTAINERS

355. Facts of the Case. In the packaging of a cereal product in 10-lb. sacks, it was suggested that a study be made to determine the advisability of using $\bar{X}$ and R charts.

It was possible to make preliminary guesses as to possible savings prior to the use of $\bar{X}$ and R charts for an experimental period. The value of the material being sacked per operator per hour was $500. Thus it was evident that a 2% overfill would cost $10 per hr. This estimate showed that if there were really an overfill and if it could be reduced without falling below specifications, there was a chance for a good saving.

A trial period of control-chart operation was required to provide a basis for judgment as to the average amount of overfill and the possibility of improvement. This showed that the filling process was not in statistical control. If the process could be brought into control, it was evident that the average overfill could be substantially reduced. An estimate indicated that the annual cost of overfill on this particular item was nearly forty thousand dollars. Although it was apparent that all overfill could not be eliminated, it was clear that even a small reduction would more than pay the cost of a control-chart program.

EXAMPLE 35. USE OF HIGH AVERAGE QUALITY AND STATISTICAL CONTROL TO REDUCE THE PROBABILITY OF A DEFECTIVE

356. Facts of the Case. C. S. Barrett describes a problem encountered in the welding of precious-metal contacts to springs for relays and other telephone equipment.[1] The engineering requirement for these welds was that a contact should withstand a shear test of 7 lb. The acceptable quality level on this quality characteristic was 0.01% defective. It was not practicable to obtain this quality assurance by a scheme involving sampling by attributes. Upon trying 100% proof load testing, it was discovered that the test damaged the contacts, particularly in cases where the welds could withstand only a few pounds over the requirement (see Art. 344, Chap. XVI, for a comment on this aspect of proof load tests). Moreover, the 100% testing was very costly in proportion to the value of the parts.

A careful study was made of the factors contributing to the variations in weld strength. Changes in the tools and techniques made it possible to produce welds of an average strength several times the specification minimum. Destructive tests were made on every two-hundredth weld. Inspection results on these tests indicated an average strength of 34 lb. with a σ' of 6.3 lb. A frequency curve was plotted from tests on over 43,000 welds during a period of statistical control. This curve was nearly normal, showing a slight positive skewness. It was evident that as long as statistical control could be maintained, the probability of a weld strength of less than 7 lb. was considerably lower than the figure of 0.0001 which corresponded to the acceptable quality level.

[1] BARRETT, C. S., Quality Control with Sampling Inspection, *Mechanical Engineering*, vol. 64, pp. 361–364, May, 1942.

With $\bar{X}'$ at 34 and σ' at 6.3, the lower 3-sigma limit on individual weld strengths was about 15 lb. Whenever a weld strength below 15 lb. was found, the machine was shut down and adjusted, and the 200 parts which had been made since the preceding test were stripped of their contacts and rewelded.

357. Some Economic Aspects of the Margin of Safety in Design Specifications.[1] Designers have not commonly thought of the margin of safety to be included in specified tolerance limits as a problem in economy. Nevertheless, because such margins are aimed at quality of conformance, they should be properly be viewed in the same way as the selection of acceptance criteria.

Serious adverse consequences of accepting unsatisfactory product and high unit costs of inspection are two conditions favorable to the economic use of large margins of safety in design specifications. These conditions were both illustrated in Example 35.

On the other hand, an uncritical use of large margins of safety under all conditions may turn out to be very costly. Generally speaking, the design specification determines the production method to be employed. Unnecessary margins of safety may require more costly materials, more precise machines, and more expensive workmanship than really needed to secure satisfactory product. Conditions favorable to small margins of safety in the design specification are as follows:

1. Evidence that the manufacturing process can be kept in good statistical control with an average and dispersion that result in product that is satisfactory for the purpose intended with very little margin of safety.

2. Evidence that a costly change in the manufacturing process will be required in order to increase this margin.

3. Either low unsatisfactory-product cost per unit of such product or relatively low cost of applying acceptance criteria to give adequate protection.

358. Quality Decisions in Choosing a Production Method. The choice of a production method is influenced by the quality objective. The quality objective, in turn, is influenced by the design and acceptance criteria. Where acceptance criteria are such that lots with moderate percentages of defectives have only a small probability of rejection, it may be more economical to have an occasional lot rejected than to increase production costs in order to prevent any rejections. This

---

[1] For additional comment on this topic, see E. L. GRANT, The Economic Relationship between Design and Acceptance Specifications, "Special Technical Publication No. 103, Symposium on Application of Statistics," American Society for Testing Materials, Philadelphia, Pa., 1950. See also E. L. GRANT, Some Possible Contributions of Statistical Quality Control to Engineering Economy, "Paper No. 1, Fourth National Convention ASQC," American Society for Quality Control, New York, 1950.

seems particularly likely to happen where the producer has some degree of statistical sophistication and where he believes that the design specifications contain enough margin of safety so that moderately defective lots are really good enough for the purpose intended.

In some instances it may be economical to adopt production methods in which a certain amount of rework or spoilage seems inevitable.   This point is illustrated in Example 36.

EXAMPLE 36.   REDUCING A HIGH PERCENTAGE OF DEFECTIVES WILL NOT NECESSARILY REDUCE COSTS

359. Facts of the Case.   In the manufacture of a certain type of pressure gage, many different types of defects were responsible for rejection at final inspection. The defects causing each rejection were shown on the inspection record.   More than half the rejections were shown to be made for one reason, associated with the zero registration of the gage.   On the average, about 20% of the gages produced had this defect.   A p chart plotted for this type of defect indicated that the process was in control at this level; the day-to-day fluctuations above and below 20% defective were such as might be attributable to chance.   This defect was always correctible by a rework operation which, for most gages, was relatively simple.

360. Analysis and Action.   An engineering study indicated that this type of defect could be almost completely eliminated by an extra operation on one of the parts of the gage.   The costs of doing this for 100% of the gages were compared with the costs of carrying out the rework operation on 20% of the gages.   This cost comparison showed it to be more economical to rework 20% of the gages than to carry out the extra operation on 100% of them.   Consequently it was decided that, until a less costly method of eliminating this defect was discovered, the 20% level for this defect would be accepted as normal.

361. Some Special Difficulties of Estimating Indirect Costs in Economy Studies.   Cost accounting systems recognize three classes of manufacturing costs, namely, direct material cost, direct labor cost, and indirect manufacturing expense, often called *burden* or *overhead*.   The classification *indirect manufacturing expense* includes a great variety of costs, such as supervision, inspection, factory transportation, janitors, repairs and maintenance on machines and buildings, heat, light, and power, manufacturing supplies, factory clerical expense, accident compensation, tools and dies, factory insurance and taxes, and depreciation on buildings and machinery.   Defective work and spoilage are sometimes charged directly to a job or process, and sometimes included as part of overhead.[1] Indirect manufacturing expense is apportioned among cost centers and applied to each job or process in proportion to something directly measurable such as direct labor cost, direct labor hours, or machine hours. The most common basis is direct labor cost.   If, for example, the machine shop carried a burden rate of 150% of direct labor cost, this would mean

---

[1] LANG, T. (ed.), "Cost Accountants' Handbook," pp. 743–746, The Ronald Press Company, New York, 1944.

that for every dollar of direct labor cost charged against a job in the machine shop, there would also be charged $1.50 of indirect manufacturing expense. This charge would be, in effect, an apportionment against the job of the many different indirect expenses, *i.e.*, supervision, janitors, heat, light, and power, factory taxes, etc.

Although such an apportionment serves many useful purposes, such as valuation of inventories of goods in process and finished goods, determination of cost of goods sold, and sometimes determination of selling price, it does not follow that the saving of a dollar of direct labor in the machine shop will save $1.50 of disbursements for indirect manufacturing expense. Neither does it follow that an increase of a dollar of direct labor cost in the machine shop increases disbursements for indirect manufacturing expense by $1.50. From the standpoint of an economy study, the real question is what receipts and disbursements are likely to be influenced by the choice between alternatives.[1]

It is a general principle of all economy studies that indirect costs should not be included in cost comparisons simply by the uncritical application of burden rates. The relevant question regarding indirect expenses is always the probable effect of the choice between the given alternatives on each separate indirect expense. If no disbursements for indirect expenses seem likely to be influenced by the choice, there is no need to consider indirect expenses in the economy study. In many economy studies relative to quality control, it may be good enough for practical purposes to limit the estimates to the direct costs involved in the alternatives being compared.

362. Did It Pay to Use Statistical Quality Control?   Up to this point the discussion in this chapter has dealt with *prospective* uses of statistical quality control techniques.   *Each* use of these techniques should be based on a favorable prospect that the particular use in question will more than pay its costs.

It sometimes happens that when statistical quality control has been newly introduced into an organization and has been used for a few months, a continuation of the *over-all* use of the techniques requires evidence satisfactory to management that their use has paid on the whole.   Management is inclined to look to the financial accounts and cost accounts for this evidence, and often wants before-and-after figures for comparison. Although in some cases a fairly satisfactory picture of the effect of statis-

---

[1] For a more extended presentation of this point of view, see E. L. GRANT, "Principles of Engineering Economy," 3d ed., The Ronald Press Company, New York, 1950, particularly Chaps. 2 and 15.

See also E. L. GRANT and P. T. NORTON, JR., "Depreciation," Chap. 16, The Ronald Press Company, New York, 1949, and B. E. GOETZ, "Management Planning and Control," McGraw-Hill Book Company, Inc., New York, 1949.

tical quality control may be had by examining costs before the use of the techniques and comparing them with costs after the techniques have been used for some time, this point of view has definite limitations that should be understood.

Where there have been reductions in the amount of spoilage and rework over a short period and these reductions are clearly due to statistical quality control, there is a good measure of cost saving. Also, where the amount of destructive testing has been reduced due to the use of the control chart for variables as a basis for acceptance, it is possible to arrive at a definite figure for the saving.

But in most cases the situation is sufficiently complicated that a fair before-and-after picture cannot be obtained solely from accounting figures. It is seldom as simple as being able to say, for example, that the charges to account 317-B-1 were $1,427 in January before statistical quality control, and $955 in May after statistical quality control. (Logically, of course, such a comparison is never appropriate. The correct comparison is between the actual costs in May with statistical quality control and the costs in May as they would have been without statistical quality control; the practical difficulty is that there is no way to be certain of the latter figure.) Too many changes are constantly taking place to make it reasonable to ascribe all cost changes over a period of time to a single influence. Any before-and-after study needs to combine all the relevant evidence; the figures in the accounts constitute only one part of this evidence.

For example, the use of the control chart may reduce the number of machine shutdowns for readjustment by 75% and thus increase productive machine time and reduce costs. In any given period, this saving might be neutralized by other causes which were responsible for idle machine time.

Or an improvement in the outgoing quality from the forge shop might reduce the number of defective forgings transmitted to the machine shop. This, in turn, might reduce excessive machining costs and tool breakage in the machine shop. These savings, however, would be only two of many possible influences on machine-shop costs. If the unit costs in the machine shop actually decreased, this improvement might be attributed by the machine-shop superintendent to causes within the machine shop, even though better forgings were really responsible for most of the savings.

Or an improvement in the quality of purchased parts might reduce the delays due to defective parts on an assembly line. But there might be enough other variations in assembly costs that the effect of this improvement could not be isolated in the accounts.

Or improvement in the quality level of final product might tend to reduce the number of customer complaints. But the time lag between production and complaints might be such that this would only be evident after a long period of time.

Moreover, it should be recognized that the chances for before-and-after studies showing spectacular cost savings come chiefly in the early days of statistical quality control. As time goes on, the function of statistical quality control becomes more and more one of holding the line of better quality and improved quality assurance, and there is no "before" figure from a few months ago that can be contrasted with current performance.

363. Who Should Get Credit for Savings from Quality Improvement? Arguing the question, "Who was responsible for making this saving?" is as futile as arguing the question, "Who was responsible for winning the war?" Any quality improvements made on the basis of a diagnosis of troubles by the control chart are necessarily based on teamwork. Inspection personnel, production personnel, methods engineers, tool engineers, design engineers, and others may all participate.

From the standpoint of managerial decisions, the important question is not, "Who gets the credit?" but rather, "What methods and policies shall we adopt?" In judging whether or not to use statistical quality control techniques, the question for management is, "What savings will be made with these techniques that will not be made without them?" All such savings are relevant in the decision whether to use statistical quality control, even though the statistical techniques are only one of the necessary links in the chain by means of which the savings are accomplished.

364. Some Problems Connected with Budgetary Control. The reduction of costs and the prevention of cost increases call for the continuous exercise of executive pressure. In modern manufacturing plants, this pressure is exerted by the use of budgets. A principle of budgetary control is that each comparison between actual performance and the budgeted figure must follow the lines of individual responsibility. Pressure, to be effective, must be exerted on individuals—on works managers, department heads, foremen, and operators.

Because department heads and foremen are judged by their superiors in terms of conformance to their own budgets, they are sometimes inclined to view all decisions and proposed actions solely in terms of the effect on those budgets. This point of view often is adverse to the best interests of the business enterprise as a whole. It frequently happens that a small increase in expenditure in one department will bring about a much larger saving in another department. Or a decrease in cost in one department may cause a much larger increase in cost elsewhere.

This concentration of attention on individual budgets may, in some organizations, constitute a serious obstacle to the effective use of statistical quality control. Control charts may cause increases in inspection costs (at least temporarily) even though they may result in much larger decreases in production costs. Quality improvements in the manufacture of parts may require increased fabrication costs, even though they result in much larger decreases in assembly costs, and so forth. Nearly every application of statistical quality control, and, for that matter, nearly all policies related to product quality, will cross the lines of departmental responsibility.

For this reason, almost all decisions related to quality should be made at a management level higher than that of the supervisors who seem to be immediately concerned. This point of view is expanded in the following chapter.

Problems

298. A certain part is made in lots that usually contain a considerable number of defectives. Only about one-fourth of the parts that are classed as defectives are really unsatisfactory for the purpose intended. Any unsatisfactory parts passed on to assembly will be detected there at an estimated average cost of 95 cents each. Or about 90% of them could be eliminated by 100% inspection at a unit cost of 0.4 cent for each item inspected. Assume that the type of inspection has no influence on production costs. Assume also that all parts technically defective but actually satisfactory will finally be used in the assembly so that total production will be the same either with 100% inspection or with no inspection; neglect costs of material review procedures to bring this about. At what per cent defective will 100% inspection just break even with no inspection? *Ans.* 1.87%.

299. In Problem 298 assume submitted product is 2% defective and that annual production is 200,000 parts. Compare the sums of annual inspection cost and unsatisfactory-product cost under 100% inspection and no inspection.
Ans. 100%, $895; no inspection, $950.

300. In Problem 298, assume product is made in lots of 5,000. Assume that 85% of the lots will contain 0.8% of defectives including only 0.1% of unsatisfactory product. The remaining 15% of the lots will contain 8% of defectives including 3% of unsatisfactory product. Compare average annual figures for the sum of inspection cost and unsatisfactory-product cost for 100% inspection, for the single sampling 2% AOQL plan $n = 70$ and $c = 2$, and for no inspection. Assume unit inspection cost under the AOQL plan to be 0.7 cent, and assume annual production to be 200,000.
Ans. 100%, $902; AOQL, $460; no inspection, $1,016.

301. A certain part is made in lots of 1,000. Under favorable conditions these lots contain 0.3% of defectives. About 5% of the time, however, they contain 2% of defectives. The average unsatisfactory-product cost per defective passed is $5. It is desired to compare 100% inspection with a single sampling acceptance/rectification plan using $n = 170$ and $c = 1$, and with no inspection. Costs per unit inspected are estimated as 2 cents under 100% inspection and 2.5 cents under sampling inspection. Compare the average annual sum of inspection costs and unsatisfactory-product costs for the three schemes. Assume annual production of 50,000 parts. Figure 61 (page 320) may be used to estimate probabilities of acceptance under sampling inspection. What factors not included in your cost comparison are favorable to the choice of the sampling inspection scheme?

CHAPTER XVIII

ORGANIZATION FOR STATISTICAL
QUALITY CONTROL

It has been said that the introduction of Quality Control transforms the Inspector from an unsympathetic detective into a helpful constable—but, however much help that constable is willing and able to give, the benefits of the scheme can only be attained if his advice is taken.—G. White[1]

We regard statistics as essentially a tool, and we recognize that in using this tool the results obtained depend primarily upon the skill of the craftsman. It is our firm conviction that next to sound common sense and good engineering judgment, statistical methods are the most valuable tools available to the quality control operator. Hence, to achieve maximum benefits, it is essential that an appreciation of statistical philosophy be nurtured in the minds of production people and that these ideas be diffused as widely as possible among operating personnel.—Fred Trowbridge and J. T. Clark[2]

365. Need for Consideration by Top Management. The statement is sometimes made, "We installed a system of statistical quality control." Strictly speaking, such a statement may be misleading. Statistical quality control is not really a "system." It is rather a set of tools—a special group of methods to be applied to certain problems of specification, production, and inspection. In some manufacturing plants, these tools are applied in a systematic way to many different problems; hence the notion of a system. But they may be used by anyone who understands their use. In many manufacturing plants they are used only at irregular intervals and on only a few of the problems for which they are really applicable; their use in such plants depends on the duties and responsibilities of those individuals in the plant who happen to have been introduced to particular statistical quality control techniques.

From the viewpoint of securing the most effective use of these tools in any given manufacturing plant, two facts about them call for particular attention. One fact is that for best results each application should be tailor-made for its particular circumstances. The other fact is that nearly all applications cross the lines of departmental authority, usually calling for action by both inspection and production personnel,

[1] From the Foreword to the "Quality Control Handbook" of The Bristol Aeroplane Company, Ltd.

[2] Quoted from *Quality Control Report* No. 5, Statistical Quality Control in Radio Manufacture, by permission of the Production Research and Development Division, U.S. Department of Commerce, formerly OPRD, WPB.

and in addition often calling for action associated with the design or engineering function.

The organization of any activity that requires cooperation among departments constitutes a problem for top management. The problems of effective organization for statistical quality control are complicated by the difficulties, mentioned in Art. 364 at the end of the preceding chapter, that are sometimes introduced by systems of budgetary control. The people responsible for statistical quality control require authority to cross departmental lines. The fact that costs may be incurred in one department in order to make a larger reduction in costs in other departments needs to be understood by the administrators of the budget system.

If each statistical quality control application is to be tailor-made to the circumstances, some individual or group of individuals must combine a knowledge of statistical quality control principles with a knowledge of the practical problems of design, tooling, production, inspection, and cost. Except in those rare instances where one individual has all this knowledge, cooperation among individuals in different departments is required in the planning as well as in the execution of each application.

366. Advantages of a Clearly Recognized Statistical Quality Control Function. The whole point of this book is that the fundamental ideas and procedures of statistical quality control are not complicated—they can be understood and used by engineers, production supervisors, machine operators, inspection supervisors, inspectors, and others. Nevertheless, management should not be misled by this simplicity into believing that the full benefits of these techniques can be obtained merely by giving an introduction to statistical quality control to a representative group of people scattered throughout an organization. In general, it should be someone's responsibility to make statistical quality control work effectively. Some of the reasons why this is true are as follows:

1. Even the best efforts at acquainting key personnel with statistical quality control principles will not be entirely successful. Someone who fully understands these principles is needed to recognize the many opportunities for their effective use.

2. If the initiation of changes involving statistical quality control techniques is left to people already fully occupied with other responsibilities, progress in the effective use of these techniques is likely to be slow. In part, this is because such people are already too busy to have enough time to devote to statistical quality control; in part, it is because they are judged by their superiors primarily on the basis of their performance of their regular duties rather than on the basis of their contributions to the use of statistical quality control techniques. In contrast, where it is someone's job to see that these techniques are used wherever they

are needed and where his performance is judged by management in terms of savings from the use of statistical quality control, it is much more likely that effective use of the techniques will be secured.

3. Someone is needed to help overcome the inevitable resistance to any new procedures by explaining the methods to the people who must use them in each new application and to deal with the diplomatic problems involved in crossing departmental lines of authority.

4. Unless statistical quality control is clearly recognized by management as someone's function, the effective use of the techniques may be severely handicapped by the transfer or resignation of an individual who understands them and has been responsible for getting them started. This is brought out in Example 37. This example, although based on one particular case, is in a sense a composite of several actual cases. That is, it describes a set of circumstances that has occurred often enough to seem to represent what is likely to happen whenever responsibility for statistical quality control is not assigned by management as a major portion of the duties of some particular job.

EXAMPLE 37.   IMPORTANCE OF CONTINUITY DIRECTING THE APPLICATIONS OF STATISTICAL QUALITY CONTROL

367. Facts of the Case.   In one manufacturing plant, a number of successful applications of $\bar{X}$ and R control charts were developed by one member of the technical staff as a side line to his regular duties.   He drew up definite explicit written instructions for each application in order to permit effective use of the control chart by foremen and inspectors who did not understand the principles.   Although some of the executives and other engineers were impressed with the results of the control chart in improving product quality and reducing costs, no one else took the trouble to try to understand the principles involved.   As a result, when the man who initiated the program left the plant, there was no one left to carry on.

The control charts were continued on the basis of the written instructions.   However, as time went on several factors combined to reduce their effectiveness.   Many of the personnel who had been working with the control charts were promoted or transferred elsewhere.   The explicitness of the directions, which had been an advantage when the program was started, became a disadvantage as the production jobs changed slightly and there was no one to adapt the written directions to the changed conditions.   The absence of anyone who had an over-all picture of control-chart principles served to limit the use of the charts to acceptance and to actions taken on out-of-control points, and prevented their use as a basis for many other actions that called for a broader interpretation of the control chart.   With changing personnel, the control charts were gradually abandoned.

Finally management became aware of the resulting deterioration in product quality and increase in costs.   A new engineer who was competent in statistical quality control was hired and assigned the duty of reviving the control-chart program.

368. Place of the Statistical Quality Control Group in a Manufacturing Organization.   If it is agreed that one or more persons should be assigned functional responsibility for the statistical quality control program, the question arises as to the best position of these persons in the organization of a manufacturing plant.

The actual functions of departments having the same name (for example, the inspection department) vary so greatly from one plant to another, and the personalities and capacities of the individuals heading departments vary so much, that there obviously can be no one right answer to this question. It is primarily a matter of where, all things considered, the statistical quality control program is likely to be most effective and to encounter the fewest obstacles to cooperation.

One common place for the statistical quality control group is in the inspection department. Considered only from the viewpoint of collection of data, this is an advantageous place. From the viewpoint of securing action, this location in the organization may present some difficulties because of the traditional arms-length relationship between production and inspection.

In some instances the group may be attached to plant engineering. This is helpful when frequent work is required by methods engineers on out-of-control processes.

In some of the most successful applications, the statistical quality control group reports directly to the plant manager and thus is not subordinate to any of the three related functions of specification (design engineering), production, or inspection. This is particularly advantageous in the many cases where it is necessary to cross the lines of departmental authority. There are obvious advantages in having direct access to plant management. However, the actual success of this scheme of organization may depend largely on the skill of the statistical quality control engineer in securing voluntary cooperation from engineering, production, and inspection without using the authority given by the managerial backing.

With the right managerial support and the requisite ability and personality in the quality control engineer, the statistical quality control program can often be successful regardless of its position in the organization chart. In some cases the right place for the program is a place which on superficial examination would not seem to be appropriate. One excellent statistical quality control program in a process industry is part of the research department. This department happens to be an appropriate place because, in addition to carrying out research and development work, it contains the plant control laboratory.

369. Responsibilities of a Statistical Quality Control Group. Where a separate statistical quality control group exists, some responsibilities that may properly be assigned to this group are as follows:

1. Devising statistical quality control procedures adapted to the needs of the particular manufacturing organization.

2. Preparing any necessary forms and written instructions needed for the effective use of these procedures.

3. Advising others (for example, production and inspection personnel) on specific applications. In some cases, this may call for a critical analysis of a problem and complete recommendations regarding actions to be taken; in other cases, it may be merely a matter of helping out with occasional difficulties.

4. Looking for good places for new applications and promoting such applications wherever they are discovered.

5. Reviewing control charts at regular intervals to see whether limits are correctly calculated and interpreted.

6. Reviewing each control chart occasionally to see whether it is still paying its way or whether it should be modified or abandoned.

7. Providing a source of information—and, in some cases, formal training—for personnel relative to statistical quality control principles and methods.

8. Making a comprehensive statistical analysis of pilot runs in connection with the development of a new design or new product.

9. Calling attention of production, inspection, and engineering executives to any situations requiring their attention as indicated by the evidence of control charts or other quality records.

10. Evaluating the quality level for management in periodic reports.

Some functions assigned to statistical quality control groups may constitute a possible source of trouble because the functions create overlapping authorities or because they can really be performed better by someone else. Some such functions are

1. Collecting the data. This is generally better done by regular inspection personnel. However, occasional cases may arise where because of special circumstances it may be necessary for the statistical quality control group to collect the data.

2. Outlining and setting up inspection methods. Generally this may be done better by the people who have direct responsibility for seeing that inspection is properly carried out, although there may be exceptions in special cases.

3. Setting quality standards. Although the statistical quality control group should be represented on a standards committee responsible for the setting of quality standards, too many policy matters are involved for this to be appropriate as an exclusive function for statistical quality control.

Although the preceding comments are intended to suggest some broad lines along which the exact responsibility of a statistical quality control group can be worked out, it is obvious that the best plan in any particular case will depend on many factors that differ from plant to plant, such as the nature of the manufacturing operations, the organization structure and the place of statistical quality control in the organization, and the abilities and personalities of the members of the statistical quality control group.

370. The Problem of Securing Cooperation. Because statistical quality control activities cross departmental lines, they must have the support of top management. Although such support is necessary if statistical quality control methods are to be used to best advantage, it is not sufficient to ensure their effective use. For really satisfactory results, there must be cooperation all along the line. In considerable measure, this is a matter of persuasion and diplomacy on the part of those persons responsible for statistical quality control activities.

It is particularly important that the control chart be presented to production foremen and supervisors as a device to help them rather than to police them. Two or three pilot applications of the control chart to carefully selected quality characteristics may assist in establishing this point of view.

Although it is essential that the quality control engineer have the ability to get along well with people, it is also necessary that he be firm and have the courage of his convictions. He cannot be effective if he is merely a "Yes" man.

In general, the introduction of statistical quality control techniques in a manufacturing plant faces human problems and obstacles similar to those encountered in the introduction of any other new techniques. The effectiveness of the statistical quality control program will depend in large measure on the skill used in overcoming these human obstacles.[1]

371. Importance of the Right Start. At the outset of the use of any new technique in a manufacturing plant, many of the people affected by the technique are bound to be skeptical. A few who fear that their prestige or authority may be diminished or that they may be otherwise caused trouble may actively oppose its use. Or, even worse, they may agree to its trial but actually take steps to interfere with its success.

In any mass-production industry, it is practically certain that many opportunities exist to use statistical quality control to reduce costs and obtain other advantages. However, in each individual plant, the only

---

[1] Three good references on this subject are:

FEIGENBAUM, A. V., "Quality Control," McGraw-Hill Book Company, Inc., New York, 1951. See particularly Chap. 13, Selling the Quality Control Program.

JURAN, J. M. (ed.), "Quality Control Handbook," McGraw-Hill Book Company, Inc., New York, 1951. See particularly Sec. 3 by C. R. Scott, Jr., Organizing for Quality.

JURAN, J. M., "Management of Inspection and Quality Control," Harper & Brothers, New York, 1945. See particularly the final chapter, Introducing a System of Modern Quality Control Techniques.

proof that will really convince many of the people requiring conviction will be a successful application in the plant itself. If, in the early stages of the statistical quality control program, the proponents of statistical quality control make a few suggestions that do not work, the entire program may be discredited in the minds of the people who must cooperate to make it successful. For this reason it is important that the first few applications be carefully chosen. Three suggestions regarding the choice of these applications are as follows:

1. Quality characteristics should be chosen where there is an evident opportunity for a useful improvement (see Art. 352, Chap. XVII).

2. The improvement aimed at should be one which, if made, is likely to be recognized without question by everyone concerned as a real advantage; for example, reduction of costly spoilage and rework, reduction of inspection costs, reduction of overfill of containers.

3. If possible, the applications should be such that they may be started with a minimum of change of existing procedures.

Example 38 describes a case in which the development of an excellent and helpful statistical quality control program was prevented by the selection of the wrong quality characteristic for the first control chart.

EXAMPLE 38. FAILURE OF A SUCCESSFUL STATISTICAL QUALITY CONTROL APPLICATION

372. Facts of the Case. A small plant with some 40 employees which in peacetime produced civilian products was manufacturing certain precision parts for several large war plants. The chief inspector of the small plant attended a statistical quality control course. On returning to her plant, she started a control chart for $\bar{X}$ and R on a dimension (which we may call dimension A) on which she knew a substantial percentage of the parts were being produced outside specified close tolerances. Dimension A proved to be badly out of control. By working a few hours on each shift of the several shifts for some weeks, she finally diagnosed the sources of trouble and after much effort she secured corrective action. Dimension A was brought into control and brought within specified tolerances.

However, the purchaser who had rejected some lots of this part in the past continued to reject as many lots as ever. Investigation disclosed that dimension A was one which, even though specified by the purchaser to very close tolerances, was really of minor importance. The purchaser could actually accept parts far outside specified tolerances on dimension A without causing any trouble; for this reason the dimension was subject only to a very perfunctory check by the receiving inspection of the purchasing company and actually had not been the cause for past rejection of lots.

The real trouble had been dimension B on which *no* departures from specified tolerances could be permitted. Although the vendor's quality level on dimension B was good, it was not perfect; a single out-of-tolerance part in a sample was cause for rejection of a lot. As she had not realized this fact, the chief inspector had not applied any control chart to dimension B.

The chief inspector was very discouraged when her strenuous efforts did not decrease the proportion of the lots rejected by the purchaser. From the viewpoint of the owner of the plant and of the foremen and machine operators who had cooperated in the trouble-shooting activity, the lack of this tangible success tended to discredit the use of statistical quality control.   As a result no further use of the control chart was made; the technique was not applied to dimension B or to other quality characteristics on which it might have been used to advantage.

373. Some Comments on Example 38.   In examining Example 38, the reader may perhaps be inclined to comment that after the control chart had demonstrated its possibilities on trouble shooting by helping to bring dimension A within the specification limits, the employer and the shop personnel were unreasonable in considering the control chart to be discredited.   The control chart had demonstrated its possibilities; the difficulty was merely that the chart had been applied to the wrong quality characteristic.   This point is well taken; the answer to it is simply that, generally speaking, people cannot be counted on to act reasonably in such matters.   Any techniques such as statistical quality control, newly introduced into a plant, are bound to suffer from any errors of judgment made by their advocates, even though such errors have nothing to do with the techniques themselves.   The converse of this is also true; a new technique will often receive credit for improvements which happen to occur after its introduction even though such improvements are really not related to its use.

374. Some Comments on Vendor–Purchaser Relationships.   Although it turned out that the chief inspector in Example 38 had selected the wrong quality characteristic in this case, her choice was a natural one under the circumstances.   She applied her attention to the quality characteristic on which her employer had found the greatest difficulty in meeting the specifications rather than to one on which the per cent failing to conform to specifications was small.   Her employer had not been told of the actual reasons for lot rejection and had not been informed that the specified tolerances on dimension A were not important but that the specified tolerances on dimension B must be strictly held.   The real fault lay with the purchaser, partly through the specification of tolerances much closer than necessary, and partly through failure to give the vendor full information as to the causes of rejection.

These faults are common ones in vendor-purchaser relationships. The point of view developed by statistical quality control can help in their correction.   Their actual correction in any case may require changes in company policies and in organizational patterns.

In this case, the action of the purchaser's receiving inspection in applying only a perfunctory check to dimension A amounted to the adoption of an acceptable quality level of a high per cent defective.   This was based on the experience of the production departments that it was not really necessary to hold the specified close tolerances.   However, the practical difficulties in securing an authorized relaxation of tolerances were sufficient that it was easier simply to disregard the tolerances than to try to get them changed. Moreover, the purchaser's representatives were not supposed to admit to any vendor that specified tolerances were being disregarded by purchaser's inspection, and it was not the regular practice to notify vendors of the exact reason why lots were rejected.

Where the viewpoint of statistical quality control is adapted to vendor-purchaser relationships, the purchaser informs the vendor as to the relative seriousness of different defects, possibly through their classification as critical, major, and minor. Moreover, once sufficient information is at hand to establish acceptable quality levels that seem practical and satisfactory, the vendor is informed of the acceptance criteria that are to be used.

The purchaser should gain two long-run advantages from telling the vendor these things. One is a quality advantage; the other is a price advantage. When the vendor knows which quality characteristics are important, he can concentrate his attention on those characteristics and thus avoid the type of mistake made in Example 38. Unless the vendor is aware of the inspection and acceptance criteria that are to be used, he may properly feel that his price needs to be based on the most severe criteria to which he might be subjected. Information on inspection and acceptance procedures may properly be incorporated in a separate inspection specification which can be included in the contract.

After the statistical point of view has been applied to relationships between vendor and purchaser for a long enough period, the purchaser may realize a still further advantage through the reduction of his inspection costs on product received from qualified vendors. In effect, the purchaser may accept product based on the vendor's quality record supplemented by greatly reduced inspection made by the purchaser. J. E. Palmer of Western Electric Company and E. G. D. Paterson of Bell Telephone Laboratories comment on this as follows:[1]

The tendency in recent years has been to reduce incoming acceptance inspection on the part of the purchaser by transfering to the supplier the responsibility for providing to the purchaser certified factual quality information of specified character and quantity. . . . Since it is possible to combine into one operation the inspections which the manufacturer as a prudent supplier necessarily makes on his own behalf with those required for assurance purposes by the customer, the inspection economies possible under this arrangement are very substantial.

[1] PALMER, J. E., and E. G. D. PATERSON, Acceptance Inspection of Purchased Material, "Quality Control Conference Papers 1951," pp. 303–320, American Society for Quality Control, New York, 1951. This paper, which reflects many years of Bell System experience, should be helpful to anyone responsible for planning inspection procedures in connection with vendor-purchaser relationships. It may also be found in the September, 1951, and November, 1951, issues of Industrial Quality Control.

W. H. Smith of Ford Motor Company describes such a program of vendor certification, in part, as follows:[1]

Another interesting offshoot of Acceptance Sampling is Quality Level Certification, in which we, for instance, as a consumer, modify our stated right to reject and send back to a supplier each and every defective item in any shipment. The Quality Level Certification Agreement . . . is an attachment to the purchase contract wherein the vendor proposes to give continuous documented assurance that each of his shipments satisfies an Acceptable Quality Level which is *mutually* established as reasonable. We, the consumers, inspect according to the standard Ford Acceptance Sampling plan and absorb, *at our cost*, the incidental defectives in any shipment which is found acceptable to the established Acceptable Quality Level. And, of course, we return the shipments found rejectable. After the supplier gives adequate proof of his consistent ability to abide by the agreement, we are able to eliminate most of our inspection and only sample shipments infrequently in a Quality Audit.

The agreement is subject to cancellation if the supplier fails to achieve the consistent quality which he claims, or if for any other reason its continuance proves undesirable to either party. In the event of such cancellation we revert to the specific powers of rejection embodied in the original purchase contract.

The question always follows—"Why formalize this procedure when your Acceptance Sampling plan seems to do the same sort of thing without formality." The answer is found in three important areas. First, it is virtually impossible for any supplier to certify his shipments without using sound methods for process quality control. If he uses Statistical Quality Control effectively in his manufacturing processes, then both he and the consumer benefit in ways which should hardly require explanation. Second, it is necessary for the supplier and consumer to agree on an Acceptable Quality Level *and* to agree on the particular quality characteristics which are to be governed in the agreement. This may be the most important aspect of all—*to be able finally to agree on what is or is not important to the consumer from the standpoint of quality.* It follows automatically that the supplier can concentrate his quality control efforts on the particular characteristics of first importance to us. The third answer has to do with the psychology of a quality commitment. The urge of a supplier to stay with the agreement will be a strong factor in perpetuating the high quality we, at Ford, are most anxious to get from all of our suppliers.

375. The Problem of Securing Action. The time factor is of first importance in securing action on a production process. The less the delay between the moment the control chart says, "Look for trouble," and the actual start of the hunt for the source of trouble, the greater the likelihood that the trouble will be diagnosed correctly. Moreover, even if delay should not interfere with the diagnosis, the sooner the source of trouble can be found, the less damage it is likely to cause.

[1] SMITH, W. H., Problems of Receiving Inspection and the Assembly Line, "Quality Control Conference Papers 1951," pp. 263–288, American Society for Quality Control, New York, 1951.

Two rules for cutting this delay to a minimum are

1. Put the control charts where they are sure to be seen by the people who are expected to use them as a basis for action. If setters and machine operators are to take action based on $\overline{X}$ and R charts, such charts should, wherever possible, be at the machine. p charts should be placed where they are readily seen by the foremen and other supervisors who are expected to take action on out-of-control points.

2. Points on the control chart should be posted promptly. On $\overline{X}$ and R charts, the average and range should be computed immediately after the measurements are made and posted at once. On p charts based on daily production, a point showing yesterday's per cent defective should be posted early each day.

In some instances there may be an advantage in using charts with squares large enough to take a rubber stamp (round or triangular or star-shaped), which may be seen at some distance by supervisors and operators. In other cases, red, yellow, and green lights, or pegboards with colored pegs have been used to present the conclusions of p charts regarding the existence of control at a satisfactory level. A peg-board installation at Sylvania Electric Products, Inc., is described by Reinhardt and Benson as follows:[1]

On this board [Fig. 83] the quality control status each day at each inspection station is indicated by colored pegs inserted in holes, somewhat like a giant cribbage board. The board contains 31 holes in each row, numbered to represent the days of the month. Golf tees in three colors—green, red, and yellow—are used for pegs.

A *green* peg, indicating safety, is used if the process is within control. Above control is represented by a *red* peg, indicating danger. Below control is represented by a *yellow* peg, indicating that a certain degree of caution, particularly on the part of the inspection department, should be exercised to make sure that the change represents a real improvement in quality, and not a shift in inspection standards or laxity in inspection methods.

The board with the colored pegs in place makes an attractive and attention-compelling display. Placed in a position where it is seen by the entire production department, it creates considerable comment regarding its meaning and purpose. The significance of the pegs is readily grasped even by persons who have no knowledge of control chart technique, and to whom a control chart would appear complex or uninteresting. With a little encouragement, a healthy spirit of competition is developed between various groups and is reflected in an over-all improvement in quality level.

376. Training for Statistical Quality Control. The effective use of statistical quality control calls for cooperation from many people such

---

[1] REINHARDT, H., and E. BENSON, Using the Chart Method to Control Quality, *Factory Management and Maintenance*, vol. 103, pp. 116–120, September, 1945.

as production and inspection supervisors, design engineers, methods engineers, and many others. In-plant training courses that meet for an hour or two once or twice a week provide a good method of introducing such people to statistical quality control principles and methods. With-

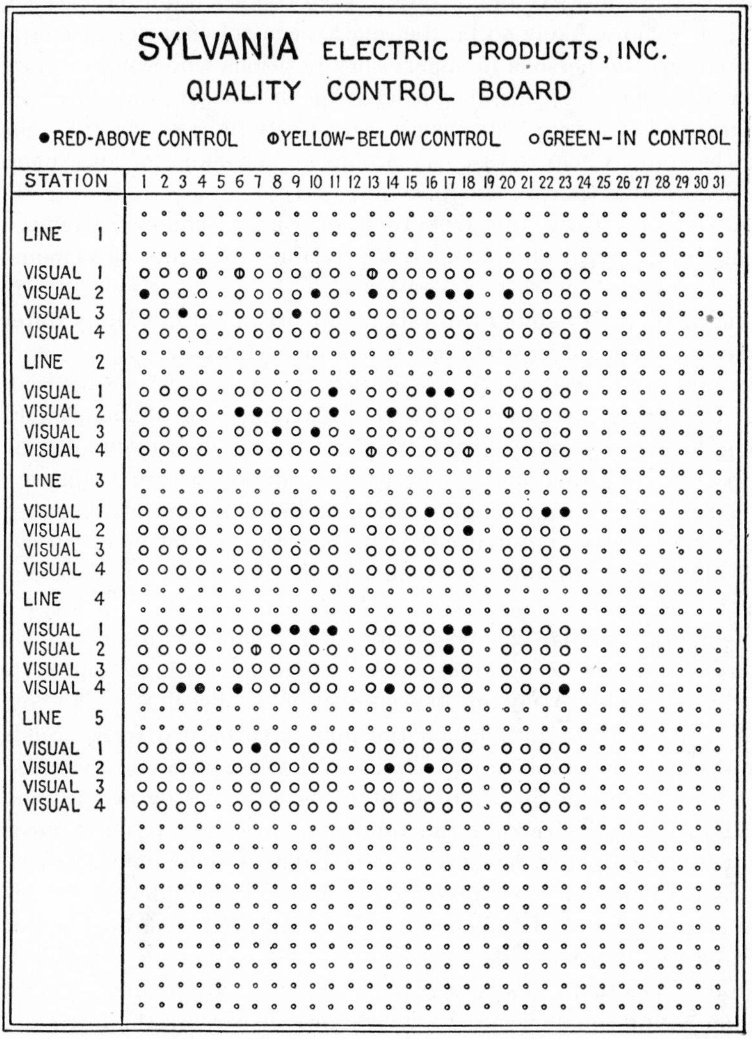

SYLVANIA ELECTRIC PRODUCTS, INC.
QUALITY CONTROL BOARD

● RED-ABOVE CONTROL   ◍ YELLOW-BELOW CONTROL   ○ GREEN- IN CONTROL

STATION	1 2 3 4 5 6 7 8 9 10 11 12 13 14 15 16 17 18 19 20 21 22 23 24 25 26 27 28 29 30 31
LINE 1	
VISUAL 1	
VISUAL 2	
VISUAL 3	
VISUAL 4	
LINE 2	
VISUAL 1	
VISUAL 2	
VISUAL 3	
VISUAL 4	
LINE 3	
VISUAL 1	
VISUAL 2	
VISUAL 3	
VISUAL 4	
LINE 4	
VISUAL 1	
VISUAL 2	
VISUAL 3	
VISUAL 4	
LINE 5	
VISUAL 1	
VISUAL 2	
VISUAL 3	
VISUAL 4	

FIG. 83. Quality control board used by Sylvania Electric Products, Inc. (*Reproduced from article by H. Reinhardt and E. Benson in Factory Management and Maintenance.*)

out some such introduction, a statistical quality control program may be handicapped by a misunderstanding of its methods and objectives, and by the distrust that often exists relative to any proposed new methods that are not understood.

Often, as in the case described in Example 1, Chap. II, such courses succeed in enlisting the active and enthusiastic cooperation of foremen and others who may then develop a number of cost-saving applications that would not otherwise be discovered. In the introduction of statistical quality control into any organization, such courses often indicate to the instructor (who is likely to be the quality control engineer in charge of the program) the persons in supervisory positions who will probably be the most cooperative; this knowledge helps in choosing the places where initial control-chart applications are most likely to be successful. Sometimes the courses help to discover promising personnel for an expanding statistical quality control group.

377. Demonstrating the Operation of Chance-cause Systems. In presenting statistical quality control principles to groups of persons, an actual demonstration of the operation of a chance-cause system is more convincing than any amount of talk about probability. Many different schemes have been developed for such demonstrations.

An interesting mechanical device for this purpose was devised by Frank C. Turner, Lecturer-in-Charge, Department of Mechanical Engineering, University of Sheffield, England. This device,[1] made chiefly from parts from a Meccano set, actually conducts a rough gaging operation that gives a visual demonstration of the variation of diameters of glass beads. It can be used either to gage the diameters of successive small subgroups or to show the frequency distribution of a bulk of several thousand beads.

A somewhat similar demonstration of a frequency distribution can be obtained by dropping steel balls through an arrangement of pins; the balls may fall into any one of a number of parallel slots at the bottom of the inclined plane into which the pins have been driven. Such an apparatus, referred to as a *quincunx*, was devised by Sir Francis Galton in the 1890's. It might be thought of as an ancestor of the modern pinball machine. Although the quincunx does not actually measure any quality characteristic of the steel balls, it does demonstrate the operation of a system of chance causes. Like Turner's device, it permits visual demonstration of the effect of chance in producing both variation within small subgroups and variation in a large frequency distribution. In standard position it tends to give a distribution approximately normal. Through tilting the device at various angles, it permits the introduction of assignable causes, giving rise to changed process averages and to skewed distributions. Figure 84 shows a quincunx developed by the Timken Roller Bearing Company. The removable horizontal wire in

[1] For a detailed description, see F. C. Turner, A Model for Quantitative Statistical Experiments, *Engineer*, vol. 178, pp. 26–27, July 14, 1944.

this quincunx makes it possible to obtain data on successive subgroups of any desired size.[1]

Doubtless the method of writing numbers on chips to be drawn from a bowl by the members of a class is the most common classroom approach to the actual demonstration of a system of chance causes giving material for $\overline{X}$ and R charts. This was illustrated at some length in Chaps. IV and V by the discussion of the drawing from Shewhart's bowl.

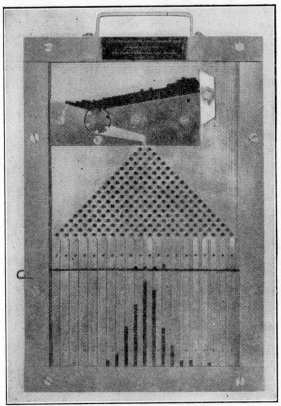

Fig. 84. Quality control chart demonstrator (quincunx) developed by Timken Roller Bearing Company.

A simple and rapid method of giving a visual illustration of sampling of attributes is the use of a sampling tray to scoop 50 wooden beads from a box containing a mixture of white and colored beads. Such a device, designed by Holbrook Working, is illustrated in Fig. 85. It can

[1] For a description of this and other useful devices for visual demonstration of statistical quality control principles, see R. E. Wagenhals, Mechanical Aids for Presenting the Quality Control Story, "Quality Control Conference Papers 1951," pp. 383–389, American Society for Quality Control, New York, 1951.

be used effectively for the production in class of data for the construction of a p chart or for the demonstration of the operation of sampling acceptance plans. White beads can be designated as acceptable and colored beads as defective. Assignable causes may be introduced by changing the quality level, *i.e.*, by varying the proportion of white and colored beads in the box. $\overline{X}$ and R charts may be developed by actual micrometer measurements of the equatorial diameters of the same wooden beads.

In the absence of such a sampling device, an ordinary deck of playing cards, or several decks put together, may be used for demonstration of sampling by attributes. Dice may also be used to demonstrate control-chart principles and sampling procedures.

378. The Relationship between the Statistical Techniques Presented in This Book and the General Body of Statistical Method. In the first chapter of this book, it was pointed out that the word *statistics* may be used in two senses. In the plural sense, *statistics* means any facts stated in terms of numbers; in the singular sense, *statistics* refers to a body of methods for collecting, organizing, and interpreting numerical data. In this book, *statistics* is used in its singular sense.

Fig. 85. Sampling scoop used to select 50 beads from a bulk of mixed white and colored beads.

Statistical methods, largely based on the mathematics of probability, have been developed to deal with problems in many different fields of activity. They are applied in agricultural experimentation, in medical research, in psychological studies, in educational measurements, in economic and sociological investigations, in business forecasting, in public opinion polls, in market research, and in innumerable other fields. There are many books on statistical method. Some of these books deal with statistical methodology in general as it might be applied in any field. Others concentrate on methods that have proved useful in some particular field of activity and illustrate their use by describing applications in that field of activity.

This book is of the latter type. It has stressed the different Shewhart control charts and that portion of sampling theory of particular importance in acceptance procedures. Experience has proved that these are the statistical methods which are of the greatest value in dealing with problems of industrial quality control. These particular methods are not adequately treated in general works on statistics; in fact, some general books on the subject do not even mention the Shewhart control chart.

However, many statistical techniques presented in general works but omitted in this book occasionally prove very useful in dealing with specific problems of industrial quality control. For example, it may be desired to substitute a nondestructive test (such as hardness) for a destructive one (such as tensile strength), or an immediate test (such as the drained weight of the contents of a can of fruit or vegetables immediately after filling) for a deferred test (such as the drained weight of the contents of the same can after processing). Or it may be desired to investigate the influence of a number of variables (such as percentages of various impurities in steel) on some measure of quality. Such quality problems may call for a use of simple linear regression and correlation, or, in some instances, multiple regression or curvilinear regression.[1]

By increasing the complexity of the statistical techniques which are used, it is sometimes possible to extract more and more information from a limited number of observations. This is of particular importance in research and development work where additional data may be costly. A small additional expense for statistical analysis may often save a much larger expense for collection of data. This is particularly true if experimental work is planned from the start with a view to the most efficient statistical analysis.[2]

From the viewpoint of the everyday problems of industrial quality control, some of the more complex statistical techniques are subject to two important limitations. One of these limitations is fairly obvious; the other is not always fully understood, even by professional statisticians.

The obvious limitation is the practical difficulty in getting complex

---

[1] The elements of regression and correlation are explained in all general works on statistics. A clear explanation for the reader who is not a mathematician may be found in A. E. Waugh, "Elements of Statistical Methods," 2d ed., pp. 372–482, McGraw-Hill Book Company, Inc., New York, 1943.

The most comprehensive work devoted primarily to correlation is M. Ezekiel, "Methods of Correlation Analysis," 2d ed., John Wiley & Sons, Inc., New York, 1940.

[2] In this connection, see particularly the following:

COCHRAN, W. G., and G. M. Cox, "Experimental Designs," John Wiley & Sons, Inc., New York, 1950.

EISENHART, CHURCHILL, M. W. HASTAY, and W. A. WALLIS (eds.), "Techniques of Statistical Analysis," McGraw-Hill Book Company, Inc., New York, 1947.

FISHER, R. A., "The Design of Experiments," 3d ed., Oliver & Boyd, Ltd., Edinburgh and London, 1942.

FISHER, R. A., "Statistical Methods for Research Workers," 7th ed., Oliver & Boyd, Ltd., Edinburgh and London, 1938.

methods understood by all the people who need to understand them if such methods are to be used successfully in dealing with ordinary quality control problems. Simpler methods, such as the control chart using 3-sigma limits, which may be slightly less efficient in the statistical sense of requiring a little more data to get the same conclusions, may actually be much more effective in industry because they can be understood and acted on by the people who need to take action.

The other limitation relates to a fundamental difference between the statistical problems encountered in research and development work and those encountered in industrial quality control. In research and development work, it often is true that the data to be interpreted by statistical methods are limited to the measurements in a single experiment or small series of experiments. In process control and in acceptance inspection, on the other hand, it is of the utmost importance to interpret the evidence of the current sample in the light of the evidence of previous samples from the same source. In these quality control problems, statistical methods which neglect the evidence of past samples are unsatisfactory no matter how good a job they do of extracting the maximum possible information out of the current sample. It is particularly for this reason that the Shewhart control chart, which combines the evidence of past samples with the evidence of current samples, is of such great value in industrial quality control, whereas many of the conventional statistical techniques which are of great use in research and development work are poorly adapted to dealing with problems in quality control.

379. Need for Advice from a Competent Mathematical Statistician. Manufacturing enterprises may encounter a number of different statistical problems, not only in connection with quality control and with research and development, but also in such diverse activities as accident prevention, market research, physical property mortality studies as a basis for depreciation estimates, and so forth. In connection with all such uses of statistical methods, the question may always be raised whether the statistical techniques being used are really the best ones for the particular problem being solved.

This question is particularly pertinent because of the rapid advances made every year in the techniques of mathematical statistics. Keeping in touch with these advances is a job for a specialist. A competent mathematical statistician who does keep up with the latest developments in his field may give much helpful advice on all uses of statistical methods in an industrial plant. Such advice may appropriately include the statistical quality control program. Many organizations are large enough to make it desirable that they employ one or more such mathematical statisticians on a full-time basis. Other smaller organizations might well use the services of a mathematical statistician occasionally on a consulting basis.

Problems

302. As an assistant to a consulting quality control engineer, you encounter the following situation in the plant of one of his clients:

A certain operation involves the packaging of a dry cereal product in 10-lb bags of heavy paper. The bags are filled by an automatic weighing and filling machine which cuts off the flow of the product when the weight of the bag and its contents has reached a certain predetermined setting. After the flow has been stopped by this automatic cutoff, there is a small amount of the cereal product which has already passed the cutoff point and which therefore goes into the bag. When operating without interruption, the machine fills 110 bags per hour. The practice of the operator appears to have been to aim at an overfill of 3 oz. (This value presumably was determined on the basis of past experience that any less overfill caused trouble with the government inspector.) The weight of an empty bag has been assumed to be 7 oz. This has given an aimed-at weight of 170 oz. (160 + 3 + 7) for the filled package. Every hour or so the operator has weighed a single filled package on a spring scales which weighs to the nearest half ounce. If this measured weight is above 170 oz., the operator changes the machine setting to cut off at a lower weight; if the measured weight is below 170 oz., the operator changes the machine setting to cut off at a higher weight.

The government inspector at this plant has the job of checking weights and other quality characteristics that are controlled by legislation and government regulations in the interests of the ultimate consumer. His time is kept fully occupied as he has the responsibility for checking many products. His practice in checking weights on this particular product has been to select 5 bags at random from each day's production. (Daily production has averaged about 1,500 bags from two 8-hr. shifts.) Each bag has been emptied and the contents weighed on a small platform scales weighing to 0.1 oz. If the contents of each of the 5 bags weigh 160 oz. or more, he approves the day's output as to weight. If 2 or more of the bags have contents weighing less than 160 oz., he requires the entire day's output to be stamped "Substandard Weight." If just 1 of the bags has contents below 160 oz., he takes an additional 5 bags for inspection. If all of this second sample is satisfactory, the day's production is considered to be satisfactory. If 1 or more of the second sample are below 160 oz., the day's output is considered to be all substandard weight. This particular acceptance procedure is not specified in any written instructions that have been given to the government inspector but appears to have been the traditional one at this plant. At least the present government inspector, who has worked on this job for the past 2 years, is simply following the acceptance procedure explained to him by his predecessor.

You talk with the government inspector and find him a conscientious and cooperative person, anxious to carry out his functions of protecting the general public and at the same time having no desire to make unreasonable demands on the manufacturer. You obtain from him the record of the measurements of weights of contents of bags for the past 50 days. (No earlier records are available.) You plot $\bar{X}$ and R charts from the first samples of 5 for these days. $\bar{\bar{X}}$ is 164.1; $\bar{R}$ is 3.9. The $\bar{X}$ chart shows definite evidence of lack of statistical control with 5 points above the upper control limit and 3 points below the lower control limit. Two points are slightly above the upper control limit on the R chart; a recomputed $\bar{R}$ with these two points eliminated is 3.6. On 5 of the 50 days a second sample of 5 was taken because one of the weights in the first sample fell below 160 oz. Two of the days requiring second samples were days on which $\bar{X}$ was below the lower control limit; on the other 3 days $\bar{X}$ was within limits. Two of the 5 second samples contained one sack with contents below 160 oz. The entire day's product for these 2 days was stamped "Substandard Weight."

Packages so stamped are accepted by the trade only at a 5% reduction from the regular factory price of $2.70 for a 10-lb. bag.

(a) Write a general discussion analyzing the statistical aspects and other related aspects of this situation. In preparing this discussion, assume that the reader is familiar with the facts as given in the preceding statement and is familiar with the terminology and general principles of statistical quality control. This discussion might be one such as you would prepare for your chief or for a colleague in your own organization.

(b) Make a proposed draft for a letter to the plant superintendent making specific proposals for any action that you recommend should be taken. Explain in as definite terms as possible the advantages that you expect will be gained by following out your proposals. In so far as possible, this letter should not assume that the plant superintendent is familiar with the terminology and concepts of statistical quality control.

(c) Assume that it is the government bureau carrying out the inspection that is your client rather than the manufacturer. Draft a report to the bureau chief discussing the problems involved in setting and enforcing specifications on filling weights with a view to consumer protection. Illustrate any general statements you make by reference to this specific case. Assume that the bureau chief (or his subordinate who reads the report) is familiar with the terminology and concepts of statistical quality control; for example, he will understand the meaning of an OC curve if one is included in your report.

CHAPTER XIX

THE PLACE OF
STATISTICAL QUALITY CONTROL
IN REPRESENTATIVE MANUFACTURING
AND INSPECTION OPERATIONS

You can't inspect quality into a product.—ANON.

380. Quality Improvement Should Be a Major Objective. This book has dealt chiefly with two techniques, namely, control charts and statistical procedures for use in acceptance sampling. Both involve inspection of manufactured product.

There are obvious reasons why inspection, in the sense of sorting good product from bad, cannot be relied on to ensure that all accepted product is good. Inspection fatigue on repetitive inspection operations will usually limit the effectiveness of 100% inspection. As has been explained in the discussion of acceptance sampling, no sampling procedure can eliminate all defectives. It follows that the best way to be sure that accepted product is good is to have the product made right in the first place. This not only ensures better outgoing product but also reduces costs associated with spoilage and rework.

There are two ways in which acceptance sampling procedures and control charts may contribute to having product made right in the first place. One way is through pressures exerted for quality improvement. The other is through providing better information regarding the reasons for quality troubles. In applying statistical quality control techniques, these two types of contribution tend to be interrelated. This chapter supplements material already presented regarding the ways in which simple statistical quality control procedures may contribute to quality improvement.

381. Some Ways in Which Pressures May Contribute to Quality Improvement. The results of inspection, properly used, may provide the basis for effective pressures for quality improvement, as follows:

1. Pressures based primarily on a sense of pride in good workmanship may be exerted on individual workers and groups of workers. This involves a policy of invoking quality-mindedness (perhaps reinforced by a plant-wide quality campaign) in combination with a policy of making current information on quality performance widely available (perhaps by large-scale control charts or other devices such as the quality control

479

board illustrated on page 471).   The mere fact that quality information is being collected and presented in a systematic way to identify products and processes on which quality is unsatisfactory often leads to striking quality improvements due to better workmanship.

2. Pressures may be exerted on supervisory personnel.   This involves the measurement of current quality performance by department or subdepartment and the comparison of current performance with some norm or standard.   In some cases, ordinary control charts for p and c may do this well enough.   Often, however, some scheme of weighting the seriousness of defects is desirable.   The plan of quality rating based on demerits per unit, referred to in Art. 227 (pages 278 to 279) may be used advantageously for this purpose.

3. In vendor-purchaser relationships involving AQL types of acceptance sampling, strong pressure for product meeting the quality standard is exerted by the threat that tightened inspection will be used unless the process average turns out to be satisfactory.

4. As brought out in Chap. XIV, AOQL procedures should be operated so that the costs of screening rejected lots create pressure for the maintenance of the quality standard.   This point is illustrated further in Example 39.

**EXAMPLE 39.   USE OF AOQL INSPECTION
TO PRODUCE QUALITY IMPROVEMENT**

382. Facts of the Case.   In a large manufacturing plant, the practice for many years had been for the inspection department to carry out 100 % inspection on numerous parts and products.   On many of these items, the average percentages of defectives had been much worse than any reasonable AOQL, and it appeared that no sampling scheme would be as economical as 100 % inspection.   (See the discussion of the break-even point in Art. 351, page 449.)

It was decided that any required 100 % inspection was properly an operating department expense and that inspection should bear only the cost of sampling inspection with sampling criteria based on reasonable quality standards.   AOQL inspection was instituted with AOQL figures set at values considered to be satisfactory objectives. Many lots were rejected, and the cost of screening was charged to the operating departments.   These charges caused greatly increased attention to quality among operating personnel.   In a surprisingly short time, quality was brought to the desired level for the great majority of items.

This new quality consciousness in the operating departments was accompanied by a new viewpoint on the relative responsibilities of operating and inspection. Product costs were considerably reduced.   Once the program reached the point where nearly all items were at qualities better than the AOQL figures adopted for them, the responsibility for carrying out all needed screening inspection was transferred to the operating departments.   This transfer of responsibility applied both to the 100 % inspection of any lots rejected under sampling inspection and to 100 % inspection prior to sampling inspection of those few items where it was not possible to produce at an average quality equal to or better than the desired AOQL.

383. Selecting an AOQL Value as a Quality Standard. Two figures may properly be considered in any decision on the AOQL. One is the maximum percentage of defectives that is tolerable in the outgoing product after inspection. The other is the capability of the production process, expressed as the percentage of defectives that will be expected in most of the submitted lots. It is evident that 100% inspection by *someone* is necessary whenever the submitted quality is appreciably worse than the tolerable percentage of defectives. As illustrated in Example 39, the chief purpose of adopting sampling inspection in this case may be to use frequent lot rejections to force the producer either to improve his quality or to carry out an adequate screening inspection.

Various considerations may enter into the decision on the maximum tolerable percentage of defectives. If the design specification for a quality characteristic contains a margin of safety, some articles that are technically classified as defectives may really be satisfactory for the purpose intended. Sometimes there may be a good chance that any defectives in the outgoing product from this inspection will be eliminated in a later manufacturing or inspection operation; in other cases this inspection may be the last chance to eliminate them. It is obviously necessary to consider the number of quality characteristics involved in the particular inspection and their importance in the functioning of the product being inspected. Comments on some economic aspects of this decision were made in Chap. XVII.

It is likely to be easier to estimate the capabilities of a production process than to decide on the maximum tolerable percentage of defectives. If nearly all of the submitted lots are to be accepted on the basis of the sample, the quality of these accepted lots needs to be somewhat better than the selected AOQL. An approximate rule for guidance is that, as things work out in practice, the net result of using an AOQL scheme will usually be an average outgoing per cent defective not worse than half to two-thirds of the AOQL value.[1] This rule may be viewed in reverse to judge the implications regarding process capability when a particular AOQL value is selected. For instance, suppose a 1.5% AOQL value is selected; this implies that it is believed that—except, perhaps, for occasional out-of-control bad lots—the process can ultimately be made capable of submitting lots that are not worse than about 1.0% defective.

384. Examples of Some Ways in Which Variables Information May Contribute to Quality Improvement. It often happens that pressure

---

[1] DODGE, H. F., Administration of a Sampling Inspection Plan, *Industrial Quality Control*, vol. 5, No. 3, pp. 12–19, November, 1948. This article contains excellent concise advice regarding the development of sampling inspection procedures in a manufacturing plant.

for better workmanship is not enough to secure desired quality improvement. What is needed in addition is a better diagnosis of the sources of quality troubles. Pressure may, however, force the use of more adequate methods of diagnosis. Better diagnosis usually involves securing variables information and frequently calls for the routine use of $\bar{X}$ and R control charts.

Examples 40 to 46 supplement material presented in the earlier chapters of this book regarding the use of control charts for variables to diagnose quality troubles and effect improvements. Examples 40 and 41 deal with vendor-purchaser relationships. Each of the remaining examples illustrates a different type of regular use of variables charts to control a manufacturing process.

EXAMPLE 40. PURCHASER'S CONTROL CHARTS MAY CAUSE VENDOR'S PROCESS IMPROVEMENT

385. Facts of the Case. A manufacturer of vacuum tubes had trouble with the cracking of a certain small cross-shaped ceramic insulator used in the tube. The cracking generally took place after the manufacturing operations were nearly completed and did so in a way that made it impossible to salvage the tube. Hence the costs resulting from each cracked insulator were many times the price of an insulator. As this was a war contract, each tube rendered defective by the failure of an insulator represented a loss of scarce materials and manpower. Moreover, the cracking of some insulators during manufacturing operations suggested that others might be likely to crack under service conditions.

In an effort to improve the situation, all incoming insulators of this type were given 100% inspection. This inspection included a proof load test in which the inspector applied a more or less standardized finger pressure in an effort to break each insulator. This 100% inspection failed to decrease the percentage of tubes rendered defective by cracked insulators.

A simple testing device was then constructed to measure the actual strength in flexure by testing insulators to destruction. From each incoming lot of insulators, 25 were tested. As the insulators came from two vendors, control charts for $\bar{X}$ and σ were maintained for each vendor. The tests showed that both vendors had approximately the same percentage of defective insulators. However, the control charts indicated that the explanations for the defectives were totally different in the two cases.

Vendor A had high average strength but complete lack of anything resembling statistical control. Vendor B had excellent statistical control but at a level such that an appreciable part of the frequency distribution was below the required minimum strength.

This diagnosis of the situation was brought to the attention of both vendors. They were encouraged to exchange information about production methods. (This exchange of information between competitors doubtless would have been possible only under wartime conditions.) Certain techniques used by vendor A (largely related to mixing and molding the clay) were adopted by vendor B to try to raise his average strength. Certain techniques used by vendor B (largely related to control of temperature and humidity during firing) were adopted by vendor A to try to bring his process into control. Both vendors established control charts to help in the maintenance of control. As a result of these actions, both vendors brought their product into control at a satisfactory level and the trouble with the cracking of the insulators was eliminated.

EXAMPLE 41. CONTROL CHARTS USED BY PURCHASER AND VENDOR DISCLOSE DISCREPANCIES BETWEEN GAGES

386. Facts of the Case. In the inspection of screw threads on a turnbuckle produced for an aircraft company by a small vendor, it was suspected that some rejections of submitted lots might be due to discrepancies between the vendor's gages and the aircraft company's gages. It was desired to check this by the use of control charts maintained by the vendor and the aircraft company. In order to put the results of gaging with go and not-go thread gages on a variables basis, the suggestion was made that if any threads were left protruding on applying the go gage, the number of such threads be recorded as a positive value; if the not-go gage went below the end of the turnbuckle, the number of threads covered by this gage be recorded as a negative value.

Control charts for both the right-hand and left-hand threads of the turnbuckle were set up on this basis. In each lot of turnbuckles shipped (750 to 1,500) the

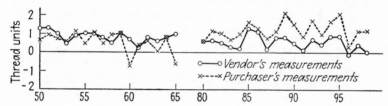

FIG. 86. Comparison of $\bar{X}$ values as obtained by gages of vendor and purchaser in Example 41.

vendor selected 25 at random. The suggested measurements were made on each of the 25, and $\bar{X}$ and R values were computed and included in a form accompanying the shipment. When the shipment was received, the company's inspectors made an independent random selection of 25 turnbuckles and made similar measurements using the company's gages. The vendor's and company's values were plotted on the same $\bar{X}$ chart.

Two sections of one of these $\bar{X}$ charts are shown in Fig. 86. (In order to concentrate attention on the comparison of the two sets of measurements, the control limits have been omitted.) In the first section, it is evident that with the exception of lots 60 and 65 the gages agree; in the second section, it is evident that there is a consistent difference between the vendor's gage and the company's gage.

Whenever a consistent small difference continued through several lots (as in the latter part of Fig. 86) or whenever a single lot showed a marked difference between the gages (as in lots 60 and 65), an investigation was called for by both vendor and company to find out which gage was in error. The resulting replacement of inaccurate gages prevented continued manufacture of bad product in cases where the vendor's gage had worn and also avoided the rejection of good product because of wear of company's gages.

387. Comment on Examples 40 and 41. In Example 40, the purchaser used control charts to diagnose vendor's quality troubles. This occurrence seems fairly common in those industries in which the use of statistical quality control techniques is growing rapidly. Other variables techniques, such as the Shainin Lot Plot method, often serve this same purpose. Just as in Example 40, the result may well be the vendor's introduction to and adoption of the control-chart method for routine process control.

Example 41 illustrates a common difficulty in vendor-purchaser relationships, namely, a discrepancy in the measuring devices. This source of trouble is not limited to dimensional gages that are subject to wear but occurs also in many other types of measurement, including chemical and biological analyses. Where both vendor and purchaser maintain control charts and the identity of individual lots is not lost in shipment, a comparison of these charts may often disclose the existence of this type of difficulty and lead to its correction.

One interesting aspect of Example 41 was that the measure used on the turnbuckle threads was, from the control-chart viewpoint, wrong in principle. According to the scheme of measurement, whenever the go gage went all the way on the threads and the not-go gage did not go at all, a zero value was recorded. As the difference between the go and no-go gages represented the tolerance spread, the so-called zero values were not all alike. The averages of plus and minus values were therefore in error, and the control limits based on $\bar{R}$ were also wrong. Despite this error of principle, the charts actually gave information which helped the vendor to improve his process and which was responsible for correcting errors in vendor's and purchaser's gages.

It should not be concluded from this that errors in principle are of no consequence in the use of the control chart. Any such errors are a possible source of incorrect conclusions and wrong action. Nevertheless, it is not uncommon to find cases like Example 41 in which substantial cost savings and other benefits have been obtained by the use of so-called "control charts" which were really incorrect. Such cases are testimonials to the advantages that may be gained from the control-chart point of view.

EXAMPLE 42. THE USE OF DIAL GAGES AND $\bar{X}$ AND R CHARTS IN DIMENSIONAL CONTROL

388. Facts of the Case. This example deals with the manufacture and inspection of brass cartridge cases for small-arms ammunition at the Eau Claire Ordnance Plant. Dr. Hugh M. Smallwood of the United States Rubber Company describes this case in part as follows:[1]

"Finished ammunition of the type under discussion comprises a bullet, or projectile, inserted in a brass case containing the propellant powder. At the head of the case there is inserted a primer which on impact of the firing pin ignites the propellant powder. The problems arising in manufacturing this product are for the most part

[1] SMALLWOOD, H. M., Quality Control in Manufacture of Small-arms Ammunition, *Mechanical Engineering*, vol. 66, pp. 179–182, March, 1944.

those problems involved in metal working processes. The starting material for the case is brass strip. From this strip, disks are blanked and cupped and these cups constitute the starting material for the majority of the manufacturing plants. The cups are first drawn to the desired length and diameter. It is standard practice in caliber .30 to employ four drawing operations, the first three of which are followed by annealing operations. The head of the case, including the primer pocket, is formed in a horizontal toggle press. The extractor groove is formed in the simplest type of screw machine. Finally, the case is shaped in a vertical dial press to conform to the chamber of the weapon for which it is intended. . . . These operations may be more readily visualized by noting the progressive change in shape of the various components shown in Figure 87.

"Apart from control of the metallurgical properties of the case and bullet, and of the ballistic properties of the finished round, the most important features of the

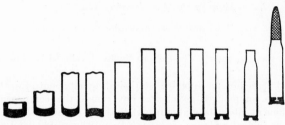

Fig. 87.   Process components of cartridge case shown in cross section.   Assembled cartridge shown at the right.

ammunition are the dimensions of the finished round.   It is apparent that every cartridge must fit the chamber and mechanism of every weapon.   This requires maintenance of fairly close tolerances in the significant dimensions of the finished round.   In order to meet these requirements, it is necessary to maintain close control over most of the dimensions of the intermediate components, since dimensions of the finished product are determined not only by tooling at final operations, but also by incoming component dimensions.   For example, excessive variation is base thickness of the fourth-draw components may cause excessive variation of primer pocket dimensions."

Traditionally, dimensional control of small-arms ammunition had been carried out with conventional go and not-go gages.   The work gages used for process inspection generally had smaller tolerances than the inspection gages subsequently used for acceptance.   As the use of the control chart for variables as a means for process control calls for actual measurement, dial gages were designed to replace the go and not-go work gages.

One of the most important dimensions established by the tapering operation, in which the case is shaped to fit the chamber of the weapon, is the so-called "head-to shoulder" length.   This dimension is indicated in Fig. 88, which shows in cross section the case after tapering.

"The conventional type of gage used for this dimension consists of a chamber in which the case is placed.   The case rests on its shoulder which is supported by a tapered constriction in the chamber.   The chamber is placed on a flat surface and slipped under a snap gage" of the go and not-go type.   "The first step in applying quality control to the head-to-shoulder length was to develop a dial gage to replace the snap gage.

"Figure 89 shows the old type of head-to-shoulder gage on the left, a receiver with case inserted in the center, and the new type of head-to-shoulder gage on the right. It will be noted that the upper arm of the original snap gage has been replaced with an arm holding a dial gage, the point of which bears upon a small plate which can move freely on two supporting pins. When a case is inserted in this gage, the movable plate is supported by the head of the case and communicates the vertical

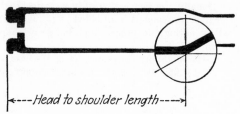

<----Head to shoulder length---->

FIG. 88. Head-to-shoulder dimension of a cartridge case.

displacement to the dial gage. The gage as finally developed is shown on the right of Figure [89]. . . .

"The detailed procedure for applying [statistical] quality control to this particular dimension may be summarized as follows: Five consecutive components are taken from each machine at intervals of approximately thirty minutes. These components are gaged, the individual readings are recorded, and the average and range plotted on an appropriate chart placed in a frame attached to the machine. Limit lines are drawn on the chart by the department which institutes and services the charts.

FIG. 89. Head-to-shoulder gages.

At regular intervals of approximately one month, the average range of all machines is computed, and, if necessary, new limit lines are placed on the charts. After the system is in use, the inspection department carries out the routine measurements and plots the points on the charts. If any point falls outside the limit lines, the tool-setter adjusts the machine and a further sample is taken."

A representative control chart for this dimension is shown in Fig. 90.

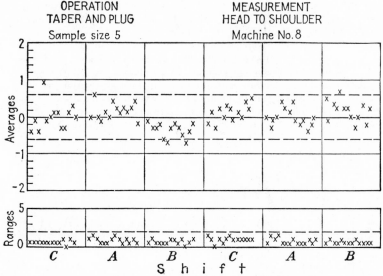

OPERATION
TAPER AND PLUG
Sample size 5

MEASUREMENT
HEAD TO SHOULDER
Machine No. 8

Fig. 90.   Control chart for head-to-shoulder dimension.

EXAMPLE 43. $\bar{X}$ AND R CHARTS ON CENTERLESS GRINDING OF A PISTON PIN

389. Facts of the Case.   E. L. Fay, Chief Inspector of the John Deere Tractor Company, describes this application to the production of a piston pin as follows:[1]

"During the final stages in the production of" a piston pin, "there are three operations: (1) rough centerless grinding, in which an endless chain or stream of pins pass along a trough or holder between two revolving stones that grind the pins rather rapidly; (2) plunge (or stop) centerless grinding and lap, in which each pin is inserted in a holder that permits it to revolve when pushed against a stone of finer grain in order to obtain a smoother finish; and (3) a polishing operation which removes practically no metal.

"The operation on the plunge (or stop) centerless grinder and lap was selected for our first installation.   As indicated by the first panel in Figure 91, the operator was producing the part on the high side of the tolerance.   As a result, a number of the pins were oversize, a condition that made necessary 100% inspection and the reworking of a considerable percentage of the pieces produced.

"In January a study was made of the process.   During this month we were able to get the average size closer to the mean dimension.   The range, however, continued at an unsatisfactory level.   Therefore, a chart was placed on the preceding rough centerless grinding operation where it was found that the major cause of the wide variation in the rough size was due to the operator's not taking the prescribed number of passes through the centerless grinder but trying instead to remove the stock in fewer passes, thus producing the observed variation in size as well as excessive taper and out-of-roundness.

[1] Quoted from E. L. Fay, "An Application of Statistical Quality Control at the John Deere Tractor Company," *O.P.R.D. Quality Control Report* No. 8, by permission of the Production Research and Development Division, U.S. Department of Commerce, formerly OPRD, WPB.

"The operator was very co-operative, and when he understood the effect the quality of his work had on the following operations, he took the prescribed number of passes and produced parts well within specifications.

"However, a few points were still out of control on the plunge (or stop) centerless grinding operation, so a further investigation was made which revealed a loose slide on the driving wheel of the plunge grinder. After making the correct adjustment the operator was able to maintain control and to produce pins within specification as illustrated in the second part of Figure 91. The control limits in each panel of this chart are process limits based on the entire series of points plotted in each of these two contrasting panels. The operators involved on all shifts observed the improve-

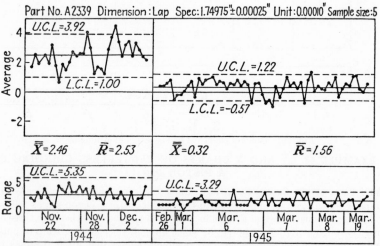

Fig. 91. $\bar{X}$ and R control chart for piston-pin centerless-grinder operation—Example 43. (*Reproduced from O.P.R.D. Quality Control Report No. 8.*)

ment reflected by this chart. They noticed the reduction in the amount of rework, and thereafter paid particular attention to individual effort and skill in operating the machines because control in this operation was the major reason for the improved quality and reduced rework.

"Actual examination of 1,800 pieces produced showed that none were outside of specifications. Four points fell outside the lower control limit on the chart for averages in the second part of Figure 91, and the general downward trend of the averages at this stage indicated impending trouble. The trend was easily checked before any bad parts were produced and control was maintained for the remainder of the run."

390. Comment on Examples 42 and 43. The practice illustrated in Example 42 of posting the $\bar{X}$ and R control charts at the machine is an excellent one. In this way, the information given by the control chart is made available to foremem, toolsetters, and machine operators. Clearly, however, the successful use of the charts by operating personnel as a basis for action is not possible without an effective program of education. This training in control-chart principles, whether conducted on an individual basis or in organized groups, is an essential part of the selling job that is necessary if $\overline{X}$ and R charts are to be used advantageously by shop personnel.

In selling the use of the control charts, either as a supplement to traditional methods of process inspection, or, as in this case, to substitute for them, it is particularly important to make it clear to supervisory personnel and operators that the main purpose of the control charts is to help them rather than to police them. Without the cooperation of foremen and supervisors, the use of $\overline{X}$ and R charts for process control is severely limited.

Anything that helps to popularize the control-chart program is advantageous. The use of well-designed dial gages as a substitute for go and not-go gages is likely to be popular with production personnel. Dr. Smallwood comments on this as follows:

This popularity, of course, is due to the substantially greater information obtained from a dial gage. It is more useful to the toolsetter to know where the product is in the tolerance band than to know simply that it is within the band. The advantage, of course, has nothing whatever to do with [statistical] quality control. In our program, however, we have capitalized on the popularity of the dial gages without severe damage to our consciences. Since the dial gages were instituted as part of the control chart procedure, the entire project was given a good start because of the popularity of the gage. The resultant good effects have justified the use of this incidental advantage.

Example 43 is typical of many trouble-shooting applications of the $\overline{X}$ and R chart. First comes a per cent defective that is too high. Second, a preliminary analysis by the control chart is made to get an idea as to the source of the trouble. This diagnosis may show that the difficulty is lack of statistical control, or too wide a natural tolerance spread, or incorrect centering of the process between the specification limits. In Example 43, the chief difficulties were incorrect centering and too much spread.

Third, there ensues a period of trial and error to test the various possible actions which have been suggested as a result of the control-chart diagnosis. Throughout this period, the control chart provides a running check on the effect of each corrective action. In Example 43, each corrective action was helpful even though several steps were required to get a satisfactory product.

Finally, the corrective actions may be discovered which bring the process into control with a satisfactory centering and a satisfactory spread. Once this desired state of affairs is reached, the problem is to ensure that it continues. This generally calls for a continuing routine use of the control chart.

EXAMPLE 44.   A BRITISH APPLICATION USING REJECT LIMITS

391. Facts of the Case.   The *Production and Engineering Bulletin* issued by the British Ministry of Labour and National Service and the Ministry of Production describes the procedures on hand-operated jobs in one factory in the London area as follows:[1]

"At this firm there is a patrol floor inspector in charge of a group of machines in each shop, who is responsible for all control charts in the group.   He goes to each controlled machine at its appropriate sampling time and takes five components from the tray.   He measures the dimensions concerned and records them on a slip of paper which he slips into the frame behind the control chart hanging above the machine. He then goes on to the next machine while a girl, who follows him, takes the slip of paper from the chart frame, works out the average and range of the five measurements written on it, and plots the corresponding points on the chart.   If both points are within their control limits the tray of components is passed, and the girl follows the patrol inspector on to the next machine.   If either point is outside its control limits the girl informs the patrol inspector who immediately takes a second sample of five from the tray.   If this second sample is satisfactory the job is allowed to continue, the tray of components being put aside for subsequent checking.   If the second sample is unsatisfactory the setter is called in.   He may run one or two components off for himself, or may set to work straight away on the machine, according to the state of the job and the chart.   When the machine or operator fault has been corrected, the operator completes five more components which are measured and referred to the chart.   If this sample is in control the job is allowed to run.   On each floor there is a quality control supervisor who calculates and draws the control limits on all charts and is responsible for the efficient working of the whole system.   Work passed under quality control may or may not be subsequently gauged, according to the importance of the dimension and the reliance which it is deemed can be placed in the operation and its chart.   The decision is based on experience in practice."

. . . "The component concerned in this example is the small brass spindle shown in Figure 92.   It is turned at the rate of 50 to 60 per hour on a $\frac{1}{2}$-inch bar capstan, working to a positive stop on the cross slide. . . . A sample of five components is taken each hour, and the three dimensions marked in Figure 92 are measured on each component.   A micrometer is used for dimensions (1) and (2), measurements being made to 0.0001-inch, and a depth micrometer, reading to 0.0005 is used for (3).   Other dimensions are also checked, but the dimensions (1), (2), and (3) are the only ones under quality control.   The inspection record card for this job is shown in Figure 92.   The drawing requirements for the three dimensions concerned are shown at the top of the card.   The five readings for any one dimension are entered in a horizontal line under the headings A, B, C, D, and E.   The number of the dimension (1, 2 or 3) is entered in the column headed 'Dim.'   A separate chart is kept for each dimension being controlled, but all three charts are made out on the same sheet of paper, as seen in Figure 92."

The limits in the three $\bar{X}$ charts shown in Figure 92 are reject limits or "modified control limits."   (See Arts. 162 and 163, Chap. VIII).   Figure 92 shows the final sheet of a production order, with all but one of the points on the $\bar{X}$ charts falling within reject limits and only one point on the R charts outside conventional control limits. All components made at this operation are later subjected to acceptance inspection in batches, using a Dodge-Romig double sampling 3 % AOQL plan.

[1] Quality Control on Hand-operated Machines, *Production and Engineering Bulletin*, vol. 3, pp. 25–31, January, 1944.

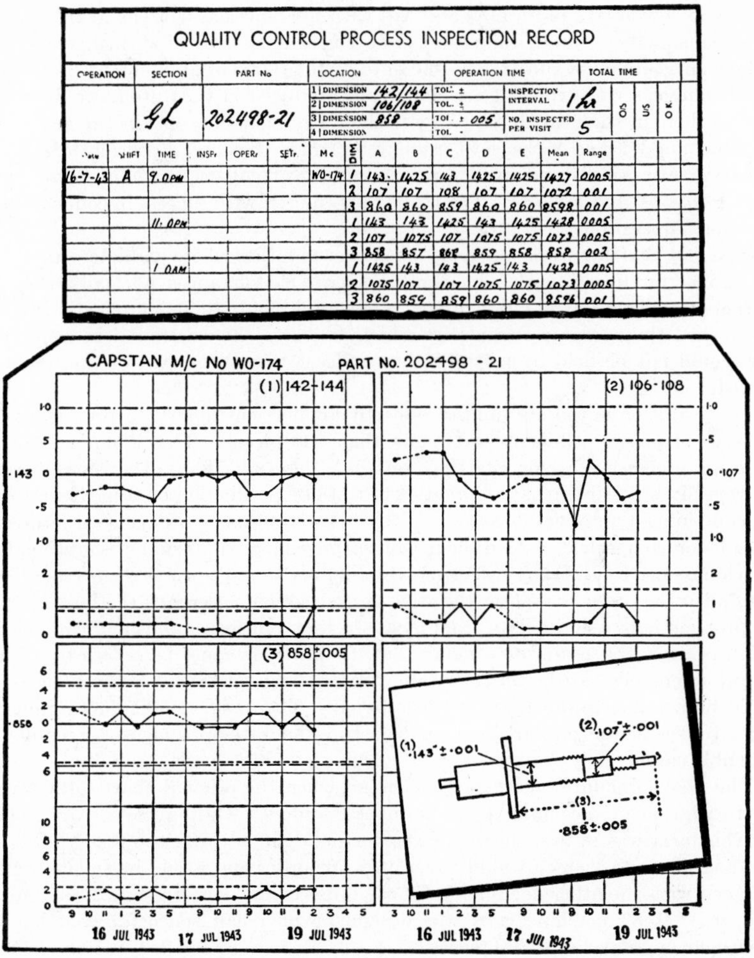

Fig. 92. $\bar{X}$ and R charts with data sheet, as applied to three dimensions of the component shown in the inset—Example 44.   (*Reproduced from Production and Engineering Bulletin.*)

EXAMPLE 45.   CONTROL CHARTS ON SHORT-RUN PRODUCTION

392. Facts of the Case.   Carl G. Schmid describes control-chart applications to the production of precision gears for fire-control instruments in the Naval Ordnance Plant at Indianapolis as follows:[1]

"The most extended and successful application of charting procedure has been made in our gear department.   The gears produced are small and of high precision.   They comprise spur, helical, and bevel gears of 64 D. P. with .000 to .001 backlash, and are made from alloy steel, stainless steel, and phosphor bronze.   Bores are small,

[1] Quoted from C. G. Schmid, "Quality Control at the Lukas-Harold Corporation," *O.P.R.D. Quality Control Report* No. 4, by permission of the Production Research and Development Division, United States Department of Commerce, formerly OPRD, WPB.

running as low as $\frac{3}{16}$ of an inch and less with tolerances as close as .0001 of an inch in some instances.   Out-of-roundness of bore is held to .0001 of an inch and the sides of the spur gears must run true to the bore within .0005 of an inch.

"In some cases the rough gear blanks are produced in the automatic department and in others in the gear department itself.   The machine tools in the gear department include Warner & Swaseys, Monarch lathes, Hardinge bench lathes, Excellos and Borematics, mills and drills, grinders, and gear cutters, including Barber-Colemans, Gleasons, and Fellows.   Charts have been used with success in connection with all of these operations.

"The first charting work was done on the bench lathes where diameters and lengths were being produced (with considerable scrap) to tolerances normally considered impractical.   The control chart proved a powerful tool in reducing rejections because it furnished the operator a guide by which to work.   It was found in general that parts could not be held in control unless at least twenty percent of the items were charted.

. . . "Outside of the automatics department it is customary to process parts on the basis of orders calling for not more than 200 pieces.   This is not an optimum figure for processing or for charting, but it is determined by other considerations. Wherever it is possible it is the practice to run line production on a particular operation combining a number of orders.   This is the exception, and in general setups must be made for each order.   The difficulty of setting control limits under these conditions is obvious, since by the time sufficient samples have been drawn to assure some degree of stability the order is well on the way to completion.   Perhaps the best answer to this problem is to use the data from a satisfactory run for establishing control limits on future runs, the assumption being that if a machine could be set up to bring the natural tolerances satisfactorily within the drawing tolerances on one occasion it should be possible to do so at a future period.   Then any violent fluctuations on a future run could be laid to inadequate setup and attempts made to remedy this assignable cause.

"The above assumption was kept in mind when the original chart form was prepared with space to accommodate a number of orders.   During the first four months that this form was in use, there was a recurring demand from the floor that a short form be substituted which would cover only one order and would be small enough to be placed with the other documents for the order in the departmental files.   Accordingly, a 5" × 8" machine card was designed which had space for charting three dimensions on an order of 200 pieces.

"The use of this card involved a number of procedures that are not strictly orthodox, but which have proved very satisfactory in our shop.   In the first place the high percentage of inspection necessary entailed heavy clerical costs.   It was decided to reduce costs as much as possible by plotting the case values rather than averages of samples of five.   The average is spotted in on the chart by eye with a different colored pencil.   The plotting of individual values permits the elimination of the range chart. The range for each sample can be obtained by inspection and the figure entered in a space provided at the top of the chart.   This chart won immediate acceptance from the shop personnel. Figure 93 is a replica of one of these charts.   Space for remarks is provided on the back of this card.

"Another procedure, which, though unorthodox, had found wide acceptance in Britain, was adopted because of the size of the orders.   This is the setting of control limits at the start of the order on the basis of the drawing limits.   A line is drawn on the chart representing the mean dimension which the operator is to 'shoot at' and the tentative control limits are established above and below the mean at a distance equal to the quotient obtained by dividing the drawing tolerance by twice the square root of the number of pieces in the sample. Thus, in the case of samples of four, tentative control limits would be set half way between the mean and the upper and lower drawing tolerances.

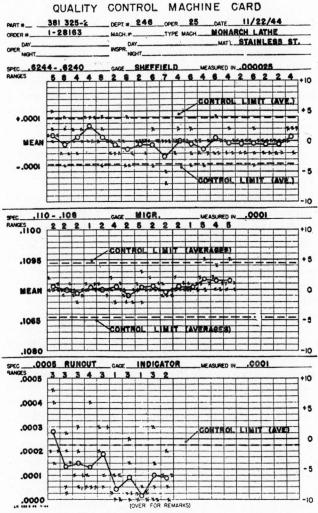

FIG. 93. Machine card used for charting three dimensions on short runs—Example 45. (*Reproduced from O.P.R.D. Quality Control Report No. 4.*)

"While the above variations from usual practice were introduced in all general-purpose machines in this department because of the special conditions encountered, it is believed that in most installations there are substantial advantages to be gained by observing the orthodox procedures explained in the manuals of the American Standards Association."

393. Some Comments on the Differences between Control-chart Applications on Automatic and Hand-operated Machines. The article in *Production and Engineering Bulletin* cited in Example 44 contains the following interesting observations:

It has often been said that quality control technique is not likely to prove of much value when applied to jobs in which the human element plays a major part in controlling the quality of the product.

Capstan lathe work, grinding, drilling and milling operations, shaping, slotting and planing, hand-pressing and most filing, finishing and polishing operations are all quoted as jobs where erratic behaviour of the operator may at any time produce a rejectable part, quite independent of the general run of quality. It is argued, therefore, that quality control, based as it is on the assumption of continuous machine performance having a definite production characteristic, and depending on the evidence of small samples to estimate the quality of the bulk, could not possibly be relied upon to deal with so unpredictable a thing as human error. The result has been that quality control has often been accepted readily for use in the auto shop, but has sometimes not even been given a trial in the hand-operated sections of the plant. One reason for this is, possibly, the widely spread impression that the object of quality control is to dispense with 100% gauging inspection.

The saving in inspection costs and personnel which often results from the introduction of quality control has been so extensively publicised that there has been a tendency to lose sight of the real object of the system, which is to improve quality, increase uniformity, reduce or prevent the production of scrap, and to provide a running commentary on the performance of machines and operators, invaluable for shop floor investigations and factory planning. This demands a fundamentally different approach to the subject. It is not a question, in the first place, of *relying on* a control chart to do our inspection for us. No control chart should ever be relied upon in this way until it has given abundant evidence that such reliance is justified. It is, in the first place, a question of using the control chart to give such information to, and keep such a check upon, operators and setters that the quality of the product is improved. If the improvement (as often happens) is so significant that the percentage of rejects at gauging inspection is found to be held invariably at an acceptable level, then of course, there is a clear case for reducing or eliminating the gauging inspection, but this is a consequence of the introduction of quality control, not its original objective. Incidentally, many factories have found that control charts and measuring equipment easily pay for themselves even though inspection cost is not reduced at all. It may even be increased, particularly when first introducing quality control.

Approaching the subject in this way, we will ask ourselves, when deciding where to introduce quality control, not "Which of our machines is sufficiently reliable to be safely entrusted to quality control?" but, "Which of our machines is so liable to variation as to be most in need of the assistance of quality control to stabilize it?" The answer to the first question, of course, is likely to be that control charts are to be used only on purely automatic jobs, and it is certainly true that this use of quality control shows up the system in its best light. The charts are easy to keep and are readily maintained in control; sampling percentages are low; causes of lack of control are more tangible, and often more easily identified and corrected than the more elusive human errors; and savings in inspection costs are often spectacular. But, on the other hand, if the subject is approached with the second question in mind, the hand-operated jobs, less reliable and more difficult to control though they are, will qualify for control charts on at least an equal footing with the autos.

Charts for hand-operated jobs should be interpreted rather differently from those on fully automatic machines. The ranges of samples from a reasonably good auto are often found to vary very little. It is the points on the chart for means that tend to wander. In other words, an automatic machine can usually produce a uniform product at least for a short period, and it is tool wear and setter's adjustments that need to be controlled, not the basic variability of the machine. In fact, so stable is the range chart often found to be on an automatic job, that some firms are not even bothering to plot it at all, on the grounds that it tells them nothing but what they know already, namely that, so long as the machine is properly set and adjusted, its product will be satisfactory. It is the mean chart which is the setter's chart. Should the *ranges* of samples from an auto be found out of control, it is quite a serious matter, for it indicates some breakdown in the basic operating characteristics of the machine, and will possibly mean that some actual repair, replacement or overhaul is necessary, as distinct from mere setting or adjustment.

On a hand-operated job, however, the position is rather different. We still have our chart of sample means to give information to the setter, but our main sources of error are likely to be the shortcomings of the operator herself. These errors are usually of a random nature—too long a dwell on one component, not long enough on another; odd, erratic performances of all kinds, due to lack of concentration or skill on the part of the operator. Such errors, when present, will result in an increase in the variability of the product and will be detected by the large ranges of the samples taken during the periods of bad workmanship. It is, thus, the chart of ranges which needs watching in this instance. It should be regarded as the operator's own personal chart, and everything possible should be done to encourage the operator herself to regard it in this way. It is a running commentary on her work—a chart standing always right before her eyes on which are recorded, faithfully and inevitably, for all the world to see, her careless slips and faults—as well as her long runs of good production.

The experience at the Indianapolis Naval Ordnance plant (Example 45) was similar to that reported by the British in the preceding quotation. Schmid says, in part:[1]

[1] *Ibid.*

Whereas on automatics, changes in level on the average chart normally result from improper setting or tool wear, on hand-operated machines they may occur simply because of the inability of the operator to index precisely the same on consecutive parts, as well as from improper setting. Likewise, in the case of the range chart, unusual fluctuations on pieces coming from an automatic often indicate that the machine is failing to repeat because of some serious trouble which justifies overhaul, whereas this type of fluctuation on a hand-operated machine may simply indicate the inability of the operator to perform satisfactorily.

The idiosyncrasies of the operator are usually more violent and less subject to control than those of an automatic machine. This condition determined the main point of divergence in the charting procedure. It was found necessary to measure and chart a much higher percentage of pieces coming from general-purpose machines than from the automatics. A five to ten percent check considered sufficient to keep the automatics running within desired control even with relatively short orders and high precision work. On lathes, grinders, bore-matics, and milling machines the percentage of check that was found necessary ran from twenty percent up to fifty percent and even one hundred percent in the case of tolerances of .0001 on small holes. Of course, when an increasingly high percentage of the parts is measured the probability of the sample being representative approaches one, or certainty, and the chart becomes an exhaustive record of performance.

394. Some Comments on Short Runs and the Use of Reject Limits.
Intermittent production of a part or article is no obstacle to the use of $\overline{X}$ and R charts on its quality characteristics. Control limits established on preceding runs may be applied at the start of a new run just as if there had been no interruption.

However, short runs which are not to be repeated do present difficulties in the way of effective use of $\overline{X}$ and R charts. The trouble is that a short run may be completed before it is possible to establish any control limits based on the run itself. In many cases this means that it will not pay to use the control chart on such operations. In other cases, particularly where tolerances are tight and the costs incident to defective work are substantial, the control chart more than pays its way if the conventional procedures are modified.

One possible modification is to use reject limits (modified control limits). In Example 45 these limits were established on the assumption that the natural tolerance range ($6\sigma'$) of each process was equal to the specified tolerance range ($X_{max} - X_{min}$). If this assumption is roughly accurate, as it may be in many cases of tight tolerances in dimensional control, it provides a simple method of establishing reject limits.

Another possible modification is, in effect, to put the control chart on the machine rather than on the part. That is, control charts may be used to estimate the capabilities of the different machines in a shop in terms of the natural tolerance range that each machine will hold on various types of operations. Such a study provides a basis for predetermining control limits on new jobs. A useful by-product may be assistance in production planning, so that the close tolerance jobs may be assigned to the machines that will hold close tolerances, and vice versa.

In a jobbing shop, another by-product of control-chart information about machine capabilities may be a better basis for judgment as to whether to undertake proposed new contracts calling for close tolerances. The lack of such information was particularly evident during the war, when many shops undertook close tolerance work which they were not equipped to perform. This resulted in spoilage and production delays that might have been avoided if the control-chart technique had been more widely understood.

EXAMPLE 46. DETERMINING THE INITIAL MACHINE SETTING WHEN A TREND IS EXPECTED IN THE VALUE OF A DIMENSION

395. Facts of the Case. On certain operations in one machine shop, it was a common experience for a definite steady trend in the average value of dimensions of machined parts to be caused by rapid tool wear. On many specified dimensions the spread of the specification limits, $X_{max} - X_{min}$, was substantially greater than the natural tolerance range of the process, $6\sigma'$. This provided an ample margin of safety against the production of defective product as long as the machine setting held the average value of the dimension somewhere close to a point midway between the specification limits. However, the tendency of the average value of a dimension to shift rapidly as a result of tool wear called for frequent new setups to restore the average value to its desired position. Each new setup involved appreciable costs, both for setup expense and for idle machine time.

The introduction of the control-chart point of view provided a basis for reducing the frequency of setups. The situation here was essentially the one discussed in Art. 98, Chap. V, and illustrated in Figs. 18c and 22. The average value of the frequency distribution of the variable X (in this case, a dimension) shifted at an approximately uniform rate, but the shape of the frequency distribution and its dispersion (measured by σ') did not change. From control-chart data properly taken, it was possible to estimate σ'. It was also possible to estimate the rate of change of the average $\bar{X}$ and to express this rate of change in terms of an equation.

The estimate of σ' made it possible to determine the aimed-at average value for an initial setup to permit the maximum run between setups. The estimate of the rate of change of the dimension provided a basis for decision as to the required frequency of new setups. Once σ' and the rate of change of X were estimated for a particular operation, it proved possible to use this information on new jobs. Even jobs involving relatively short runs were benefited, as many such jobs were completed with a single setup in contrast to the two or three setups usually required for similar jobs before the use of the control chart.

396. Fitting a Trend Line to an $\bar{X}$ Chart. Consider the following values of $\bar{X}$ and R for a dimension specified as 0.644 ± 0.004 in. Subgroups of five components were measured every half-hour.

Subgroup number	$\bar{X}$	R
1	0.6417	0.0011
2	0.6418	0.0016
3	0.6424	0.0010
4	0.6431	0.0015
5	0.6433	0.0009
6	0.6437	0.0010
7	0.6433	0.0014
8	0.6436	0.0004
9	0.6441	0.0006
10	0.6444	0.0011
11	0.6456	0.0009
12	0.6457	0.0007
13	0.6454	0.0009
Totals.....	8.3681	0.0131

$$\bar{\bar{X}} = \frac{8.3681}{13} = 0.6437$$

$$\bar{R} = \frac{0.0131}{13} = 0.0010$$

Certain precautions should be taken in the collection of data to be used for the calculation of a trend line and control limits. The production between successive subgroups should be approximately constant.[1] The components included in a subgroup should be produced in succession so that the trend will have little effect on the range of a subgroup.

On the conventional $\bar{X}$ chart, the central line is horizontal. With an upward trend of $\bar{X}$ values, the central line must be a sloping line. The position of this central line may be described by an equation of the form $\bar{X} = a + bh$, with the symbol h used to represent the subgroup number (preferably with a revised subgroup numbering using the middle subgroup as the origin). a is the value of $\bar{X}$ when $h = 0$, and b is the slope of the line. The method of least squares provides a satisfactory way of finding the values of a and b corresponding to any given set of measurements.[2]

Under certain special circumstances, computing a least squares trend line is a very simple operation. These circumstances are that the observed values of the variable plotted on the vertical axis of the chart (in this case, values of $\bar{X}$) are uniformly

[1] If the total production up to each subgroup were recorded, it would be possible to plot $\bar{X}$ as a function of production even though the production were not uniform from subgroup to subgroup. In such a case, however, the fitting of a least squares trend line is somewhat more complicated than is the simple method illustrated in Table 50. Methods of fitting least squares lines in such cases are explained in standard texts on statistical methods.

[2] Although fair results may often be obtained by drawing a trend line by eye on the chart, the personal equation enters into such fits to the extent that no two people are likely to agree exactly. As the least squares line is so easy to compute in this special case, it will generally pay to take the slight additional time required to obtain the least squares fit.

spaced along the horizontal axis of the chart (in this case, on the scale of subgroup numbers h); that there are an odd number of observed values; and that the origin on the horizontal axis is taken as the mid-point of that axis (that is, the 0 value of h is assumed at the middle subgroup). Under these circumstances $a = \bar{X}$, and $b = \dfrac{\Sigma h \bar{X}}{\Sigma h^2}$.
(The symbol Σ represents summation.) The method of calculation is illustrated in Table 50 as shown on page 500.

For simplicity in calculations, the $\bar{X}$ values in Table 50 are expressed in units of 0.0001 in excess of 0.6400. The equation $\bar{X} = 37.0 + 3.29h$ is, of course, expressed

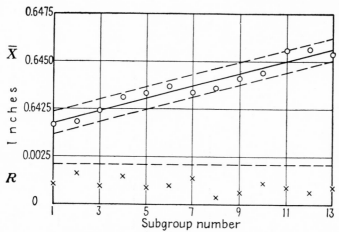

FIG. 94. Illustration of trend line on $\bar{X}$ chart—Example 46.

in these units. In terms of the actual dimension in inches, the equation becomes $\bar{X} = 0.6437 + 0.000329h$.

To plot this line on the control chart (Fig. 94), it is necessary to locate two points on the line and connect them.

For example, for $h = -6$, $\bar{X} = 0.6437 + (0.000329)(-6) = 0.6417$
for $h = +6$, $\bar{X} = 0.6437 + (0.000329)(6) = 0.6457$

397. Interpreting the Control Chart as a Basis for Action. The control limits are sloping lines parallel to the central trend line. The upper control limit is $A_2\bar{R}$ above the trend line, and the lower control limit is $A_2\bar{R}$ below it. In this case, $A_2\bar{R} = 0.58(0.0010) = 0.0006$. Figure 94 shows sloping limits plotted at this distance from the central line.

To decide on the value of the average dimension to be aimed at in the initial machine setting, it is first necessary to estimate σ'. This is $\bar{R}/d_2 = 0.0010/2.326 = 0.00043$. The tolerance spread $X_{\max} - X_{\min}$ may then be compared with σ'. In this case

$$X_{\max} - X_{\min} = 0.6480 - 0.6400 = 0.0080$$

This is equal to $18.6\sigma'$.

A decision must then be made as to how many multiples of σ' the initial setting should be from the lower specification limit. In some instances this might be $3\sigma'$; in others, it might be a greater multiple of σ' such as $4\sigma'$. Where the tolerance spread is great enough to allow a considerable run between settings, as in this case, the additional margin of safety involved in the use of $4\sigma'$ is likely to be justified. The same multiple of σ' should be used to determine the time of a new setup. Using $4\sigma'$ in this case, we obtain the following directions: On initial setup, aim at

$$\bar{X} = X_{min} + 4\sigma' = 0.6400 + 0.0017 = 0.6417$$

Make a new setup when trend line $= X_{max} - 4\sigma' = 0.6480 - 0.0017 = 0.6463$.

The slope of the trend line, $b = 0.000329$, is the expected change in average dimension from one subgroup to the next. The interval between setups may be estimated as $(0.6463 - 0.6417)/0.000329 = 14$ subgroup intervals. With subgroups spaced half an hour apart, this indicates that a new setup is required every 7 hr.

TABLE 50. CALCULATION OF EQUATION OF LEAST SQUARES TREND LINE FOR $\bar{X}$
($\bar{X}$ expressed in units of 0.0001 in excess of 0.6400)

Subgroup number	Revised subgroup number h	Subgroup average $\bar{X}$	$h\bar{X}$	h^2
1	−6	17	−102	36
2	−5	18	− 90	25
3	−4	24	− 96	16
4	−3	31	− 93	9
5	−2	33	− 66	4
6	−1	37	− 37	1
7	0	33	0	0
8	1	36	36	1
9	2	41	82	4
10	3	44	132	9
11	4	56	224	16
12	5	57	285	25
13	6	54	324	36
Totals.....	0	481	599	182

$$a = \bar{\bar{X}} = \frac{481}{13} = 37.0$$

$$b = \frac{\Sigma h\bar{X}}{\Sigma h^2} = \frac{599}{182} = 3.29$$

$$\bar{X} = a + bh = 37.0 + 3.29h$$

When a point falls outside control limits on an $\bar{X}$ chart with a sloping central line, there are two possible interpretations. One is the conventional one that an assignable cause of variation is responsible for the point falling outside the limits. The other is that the limits are based on a trend line that is wrong. For example, a control chart might be started for a new job using a slope of a trend line determined from a previous similar job; it might turn out that the jobs were really sufficiently different for the slopes to differ. As another example, tool wear is a factor that does not necessarily operate at a uniform rate; on jobs where the rate of change of the average value of a dimension is variable, no straight line fitted to $\bar{X}$ values will provide a satisfactory central line for a control chart.

APPENDIXES

GLOSSARY OF SYMBOLS

The symbols used in the literature of statistical method are not fully standardized. The same statistical quantity may be represented by different symbols by different writers. Moreover, statistical problems are so numerous and diverse that any given symbol may be used in a number of different meanings, each meaning referring to a particular type of statistical problem. This lack of standardization complicates matters for the reader who consults a number of statistical books and articles.

The principle used in the selection of symbols for this book has been to try to minimize the reader's difficulties of transition to other quality control literature by the adoption for each statistical quantity of the symbol for it which is most common in the literature of statistical quality control in the United States. In general, the control-chart symbols used follow the standards of the American Society for Quality Control and also agree with the symbols used in the publications of the American Society for Testing Materials and the American Standards Association.

In the case of a few symbols, this conformance to common practice in the literature of quality control has involved the use of one symbol with two or more meanings. However, in every case the appropriate meaning should be clear from the context. This duplication of meanings for a few symbols seemed less likely to cause confusion than the adoption for this book of symbols that are not in common use in the other literature of the subject.

A = a multiplier of σ' to determine the distance from central line to 3-sigma control limits on an $\bar{X}$ chart. It equals $3/\sqrt{n}$ and is given for values of n from 2 to 100 in Table E, Appendix III.

A_1 = a multiplier of $\bar{\sigma}$ to determine the distance from central line to 3-sigma control limits on an $\bar{X}$ chart. It equals $3/c_2 \sqrt{n}$ and is given for values of n from 2 to 100 in Table D, Appendix III.

A_2 = a multiplier of $\bar{R}$ to determine the distance from central line to 3-sigma control limits on an $\bar{X}$ chart. It equals $3/d_2 \sqrt{n}$ and is given for values of n from 2 to 20 in Table C, Appendix III.

AOQL = average outgoing quality limit.

AQL = acceptable quality level.

B_1 = a multiplier of σ' to determine the 3-sigma lower control limit on a chart for σ. It is given for values of n from 2 to 100 in Table E, Appendix III.

B_2 = a multiplier of σ' to determine the 3-sigma upper control limit on a chart for σ. It is given for values of n from 2 to 100 in Table E, Appendix III.

B_3 = a multiplier of $\bar{\sigma}$ to determine the 3-sigma lower control limit on a chart for σ. It is given for values of n from 2 to 100 in Table D, Appendix III.

B_4 = a multiplier of $\bar{\sigma}$ to determine the 3-sigma upper control limit on a chart for σ. It is given for values of n from 2 to 100 in Table D, Appendix III.

$B_{.001}$, $B_{.005}$, $B_{.025}$, $B_{.975}$, $B_{.995}$, $B_{.999}$ = factors for computing probability limits for control charts for σ. See Table 23, Chap. VIII.

c = number of defects, usually in a sample of stated size. c may also refer to the number of occurrences of some other chosen event in a sample of stated size.

502

c = in single sampling acceptance schemes, the acceptance number, *i.e.*, the maximum allowable number of defective pieces in a sample of size n.

$\bar{c}$ = average number of defects per sample in a series of samples of equal size.

c' = standard or aimed-at average number of defects in a sample of stated size. c' may refer also to the universe average number of defects per sample.

c_1 = in double sampling acceptance schemes, the acceptance number for the first sample, *i.e.*, the maximum number of defectives that will permit acceptance of the lot on the basis of the first sample.

c_2 = in double sampling acceptance schemes, the acceptance number for the two samples combined, *i.e.*, the maximum number of defectives that will permit acceptance of the lot on the basis of the two samples.

c_2 = a factor used in connection with sampling by variables that is a function of n and expresses the ratio between the expected value of $\bar{\sigma}$ from a long series of samples from a normal universe and the σ' of that universe. Values of c_2 are given in Table B, Appendix III.

C_r^n = the number of combinations of n things taken r at a time.

d = deviation in cells from the assumed origin of a frequency distribution.

d_2 = a factor used in connection with sampling by variables that is a function of n and expresses the ratio between the expected value of R from a long series of samples from a normal universe and the σ' of that universe. Values of d_2 are given in Table B, Appendix III.

D_1 = a multiplier of σ' to determine the 3-sigma lower control limit on a chart for R. It is given for values of n from 2 to 20 in Table E, Appendix III.

D_2 = a multiplier of σ' to determine the 3-sigma upper control limit on a chart for R. It is given for values of n from 2 to 20 in Table E, Appendix III.

D_3 = a multiplier of $\bar{R}$ to determine the 3-sigma lower control limit on a chart for R. It is given for values of n from 2 to 20 in Table C, Appendix III.

D_4 = a multiplier of $\bar{R}$ to determine the 3-sigma upper control limit on a chart for R. It is given for values of n from 2 to 20 in Table C, Appendix III.

$D_{.001}$, $D_{.005}$, $D_{.025}$, $D_{.975}$, $D_{.995}$, $D_{.999}$ = factors for computing probability limits for control chart for R. See Table 24, Chap. VIII.

e = Naperian or natural base of logarithms, 2.71828+.

f = frequency; generally, the number of observed values within a cell of a frequency distribution.

f = in Dodge's AOQL plan for continuous production (Art. 283), the fraction of units that are inspected during the periods when sampling inspection is used.

i = in Dodge's AOQL plan for continuous production (Art. 283), the number of successive units that must be found by 100 % inspection to be free from all defects before acceptance may be carried out by sampling.

I_Q = incomplete beta function. Gen. L. E. Simon's "An Engineers' Manual of Statistical Method" contains I_Q charts of probability limits for the binomial distribution.

k = a factor used in connection with unknown-sigma variables acceptance plans. With a one-sided specification, $\bar{X} \geqq L + ks$ or $U - ks \geqq \bar{X}$.

k' = a factor used in connection with known-sigma variables acceptance plans. With a one-sided specification, $\bar{X} \geqq L + k'\sigma'$ or $U - k'\sigma' \geqq \bar{X}$.

k'^* = a factor used in connection with known-sigma variables acceptance plans involving two-sided specifications. $\bar{X} \geqq L + k'^*\sigma'$ and $U - k'^*\sigma' \geqq \bar{X}$.

L = lower specification limit.

LCL = lower control limit on a control chart. $LCL_{\bar{X}}$ refers to the lower control limit on an $\bar{X}$ chart, LCL_p to lower control limit on a p chart, etc.

$LRL_{\bar{X}}$ = lower reject limit for averages, the lowest possible satisfactory value of the lower control limit on an $\bar{X}$ chart.

LTPD = lot tolerance per cent defective.

m = number of defective pieces in a given sample of size n.

M = number of defective pieces in a given lot of size N.

n = the number of pieces or observed values in any given sample or subgroup.

np = number of defectives in a sample of size n.

n_1 = in double sampling, the number of pieces in the first sample.

n_2 = in double sampling, the number of pieces in the second sample.

N = number of pieces in a given lot to be sampled for purposes of acceptance.

p = fraction defective, the ratio of the number of defectives to the total number inspected.

$100p$ = per cent defective.

$\bar{p}$ = average fraction defective, the ratio of the sum of the number of defectives found in a set of samples to the sum of the number of articles inspected in the same samples.

p' = the probability that a particular event will happen in a single trial. In statistical quality control the event in question is usually the occurrence of a defective article. In control-chart applications, p' generally refers to an aimed-at or standard value of the probability of a defective. In sampling acceptance theory, p' generally refers to the true process average fraction defective of a product submitted for inspection.

$p_{0.95}$ = product fraction defective having a probability of acceptance of 0.95 under given acceptance criteria.

$p_{0.50}$ = product fraction defective having a probability of acceptance of 0.50 under given acceptance criteria. In the Philips Standard Sampling System (Table 46, Art. 318) this is referred to as the point of control.

$p_{0.10}$ = product fraction defective having a probability of acceptance of 0.10 under given acceptance criteria.

P_0, P_1, P_2, etc. = probabilities of exactly 0, 1, 2, etc., defectives, respectively.

P_a = probability of accepting any given lot or product.

P_c = the consumer's risk, *i.e.*, the probability of accepting product meeting some given quality standard.

P_r^n = the number of permutations of n things taken r at a time.

q' = $(1 - p')$, the probability that a particular event will not happen in a single trial.

Q = a factor (given in Table 49, page 433) for use in the Schwartz-Kaufman unknown-sigma variables acceptance test to be used when specifications apply to lot averages. A sample average should fall outside specification limits for lot average by not more than QR.

r = a constant referring to the number of occurrences of some event.

R = the range, the difference between the largest value and the smallest value in any set of numbers.

$\bar{R}$ = the average of a set of ranges.

$s = \sqrt{\dfrac{\Sigma(X - \bar{X})^2}{n - 1}}.$ The sample value of s is used rather than the sample value of σ in certain unknown-sigma plans in acceptance sampling by variables.

t = an arbitrary constant used to represent the position of some given X value in terms of multiples of the standard deviation above or below the average of a universe or frequency distribution.

u = defects per unit, the ratio of the number of defects in a sample to the total number of units in the sample; $u = c/n$.

$\bar{u}$ = average defects per unit; the total number of defects in a set of samples divided by the total number of units in the set.

u' = the aimed-at or standard value of defects per unit used for purposes of computing control limits on a control chart for u; also used to refer to the true universe average number of defects per unit.

U = a factor (given in Table 49, page 433) for use in the Schwartz-Kaufman known-sigma variables acceptance test to be used when specifications apply to lot averages. A sample average should fall outside specification limits for lot average by not more than $U(6\sigma')$.

U = upper specification limit.

UCL = upper control limit on a control chart. $UCL_{\overline{X}}$ refers to the upper control limit on an $\overline{X}$ chart, UCL_p to the upper control limit on a p chart, etc.

$URL_{\overline{X}}$ = upper reject limit for averages, the highest possible satisfactory value of the upper control limit on an $\overline{X}$ chart.

V = factor for reject limits. It equals $3 - 3/\sqrt{n}$ and is given in Table 25, Chap. VIII.

X = a number representing a value of some variable; in statistical quality control, X is usually the observed value of some quality characteristic for an individual unit. Specific observed values may be designated as $X_1, X_2, X_3, \ldots, X_i, \ldots, X_n$.

$\overline{X}$ = (X bar), the average (arithmetic mean) of two or more X values. The average of n X values is the sum of the X values divided by n.

$\overline{\overline{X}}$ = (X double bar), the average of a set of $\overline{X}$ values, sometimes called the grand average.

$\overline{X}'$ = (X bar prime), an aimed-at or standard average value of a quality characteristic; also used to represent the true universe average.

$X_{\max}$ = upper specification limit for value of the variable X.

$X_{\min}$ = lower specification limit for value of the variable X.

σ = (sigma), the standard deviation of a set of numbers, *i.e.*, the root-mean-square deviation about the average.

$\bar{\sigma}$ = (sigma bar), the average of a set of σ values.

σ' = (sigma prime), the known or estimated or aimed-at value of universe standard deviation.

$\sigma_{\overline{X}}$ = the standard deviation of the expected frequency distribution of the averages $\overline{X}$ of samples of size n. It is equal to $\sigma'/\sqrt{n}$.

$\sigma_c, \sigma_{np}, \sigma_p, \sigma_R, \sigma_u, \sigma_\sigma$ = the standard deviation of the sampling distribution of c, np, p, R, u, and σ, respectively.

$!$ = symbol for factorial. $n!$ is the product of the first n integers.

BIBLIOGRAPHY

The following bibliography is limited to books and pamphlets. Nearly all of the volumes listed give considerable attention to one or more aspects of statistical quality control. A few recent works on mathematical and applied statistics have also been included where the material covered appears to have direct application to certain quality control problems.

Most of the available published information on statistical quality control applications in different industries is contained in periodical articles. For the most complete bibliography of periodical articles (and other writings) on the subject, see the two Butterbaugh volumes listed below. These two volumes of bibliography cover the period from the beginnings of statistical quality control in 1924 through June, 1949. The second volume contains an index by industries, applicable to the material in both volumes.

It is significant that the first Butterbaugh bibliography, covering the first 22 years of this period, contained 712 items, whereas the second one, covering only the final 3½ years, contained 725 items. Starting with the issue of July, 1949, *Industrial Quality Control* has carried a current bibliography including short digests of many of the articles appearing in other periodicals.

"Acceptance Sampling—A Symposium," The American Statistical Association, Washington, D.C., 1950. (Contains papers by Paul Peach, E. G. Olds, J. H. Curtiss, and W. A. Wallis, and discussion by many others.)

ALFORD, L. P., and J. R. BANGS, JR. (eds.), "Production Handbook," The Ronald Press Company, New York, 1944. (Section 10, pp. 675–725, deals with statistical quality control.)

American War Standards Z1.1—1941 and Z1.2—1941, "Guide for Quality Control and Control Chart Method of Analyzing Data," American Standards Association, New York, 1941.

American War Standard Z1.3—1942; "Control Chart Method of Controlling Quality During Production," American Standards Association, New York, 1942. (The authoritative, concise statement of American control-chart practices.)

"A.S.T.M. Manual on Quality Control of Materials," American Society for Testing Materials, Philadelphia, Pa., 1951.

BOWKER, A. H., and H. P. GOODE, "Sampling Inspection by Variables," McGraw-Hill Book Company, Inc., New York, 1952.

BROWNLEE, K. A., "Industrial Experimentation," Chemical Publishing Company, Inc., Brooklyn, 1947.

BUREAU OF ORDNANCE OF THE DEPARTMENT OF THE NAVY, "An Introduction to Statistical Quality Control," Superintendent of Documents, Government Printing Office, Washington, D.C., 1950.

BUTTERBAUGH, G. I., "A Bibliography of Statistical Quality Control," University of Washington Press, Seattle, 1946.

BUTTERBAUGH, G. I., "A Bibliography of Statistical Quality Control—Supplement," University of Washington Press, Seattle, 1951.

COCHRAN, W. G., and G. M. COX, "Experimental Designs," John Wiley & Sons, Inc., New York, 1950.

"Conference Papers—First Annual Convention American Society for Quality Control and Second Midwest Quality Control Conference," John S. Swift Company, Inc., Chicago, 1947.

DAVIES, O. L. (ed.), "Statistical Methods in Research and Production with Special Reference to the Chemical Industry," Oliver & Boyd, Ltd., Edinburgh and London, 1947.

DEMING, W. E., "Some Theory of Sampling," John Wiley & Sons, Inc., New York, 1950.

DIXON, W. J., and F. J. MASSEY, JR., "An Introduction to Statistical Analysis," McGraw-Hill Book Company, Inc., New York, 1951.

DODGE, H. F., and H. G. ROMIG, "Sampling Inspection Tables—Single and Double Sampling," John Wiley & Sons, Inc., New York, 1944. (The complete Dodge-Romig tables, with an explanation of how they were derived and an illustration of their use at Western Electric Company. Every inspection department in a mass-production industry should have a copy of this book.)

DUDDING, B. P., and W. J. JENNETT, Quality Control Charts, *British Standard* 600R: 1942, British Standards Institution, London, 1942.

DUDDING, B. P., and W. J. JENNETT, "Quality Control Chart Techniques When Manufacturing to a Specification," General Electric Company, Ltd., of England, London, 1944.

DUDLEY, J. W., JR., "Examination of Industrial Measurements," McGraw-Hill Book Company, Inc., New York, 1946.

DUNCAN, A. J., "Quality Control and Industrial Statistics," Richard D. Irwin, Inc., Homewood, Ill., 1952.

EISENHART, CHURCHILL, M. W. HASTAY, and W. A. WALLIS, (eds.), "Techniques of Statistical Analysis," McGraw-Hill Book Company, Inc., New York, 1947.

ENRICK, N. L., "Quality Control," Industrial Press, New York, 1948.

FEIGENBAUM, A. V., "Quality Control," McGraw-Hill Book Company, Inc., New York, 1951.

FELLER, WILLIAM, "An Introduction to Probability Theory and Its Applications," vol. I, John Wiley & Sons, Inc., New York, 1950.

FREEDMAN, RUDOLPH, and JOSEPH MOVSHIN, "A Basic Training Manual on Statistical Quality Control," St. Louis Society for Quality Control, St. Louis, 1950.

FREEMAN, H. A., "Industrial Statistics," John Wiley & Sons, Inc., New York, 1942.

FREEMAN, H. A., and others, "Proceedings of the Industrial Statistics Conference Held at Massachusetts Institute of Technology, September 8–9, 1938," Pitman Publishing Corp., New York, 1939. (Includes papers by Shewhart, Dodge, Simon, Tippett, Wilks, and others.)

FREEMAN, H. A., MILTON FRIEDMAN, FREDERICK MOSTELLER, and W. A. WALLIS (eds.), "Sampling Inspection," McGraw-Hill Book Company, Inc., New York, 1948. (Because of its matched sets of single, double, and multiple plans with OC curves for every plan, this book is an extremely useful source of attributes acceptance plans.)

FRY, T. C., "Probability and Its Engineering Uses," D. Van Nostrand Company, Inc., New York, 1928.

HALD, ANDERS, "Statistical Tables and Formulas," John Wiley & Sons, Inc., New York, 1952.

HALD, ANDERS, "Statistical Theory with Engineering Applications," John Wiley & Sons, Inc., New York, 1952.

HEIDE, J. D., "Industrial Process Control by Statistical Methods," McGraw-Hill Book Company, Inc., New York, 1952.

HOEL, P. G., "Introduction to Mathematical Statistics," John Wiley & Sons, Inc., New York, 1947.

JURAN, J. M., "Management of Inspection and Quality Control," Harper & Brothers, New York, 1945.

JURAN, J. M., "Quality Control Handbook," McGraw-Hill Book Company, Inc., New York, 1951.

KEMPTHORNE, OSCAR, "The Design and Analysis of Experiments," John Wiley & Sons, Inc., New York, 1952.

KENNEDY, C. W., "Quality Control Methods," Prentice-Hall, Inc., New York, 1948.

"Military Standard 105A—Sampling Procedures and Tables for Inspection by Attributes," Superintendent of Documents, Government Printing Office, Washington, D.C., 1950.

MOOD, A. M., "Introduction to the Theory of Statistics," McGraw-Hill Book Company, Inc., New York, 1950.

MOLINA, E. C., "Poisson's Exponential Binomial Limit," D. Van Nostrand Company, Inc., New York, 1942. (Molina's tables contain individual values and cumulative values of the Poisson, both to six decimal places.)

PEACH, PAUL, "Introduction to Industrial Statistics and Quality Control," Edwards and Broughton Co., Raleigh, N.C., 1947.

PEARSON, E. S., "The Application of Statistical Methods to Industrial Standardization and Quality Control," British Standard 600I:1935, British Standards Institution, London. (This is out of print, as the plates for this volume were destroyed in the bombing of London. It is, however, available in many libraries.)

REYNOLDS, E. A., and G. M. REYNOLDS, "Industrial Project in Statistical Quality Control," Syracuse University Institute of Industrial Research, Syracuse, N.Y., 1948.

RICE, W. B., "Control Charts in Factory Management," John Wiley & Sons, Inc., New York, 1947.

RISSIK, H., "Quality Control in Production," Sir Isaac Pitman & Sons, Ltd., London, 1947.

RUTHERFORD, J. G., "Quality Control in Industry," Pitman Publishing Corp., New York, 1948.

SCHROCK, E. M., "Quality Control and Statistical Methods," Reinhold Publishing Corporation, New York, 1950.

SEALY, E. H., "A First Guide to Quality Control for Engineers," British Ministry of Supply, Advisory Service on Quality Control, London, 1943. (A short, clearly written pamphlet describing British practices in statistical quality control.)

SHEWHART, W. A., "Economic Control of Quality of Manufactured Product," D. Van Nostrand Company, Inc., New York, 1931. (This is the classic in the field of statistical quality control. In it, the control chart is described as "Criterion I" for detection of lack of control.)

SHEWHART, W. A. (ed. by W. E. Deming), "Statistical Method from the Viewpoint of Quality Control," The Graduate School, Department of Agriculture, Washington, D.C., 1939. (Four lectures by Dr. Shewhart that throw light on the statistical philosophy behind the control chart.)

SIMON, L. E., "An Engineers' Manual of Statistical Methods," John Wiley & Sons, Inc., New York, 1941. (This volume is helpful on applications of statistics to engineering problems in general as well as to acceptance problems. An insert containing Simon's I_Q charts may also be purchased separately from the publisher in enlarged form.)

SMITH, E. S., "Control Charts," McGraw-Hill Book Company, Inc., New York, 1947.

STATISTICAL ENGINEERING LABORATORY OF THE NATIONAL BUREAU OF STANDARDS, "Tables of the Binomial Probability Distribution," Superintendent of Documents, Government Printing Office, Washington, D.C., 1950.

STATISTICAL RESEARCH GROUP, COLUMBIA UNIVERSITY, "Sequential Analysis of Statistical Data: Applications," Columbia University Press, New York, 1945.

TIPPETT, L. H. C., "Statistical Methods in Industry," Iron and Steel Industrial Research Council, British Iron and Steel Federation, London, 1943. (Brief presentation emphasizing applications in the steel industry.)

TIPPETT, L. H. C., "Technological Applications of Statistics," John Wiley & Sons, New York, 1950.

UNIVERSITY OF PENNSYLVANIA BICENTENNIAL CONFERENCE, 1940, "Fluid Mechanics and Statistical Methods in Engineering," University of Pennsylvania Press, Philadelphia. (Contains papers by Wilks, Shewhart, Simon, and Pound.)

WALD, ABRAHAM, "Sequential Analysis," John Wiley & Sons, Inc., New York, 1947.

WALD, ABRAHAM, "Statistical Decision Functions," John Wiley & Sons, Inc., New York, 1950.

WALLACE, W. N. W. (ed.), "Lectures on Statistical Methods of Inspecting and Controlling Quality," Commonwealth of Australia, Ministry of Munitions, Melbourne, 1944.

WESTMAN, A. E. R., "An Extension Course in Statistical Quality Control," Consolidated Press, Ltd., Toronto, 1947.

WHARTON, A. S., "Quality through Statistics," Philips Lamps, Ltd., London, 1945. (Describes applications at Philips Lamps, Ltd.)

WORKING, H., "A Guide to Utilization of the Binomial and Poisson Distributions in Industrial Quality Control," Stanford University Press, Stanford University, Calif., 1944.

YOUDEN, W. J., "Statistical Methods for Chemists," John Wiley & Sons, Inc., New York, 1951.

TABLES

TABLE A. AREAS UNDER THE NORMAL CURVE

Proportion of total area under the curve that is under the portion of the curve from $-\infty$ to $\dfrac{X_i - \bar{X}'}{\sigma'}$. ($X_i$ represents any desired value of the variable X)

$\frac{X_i-\bar{X}'}{\sigma'}$	0.09	0.08	0.07	0.06	0.05	0.04	0.03	0.02	0.01	0.00
−3.5	0.00017	0.00017	0.00018	0.00019	0.00019	0.00020	0.00021	0.00022	0.00022	0.00023
−3.4	0.00024	0.00025	0.00026	0.00027	0.00028	0.00029	0.00030	0.00031	0.00033	0.00034
−3.3	0.00035	0.00036	0.00038	0.00039	0.00040	0.00042	0.00043	0.00045	0.00047	0.00048
−3.2	0.00050	0.00052	0.00054	0.00056	0.00058	0.00060	0.00062	0.00064	0.00066	0.00069
−3.1	0.00071	0.00074	0.00076	0.00079	0.00082	0.00085	0.00087	0.00090	0.00094	0.00097
−3.0	0.00100	0.00104	0.00107	0.00111	0.00114	0.00118	0.00122	0.00126	0.00131	0.00135
−2.9	0.0014	0.0014	0.0015	0.0015	0.0016	0.0016	0.0017	0.0017	0.0018	0.0019
−2.8	0.0019	0.0020	0.0021	0.0021	0.0022	0.0023	0.0023	0.0024	0.0025	0.0026
−2.7	0.0026	0.0027	0.0028	0.0029	0.0030	0.0031	0.0032	0.0033	0.0034	0.0035
−2.6	0.0036	0.0037	0.0038	0.0039	0.0040	0.0041	0.0043	0.0044	0.0045	0.0047
−2.5	0.0048	0.0049	0.0051	0.0052	0.0054	0.0055	0.0057	0.0059	0.0060	0.0062
−2.4	0.0064	0.0066	0.0068	0.0069	0.0071	0.0073	0.0075	0.0078	0.0080	0.0082
−2.3	0.0084	0.0087	0.0089	0.0091	0.0094	0.0096	0.0099	0.0102	0.0104	0.0107
−2.2	0.0110	0.0113	0.0116	0.0119	0.0122	0.0125	0.0129	0.0132	0.0136	0.0139
−2.1	0.0143	0.0146	0.0150	0.0154	0.0158	0.0162	0.0166	0.0170	0.0174	0.0179
−2.0	0.0183	0.0188	0.0192	0.0197	0.0202	0.0207	0.0212	0.0217	0.0222	0.0228
−1.9	0.0233	0.0239	0.0244	0.0250	0.0256	0.0262	0.0268	0.0274	0.0281	0.0287
−1.8	0.0294	0.0301	0.0307	0.0314	0.0322	0.0329	0.0336	0.0344	0.0351	0.0359
−1.7	0.0367	0.0375	0.0384	0.0392	0.0401	0.0409	0.0418	0.0427	0.0436	0.0446
−1.6	0.0455	0.0465	0.0475	0.0485	0.0495	0.0505	0.0516	0.0526	0.0537	0.0548
−1.5	0.0559	0.0571	0.0582	0.0594	0.0606	0.0618	0.0630	0.0643	0.0655	0.0668
−1.4	0.0681	0.0694	0.0708	0.0721	0.0735	0.0749	0.0764	0.0778	0.0793	0.0808
−1.3	0.0823	0.0838	0.0853	0.0869	0.0885	0.0901	0.0918	0.0934	0.0951	0.0968
−1.2	0.0985	0.1003	0.1020	0.1038	0.1057	0.1075	0.1093	0.1112	0.1131	0.1151
−1.1	0.1170	0.1190	0.1210	0.1230	0.1251	0.1271	0.1292	0.1314	0.1335	0.1357
−1.0	0.1379	0.1401	0.1423	0.1446	0.1469	0.1492	0.1515	0.1539	0.1562	0.1587
−0.9	0.1611	0.1635	0.1660	0.1685	0.1711	0.1736	0.1762	0.1788	0.1814	0.1841
−0.8	0.1867	0.1894	0.1922	0.1949	0.1977	0.2005	0.2033	0.2061	0.2090	0.2119
−0.7	0.2148	0.2177	0.2207	0.2236	0.2266	0.2297	0.2327	0.2358	0.2389	0.2420
−0.6	0.2451	0.2483	0.2514	0.2546	0.2578	0.2611	0.2643	0.2676	0.2709	0.2743
−0.5	0.2776	0.2810	0.2843	0.2877	0.2912	0.2946	0.2981	0.3015	0.3050	0.3085
−0.4	0.3121	0.3156	0.3192	0.3228	0.3264	0.3300	0.3336	0.3372	0.3409	0.3446
−0.3	0.3483	0.3520	0.3557	0.3594	0.3632	0.3669	0.3707	0.3745	0.3783	0.3821
−0.2	0.3859	0.3897	0.3936	0.3974	0.4013	0.4052	0.4090	0.4129	0.4168	0.4207
−0.1	0.4247	0.4286	0.4325	0.4364	0.4404	0.4443	0.4483	0.4522	0.4562	0.4602
−0.0	0.4641	0.4681	0.4721	0.4761	0.4801	0.4840	0.4880	0.4920	0.4960	0.5000

TABLE *A*. AREAS UNDER THE NORMAL CURVE.—(*Continued*)

$\frac{X_i-\overline{X}'}{\sigma'}$	0.00	0.01	0.02	0.03	0.04	0.05	0.06	0.07	0.08	0.09
+0.0	0.5000	0.5040	0.5080	0.5120	0.5160	0.5199	0.5239	0.5279	0.5319	0.5359
+0.1	0.5398	0.5438	0.5478	0.5517	0.5557	0.5596	0.5636	0.5675	0.5714	0.5753
+0.2	0.5793	0.5832	0.5871	0.5910	0.5948	0.5987	0.6026	0.6064	0.6103	0.6141
+0.3	0.6179	0.6217	0.6255	0.6293	0.6331	0.6368	0.6406	0.6443	0.6480	0.6517
+0.4	0.6554	0.6591	0.6628	0.6664	0.6700	0.6736	0.6772	0.6808	0.6844	0.6879
+0.5	0.6915	0.6950	0.6985	0.7019	0.7054	0.7088	0.7123	0.7157	0.7190	0.7224
+0.6	0.7257	0.7291	0.7324	0.7357	0.7389	0.7422	0.7454	0.7486	0.7517	0.7549
+0.7	0.7580	0.7611	0.7642	0.7673	0.7704	0.7734	0.7764	0.7794	0.7823	0.7852
+0.8	0.7881	0.7910	0.7939	0.7967	0.7995	0.8023	0.8051	0.8079	0.8106	0.8133
+0.9	0.8159	0.8186	0.8212	0.8238	0.8264	0.8289	0.8315	0.8340	0.8365	0.8389
+1.0	0.8413	0.8438	0.8461	0.8485	0.8508	0.8531	0.8554	0.8577	0.8599	0.8621
+1.1	0.8643	0.8665	0.8686	0.8708	0.8729	0.8749	0.8770	0.8790	0.8810	0.8830
+1.2	0.8849	0.8869	0.8888	0.8907	0.8925	0.8944	0.8962	0.8980	0.8997	0.9015
+1.3	0.9032	0.9049	0.9066	0.9082	0.9099	0.9115	0.9131	0.9147	0.9162	0.9177
+1.4	0.9192	0.9207	0.9222	0.9236	0.9251	0.9265	0.9279	0.9292	0.9306	0.9319
+1.5	0.9332	0.9345	0.9357	0.9370	0.9382	0.9394	0.9406	0.9418	0.9429	0.9441
+1.6	0.9452	0.9463	0.9474	0.9484	0.9495	0.9505	0.9515	0.9525	0.9535	0.9545
+1.7	0.9554	0.9564	0.9573	0.9582	0.9591	0.9599	0.9608	0.9616	0.9625	0.9633
+1.8	0.9641	0.9649	0.9656	0.9664	0.9671	0.9678	0.9686	0.9693	0.9699	0.9706
+1.9	0.9713	0.9719	0.9726	0.9732	0.9738	0.9744	0.9750	0.9756	0.9761	0.9767
+2.0	0.9773	0.9778	0.9783	0.9788	0.9793	0.9798	0.9803	0.9808	0.9812	0.9817
+2.1	0.9821	0.9826	0.9830	0.9834	0.9838	0.9842	0.9846	0.9850	0.9854	0.9857
+2.2	0.9861	0.9864	0.9868	0.9871	0.9875	0.9878	0.9881	0.9884	0.9887	0.9890
+2.3	0.9893	0.9896	0.9898	0.9901	0.9904	0.9906	0.9909	0.9911	0.9913	0.9916
+2.4	0.9918	0.9920	0.9922	0.9925	0.9927	0.9929	0.9931	0.9932	0.9934	0.9936
+2.5	0.9938	0.9940	0.9941	0.9943	0.9945	0.9946	0.9948	0.9949	0.9951	0.9952
+2.6	0.9953	0.9955	0.9956	0.9957	0.9959	0.9960	0.9961	0.9962	0.9963	0.9964
+2.7	0.9965	0.9966	0.9967	0.9968	0.9969	0.9970	0.9971	0.9972	0.9973	0.9974
+2.8	0.9974	0.9975	0.9976	0.9977	0.9977	0.9978	0.9979	0.9979	0.9980	0.9981
+2.9	0.9981	0.9982	0.9983	0.9983	0.9984	0.9984	0.9985	0.9985	0.9986	0.9986
+3.0	0.99865	0.99869	0.99874	0.99878	0.99882	0.99886	0.99889	0.99893	0.99896	0.99900
+3.1	0.99903	0.99906	0.99910	0.99913	0.99915	0.99918	0.99921	0.99924	0.99926	0.99929
+3.2	0.99931	0.99934	0.99936	0.99938	0.99940	0.99942	0.99944	0.99946	0.99948	0.99950
+3.3	0.99952	0.99953	0.99955	0.99957	0.99958	0.99960	0.99961	0.99962	0.99964	0.99965
+3.4	0.99966	0.99967	0.99969	0.99970	0.99971	0.99972	0.99973	0.99974	0.99975	0.99976
+3.5	0.99977	0.99978	0.99978	0.99979	0.99980	0.99981	0.99981	0.99982	0.99983	0.99983

TABLE B. FACTORS FOR ESTIMATING σ' FROM $\bar{R}$ OR $\bar{\sigma}$

Number of observations in subgroup	Factor for estimate from R	Factor for estimate from $\bar{\sigma}$
n	$d_2 = \bar{R}/\sigma'$	$c_2 = \bar{\sigma}/\sigma'$
2	1.128	0.5642
3	1.693	0.7236
4	2.059	0.7979
5	2.326	0.8407
6	2.534	0.8686
7	2.704	0.8882
8	2.847	0.9027
9	2.970	0.9139
10	3.078	0.9227
11	3.173	0.9300
12	3.258	0.9359
13	3.336	0.9410
14	3.407	0.9453
15	3.472	0.9490
16	3.532	0.9523
17	3.588	0.9551
18	3.640	0.9576
19	3.689	0.9599
20	3.735	0.9619
21	3.778	0.9638
22	3.819	0.9655
23	3.858	0.9670
24	3.895	0.9684
25	3.931	0.9696
30	4.086	0.9748
35	4.213	0.9784
40	4.322	0.9811
45	4.415	0.9832
50	4.498	0.9849
55	4.572	0.9863
60	4.639	0.9874
65	4.699	0.9884
70	4.755	0.9892
75	4.806	0.9900
80	4.854	0.9906
85	4.898	0.9912
90	4.939	0.9916
95	4.978	0.9921
100	5.015	0.9925

Estimate of $\sigma' = \bar{R}/d_2$ or $\bar{\sigma}/c_2$.
These factors assume sampling from a normal universe.

TABLE *C*. FACTORS FOR DETERMINING FROM $\bar{R}$ THE 3-SIGMA CONTROL LIMITS FOR $\bar{X}$ AND R CHARTS

Number of observations in subgroup	Factor for $\bar{X}$ chart	Factors for R chart	
		Lower control limit	Upper control limit
n	A_2	D_3	D_4
2	1.88	0	3.27
3	1.02	0	2.57
4	0.73	0	2.28
5	0.58	0	2.11
6	0.48	0	2.00
7	0.42	0.08	1.92
8	0.37	0.14	1.86
9	0.34	0.18	1.82
10	0.31	0.22	1.78
11	0.29	0.26	1.74
12	0.27	0.28	1.72
13	0.25	0.31	1.69
14	0.24	0.33	1.67
15	0.22	0.35	1.65
16	0.21	0.36	1.64
17	0.20	0.38	1.62
18	0.19	0.39	1.61
19	0.19	0.40	1.60
20	0.18	0.41	1.59

Upper Control Limit for $\bar{X} = UCL_{\bar{X}} = \bar{\bar{X}} + A_2\bar{R}$
Lower Control Limit for $\bar{X} = LCL_{\bar{X}} = \bar{\bar{X}} - A_2\bar{R}$

(If aimed-at or standard value $\bar{X}'$ is used rather than $\bar{\bar{X}}$ as the central line on the control chart, $\bar{X}'$ should be substituted for $\bar{\bar{X}}$ in the preceding formulas.)

Upper Control Limit for $R = UCL_R = D_4\bar{R}$
Lower Control Limit for $R = LCL_R = D_3\bar{R}$

All factors in Table *C* are based on the normal distribution.

TABLE D. FACTORS FOR DETERMINING FROM $\bar{\sigma}$ THE 3-SIGMA CONTROL LIMITS FOR $\bar{X}$ AND σ CHARTS

Number of observations in subgroup n	Factor for $\bar{X}$ chart A_1	Factors for σ chart	
		Lower control limit B_3	Upper control limit B_4
2	3.76	0	3.27
3	2.39	0	2.57
4	1.88	0	2.27
5	1.60	0	2.09
6	1.41	0.03	1.97
7	1.28	0.12	1.88
8	1.17	0.19	1.81
9	1.09	0.24	1.76
10	1.03	0.28	1.72
11	0.97	0.32	1.68
12	0.93	0.35	1.65
13	0.88	0.38	1.62
14	0.85	0.41	1.59
15	0.82	0.43	1.57
16	0.79	0.45	1.55
17	0.76	0.47	1.53
18	0.74	0.48	1.52
19	0.72	0.50	1.50
20	0.70	0.51	1.49
21	0.68	0.52	1.48
22	0.66	0.53	1.47
23	0.65	0.54	1.46
24	0.63	0.55	1.45
25	0.62	0.56	1.44
30	0.56	0.60	1.40
35	0.52	0.63	1.37
40	0.48	0.66	1.34
45	0.45	0.68	1.32
50	0.43	0.70	1.30
55	0.41	0.71	1.29
60	0.39	0.72	1.28
65	0.38	0.73	1.27
70	0.36	0.74	1.26
75	0.35	0.75	1.25
80	0.34	0.76	1.24
85	0.33	0.77	1.23
90	0.32	0.77	1.23
95	0.31	0.78	1.22
100	0.30	0.79	1.21

Upper Control Limit for $\bar{X} = UCL_{\bar{X}} = \bar{\bar{X}} + A_1\bar{\sigma}$
Lower Control Limit for $\bar{X} = LCL_{\bar{X}} = \bar{\bar{X}} - A_1\bar{\sigma}$

(If aimed-at or standard value $\bar{X}'$ is used rather than $\bar{\bar{X}}$ as the central line on the control chart, $\bar{X}'$ should be substituted for $\bar{\bar{X}}$ in the preceding formulas.)

Upper Control Limit for $\sigma = UCL_{\sigma} = B_4\bar{\sigma}$
Lower Control Limit for $\sigma = LCL_{\sigma} = B_3\bar{\sigma}$

All factors in Table D are based on the normal distribution.

TABLE E. FACTORS FOR DETERMINING FROM σ' THE 3-SIGMA CONTROL LIMITS FOR $\overline{X}$, R, AND σ CHARTS

Number of observations in subgroup n	Factor for $\overline{X}$ chart A	Factors for R chart		Factors for σ chart	
		Lower control limit D_1	Upper control limit D_2	Lower control limit B_1	Upper control limit B_2
2	2.12	0	3.69	0	1.84
3	1.73	0	4.36	0	1.86
4	1.50	0	4.70	0	1.81
5	1.34	0	4.92	0	1.76
6	1.22	0	5.08	0.03	1.71
7	1.13	0.20	5.20	0.10	1.67
8	1.06	0.39	5.31	0.17	1.64
9	1.00	0.55	5.39	0.22	1.61
10	0.95	0.69	5.47	0.26	1.58
11	0.90	0.81	5.53	0.30	1.56
12	0.87	0.92	5.59	0.33	1.54
13	0.83	1.03	5.65	0.36	1.52
14	0.80	1.12	5.69	0.38	1.51
15	0.77	1.21	5.74	0.41	1.49
16	0.75	1.28	5.78	0.43	1.48
17	0.73	1.36	5.82	0.44	1.47
18	0.71	1.43	5.85	0.46	1.45
19	0.69	1.49	5.89	0.48	1.44
20	0.67	1.55	5.92	0.49	1.43
21	0.65			0.50	1.42
22	0.64			0.52	1.41
23	0.63			0.53	1.41
24	0.61			0.54	1.40
25	0.60			0.55	1.39
30	0.55			0.59	1.36
35	0.51			0.62	1.33
40	0.47			0.65	1.31
45	0.45			0.67	1.30
50	0.42			0.68	1.28
55	0.40			0.70	1.27
60	0.39			0.71	1.26
65	0.37			0.72	1.25
70	0.36			0.74	1.24
75	0.35			0.75	1.23
80	0.34			0.75	1.23
85	0.33			0.76	1.22
90	0.32			0.77	1.22
95	0.31			0.77	1.21
100	0.30			0.78	1.20

$$UCL_{\overline{X}} = \overline{X}' + A\sigma'$$
$$LCL_{\overline{X}} = \overline{X}' - A\sigma'$$

(If actual average is to be used rather than standard or aimed-at average, $\overline{\overline{X}}$ should be substituted for $\overline{X}'$ in the preceding formulas.)

$$\begin{cases} UCL_R = D_2\sigma' \\ \text{Central line}_R = d_2\sigma' \\ LCL_R = D_1\sigma' \\ UCL_\sigma = B_2\sigma' \\ \text{Central line}_\sigma = c_2\sigma' \\ LCL_\sigma = B_1\sigma' \end{cases}$$

TABLE F. 3-SIGMA CONTROL LIMITS FOR CONTROL CHARTS FOR PER CENT DEFECTIVE

Upper control limit

Standard per cent defective (100p')	Subgroup size																	
	100	150	200	300	400	500	600	800	1,000	1,500	2,000	3,000	4,000	5,000	10,000	20,000	50,000	100,000
0.1	1.05	0.87	0.77	0.65	0.57	0.52	0.49	0.44	0.40	0.34	0.31	0.27	0.25	0.23	0.19	0.17	0.14	0.13
0.2	1.54	1.29	1.15	0.97	0.87	0.80	0.75	0.67	0.62	0.55	0.50	0.44	0.41	0.39	0.33	0.29	0.26	0.24
0.4	2.29	1.95	1.74	1.49	1.34	1.25	1.17	1.07	1.00	0.89	0.82	0.75	0.70	0.67	0.59	0.53	0.48	0.46
0.6	2.92	2.49	2.24	1.94	1.76	1.64	1.55	1.42	1.33	1.20	1.12	1.02	0.97	0.93	0.83	0.76	0.70	0.67
0.8	3.47	2.98	2.69	2.34	2.14	2.00	1.89	1.75	1.65	1.49	1.40	1.29	1.22	1.18	1.07	0.99	0.92	0.88
1.0	3.98	3.44	3.11	2.72	2.49	2.33	2.22	2.06	1.94	1.77	1.67	1.54	1.47	1.42	1.30	1.21	1.13	1.09
1.2	4.47	3.87	3.51	3.09	2.83	2.66	2.53	2.35	2.23	2.04	1.93	1.80	1.72	1.66	1.53	1.43	1.35	1.30
1.4	4.92	4.28	3.89	3.43	3.16	2.98	2.84	2.65	2.51	2.31	2.19	2.04	1.96	1.90	1.75	1.65	1.56	1.51
1.6	5.36	4.70	4.26	3.77	3.48	3.28	3.14	2.93	2.79	2.57	2.44	2.29	2.20	2.13	1.98	1.87	1.77	1.72
1.8	5.79	5.05	4.62	4.10	3.79	3.58	3.43	3.21	3.06	2.83	2.69	2.53	2.43	2.36	2.20	2.08	1.98	1.93
2.0	6.20	5.43	4.97	4.42	4.10	3.88	3.71	3.49	3.33	3.08	2.94	2.77	2.66	2.59	2.42	2.30	2.19	2.13
2.5	7.18	6.32	5.81	5.20	4.84	4.59	4.41	4.16	3.98	3.71	3.55	3.36	3.24	3.16	2.97	2.83	2.71	2.65
3.0	8.01	7.18	6.62	5.56	5.56	5.29	5.09	4.81	4.62	4.32	4.14	3.93	3.81	3.72	3.51	3.36	3.23	3.16
3.5	9.01	8.03	7.40	6.68	6.26	5.97	5.75	5.45	5.24	4.92	4.73	4.51	4.37	4.28	4.05	3.89	3.75	3.67
4.0	9.88	8.80	8.16	7.39	6.94	6.63	6.40	6.08	5.86	5.52	5.31	5.07	4.93	4.83	4.59	4.42	4.26	4.19
5	11.54	10.34	9.62	8.77	8.27	7.92	7.67	7.31	7.07	6.69	6.46	6.19	6.03	5.92	5.65	5.46	5.29	5.21
6	13.12	11.82	11.04	10.11	9.56	9.19	8.91	8.52	8.25	7.84	7.59	7.30	7.13	7.01	6.71	6.50	6.32	6.23
7	14.65	13.25	12.41	11.42	10.83	10.42	10.12	9.71	9.42	8.98	8.71	8.40	8.21	8.08	7.77	7.54	7.34	7.24
8	16.14	14.65	13.76	12.70	12.07	11.64	11.32	10.88	10.57	10.10	9.82	9.49	9.29	9.15	8.81	8.58	8.36	8.26
9	17.59	16.01	15.07	13.96	13.29	12.84	12.51	12.04	11.71	11.22	10.92	10.57	10.36	10.21	9.86	9.61	9.38	9.27
10	19.00	17.35	16.36	15.20	14.50	14.02	13.67	13.18	12.85	12.32	12.01	11.64	11.42	11.27	10.90	10.64	10.40	10.28
12	21.75	19.36	18.89	17.63	16.87	16.36	15.98	15.45	15.08	14.52	14.18	13.78	13.54	13.38	12.97	12.69	12.44	12.31
14	24.41	22.50	21.36	20.01	19.20	18.66	18.25	17.68	17.29	16.69	16.33	15.90	15.65	15.47	15.04	14.74	14.47	14.33
16	27.00	24.98	23.78	22.35	21.50	20.92	20.49	19.89	19.48	18.84	18.46	18.01	17.74	17.56	17.10	16.78	16.49	16.35
18	29.53	27.41	26.15	24.65	23.76	23.15	22.71	22.07	21.64	20.97	20.58	20.10	19.82	19.63	19.15	18.81	18.52	18.36
20	32.00	29.80	28.49	26.93	26.00	25.37	24.90	24.24	23.79	23.10	22.68	22.19	21.90	21.70	21.20	20.85	20.54	20.38
25	37.99	35.61	34.19	32.50	31.50	30.81	30.30	29.59	29.11	28.35	27.90	27.37	27.05	26.84	26.30	25.92	25.58	25.41
30	43.75	41.23	39.72	37.94	36.87	36.15	35.61	34.86	34.35	33.55	33.07	32.51	32.17	31.94	31.37	30.97	30.61	30.45
35	49.31	46.68	45.12	43.26	42.15	41.40	40.84	40.06	39.52	38.70	38.20	37.61	37.26	37.02	36.43	36.01	35.64	35.45
40	54.70	52.00	50.39	48.49	47.35	46.57	46.00	45.20	44.65	43.79	43.28	42.68	42.32	42.08	41.47	41.04	40.66	40.46

TABLE F. 3-SIGMA CONTROL LIMITS FOR CONTROL CHARTS FOR PER CENT DEFECTIVE.—(Continued)

Lower control limit

Standard per cent defective (100p')	\									Subgroup size								
	100	150	200	300	400	500	600	800	1,000	1,500	2,000	3,000	4,000	5,000	10,000	20,000	50,000	100,000
0.1	0.00	0.00	0.00	0.00	0.00	0.00	0.00	0.00	0.00	0.00	0.00	0.00	0.00	0.00	0.01	0.03	0.06	0.07
0.2	0.00	0.00	0.00	0.00	0.00	0.00	0.00	0.00	0.00	0.00	0.00	0.00	0.00	0.01	0.07	0.11	0.14	0.16
0.4	0.00	0.00	0.00	0.00	0.00	0.00	0.00	0.00	0.00	0.00	0.00	0.05	0.10	0.13	0.21	0.27	0.32	0.34
0.6	0.00	0.00	0.00	0.00	0.00	0.00	0.00	0.00	0.00	0.00	0.08	0.18	0.23	0.27	0.37	0.44	0.50	0.53
0.8	0.00	0.00	0.00	0.00	0.00	0.00	0.00	0.00	0.00	0.11	0.20	0.31	0.38	0.42	0.53	0.61	0.68	0.72
1.0	0.00	0.00	0.00	0.00	0.00	0.00	0.00	0.00	0.06	0.23	0.33	0.46	0.53	0.58	0.70	0.79	0.87	0.91
1.2	0.00	0.00	0.00	0.00	0.00	0.00	0.00	0.05	0.17	0.36	0.47	0.60	0.68	0.74	0.87	0.97	1.05	1.10
1.4	0.00	0.00	0.00	0.00	0.00	0.00	0.00	0.15	0.29	0.49	0.61	0.76	0.84	0.90	1.05	1.15	1.24	1.29
1.6	0.00	0.00	0.00	0.00	0.00	0.00	0.06	0.27	0.41	0.63	0.76	0.91	1.00	1.07	1.22	1.33	1.43	1.48
1.8	0.00	0.00	0.00	0.00	0.00	0.00	0.17	0.39	0.54	0.77	0.91	1.07	1.17	1.24	1.40	1.52	1.62	1.67
2.0	0.00	0.00	0.00	0.00	0.00	0.00	0.29	0.51	0.67	0.92	1.06	1.23	1.34	1.41	1.58	1.70	1.81	1.87
2.5	0.00	0.00	0.38	0.00	0.16	0.41	0.59	0.84	1.02	1.29	1.45	1.64	1.76	1.84	2.03	2.17	2.29	2.35
3.0	0.00	0.00	0.96	0.05	0.44	0.71	0.91	1.19	1.38	1.68	1.86	2.07	2.19	2.28	2.49	2.64	2.77	2.84
3.5	0.00	0.75	1.59	0.32	0.74	1.03	1.25	1.55	1.76	2.08	2.27	2.49	2.63	2.72	2.95	3.11	3.25	3.33
4.0	0.00	1.35	2.24	0.61	1.06	1.37	1.60	1.92	2.14	2.48	2.69	2.93	3.07	3.17	3.41	3.58	3.74	3.81
5	0.00	0.18	2.93	1.23	1.73	2.08	2.33	2.69	2.93	3.31	3.54	3.81	3.97	4.08	4.35	4.54	4.71	4.79
6	0.00	0.75	3.64	1.89	2.44	2.81	3.09	3.48	3.75	4.16	4.41	4.70	4.87	4.99	5.29	5.50	5.68	5.77
7	0.00	1.35	5.11	2.58	3.17	3.58	3.88	4.29	4.58	5.02	5.29	5.60	5.79	5.92	6.23	6.46	6.66	6.76
8	0.41	1.99	6.64	3.30	3.93	4.36	4.68	5.12	5.43	5.90	6.18	6.51	6.71	6.85	7.19	7.42	7.64	7.74
9	1.00	2.65	8.22	4.04	4.71	5.16	5.49	5.96	6.29	6.78	7.08	7.43	7.64	7.79	8.14	8.39	8.62	8.73
10	2.25	4.04	9.85	4.80	5.50	5.98	6.33	6.82	7.15	7.68	7.99	8.36	8.58	8.73	9.10	9.36	9.60	9.72
12	3.59	5.50	11.51	6.37	7.13	7.64	8.02	8.55	8.92	9.48	9.82	10.22	10.46	10.62	11.03	11.31	11.56	11.69
14	5.00	7.02	15.81	7.99	8.80	9.34	9.75	10.32	10.71	11.31	11.67	12.10	12.35	12.53	12.96	13.26	13.53	13.67
16	6.47	8.59	20.28	9.65	10.50	11.08	11.51	12.11	12.52	13.16	13.54	13.99	14.26	14.44	14.90	15.22	15.51	15.65
18	8.00	10.20	24.88	11.35	12.24	12.85	13.29	13.93	14.36	15.03	15.42	15.90	16.18	16.37	16.85	17.19	17.48	17.64
20	12.01	14.39	29.61	13.07	14.00	14.63	15.10	15.76	16.21	16.90	17.32	17.81	18.10	18.30	18.80	19.15	19.46	19.62
25	16.25	18.77	11.51	17.50	18.50	19.19	19.70	20.41	20.89	21.65	22.10	22.63	22.95	23.16	23.70	24.08	24.42	24.59
30	20.69	23.32	15.81	22.06	23.18	23.85	24.39	25.14	25.65	26.45	26.93	27.49	27.83	28.06	28.63	29.03	29.39	29.57
35	25.30	28.00	20.28	26.74	27.85	28.60	29.16	29.94	30.48	31.30	31.80	32.39	32.74	32.98	33.57	33.99	34.36	34.55
40			24.88	31.51	32.65	33.43	34.00	34.80	35.35	36.21	36.72	37.32	37.68	37.92	38.53	38.96	39.34	39.54

TABLE G. SUMMATION OF TERMS OF POISSON'S EXPONENTIAL BINOMIAL LIMIT
1,000 × probability of c or less occurrences of event that has average number of occurrences equal to c' or np'

c' or np' \ c	0	1	2	3	4	5	6	7	8	9
0.02	980	1,000								
0.04	961	999	1,000							
0.06	942	998	1,000							
0.08	923	997	1,000							
0.10	905	995	1,000							
0.15	861	990	999	1,000						
0.20	819	982	999	1,000						
0.25	779	974	998	1,000						
0.30	741	963	996	1,000						
0.35	705	951	994	1,000						
0.40	670	938	992	999	1,000					
0.45	638	925	989	999	1,000					
0.50	607	910	986	998	1,000					
0.55	577	894	982	998	1,000					
0.60	549	878	977	997	1,000					
0.65	522	861	972	996	999	1,000				
0.70	497	844	966	994	999	1,000				
0.75	472	827	959	993	999	1,000				
0.80	449	809	953	991	999	1,000				
0.85	427	791	945	989	998	1,000				
0.90	407	772	937	987	998	1,000				
0.95	387	754	929	984	997	1,000				
1.00	368	736	920	981	996	999	1,000			
1.1	333	699	900	974	995	999	1,000			
1.2	301	663	879	966	992	998	1,000			
1.3	273	627	857	957	989	998	1,000			
1.4	247	592	833	946	986	997	999	1,000		
1.5	223	558	809	934	981	996	999	1,000		
1.6	202	525	783	921	976	994	999	1,000		
1.7	183	493	757	907	970	992	998	1,000		
1.8	165	463	731	891	964	990	997	999	1,000	
1.9	150	434	704	875	956	987	997	999	1,000	
2.0	135	406	677	857	947	983	995	999	1,000	

TABLE *G*. SUMMATION OF TERMS OF POISSON'S EXPONENTIAL BINOMIAL LIMIT.—(Continued)

c / (c' or np')	0	1	2	3	4	5	6	7	8	9
2.2	111	355	623	819	928	975	993	998	1,000	
2.4	091	308	570	779	904	964	988	997	999	1,000
2.6	074	267	518	736	877	951	983	995	999	1,000
2.8	061	231	469	692	848	935	976	992	998	999
3.0	050	199	423	647	815	916	966	988	996	999
3.2	041	171	380	603	781	895	955	983	994	998
3.4	033	147	340	558	744	871	942	977	992	997
3.6	027	126	303	515	706	844	927	969	988	996
3.8	022	107	269	473	668	816	909	960	984	994
4.0	018	092	238	433	629	785	889	949	979	992
4.2	015	078	210	395	590	753	867	936	972	989
4.4	012	066	185	359	551	720	844	921	964	985
4.6	010	056	163	326	513	686	818	905	955	980
4.8	008	048	143	294	476	651	791	887	944	975
5.0	007	040	125	265	440	616	762	867	932	968
5.2	006	034	109	238	406	581	732	845	918	960
5.4	005	029	095	213	373	546	702	822	903	951
5.6	004	024	082	191	342	512	670	797	886	941
5.8	003	021	072	170	313	478	638	771	867	929
6.0	002	017	062	151	285	446	606	744	847	916

	10	11	12	13	14	15	16
2.8	1,000						
3.0	1,000						
3.2	1,000						
3.4	999	1,000					
3.6	999	1,000					
3.8	998	999	1,000				
4.0	997	999	1,000				
4.2	996	999	1,000				
4.4	994	998	999	1,000			
4.6	992	997	999	1,000			
4.8	990	996	999	1,000			
5.0	986	995	998	999	1,000		
5.2	982	993	997	999	1,000		
5.4	977	990	996	999	1,000		
5.6	972	988	995	998	999	1,000	
5.8	965	984	993	997	999	1,000	
6.0	957	980	991	996	999	999	1,000

TABLE *G*. SUMMATION OF TERMS OF POISSON'S EXPONENTIAL BINOMIAL LIMIT.—
(*Continued*)

c c' or np'	0	1	2	3	4	5	6	7	8	9
6.2	002	015	054	134	259	414	574	716	826	902
6.4	002	012	046	119	235	384	542	687	803	886
6.6	001	010	040	105	213	355	511	658	780	869
6.8	001	009	034	093	192	327	480	628	755	850
7.0	001	007	030	082	173	301	450	599	729	830
7.2	001	006	025	072	156	276	420	569	703	810
7.4	001	005	022	063	140	253	392	539	676	788
7.6	001	004	019	055	125	231	365	510	648	765
7.8	000	004	016	048	112	210	338	481	620	741
8.0	000	003	014	042	100	191	313	453	593	717
8.5	000	002	009	030	074	150	256	386	523	653
9.0	000	001	006	021	055	116	207	324	456	587
9.5	000	001	004	015	040	089	165	269	392	522
10.0	000	000	003	010	029	067	130	220	333	458

	10	11	12	13	14	15	16	17	18	19
6.2	949	975	989	995	998	999	1,000			
6.4	939	969	986	994	997	999	1,000			
6.6	927	963	982	992	997	999	999	1,000		
6.8	915	955	978	990	996	998	999	1,000		
7.0	901	947	973	987	994	998	999	1,000		
7.2	887	937	967	984	993	997	999	999	1,000	
7.4	871	926	961	980	991	996	998	999	1,000	
7.6	854	915	954	976	989	995	998	999	1,000	
7.8	835	902	945	971	986	993	997	999	1,000	
8.0	816	888	936	966	983	992	996	998	999	1,000
8.5	763	849	909	949	973	986	993	997	999	999
9.0	706	803	876	926	959	978	989	995	998	999
9.5	645	752	836	898	940	967	982	991	996	998
10.0	583	697	792	864	917	951	973	986	993	997

	20	21	22
8.5	1,000		
9.0	1,000		
9.5	999	1,000	
10.0	998	999	1,000

TABLE *G*. SUMMATION OF TERMS OF POISSON'S EXPONENTIAL BINOMIAL LIMIT.—
(*Continued*)

c / c' or np'	0	1	2	3	4	5	6	7	8	9
10.5	000	000	002	007	021	050	102	179	279	397
11.0	000	000	001	005	015	038	079	143	232	341
11.5	000	000	001	003	011	028	060	114	191	289
12.0	000	000	001	002	008	020	046	090	155	242
12.5	000	000	000	002	005	015	035	070	125	201
13.0	000	000	000	001	004	011	026	054	100	166
13.5	000	000	000	001	003	008	019	041	079	135
14.0	000	000	000	000	002	006	014	032	062	109
14.5	000	000	000	000	001	004	010	024	048	088
15.0	000	000	000	000	001	003	008	018	037	070

	10	11	12	13	14	15	16	17	18	19
10.5	521	639	742	825	888	932	960	978	988	994
11.0	460	579	689	781	854	907	944	968	982	991
11.5	402	520	633	733	815	878	924	954	974	986
12.0	347	462	576	682	772	844	899	937	963	979
12.5	297	406	519	628	725	806	869	916	948	969
13.0	252	353	463	573	675	764	835	890	930	957
13.5	211	304	409	518	623	718	798	861	908	942
14.0	176	260	358	464	570	669	756	827	883	923
14.5	145	220	311	413	518	619	711	790	853	901
15.0	118	185	268	363	466	568	664	749	819	875

	20	21	22	23	24	25	26	27	28	29
10.5	997	999	999	1,000						
11.0	995	998	999	1,000						
11.5	992	996	998	999	1,000					
12.0	988	994	997	999	999	1,000				
12.5	983	991	995	998	999	999	1,000			
13.0	975	986	992	996	998	999	1,000			
13.5	965	980	989	994	997	998	999	1,000		
14.0	952	971	983	991	995	997	999	999	1,000	
14.5	936	960	976	986	992	996	998	999	999	1,000
15.0	917	947	967	981	989	994	997	998	999	1,000

TABLE G. SUMMATION OF TERMS OF POISSON'S EXPONENTIAL BINOMIAL LIMIT.—
(Continued)

c' or np' \ c	4	5	6	7	8	9	10	11	12	13
16	000	001	004	010	022	043	077	127	193	275
17	000	001	002	005	013	026	049	085	135	201
18	000	000	001	003	007	015	030	055	092	143
19	000	000	001	002	004	009	018	035	061	098
20	000	000	000	001	002	005	011	021	039	066
21	000	000	000	000	001	003	006	013	025	043
22	000	000	000	000	001	002	004	008	015	028
23	000	000	000	000	000	001	002	004	009	017
24	000	000	000	000	000	000	001	003	005	011
25	000	000	000	000	000	000	001	001	003	006

	14	15	16	17	18	19	20	21	22	23
16	368	467	566	659	742	812	868	911	942	963
17	281	371	468	564	655	736	805	861	905	937
18	208	287	375	469	562	651	731	799	855	899
19	150	215	292	378	469	561	647	725	793	849
20	105	157	221	297	381	470	559	644	721	787
21	072	111	163	227	302	384	471	558	640	716
22	048	077	117	169	232	306	387	472	556	637
23	031	052	082	123	175	238	310	389	472	555
24	020	034	056	087	128	180	243	314	392	473
25	012	022	038	060	092	134	185	247	318	394

	24	25	26	27	28	29	30	31	32	33
16	978	987	993	996	998	999	999	1,000		
17	959	975	985	991	995	997	999	999	1,000	
18	932	955	972	983	990	994	997	998	999	1,000
19	893	927	951	969	980	988	993	996	998	999
20	843	888	922	948	966	978	987	992	995	997
21	782	838	883	917	944	963	976	985	991	994
22	712	777	832	877	913	940	959	973	983	989
23	635	708	772	827	873	908	936	956	971	981
24	554	632	704	768	823	868	904	932	953	969
25	473	553	629	700	763	818	863	900	929	950

	34	35	36	37	38	39	40	41	42	43
19	999	1,000								
20	999	999	1,000							
21	997	998	999	999	1,000					
22	994	996	998	999	999	1,000				
23	988	993	996	997	999	999	1,000			
24	979	987	992	995	997	998	999	999	1,000	
25	966	978	985	991	994	997	998	999	999	1,000

Table *H*. Logarithms of Factorials

	0	1	2	3	4	5	6	7	8	9
00	0.0000	0.0000	0.3010	0.7782	1.3802	2.0792	2.8573	3.7024	4.6055	5.5598
10	6.5598	7.6012	8.6803	9.7943	10.9404	12.1165	13.3206	14.5511	15.8063	17.0851
20	18.3861	19.7083	21.0508	22.4125	23.7927	25.1906	26.6056	28.0370	29.4841	30.9465
30	32.4237	33.9150	35.4202	36.9387	38.4702	40.0142	41.5705	43.1387	44.7185	46.3096
40	47.9116	49.5244	51.1477	52.7811	54.4246	56.0778	57.7406	59.4127	61.0939	62.7841
50	64.4831	66.1906	67.9066	69.6309	71.3633	73.1037	74.8519	76.6077	78.3712	80.1420
60	81.9202	83.7055	85.4979	87.2972	89.1034	90.9163	92.7359	94.5619	96.3945	98.2333
70	100.0784	101.9297	103.7870	105.6503	107.5196	109.3946	111.2754	113.1619	115.0540	116.9516
80	118.8547	120.7632	122.6770	124.5961	126.5204	128.4498	130.3843	132.3238	134.2683	136.2177
90	138.1719	140.1310	142.0948	144.0632	146.0364	148.0141	149.9964	151.9831	153.9744	155.9700
100	157.9700	159.9743	161.9829	163.9958	166.0128	168.0340	170.0593	172.0887	174.1221	176.1595
110	178.2009	180.2462	182.2955	184.3485	186.4054	188.4661	190.5306	192.5988	194.6707	196.7462
120	198.8254	200.9082	202.9945	205.0844	207.1779	209.2748	211.3751	213.4790	215.5862	217.6967
130	219.8107	221.9280	224.0485	226.1724	228.2995	230.4298	232.5634	234.7001	236.8400	238.9830
140	241.1291	243.2783	245.4306	247.5860	249.7443	251.9057	254.0700	256.2374	258.4076	260.5808
150	262.7569	264.9359	267.1177	269.3024	271.4899	273.6803	275.8734	278.0693	280.2679	282.4693
160	284.6735	286.8803	289.0898	291.3020	293.5168	295.7343	297.9544	300.1771	302.4024	304.6303
170	306.8608	309.0938	311.3293	313.5674	315.8079	318.0509	320.2965	322.5444	324.7948	327.0477
180	329.3030	331.5606	333.8207	336.0832	338.3480	340.6152	342.8847	345.1565	347.4307	349.7071
190	351.9859	354.2669	356.5502	358.8358	361.1236	363.4136	365.7059	368.0003	370.2970	372.5959

TABLE *H.* LOGARITHMS OF FACTORIALS.—(*Continued*)

	0	1	2	3	4	5	6	7	8	9
200	374.8969	377.2001	379.5054	381.8129	384.1226	386.4343	388.7482	391.0642	393.3822	395.7024
210	398.0246	400.3489	402.6752	405.0036	407.3340	409.6664	412.0009	414.3373	416.6758	419.0162
220	421.3587	423.7031	426.0494	428.3977	430.7480	433.1002	435.4543	437.8103	440.1682	442.5281
230	444.8898	447.2534	449.6189	451.9862	454.3555	456.7265	459.0994	461.4742	463.8508	466.2292
240	468.6094	470.9914	473.3752	475.7608	478.1482	480.5374	482.9283	485.3210	487.7154	490.1116
250	492.5096	494.9093	497.3107	499.7138	502.1186	504.5252	506.9334	509.3433	511.7549	514.1682
260	516.5832	518.9999	521.4182	523.8381	526.2597	528.6830	531.1078	533.5344	535.9625	538.3922
270	540.8236	543.2566	545.6912	548.1273	550.5651	553.0044	555.4453	557.8878	560.3318	562.7774
280	565.2246	567.6733	570.1235	572.5753	575.0287	577.4835	579.9399	582.3977	584.8571	587.3180
290	589.7804	592.2443	594.7097	597.1766	599.6449	602.1147	604.5860	607.0588	609.5330	612.0087
300	614.4858	616.9644	619.4444	621.9258	624.4087	626.8930	629.3787	631.8659	634.3544	636.8444
310	639.3357	641.8285	644.3226	646.8182	649.3151	651.8134	654.3131	656.8142	659.3166	661.8204
320	664.3255	666.8320	669.3399	671.8491	674.3596	676.8715	679.3847	681.8993	684.4152	686.9324
330	689.4509	691.9707	694.4918	697.0143	699.5380	702.0631	704.5894	707.1170	709.6460	712.1762
340	714.7076	717.2404	719.7744	722.3097	724.8463	727.3841	729.9232	732.4635	735.0051	737.5479
350	740.0920	742.6373	745.1838	747.7316	750.2806	752.8308	755.3823	757.9349	760.4888	763.0439
360	765.6002	768.1577	770.7164	773.2764	775.8375	778.3997	780.9632	783.5279	786.0937	788.6608
370	791.2290	793.7983	796.3689	798.9406	801.5135	804.0875	806.6627	809.2390	811.8165	814.3952
380	816.9749	819.5559	822.1379	824.7211	827.3055	829.8909	832.4775	835.0652	837.6540	840.2440
390	842.8351	845.4272	848.0205	850.6149	853.2104	855.8070	858.4047	861.0035	863.6034	866.2044

TABLE H. LOGARITHMS OF FACTORIALS.—(Continued)

	0	1	2	3	4	5	6	7	8	9
400	868.8064	871.4096	874.0138	876.6191	879.2255	881.8329	884.4415	887.0510	889.6617	892.2734
410	894.8862	897.5001	900.1150	902.7309	905.3479	907.9660	910.5850	913.2052	915.8264	918.4486
420	921.0718	923.6961	926.3214	928.9478	931.5751	934.2035	936.8329	939.4633	942.0948	944.7272
430	947.3607	949.9952	952.6307	955.2672	957.9047	960.5431	963.1826	965.8231	968.4646	971.1071
440	973.7505	976.3949	979.0404	981.6868	984.3342	986.9825	989.6318	992.2822	994.9334	997.5857
450	1000.2389	1002.8931	1005.5482	1008.2043	1010.8614	1013.5194	1016.1783	1018.8383	1021.4991	1024.1609
460	1026.8237	1029.4874	1032.1520	1034.8176	1037.4841	1040.1516	1042.8200	1045.4893	1048.1595	1050.8307
470	1053.5028	1056.1758	1058.8498	1061.5246	1064.2004	1066.8771	1069.5547	1072.2332	1074.9127	1077.5930
480	1080.2742	1082.9564	1085.6394	1088.3234	1091.0082	1093.6940	1096.3806	1099.0681	1101.7565	1104.4458
490	1107.1360	1109.8271	1112.5191	1115.2119	1117.9057	1120.6003	1123.2958	1125.9921	1128.6893	1131.3874
500	1134.0864	1136.7862	1139.4869	1142.1885	1144.8909	1147.5942	1150.2984	1153.0034	1155.7093	1158.4160
510	1161.1236	1163.8320	1166.5412	1169.2514	1171.9623	1174.6741	1177.3868	1180.1003	1182.8146	1185.5298
520	1188.2458	1190.9626	1193.6803	1196.3988	1199.1181	1201.8383	1204.5593	1207.2811	1210.0037	1212.7272
530	1215.4514	1218.1765	1220.9024	1223.6292	1226.3567	1229.0851	1231.8142	1234.5442	1237.2750	1240.0066
540	1242.7390	1245.4722	1248.2062	1250.9410	1253.6766	1256.4130	1259.1501	1261.8881	1264.6269	1267.3665
550	1270.1069	1272.8480	1275.5899	1278.3327	1281.0762	1283.8205	1286.5655	1289.3114	1292.0580	1294.8054
560	1297.5536	1300.3026	1303.0523	1305.8028	1308.5541	1311.3062	1314.0590	1316.8126	1319.5669	1322.3220
570	1325.0779	1327.8345	1330.5919	1333.3501	1336.1090	1338.8687	1341.6291	1344.3903	1347.1522	1349.9149
580	1352.6783	1355.4425	1358.2074	1360.9731	1363.7395	1366.5066	1369.2745	1372.0432	1374.8126	1377.5827
590	1380.3535	1383.1251	1385.8974	1388.6705	1391.4443	1394.2188	1396.9940	1399.7700	1402.5467	1405.3241

TABLE H. LOGARITHMS OF FACTORIALS.—(Continued)

	0	1	2	3	4	5	6	7	8	9
600	1408.1023	1410.8812	1413.6608	1416.4411	1419.2221	1422.0039	1424.7863	1427.5695	1430.3534	1433.1380
610	1435.9234	1438.7094	1441.4962	1444.2836	1447.0718	1449.8607	1452.6503	1455.4405	1458.2315	1461.0232
620	1463.8156	1466.6087	1469.4025	1472.1970	1474.9922	1477.7880	1480.5846	1483.3819	1486.1798	1488.9785
630	1491.7778	1494.5779	1497.3786	1500.1800	1502.9821	1505.7849	1508.5883	1511.3924	1514.1973	1517.0028
640	1519.8090	1522.6158	1525.4233	1528.2316	1531.0404	1533.8500	1536.6602	1539.4711	1542.2827	1545.0950
650	1547.9079	1550.7215	1553.5357	1556.3506	1559.1662	1561.9824	1564.7993	1567.6169	1570.4351	1573.2540
660	1576.0736	1578.8938	1581.7146	1584.5361	1587.3583	1590.1811	1593.0046	1595.8287	1598.6535	1601.4789
670	1604.3050	1607.1317	1609.9591	1612.7871	1615.6158	1618.4451	1621.2750	1624.1056	1626.9368	1629.7687
680	1632.6012	1635.4344	1638.2681	1641.1026	1643.9376	1646.7733	1649.6096	1652.4466	1655.2842	1658.1224
690	1660.9612	1663.8007	1666.6408	1669.4816	1672.3229	1675.1649	1678.0075	1680.8508	1683.6946	1686.5391
700	1689.3842	1692.2299	1695.0762	1697.9232	1700.7708	1703.6190	1706.4678	1709.3172	1712.1672	1715.0179
710	1717.8691	1720.7210	1723.5735	1726.4266	1729.2803	1732.1346	1734.9895	1737.8450	1740.7011	1743.5578
720	1746.4152	1749.2731	1752.1316	1754.9908	1757.8505	1760.7109	1763.5718	1766.4333	1769.2955	1772.1582
730	1775.0215	1777.8854	1780.7499	1783.6150	1786.4807	1789.3470	1792.2139	1795.0814	1797.9494	1800.8181
740	1803.6873	1806.5571	1809.4275	1812.2985	1815.1701	1818.0423	1820.9150	1823.7883	1826.6622	1829.5367
750	1832.4118	1835.2874	1838.1636	1841.0404	1843.9178	1846.7957	1849.6742	1852.5533	1855.4330	1858.3133
760	1861.1941	1864.0755	1866.9574	1869.8399	1872.7230	1875.6067	1878.4909	1881.3757	1884.2611	1887.1470
770	1890.0335	1892.9205	1895.8082	1898.6963	1901.5851	1904.4744	1907.3642	1910.2547	1913.1456	1916.0372
780	1918.9293	1921.8219	1924.7151	1927.6089	1930.5032	1933.3981	1936.2935	1939.1895	1942.0860	1944.9831
790	1947.8807	1950.7789	1953.6776	1956.5769	1959.4767	1962.3771	1965.2780	1968.1794	1971.0814	1973.9840

TABLE *H*. LOGARITHMS OF FACTORIALS.—(*Continued*)

	0	1	2	3	4	5	6	7	8	9
800	1976.8871	1979.7907	1982.6949	1985.5996	1988.5049	1991.4107	1994.3170	1997.2239	2000.1313	2003.0392
810	2005.9477	2008.8567	2011.7663	2014.6764	2017.5870	2020.4982	2023.4099	2026.3221	2029.2348	2032.1481
820	2035.0619	2037.9763	2040.8911	2043.8065	2046.7225	2049.6389	2052.5559	2055.4734	2058.3914	2061.3100
830	2064.2291	2067.1487	2070.0688	2072.9894	2075.9106	2078.8323	2081.7545	2084.6772	2087.6005	2090.5242
840	2093.4485	2096.3733	2099.2986	2102.2244	2105.1508	2108.0776	2111.0050	2113.9329	2116.8613	2119.7902
850	2122.7196	2125.6495	2128.5800	2131.5109	2134.4424	2137.3744	2140.3068	2143.2398	2146.1733	2149.1073
860	2152.0418	2154.9768	2157.9123	2160.8483	2163.7848	2166.7218	2169.6594	2172.5974	2175.5359	2178.4749
870	2181.4144	2184.3545	2187.2950	2190.2360	2193.1775	2196.1195	2199.0620	2202.0050	2204.9485	2207.8925
880	2210.8370	2213.7820	2216.7274	2219.6734	2222.6198	2225.5668	2228.5142	2231.4621	2234.4106	2237.3595
890	2240.3088	2243.2587	2246.2091	2249.1599	2252.1113	2255.0631	2258.0154	2260.9682	2263.9215	2266.8752
900	2269.8295	2272.7842	2275.7394	2278.6951	2281.6513	2284.6079	2287.5650	2290.5226	2293.4807	2296.4393
910	2299.3983	2302.3579	2305.3179	2308.2783	2311.2393	2314.2007	2317.1626	2320.1250	2323.0878	2326.0511
920	2329.0149	2331.9792	2334.9439	2337.9091	2340.8748	2343.8409	2346.8075	2349.7746	2352.7421	2355.7102
930	2358.6786	2361.6476	2364.6170	2367.5869	2370.5572	2373.5281	2376.4993	2379.4711	2382.4433	2385.4159
940	2388.3891	2391.3627	2394.3367	2397.3112	2400.2862	2403.2616	2406.2375	2409.2139	2412.1907	2415.1679
950	2418.1457	2421.1238	2424.1025	2427.0816	2430.0611	2433.0411	2436.0216	2439.0025	2441.9839	2444.9657
960	2447.9479	2450.9307	2453.9138	2456.8975	2459.8815	2462.8661	2465.8511	2468.8365	2471.8224	2474.8087
970	2477.7954	2480.7827	2483.7703	2486.7584	2489.7470	2492.7360	2495.7255	2498.7154	2501.7057	2504.6965
980	2507.6877	2510.6794	2513.6715	2516.6640	2519.6570	2522.6505	2525.6443	2528.6387	2531.6334	2534.6286
990	2537.6242	2540.6203	2543.6168	2546.6138	2549.6112	2552.6090	2555.6073	2558.6059	2561.6051	2564.6046
1,000	2567.6046	2570.6051	2573.6059	2576.6072	2579.6090	2582.6111	2585.6137	2588.6168	2591.6202	2594.6241

TABLE *J*. LOGARITHMS OF NUMBERS

N	0	1	2	3	4	5	6	7	8	9
10	0000	0043	0086	0128	0170	0212	0253	0294	0334	0374
11	0414	0453	0492	0531	0569	0607	0645	0682	0719	0755
12	0792	0828	0864	0899	0934	0969	1004	1038	1072	1106
13	1139	1173	1206	1239	1271	1303	1335	1367	1399	1430
14	1461	1492	1523	1553	1584	1614	1644	1673	1703	1732
15	1761	1790	1818	1847	1875	1903	1931	1959	1987	2014
16	2041	2068	2095	2122	2148	2175	2201	2227	2253	2279
17	2304	2330	2355	2380	2405	2430	2455	2480	2504	2529
18	2553	2577	2601	2625	2648	2672	2695	2718	2742	2765
19	2788	2810	2833	2856	2878	2900	2923	2945	2967	2989
20	3010	3032	3054	3075	3096	3118	3139	3160	3181	3201
21	3222	3243	3263	3284	3304	3324	3345	3365	3385	3404
22	3424	3444	3464	3483	3502	3522	3541	3560	3579	3598
23	3617	3636	3655	3674	3692	3711	3729	3747	3766	3784
24	3802	3820	3838	3856	3874	3892	3909	3927	3945	3962
25	3979	3997	4014	4031	4048	4065	4082	4099	4116	4133
26	4150	4166	4183	4200	4216	4232	4249	4265	4281	4298
27	4314	4330	4346	4362	4378	4393	4409	4425	4440	4456
28	4472	4487	4502	4518	4533	4548	4564	4579	4594	4609
29	4624	4639	4654	4669	4683	4698	4713	4728	4742	4757
30	4771	4786	4800	4814	4829	4843	4857	4871	4866	4900
31	4914	4928	4942	4955	4969	4983	4997	5011	5024	503⁸
32	5051	5065	5079	5092	5105	5119	5132	5145	5159	5172
33	5185	5198	5211	5224	5237	5250	5263	5276	5289	5302
34	5315	5328	5340	5353	5366	5378	5391	5403	5416	5428
35	5441	5453	5465	5478	5490	5502	5514	5527	5539	5551
36	5563	5575	5587	5599	5611	5623	5635	5647	5658	5670
37	5682	5694	5705	5717	5729	5740	5752	5763	5775	5786
38	5798	5809	5821	5832	5843	5855	5866	5877	5888	5899
39	5911	5922	5933	5944	5955	5966	5977	5988	5999	6010
40	6021	6031	6042	6053	6064	6075	6085	6096	6107	6117
41	6128	6138	6149	6160	6170	6180	6191	6201	6212	6222
42	6232	6243	6253	6263	6274	6284	6294	6304	6314	6325
43	6335	6345	6355	6365	6375	6385	6395	6405	6415	6425
44	6435	6444	6454	6464	6474	6484	6493	6503	6513	6522
45	6532	6542	6551	6561	6571	6580	6590	5699	6609	6618
46	6628	6637	6646	6656	6665	6675	6684	6693	6702	6712
47	6721	6730	6739	6749	6758	6767	6776	6785	6794	6803
48	6812	6821	6830	6839	6848	6857	6886	6875	6884	6893
49	6902	6911	6920	6928	6937	6946	6955	6964	6972	6981
50	6990	6998	7007	7016	7024	7033	7042	7050	7059	7067
51	7076	7084	7093	7101	7110	7118	7126	7135	7143	7152
52	7160	7168	7177	7185	7193	7202	7210	7218	7226	7235
53	7243	7251	7259	7267	7275	7284	7292	7300	7308	7316
54	7324	7332	7340	7348	7356	7364	7372	7380	7388	7396
N	0	1	2	3	4	5	6	7	8	9

TABLE *J.* LOGARITHMS OF NUMBERS.—(*Continued*)

N	0	1	2	3	4	5	6	7	8	9
55	7404	7412	7419	7427	7435	7443	7451	7459	7466	7474
56	7482	7490	7497	7505	7513	7520	7528	7536	7543	7551
57	7559	7566	7574	7582	7589	7597	7604	7612	7619	7627
58	7634	7642	7649	7657	7664	7672	7679	7686	7694	7701
59	7709	7716	7723	7731	7738	7745	7752	7760	7767	7774
60	7782	7789	7796	7803	7810	7818	7825	7832	7839	7846
61	7853	7860	7868	7875	7882	7889	7896	7903	7910	7917
62	7924	7931	7938	7945	7952	7959	7966	7973	7980	7987
63	7993	8000	8007	8014	8021	8028	8035	8041	8048	8055
64	8062	8069	8075	8082	8089	8096	8102	8109	8116	8122
65	8129	8136	8142	8149	8156	8162	8169	8176	8182	8189
66	8195	8202	8209	8215	8222	8228	8235	8241	8248	8254
67	8261	8267	8274	8280	8287	8293	8299	8306	8312	8319
68	8325	8331	8338	8344	8351	8357	8363	8370	8376	8382
69	8388	8395	8401	8407	8414	8420	8426	8432	8439	8445
70	8451	8457	8463	8470	8476	8482	8488	8494	8500	8506
71	8513	8519	8525	8531	8537	8543	8549	8555	8561	8567
72	8573	8579	8585	8591	8597	8603	8609	8615	8621	8627
73	8633	8639	8645	8651	8657	8663	8669	8675	8681	8686
74	8692	8698	8704	8710	8716	8722	8727	8733	8739	8745
75	8751	8756	8762	8768	8774	8779	8785	8791	8797	8802
76	8808	8814	8820	8825	8831	8837	8842	8848	8854	8859
77	8865	8871	8876	8882	8887	8893	8899	8904	8910	8915
78	8921	8927	8932	8938	8943	8949	8954	8960	8965	8971
79	8976	8982	8987	8993	8998	9004	9009	9015	9020	9025
80	9031	9036	9042	9047	9053	9058	9063	9069	9074	9079
81	9085	9090	9096	9101	9106	9112	9117	9122	9128	9133
82	9138	9143	9149	9154	9159	9165	9170	9175	9180	9186
83	9191	9196	9201	9206	9212	9217	9222	9227	9232	9238
84	9243	9248	9253	9258	9263	9269	9274	9279	9284	9289
85	9294	9299	9304	9309	9315	9320	9325	9330	9335	9340
86	9345	9350	9355	9360	9365	9370	9375	9380	9385	9390
87	9395	9400	9405	9410	9415	9420	9425	9430	9435	9440
88	9445	9450	9455	9460	9465	9469	9474	9479	9484	9489
89	9494	9499	9504	9509	9513	9518	9523	9528	9533	9538
90	9542	9547	9552	9557	9562	9566	9571	9576	9581	9586
91	9590	9595	9600	9605	9609	9614	9619	9624	9628	9633
92	9638	9643	9647	9652	9657	9661	9666	9671	9675	9680
93	9685	9689	9694	9699	9703	9708	9713	9717	9722	9727
94	9731	9736	9741	9745	9750	9754	9759	9763	9768	9773
95	9777	9782	9786	9791	9795	9800	9805	8909	9814	9818
96	9823	9827	9832	9836	9841	9845	9850	9854	9859	9663
97	9868	8772	9877	9881	9886	9890	9894	9899	9903	9908
98	9912	9917	9921	9926	9930	9934	9939	9943	9948	9952
99	9956	9961	9965	9969	9974	9978	9983	9987	9991	9996
N	0	1	2	3	4	5	6	7	8	9

TABLE *M*.   MASTER TABLE FOR NORMAL AND

Sample size code letter	Sample size	Acceptable Quality Levels (normal inspection)										
		0.015 (Ac Re)	0.035 (Ac Re)	0.065 (Ac Re)	0.10 (Ac Re)	0.15 (Ac Re)	0.25 (Ac Re)	0.40 (Ac Re)	0.65 (Ac Re)	1.0 (Ac Re)	1.5 (Ac Re)	2.5 (Ac Re)
A	2	↓	↓	↓	↓	↓	↓	↓	↓	↓	↓	↓
B	3											
C	5											
D	7										↓	0 1
E	10										0 1	↑
F	15									0 1	↑	↑
G	25							↓	0 1	↓	1 2	1 2
H	35							0 1	↓	↓	2 3	2 3
I	50						0 1	↑	↓	1 2	2 3	3 4
J	75					0 1	↓	↓	1 2	2 3	3 4	4 5
K	110				0 1	↓		1 2	2 3	3 4	4 5	6 7
L	150			0 1	↑	↑	1 2	2 3	3 4	4 5	5 6	8 9
M	225	↓	0 1	↓	↓	1 2	2 3	3 4	4 5	5 6	8 9	11 12
N	300	0 1	↑	↓	↓	2 3	3 4	4 5	5 6	7 8	10 11	14 15
O	450	↑	↑	↓	1 2	2 3	3 4	4 5	5 6	7 8	14 15	20 21
P	750	↓	1 2	2 3	3 4	4 5	6 7	8 9	11 12	15 16	20 21	31 32
Q	1,500	1 2	2 3	3 4	5 6	7 8	9 10	13 14	18 19	25 26	35 36	56 57
		0.035	0.065	0.10	0.15	0.25	0.40	0.65	1.0	1.5	2.5	4.0

Acceptable Quality Levels (tightened inspection)

TABLE *K*.   CONVERSION OF A SPECIFIED AQL TO AN AQL VALUE USED IN MIL-STD-105A

For specified AQL values falling within these ranges	Use AQL values below	For specified AQL values falling within these range	Use AQL value below
..... to 0.018	0.015	4.40 to 6.99	6.5
0.019 to 0.039	0.035	7.00 to 10.9	10.0
0.040 to 0.069	0.065	11.0 to 16.4	15.0
0.070 to 0.109	0.10	16.5 to 27.9	25.0
0.110 to 0.164	0.15	28.0 to 43.9	40.0
0.165 to 0.279	0.25	44.0 to 69.9	65.0
0.280 to 0.439	0.40	70.0 to 109	100.0
0.440 to 0.699	0.65	110 to 164	150.0
0.700 to 1.09	1.0	165 to 279	250.0
1.10 to 1.64	1.5	280 to 439	400.0
1.65 to 2.79	2.5	440 to 699	650.0
2.80 to 4.39	4.0	700 to 1090	1000.0

Tightened Inspection (Single Sampling)—MIL-STD-105A

Acceptable Quality Levels (normal inspection)

Each cell gives the Ac (acceptance) and Re (rejection) numbers. ↓ = use first sampling plan below arrow; ↑ = use first sampling plan above arrow.

4.0	6.5	10.0	15.0	25.0	40.0	65.0	100.0	150.0	250.0	400.0	650.0	1,000.0
Ac Re	Ac Re	Ac Re	Ac Re	Ac Re	Ac Re	Ac Re	Ac Re	Ac Re	Ac Re	Ac Re	Ac Re	Ac Re
↓	↓	0 1	↓		1 2	2 3	3 4	5 6	8 9	12 13	19 20	28 29
	0 1	↓		1 2	2 3	3 4	5 6	8 9	12 13	18 19	28 29	41 42
0 1			1 2	2 3	3 4	5 6	8 9	12 13	19 20	29 30	44 45	65 66
2 3	3 4	5 6	7 8	11 12	16 17	24 25	35 36	51 52	80 81	124 125	192 193	↑
3 4	5 6	7 8	10 11	15 16	22 23	33 34	48 49	69 70	110 111	168 169	↑	
4 5	6 7	9 10	13 14	20 21	30 31	46 47	67 68	96 97	151 152	↑		
6 7	9 10	13 14	19 20	29 30	43 44	66 67	96 97	138 139	↑			
8 9	12 13	18 19	26 27	40 41	60 61	93 94	135 136	↑				
11 12	17 18	24 25	34 35	53 54	80 81	123 124	↑					
17 18	24 25	34 35	48 49	76 77	115 116	↑						
20 21	32 33	44 45	63 64	98 99	↑							
29 30	43 44	62 63	89 90	↑								
45 46	68 69	98 99	↑									
81 82	124 125	184 185	↑									
6.5	10.0	15.0	25.0	40.0	65.0	100.0	150.0	250.0	400.0	650.0	1,000.0	✕

Acceptable Quality Levels (tightened inspection)

↓ Use first sampling plan below arrow. When sample size equals or exceeds lot size, do 100 per cent inspection.
↑ Use first sampling plan above arrow.
Ac = Acceptance number
Re = Rejection number
Tightened sampling plans are not provided for AQL: 0.015

Table *L*. Sample Size Code Letters—MIL-STD-105A*

Lot size	Inspection levels		
	I	II	III
2–8	A	A	C
9–15	A	B	D
16–25	B	C	E
26–40	B	D	F
41–65	C	E	G
66–110	D	F	H
111–180	E	G	I
181–300	F	H	J
301–500	G	I	K
501–800	H	J	L
801–1,300	I	K	L
1,301–3,200	J	L	M
3,201–8,000	L	M	N
8,001–22,000	M	N	O
22,001–110,000	N	O	P
110,001–550,000	O	P	Q
550,001 and over	P	Q	Q

* Sample-size code letters given in body of table are applicable when the indicated inspection levels are to be used.

TABLE N. MASTER TABLE FOR NORMAL AND TIGHTENED INSPECTION (DOUBLE SAMPLING)—MIL-STD-105A

Note: In the original, the upper-left triangular region of each Acceptable Quality Level column is occupied by directional arrows (↓ "use first sampling below arrow", ↑/→ "use first sampling plan above arrow") and "*" markers. Those cells are left blank below. Ac = Acceptance number, Re = Rejection number (given as "Ac Re").

Sample-size code letter	Sample	Sample size	Cumulative sample size	0.015	0.035	0.065	0.10	0.15	0.25	0.40	0.65	1.0	1.5	2.5	4.0	6.5	10.0
A, B, C	— No double sampling plans for these sample-size code letters. Use single sampling.																
D	First	5	5														0 3
D	Second	10	15														2 3
E	First	7	7													0 3	1 4
E	Second	14	21													2 3	3 4
F	First	10	10												0 3	1 4	2 5
F	Second	20	30												2 3	3 4	4 5
G	First	15	15											0 3	1 3	1 5	2 6
G	Second	30	45											2 3	3 4	4 5	5 6
H	First	25	25										0 3	1 3	2 5	3 6	3 7
H	Second	50	75										2 3	3 4	4 5	6 7	6 7
I	First	35	35									0 3	1 3	2 5	2 6	3 7	5 11
I	Second	70	105									2 3	2 3	4 5	6 7	6 7	10 11
J	First	50	50								0 3	1 3	1 6	2 7	3 10	3 12	6 15
J	Second	100	150								2 3	3 4	5 6	6 7	9 10	11 12	14 15
K	First	75	75							0 3	1 3	1 6	2 7	4 9	5 12	5 15	8 21
K	Second	150	225							2 3	2 3	5 6	6 7	8 9	11 12	14 15	20 21
L	First	100	100						0 3	1 3	1 6	2 6	3 8	5 12	7 16	7 20	8 29
L	Second	200	300						2 3	3 4	5 6	5 6	7 8	11 12	16 17	19 20	28 29
M	First	150	150					0 3	1 3	2 5	2 7	3 8	5 14	7 19	11 29	10 31	14 49
M	Second	300	450					2 3	2 3	4 5	6 7	7 8	13 14	18 19	28 29	30 31	48 49
N	First	200	200				0 3	1 3	1 6	2 7	3 8	4 10	6 17	9 25	12 35	15 46	21 65
N	Second	400	600				2 3	2 3	5 6	6 7	7 8	9 10	16 17	24 25	35 36	46 47	64 65
O	First	300	300			0 3	1 3	1 6	2 7	3 9	4 11	6 17	8 26	12 35	18 54	26 87	38 123
O	Second	600	900			2 3	2 3	5 6	6 7	8 9	10 11	16 17	25 26	34 35	54 55	87 88	122 123
P	First	500	500		0 3	1 4	1 6	2 7	3 10	5 13	6 22	9 25	12 37	18 65	27 89	43 131	62 191
P	Second	1000	1500		2 3	3 4	5 6	6 7	9 10	12 13	21 22	24 25	36 37	64 65	88 89	130 131	190 191
Q	First	1000	1000	0 3	1 4	1 6	2 9	4 13	5 17	7 26	11 33	15 47	22 65	34 113	50 160	79 243	119 348
Q	Second	2000	3000	2 3	3 4	5 6	8 9	12 13	16 17	25 26	32 33	46 47	64 65	112 113	159 160	242 243	347 348

Acceptable Quality Levels (tightened inspection), aligned under the normal-inspection columns:

	0.035	0.065	0.10	0.15	0.25	0.40	0.65	1.0	1.5	2.5	4.0	6.5	10.0

✗ Use first sampling below arrow. When sample size equals or exceeds lot size, do 100 per cent inspection.
* Use first sampling plan above arrow.
Use corresponding single sampling plan, Table M.
Ac = Acceptance number.
Re = Rejection number.
Tightened sampling plans are not provided for AQL: 0.015.

TABLE O. MASTER TABLE FOR NORMAL AND TIGHTENED INSPECTION (MULTIPLE SAMPLING)—MIL-STD-105A

Acceptable Quality Levels (normal inspection)

Sample-size code letter	Sample	Sample size	Cumulative sample size	0.015	0.035	0.065	0.10	0.15	0.25	0.40	0.65	1.0	1.5	2.5	4.0	6.5	10.0
				Ac Re	Ac Re	Ac Re	Ac Re	Ac Re	Ac Re	Ac Re	Ac Re	Ac Re	Ac Re	Ac Re	Ac Re	Ac Re	Ac Re
A	No multiple sampling plan for these sample-size code letters. Use single sampling.																
B																	
C																	
D	First	3	3	↓								↓	→	*	*	→	†
	Second	3	6														
	Third	3	9														
	Fourth	3	12														
E	First	4	4	↓								↓	*	→	*	+ 2	+ 2
	Second	4	8													+ 3	+ 3
	Third	4	12													1 4	1 4
	Fourth	4	16													2 5	2 5
	Fifth	4	20													3 5	3 5
F	First	5	5	↓							*	→	←	→	+ 2	+ 2	+ 2
	Second	5	10												+ 3	1 3	1 4
	Third	5	15												1 3	2 4	2 5
	Fourth	5	20												2 4	4 4	4 6
	Fifth	5	25												3 4	5 6	6 7
G	First	7	7	↓						*	←	←	→	+ 2	+ 3	0 3	0 4
	Second	7	14											+ 2	0 3	1 4	2 6
	Third	7	21											0 2	1 3	3 5	3 8
	Fourth	7	28											1 3	2 4	4 6	5 9
	Fifth	7	35											2 3	3 4	6 6	6 9
	Sixth	7	42											3 4	4 5	6 6	8 9
H	First	10	10	↓						←	←	→	←	→	0 3	0 4	0 4
	Second	10	20											1 3	3 5	3 6
	Third	10	30											3 6	5 7	5 8
	Fourth	10	40											4 7	6 8	6 10
	Fifth	10	50											6 8	7 9	8 12
	Sixth	10	60											8 10	10 10	11 14
	Seventh	10	70											10 11	11 11	13 14
				0.035	0.065	0.10	0.15	0.25	0.40	0.65	1.0	1.5	2.5	4.0	6.6	10.0	10.0

Acceptable Quality Levels (tightened inspection)

TABLE O. MASTER TABLE FOR NORMAL AND TIGHTENED INSPECTION (MULTIPLE SAMPLING)—MIL-STD-105A.—(Continued)

Acceptable Quality Levels (normal inspection)

Sample-size code letter	Sample	Sample size	Cumulative sample size	10.0 Ac Re	6.5 Ac Re	4.0 Ac Re	2.5 Ac Re	1.5 Ac Re	1.0 Ac Re	0.65 Ac Re	0.40 Ac Re	0.25 Ac Re	0.15 Ac Re	0.10 Ac Re	0.065 Ac Re	0.035 Ac Re	0.015 Ac Re
I	First	14	14	1 5	0 4	+ 3	+ 3	+ 2	+ 2	→	←		→	←		→	→
	Second	14	28	3 8	2 5	1 4	+ 3	+ 3	+ 2								
	Third	14	42	5 10	4 8	2 4	0 4	1 3	0 2								
	Fourth	14	56	8 12	6 9	3 6	1 5	1 3	0 2				*				
	Fifth	14	70	11 14	9 11	4 6	3 5	2 4	1 3								
	Sixth	14	84	13 16	11 12	5 7	3 5	3 5	2 3								
	Seventh	14	98	15 16	11 12	6 7	4 5	3 5	2 3								
J	First	20	20	1 6	1 5	0 4	+ 3	+ 3	+ 2	2 2				→	←		→
	Second	20	40	5 10	3 7	1 5	+ 3	+ 3	+ 2	2 2							
	Third	20	60	9 12	5 9	3 6	1 4	0 2	0 2	+ 3							
	Fourth	20	80	12 14	7 12	5 8	2 5	1 4	1 2	1 3			*				
	Fifth	20	100	15 19	9 13	8 10	3 6	2 4	2 3	1 3							
	Sixth	20	120	19 22	12 16	9 11	6 7	4 6	3 4	1 3							
	Seventh	20	140	22 23	16 17	10 11	8 8	6 6	4 4	2 3							
K	First	30	30	2 8	1 6	0 4	0 3	+ 3	+ 3	2 2	2 2				→	←	
	Second	30	60	8 13	5 9	3 7	2 3	1 4	+ 3	2 3	2 2						
	Third	30	90	12 18	9 13	5 9	3 6	2 5	1 3	3 4	0 3						
	Fourth	30	120	17 22	11 16	7 11	4 8	3 6	2 4	5 6	1 3		*				
	Fifth	30	150	21 27	13 19	9 13	6 8	5 7	3 5	6 6	3 3						
	Sixth	30	180	27 32	16 22	12 15	8 10	6 8	5 6	8 8	3 3						
	Seventh	30	210	35 36	21 22	15 15	11 12	8 8	6 7	8 8	4 4						
L	First	40	40	4 10	2 8	1 6	0 4	0 4	+ 3	3 3	2 2	2 2				→	←
	Second	40	80	10 16	6 12	4 8	3 5	2 5	1 4	4 4	2 4	2 3					
	Third	40	120	16 23	11 16	7 11	5 7	4 6	2 5	6 7	3 5	3 4					
	Fourth	40	160	22 29	16 21	10 14	8 9	5 7	3 6	7 8	4 6	4 4			*		
	Fifth	40	200	28 35	22 26	13 17	10 13	7 9	5 7	8 8	5 7	4 4					
	Sixth	40	240	36 42	28 31	16 21	13 18	9 14	7 9	9 10	6 7	6 6					
	Seventh	40	280	44 45	30 31	20 21	15 16	11 16	9 10	9 10	7 7	6 6					
M	First	50	50	5 12	3 10	2 7	0 5	0 4	+ 3	3 4	0 2	2 2	2 2				
	Second	50	100	12 20	8 15	4 11	3 8	2 6	1 4	4 4	2 4	2 3	2 3				
	Third	50	150	19 28	13 19	8 12	5 10	3 8	2 5	6 7	2 5	3 4	3 4				
	Fourth	50	200	26 35	18 24	12 16	8 13	6 10	3 7	8 9	3 7	4 4	3 4		*		
	Fifth	50	250	33 42	23 30	16 19	10 15	9 12	5 8	9 10	4 7	5 6	4 4				
	Sixth	50	300	40 49	28 35	22 24	13 18	11 16	7 10	9 10	5 7	6 7	5 5				
	Seventh	50	350	48 56	33 40	25 29	15 20	14 16	8 10		6 7	7 7	5 5				
	Eighth	50	400	56 57	40 41	29 29	19 20	16 16	9 10		7 8	7 7	6 6				

10.0	6.5	4.0	2.5	1.5	1.0	0.65	0.40	0.25	0.15	0.10	0.065	0.035

Acceptable Quality Levels (tightened inspection)

TABLE O. MASTER TABLE FOR NORMAL AND TIGHTENED INSPECTION (MULTIPLE SAMPLING)—MIL-STD-105A.—*(Continued)*

Code	Sample	Sample size	Cumulative sample size
N	First	75	75
	Second	75	150
	Third	75	225
	Fourth	75	300
	Fifth	75	375
	Sixth	75	450
	Seventh	75	525
O	First	100	100
	Second	100	200
	Third	100	300
	Fourth	100	400
	Fifth	100	500
	Sixth	100	600
	Seventh	100	700
	Eighth	100	800
P	First	150	150
	Second	150	300
	Third	150	450
	Fourth	150	600
	Fifth	150	750
	Sixth	150	900
	Seventh	150	1050
	Eighth	150	1200
	Ninth	150	1350
Q	First	300	300
	Second	300	600
	Third	300	900
	Fourth	300	1200
	Fifth	300	1500
	Sixth	300	1800
	Seventh	300	2100
	Eighth	300	2400
	Ninth	300	2700

Acceptable Quality Levels (tightened inspection): 0.035, 0.065, 0.10, 0.15, 0.25, 0.40, 0.65, 1.0, 1.5, 2.5, 4.0, 6.5, 10.0 (each with Acceptance and Rejection numbers). In the low-AQL columns the cells contain directional arrows (↑ "use first sampling plan above arrow," ↓ "use first sampling plan below arrow") and an asterisk (*), as described in the footnotes.

↓ Use first sampling plan below arrow. When sample size equals or exceeds lot size, do 100 per cent inspection.
↑ Use first sampling plan above arrow.
* Use corresponding double sampling plan.
† Use corresponding single sampling plan in Table M.
‡ Acceptance not permitted at this sample size.
Ac = Acceptance number.
Re = Rejection number.
Tightened sampling plans are not provided for AQL 0.015.

TABLE *P.* HIGHEST PROCESS AVERAGE PERMITTING
(Upper limits for AQL's

Number of sample units included in estimated process average	Acceptable quality levels										
	0.015	0.035	0.065	0.10	0.15	0.25	0.40	0.65	1.0	1.5	2.5
25–34	*	*	*	*	*	*	*	5.103	6.52	8.27	11.23
35–49	*	*	*	*	*	*	3.328	4.383	5.63	7.17	9.82
50–74	*	*	*	*	*	2.155	2.810	3.722	4.81	6.17	8.52
75–99	*	*	*	*	1.396	1.858	2.434	3.243	4.22	5.44	7.59
100–124	*	*	*	0.996	1.248	1.667	2.193	2.935	3.83	4.97	6.98
125–149	*	*	*	0.911	1.143	1.532	2.021	2.716	3.56	4.64	6.55
150–199	*	*	0.644	0.818	1.030	1.386	1.836	2.481	3.27	4.28	6.09
200–249	*	0.410	0.575	0.733	0.926	1.251	1.666	2.264	3.00	3.95	5.67
250–299	*	0.374	0.527	0.673	0.851	1.155	1.545	2.110	2.81	3.72	5.36
300–349	0.219	0.347	0.490	0.627	0.795	1.083	1.453	1.993	2.67	3.54	5.13
350–399	0.205	0.325	0.460	0.590	0.750	1.025	1.380	1.900	2.55	3.40	4.95
400–449	0.193	0.307	0.436	0.561	0.714	0.978	1.321	1.824	2.46	3.28	4.80
450–549	0.179	0.286	0.407	0.525	0.670	0.921	1.249	1.732	2.34	3.14	4.62
550–649	0.165	0.264	0.377	0.488	0.625	0.863	1.175	1.638	2.23	3.00	4.44
650–749	0.151	0.247	0.354	0.459	0.589	0.817	1.117	1.564	2.13	2.89	4.29
750–899	0.143	0.231	0.331	0.430	0.555	0.772	1.061	1.492	2.04	2.78	4.15
900–1,099	0.131	0.213	0.307	0.400	0.518	0.724	1.000	1.415	1.95	2.66	4.00
1,100–1,299	0.121	0.197	0.286	0.374	0.485	0.683	0.948	1.348	1.87	2.56	3.87
1,300–1,499	0.113	0.185	0.270	0.354	0.461	0.651	0.907	1.296	1.80	2.48	3.77
1,500–1,699	0.107	0.175	0.256	0.337	0.440	0.625	0.874	1.255	1.75	2.42	3.69
1,700–1,899	0.102	0.167	0.245	0.324	0.424	0.604	0.847	1.220	1.71	2.37	3.59
1,900–2,249	0.096	0.158	0.233	0.308	0.405	0.579	0.817	1.181	1.66	2.31	3.54
2,250–2,749	0.089	0.147	0.218	0.290	0.383	0.550	0.779	1.134	1.60	2.23	3.45
2,750–3,499	0.081	0.136	0.202	0.270	0.358	0.518	0.739	1.083	1.54	2.16	3.35
3,500–4,999	0.071	0.121	0.182	0.246	0.328	0.480	0.691	1.021	1.46	2.06	3.23
5,000–6,999	0.062	0.108	0.164	0.222	0.300	0.444	0.645	0.962	1.39	1.97	3.11
7,000–8,999	0.056	0.098	0.151	0.206	0.280	0.418	0.612	0.920	1.34	1.91	3.03
9,000–10,999	0.052	0.091	0.142	0.195	0.266	0.400	0.590	0.892	1.30	1.87	2.97
11,000–13,499	0.048	0.085	0.133	0.185	0.254	0.384	0.570	0.866	1.27	1.83	2.92
13,500–17,499	0.044	0.080	0.127	0.176	0.243	0.371	0.552	0.844	1.24	1.80	2.88
17,500–22,499	0.041	0.075	0.119	0.167	0.232	0.356	0.534	0.821	1.21	1.76	2.84
22,500 and up	0.036	0.067	0.109	0.155	0.217	0.337	0.510	0.790	1.17	1.71	2.77

* Normal inspection for these AQL's does not provide sample sizes this small.

CONTINUANCE OF NORMAL INSPECTION—MIL-STD-105A
from 0.015 to 1000.0)

						Acceptable quality levels							
4.0	6.5	10.0	15.0	25.0	40.0	65.0	100.0	150.0	250.0	400.0	650.0	1000.0
15.05	20.58	27.47	36.39	52.62	74.93	109.53	155.2	217.6	337.3	510.5	790.8	1174.7
13.26	18.30	24.64	32.93	48.14	69.28	102.33	146.3	206.7	323.2	492.6	768.0	1146.4
11.62	16.21	22.05	29.75	44.05	64.10	95.72	138.1	196.7	310.2	476.2	747.1	1120.5
10.43	14.70	20.17	27.46	41.08	60.34	90.93	132.2	189.4	300.9	464.3	732.0	1101.7
9.67	13.73	18.96	25.98	39.17	57.93	87.86	128.3	184.7	294.8	456.7	722.3	1089.6
9.13	13.03	18.11	24.93	37.82	56.21	85.67	125.6	181.4	290.5	451.3	715.3	1081.1
8.54	12.29	17.18	23.80	36.36	54.36	83.31	122.7	177.8	285.9	445.4	707.9	1071.8
8.00	11.60	16.33	22.76	35.01	52.66	81.14	120.0	174.5	281.7	440.0	701.0	1063.3
7.62	11.12	15.73	22.01	34.05	51.45	79.60	118.1	172.2	278.6	436.2	696.2	1057.3
7.33	10.75	15.27	21.45	33.33	50.53	78.43	116.7	170.4	276.3	433.3	692.5	1052.7
7.10	10.45	14.90	21.00	32.75	49.83	77.50	115.5	169.0	274.5	431.0	689.5	1049.0
6.91	10.21	14.60	20.64	32.28	49.21	76.74	114.6	167.8	273.0	429.1	687.1	1046.0
6.68	9.92	14.24	20.20	31.71	48.49	75.82	113.4	166.4	271.2	426.8	684.2	1042.4
6.45	9.62	13.87	19.75	31.13	47.75	74.88	112.3	165.0	269.4	424.5	681.2	1038.7
6.27	9.39	13.59	19.39	30.67	47.17	74.14	111.3	163.9	267.9	422.7	678.9	1035.9
6.09	9.16	13.30	19.05	30.22	46.61	73.42	110.4	162.8	266.5	420.9	676.6	1033.0
5.90	8.92	13.00	18.68	29.74	46.00	72.65	109.5	161.6	265.0	419.0	674.2	1030.0
5.73	8.71	12.74	18.36	29.33	45.48	71.98	108.7	160.6	263.7	417.3	672.1	1027.4
5.60	8.54	12.54	18.11	29.01	45.07	71.47	108.0	159.8	262.7	416.0	670.4	1025.4
5.50	8.41	12.37	17.91	28.75	44.74	71.05	107.5	159.2	261.9	415.0	669.1	1023.7
5 41	8.30	12.24	17.74	28.54	44.47	70.70	107.1	158.7	261.2	414.1	668.0	†
5.32	8.18	12.08	17.55	28.29	44.17	70.31	106.6	158.1	260.4	413.2	†	†
5.20	8.03	11.90	17.32	28.00	43.79	69.84	106.0	157.3	259.5	†	†	†
5.07	7.87	11.70	17.08	27.68	43.39	69.33	105.4	156.6	†	†	†	†
4.92	7.67	11.46	16.78	27.30	42.91	68.71	104.6	†	†	†	†	†
4.77	7.49	11.22	16.50	26.94	42.45	68.12	†	†	†	†	†	†
4.67	7.36	11.06	16.30	26.68	42.12	†	†	†	†	†	†	†
4.60	7.27	10.95	16.16	26.50	†	†	†	†	†	†	†	†
4.54	7.18	10.85	16.04	†	†	†	†	†	†	†	†	†
4.48	7.11	10.76	†	†	†	†	†	†	†	†	†	†
4.42	7.04	†	†	†	†	† ⌐	†	†	†	†	†	†
4.35	†	†	†	†	†	†	†	†	†	†	†	†

† Number of sample units included in estimated process average is too great.   Discard older results.

TABLE Q.   PROCESS AVERAGES NEEDED TO BECOME
(Lower limits for AQL's

Number of sample units included in estimated process average	Acceptable quality levels										
	0.015	0.035	0.065	0.10	0.15	0.25	0.40	0.65	1.0	1.5	2.5
25–34	*	*	*	*	*	*	*	*	*	*	*
35–49	*	*	*	*	*	*	*	*	*	*	*
50–74	*	*	*	*	*	*	*	*	*	*	*
75–99	*	*	*	*	*	*	*	*	*	*	*
100–124	*	*	*	*	*	*	*	*	*	*	*
125–149	*	*	*	*	*	*	*	*	*	*	*
150–199	*	*	*	*	*	*	*	*	*	*	*
200–249	*	*	*	*	*	*	*	*	*	*	*
250–299	*	*	*	*	*	*	*	*	*	*	*
300–349	*	*	*	*	*	*	*	*	*	*	*
350–399	*	*	*	*	*	*	*	*	*	*	0.05
400–449	*	*	*	*	*	*	*	*	*	*	0.20
450–549	*	*	*	*	*	*	*	*	*	*	0.38
550–649	*	*	*	*	*	*	*	*	*	*	0.56
650–749	*	*	*	*	*	*	*	*	*	0.11	0.71
750–899	*	*	*	*	*	*	*	*	*	0.22	0.85
900–1,099	*	*	*	*	*	*	*	*	0.05	0.34	1.00
1,100–1,299	*	*	*	*	*	*	*	*	0.13	0.44	1.13
1,300–1,499	*	*	*	*	*	*	*	0.004	0.20	0.52	1.23
1,500–1,699	*	*	*	*	*	*	*	0.045	0.25	0.58	1.31
1,700–1,899	*	*	*	*	*	*	*	0.080	0.29	0.63	1.41
1,900–2,249	*	*	*	*	*	*	*	0.119	0.34	0.69	1.46
2,250–2,749	*	*	*	*	*	*	0.021	0.166	0.40	0.77	1.55
2,750–3,499	*	*	*	*	*	*	0.061	0.217	0.46	0.84	1.65
3,500–4,999	*	*	*	*	*	0.020	0.109	0.279	0.54	0.94	1.77
5,000–6,999	*	*	*	*	*	0.056	0.155	0.338	0.61	1.03	1.89
7,000–8,999	*	*	*	*	0.020	0.082	0.188	0.380	0.66	1.09	1.97
9,000–10,999	*	*	*	0.005	0.034	0.100	0.210	0.408	0.70	1.13	2.03
11,000–13,499	*	*	*	0.015	0.046	0.116	0.230	0.434	0.73	1.17	2.08
13,500–17,499	*	*	0.003	0.024	0.057	0.129	0.248	0.456	0.76	1.20	2.12
17,500–22,499	*	*	0.011	0.033	0.068	0.144	0.266	0.479	0.79	1.24	2.16
22,500 and up	*	0.003	0.021	0.045	0.083	0.163	0.290	0.510	0.83	1.29	2.23

* Number of sample units included in estimated process average is insufficient for reduced inspection.

ELIGIBLE FOR REDUCED INSPECTION—MIL-STD-105A
from 0.015 to 1000.0)

Acceptable quality levels

4.0	6.5	10.0	15.0	25.0	40.0	65.0	100.0	150.0	250.0	400.0	650.0	1000.0
*	*	*	*	*	5.07	20.47	44.8	82.4	162.7	289.5	509.2	825.3
*	*	*	*	1.86	10.72	27.67	53.7	93.3	176.8	307.4	532.0	853.6
*	*	*	0.25	5.95	15.90	34.28	61.9	103.3	189.8	323.8	552.9	879.5
*	*	*	2.54	8.92	19.66	39.07	67.8	110.6	199.1	335.7	568.0	898.3
*	*	1.04	4.02	10.83	22.07	42.14	71.7	115.3	205.2	343.3	577.7	910.4
*	*	1.89	5.07	12.18	23.79	44.33	74.4	118.6	209.5	348.7	584.7	918.9
*	0.71	2.82	6.20	13.64	25.64	46.69	77.3	122.2	214.1	354.6	592.1	928.2
*	1.40	3.67	7.24	14.99	27.34	48.86	80.0	125.5	218.3	360.0	599.0	936.7
0.38	1.88	4.27	7.99	15.95	28.55	50.40	81.9	127.8	221.4	363.8	603.8	942.7
0.67	2.25	4.73	8.55	16.67	29.47	51.57	83.3	129.6	223.7	366.7	607.5	947.3
0.90	2.55	5.10	9.00	17.25	30.17	52.50	84.5	131.0	225.5	369.0	610.5	951.0
1.09	2.79	5.40	9.36	17.72	30.79	53.26	85.4	132.2	227.0	370.9	612.9	954.0
1.32	3.08	5.76	9.80	18.29	31.51	54.18	86.6	133.6	228.8	373.2	615.8	957.6
1.55	3.38	6.13	10.25	18.87	32.25	55.12	87.7	135.0	230.6	375.5	618.8	961.3
1.73	3.61	6.41	10.61	19.33	32.83	55.86	88.7	136.1	232.1	377.3	621.1	964.1
1.91	3.84	6.70	10.95	19.78	33.39	56.58	89.6	137.2	233.5	379.1	623.4	967.0
2.10	4.08	7.00	11.32	20.26	34.00	57.35	90.5	138.4	235.0	381.0	625.8	970.0
2.27	4.29	7.26	11.64	20.67	34.52	58.02	91.3	139.4	236.3	382.7	627.9	972.6
2.40	4.46	7.46	11.89	20.99	34.93	58.53	92.0	140.2	237.3	384.0	629.6	974.6
2.50	4.59	7.63	12.09	21.25	35.26	58.95	92.5	140.8	238.1	385.0	630.9	976.3
2.59	4.70	7.76	12.26	21.46	35.53	59.30	92.9	141.3	238.8	385.9	632.0	†
2.68	4.82	7.92	12.45	21.71	35.83	59.69	93.4	141.9	239.6	386.8	†	†
2.80	4.97	8.10	12.68	22.00	36.21	60.16	94.0	142.7	240.5	†	†	†
2.93	5.13	8.30	12.92	22.32	36.61	60.67	94.6	143.4	†	†	†	†
3.08	5.33	8.54	13.22	22.70	37.09	61.29	95.4	†	†	†	†	†
3.23	5.51	8.78	13.50	23.06	37.55	61.88	†	†	†	†	†	†
3.33	5.64	8.94	13.70	23.32	37.88	†	†	†	†	†	†	†
3.40	5.73	9.05	13.84	23.50	†	†	†	†	†	†	†	†
3.46	5.82	9.15	13.96	†	†	†	†	†	†	†	†	†
3.52	5.89	9.24	†	†	†	†	†	†	†	†	†	†
3.58	5.96	†	†	†	†	†	†	†	†	†	†	†
3 65	†	†	†	†	†	†	†	†	†	†	†	†

† Number of sample units included in estimated process average is too great.   Discard older results.

TABLE R. MASTER TABLE FOR

Sample-size code letter	Sample size	Acceptable Quality Levels										
		0.015	0.035	0.065	0.10	0.15	0.25	0.40	0.65	1.0	1.5	2.5
		Ac Re	Ac Re	Ac Re	Ac Re	Ac Re	Ac Re	Ac Re	Ac Re	Ac Re	Ac Re	Ac Re
A, B, C, D	2*									↓	0 1	↓
E	2									↓	0 1	
F	3								↓	0 1	↑	↓
G	5							↓	0 1	↑	↓	1 2
H	7						↓	0 1	↑	↑	1 2	1 2
I	10	Reduced inspection not available for AQL: 0.015				↓	0 1	↑	↓	1 2	1 2	2 3
J	15					0 1	↑	↓	1 2	1 2	2 3	2 3
K	22			↓	0 1	↑	↑	1 2	1 2	2 3	2 3	3 4
L	30		↓	0 1	↑		1 2	1 2	2 3	2 3	3 4	4 5
M	45		0 1	↑	↓	1 2	1 2	2 3	2 3	3 4	4 5	5 6
N	60		↓	↓	1 2	1 2	1 2	2 3	3 4	4 5	5 6	6 7
O	90			1 2	1 2	2 3	2 3	3 4	4 5	5 6	6 7	9 10
P	150	1 2	1 2	2 3	2 3	3 4	4 5	5 6	7 8	9 10	11 12	
Q	300	1 2	2 3	3 4	4 5	5 6	6 7	8 9	11 12	13 14	16 17	

Reduced Inspection—MIL-STD-105A

Acceptable Quality Levels

4.0	6.5	10.0	15.0	25.0	40.0	65.0	100.0	150.0	250.0	400.0	650.0	1000.0
Ac Re	Ac Re	Ac Re	Ac Re	Ac Re	Ac Re	Ac Re	Ac Re	Ac Re	Ac Re	Ac Re	Ac Re	Ac Re
↓			1 2	1 2	1 2	2 3	4 5	5 6	8 9	12 13	15 16	19 20
↓	1 2	1 2	2 3	3 4	3 4	4 5	7 8	10 11	13 14	17 18	22 23	29 30
1 2	1 2	2 3	2 3	3 4	5 6	7 8	10 11	13 14	17 18	21 22	29 30	37 38
1 2	2 3	3 4	3 4	5 6	7 8	10 11	13 14	17 18	22 23	29 30	39 40	↑
2 3	3 4	3 4	5 6	7 8	9 10	13 14	16 17	20 21	27 28	36 37	↑	
2 3	3 4	4 5	6 7	9 10	12 13	16 17	19 20	24 25	33 34	↑		
3 4	4 5	6 7	8 9	12 13	15 16	19 20	24 25	31 32	↑			
4 5	5 6	8 9	11 12	14 15	18 19	23 24	31 32	↑				
5 6	7 8	11 12	12 13	16 17	21 22	29 30	↑					
7 8	10 11	13 14	15 16	20 21	27 28	↑						
9 10	12 13	15 16	18 19	24 25	↑							
11 12	14 15	18 19	23 24	↑								
14 15	18 19	23 24	↑									
21 22	28 29	37 38										

↓ Use first sampling plan below arrow. When sample size equals or exceeds lot size, do 100 per cent inspection.

↑ Use first sampling plan above arrow.

Ac = Acceptance number.

Re = Rejection number.

* For code letters A, B, C, and D, sample size is 1 for AQL values 15.0 to 1000.0.

TABLE *S*. SOME FACTORS FOR USE IN ACCEPTANCE SAMPLING BY VARIABLES

This table gives factors taken from "Sampling Inspection by Variables" by A. H. Bowker and H. P. Goode, McGraw-Hill Book Company, Inc., New York, 1952. These factors are representative of much more extensive sets of variables plans given in that volume. For a brief explanation of the use of these factors, see Chap. XVI.

The Bowker-Goode volume gives sample size code letters (not reproduced here) that correspond to those used in the attributes tables in the Columbia Statistical Research Group's (SRG's) volume "Sampling Inspection" and in JAN-STD-105. AQL classes also correspond to the AQL classes in these attributes tables, and the same definition of AQL ($100p_{0.95}$) is used. Each line of the following table gives factors for three different types of variables plans as well as the corresponding single sampling attributes plan. The four plans on any line have the same AQL class and are selected using the same sample size code letter. The OC curves of all plans on a given line match as closely as practicable under the restriction imposed by the use of standard sample sizes for each code letter for the one-sided variables plans. The Bowker-Goode volume gives full OC curves for all its unknown-sigma plans that relate to one-sided specifications.

Known-sigma plans for-one sided specifications				Unknown-sigma plans for one-sided specifications		Known-sigma plans for two-sided specifications		Single sampling attributes plan	
n	k'	$100p_{0.95}$	$100p_{0.10}$	n	k	n	k'^*	n	c
5	1.748	0.65	12.00	7	1.636	3	1.587	10	0
5	1.522	1.20	17.15	7	1.449	4	1.404	30	1
5	1.278	2.20	24.03	7	1.242	4	1.201	20	1
5	1.117	3.20	29.34	7	1.107	5	1.070	15	1
5	1.027	3.90	32.50	7	1.053	5	1.017	10	1
5	1.015	4.00	32.93	7	0.969	5	0.935	10	1
6	1.812	0.65	9.87	10	1.757	4	1.720	15	0
6	1.586	1.20	14.40	10	1.562	5	1.529	30	1
6	1.343	2.20	20.63	10	1.400	5	1.303	20	1
6	1.272	2.60	22.71	10	1.287	6	1.162	15	1
6	1.181	3.20	25.54	10	1.186	6	1.119	15	1
6	0.973	5.00	32.63	10	0.994	7	1.060	15	2
7	2.105	0.32	5.26	13	1.957	5	1.927	20	0
7	1.862	0.65	8.41	13	1.764	5	1.736	55	1
7	1.635	1.20	12.49	13	1.583	6	1.557	30	1
7	1.432	2.00	17.16	13	1.472	6	1.448	20	1
7	1.392	2.20	18.19	13	1.371	7	1.348	20	1
7	1.177	3.60	24.41	13	1.189	8	1.169	20	2
7	1.084	4.40	27.43	13	1.132	8	1.113	20	2

Table *S.* Some Factors for Use in Acceptance Sampling by Variables.— *(Continued)*

Known-sigma plans for one-sided specifications				Unknown-sigma plans for one-sided specifications		Known-sigma plans for two-sided specifications		Single sampling attributes plan	
n	k'	$100p_{0.95}$	$100p_{0.10}$	n	k	n	k'^*	n	c
9	2.300	0.22	3.06	16	2.116	5	2.090	30	0
9	2.178	0.32	4.00	16	2.018	6	1.994	150	1
9	1.935	0.65	6.57	16	1.822	6	1.799	55	1
9	1.709	1.20	10.00	16	1.694	7	1.672	30	1
9	1.466	2.20	14.95	16	1.437	8	1.418	30	2
9	1.363	2.80	17.47	16	1.378	8	1.360	30	2
9	1.226	3.80	21.22	16	1.217	9	1.201	30	3
9	1.158	4.40	23.25	16	1.180	10	1.164	30	3
11	2.433	0.17	2.03	20	2.246	6	2.225	40	0
11	2.352	0.22	2.47	20	2.180	6	2.159	225	1
11	2.231	0.32	3.26	20	2.080	7	2.060	150	1
11	1.988	0.65	5.46	20	1.880	7	1.861	55	1
11	1.761	1.20	8.46	20	1.749	8	1.732	40	1
11	1.518	2.20	12.89	20	1.504	10	1.489	40	2
11	1.400	2.90	15.54	20	1.388	10	1.374	40	3
11	1.356	3.20	16.61	20	1.351	11	1.337	40	3
11	1.210	4.40	20.51	20	1.218	12	1.205	40	4
13	2.579	0.12	1.31	25	2.395	7	2.378	55	0
13	2.473	0.17	1.71	25	2.306	7	2.289	300	1
13	2.392	0.22	2.09	25	2.239	7	2.222	225	1
13	2.270	0.32	2.78	25	2.137	8	2.121	150	1
13	2.028	0.65	4.72	25	1.933	9	1.918	55	1
13	1.781	1.20	7.42	25	1.756	10	1.742	55	2
13	1.558	2.20	11.46	25	1.569	11	1.556	55	3
13	1.539	2.30	11.83	25	1.504	12	1.492	55	3
13	1.396	3.20	14.90	25	1.385	13	1.373	55	4
13	1.250	4.40	18.56	25	1.261	14	1.250	55	5
16	2.828	0.06	0.61	35	2.653	8	2.640	750	1
16	2.624	0.12	1.06	35	2.480	9	2.467	450	1
16	2.518	0.17	1.40	35	2.389	9	2.377	300	1
16	2.437	0.22	1.72	35	2.319	10	2.307	225	1
16	2.315	0.32	2.30	35	2.234	10	2.222	150	1
16	2.073	0.65	3.99	35	2.031	12	2.020	75	1
16	1.846	1.20	6.36	35	1.811	13	1.795	75	2
16	1.664	1.90	8.96	35	1.672	15	1.662	75	3
16	1.532	2.60	11.28	35	1.552	16	1.543	75	4
16	1.351	3.90	15.13	35	1.390	18	1.381	75	6
16	1.253	4.80	17.54	35	1.284	19	1.276	75	7

TABLE *T.*—OPERATING CHARACTERISTICS OF CERTAIN UNKNOWN-SIGMA AND KNOWN-SIGMA VARIABLES ACCEPTANCE PLANS FOR ONE-SIDED SPECIFICATIONS

In this table, n is the sample size for an unknown-sigma plan of the type described in Art. 329. The values of $p_{0.95}$, $p_{0.50}$, and $p_{0.10}$ apply to the unknown-sigma plans for the stated values of k and n. The symbol n^* is used to show the sample size for the known-sigma plan having an OC curve that comes closest to matching the OC curve of the given unknown-sigma plan when the k' of the known-sigma plan is made equal to the k of the given unknown-sigma plan. The information in this table is taken from W. G. Ireson, "Sampling Tables for Inspection by Variables," Technical Report No. 7, Applied Mathematics and Statistics Laboratory, Stanford University.

k	$100p_{0.95}$	$100p_{0.50}$	$100p_{0.10}$	n^*	$100p_{0.95}$	$100p_{0.50}$	$100p_{0.10}$	n^*
	$n = 5$				$n = 7$			
0.6	8.42	28.73	52.58	5	10.39	28.30	48.17	6
0.8	5.23	22.77	46.65	4	6.72	22.24	41.87	6
1.0	3.00	17.59	41.09	4	4.05	17.00	36.00	5
1.2	1.59	13.24	35.95	3	2.28	12.64	30.63	4
1.4	0.77	9.70	31.25	3	1.19	9.13	25.80	4
1.6	0.34	6.92	26.95	2	0.57	6.41	21.49	3
1.8	0.14	4.80	23.06	2	0.26	4.37	17.70	3
2.0	0.05	3.24	19.62	2	0.11	2.89	14.42	3
2.25	0.01	1.90	15.83	2	0.03	1.64	10.99	2
2.5	0.00	1.06	12.61	2	0.01	0.89	8.21	2
3.0	0.00	0.29	7.72	1	0.00	0.23	4.34	2
	$n = 10$				$n = 15$			
0.6	12.43	28.01	44.38	9	14.61	27.80	40.95	10
0.8	8.30	21.89	37.85	8	10.05	21.63	34.31	9
1.0	5.22	16.62	31.84	7	6.55	16.35	28.27	8
1.2	3.08	12.26	26.42	5	4.03	11.99	22.89	7
1.4	1.70	8.78	21.62	5	2.34	8.52	18.23	6
1.6	0.88	6.09	17.44	5	1.28	5.87	14.26	6
1.8	0.42	4.10	13.87	4	0.66	3.91	10.96	5
2.0	0.19	2.67	10.87	4	0.32	2.52	8.27	4
2.25	0.06	1.49	7.84	3	0.12	1.39	5.67	4
2.5	0.02	0.79	5.53	3	0.04	0.73	3.77	3
3.0	0.00	0.19	2.55	2	0.00	0.17	1.52	3

TABLE *T*. OPERATING CHARACTERISTICS OF CERTAIN UNKNOWN-SIGMA AND KNOWN-SIGMA VARIABLES ACCEPTANCE PLANS FOR ONE-SIDED SPECIFICATIONS.—(*Continued*)

k	$100p_{0.95}$	$100p_{0.50}$	$100p_{0.10}$	n^*	$100p_{0.95}$	$100p_{0.50}$	$100p_{0.10}$	n^*
	$n = 20$				$n = 25$			
0.6	16.02	27.70	38.96	17	17.04	27.64	37.64	22
0.8	11.21	21.52	32.30	15	12.05	21.45	30.97	19
1.0	7.45	16.22	26.28	14	8.13	16.15	24.99	17
1.2	4.70	11.86	20.98	12	5.21	11.78	19.75	15
1.4	2.81	8.40	16.44	10	3.17	8.33	15.30	13
1.6	1.59	5.76	12.62	9	1.83	5.70	11.60	11
1.8	0.85	3.82	9.50	8	1.00	3.78	8.61	10
2.0	0.43	2.45	7.01	7	0.62	2.42	6.25	9
2.25	0.17	1.34	4.65	6	0.21	1.32	4.06	7
2.5	0.06	0.70	2.99	5	0.08	0.68	2.55	6
3.0	0.01	0.16	1.12	4	0.01	0.15	0.90	5
	$n = 30$				$n = 35$			
0.6	17.82	27.61	36.68	26	18.45	27.58	35.94	30
0.8	12.71	21.40	30.02	23	13.24	21.37	29.29	27
1.0	8.65	16.10	24.06	20	9.08	16.06	23.36	24
1.2	5.61	11.74	18.88	18	5.94	11.70	18.23	21
1.4	3.46	8.29	14.50	15	3.70	8.26	13.91	18
1.6	2.03	5.66	10.89	13	2.20	5.64	10.37	16
1.8	1.13	3.74	8.00	12	1.24	3.72	7.56	14
2.0	0.60	2.39	5.74	10	0.66	2.37	5.37	12
2.25	0.25	1.30	3.67	9	0.28	1.29	3.39	10
2.5	0.10	0.67	2.26	8	0.11	0.66	2.06	9
3.0	0.01	0.15	0.77	6	0.01	0.15	0.68	7
	$n = 40$				$n = 50$			
0.6	18.96	27.56	35.35	34	19.76	27.53	34.46	43
0.8	13.67	21.35	28.71	31	14.36	21.31	27.84	38
1.0	9.44	16.04	22.81	27	10.00	16.00	21.98	34
1.2	6.22	11.68	17.71	23	6.66	11.64	16.95	29
1.4	3.91	8.23	13.45	20	4.24	8.20	12.76	25
1.6	2.34	5.62	9.97	18	2.58	5.59	9.37	22
1.8	1.33	3.70	7.21	15	1.49	3.68	6.71	19
2.0	0.72	2.36	5.19	14	0.82	2.34	4.69	17
2.25	0.31	1.28	3.18	12	0.37	1.27	2.89	14
2.5	0.13	0.66	1.91	10	0.15	0.65	1.70	12
3.0	0.02	0.15	0.61	8	0.02	0.14	0.52	9

NAME INDEX

A

American Society for Quality Control (A.S.Q.C.), 82, 412n.
American Society for Testing Materials (A.S.T.M.), 44n., 101, 302n., 412n.
American Standards Association (A.S.A.), 17, 82, 105, 156, 260, 271, 412n.
American Telephone & Telegraph Company, Comptroller's Department, 361n.
Anscombe, F. J., 399
Ashcroft, A. G., 106n.

B

Ballowe, J. M., 362
Barrett, C. S., 453
Baten, W. D., 207n., 294n.
Beckwith, O. P., 305, 342
Bell Aircraft Corporation, 12, 402
Bell Telephone Laboratories, 279n., 366
Bell Telephone System, 279
Bellinson, H. R., 369
Benson, E., 470, 471
Birge, R. T., 58n., 70
Bowker, A. H., 333, 409, 411, 413, 415
Brinegar, Claude, 359n.
Bristol Aeroplane Company, Ltd., 460n.
British Standards Institution, 106

C

Campbell, G. A., 394n.
Campbell, W. E., 113n.
Chase, Herbert, 12n.
Cisne, L. E., 351
Clark, J. T., 460
Cochran, W. G., 475n.
Coggins, Paul, 197
Columbia Statistical Research Group, 10, 325, 343, 353, 366, 389, 390, 401n., 409
Cox, G. M., 475n.

D

Darwin, C. G., 41, 285, 287
Deming, W. E., 58n., 75, 106n., 130, 173n., 175, 323

D (continued)

De Morgan, 100
Dodge, H. F., 106n., 109, 210, 212, 279, 323, 325n., 343–358, 366n., 402n., 481n.
Dudding, B. P., 106n.
DuMont Laboratories, 248

E

Edwards, G. D., 311, 364, 366n., 407
Eisenhart, Churchill, 475n.
Enell, J. W., 385
Enrick, N. L., 366n.
Epstein, B., 294
Ezekiel, M., 475n.

F

Fay, E. L., 487
Feigenbaum, A. V., 399n., 465n.
Fisher, R. A., 222n., 389n., 475n.
Ford Motor Company, 469
Freeman, H. A., 343n., 372n., 374n., 381n., 384n., 388n., 389n., 409n.
Friedman, Milton, 343n., 372n., 374n., 381n., 384n., 388n., 389n., 409n.
Fry, T. C., 202n., 209n., 223

G

Gaillard, John, 106n.
Galton, Francis, 472
Gartner, C. L., 248
Gause, G. R., 366n.
General Electric Company, 249
Geschelin, Joseph, 229
Girshick, M. A., 357, 358n.
Goetz, B. E., 456n.
Goode, H. P., 280n., 333, 393n., 409, 411, 413, 415
Grant, B. E., 213

H

Hamaker, H. C., 393, 394
Hanna, R. W., 300, 301
Hastay, M. W., 475n.
Hazen, Allen, 46n.
Hill, D. A., 279n.

SUBJECT INDEX

A